A History of the British Steam Tram

Volume 1

by David Gladwin

Published by Adam Gordon

ACKNOWLEDGEMENTS

Thanks are due to many people, and it is intended to give full credits in the last volume (planned to be no.4). However, the author would like to give the following advance credits to: "Ms Rachel Ford, Professional Support Officer, Patents Archives, Birmingham Central Library, and her colleagues for their assistance in tracing, often from the vaguest of clues, a number of obscure and long forgotten tramway patents. Their difficulties were compounded by a massive computerisation/updating of Patent Records which made physical research difficult. In this context I must also thank Leeds Patent Office for their prompt supply of prints. Mike Haddon, Industrial History Officer, Wigan, for saving me many trips to Wigan and for enabling me to trace more of the history of William Wilkinson and his foundry. If there are perceived errors in my interpretation of the material available it is not the fault of Mike. I find it difficult to believe there are no descendants of William Wilkinson still in the area, so little documentation has survived that any source material would help. The Editor and staff of The Engineer for the courteous replies to queries and for permission to use text and illustrations from The Engineer and Engineering without restriction; the difference this has made to both this and succeeding volumes is immeasurable."

The following images are credited to the Science Museum/Science & Society Picture Library (South Kensington): 10, 13, 14, 25, 40, 48, 51, 60, 61, 63, 64, 87, 157, 167, 170 & 172. As an exception to the above statement re acknowledgements the Museum requested that each volume contains the relevant credits.

ISBN: 1 874422 46 X

A catalogue entry for this book is available from the British Library.

Publication no.48.

Published 2004 by Adam Gordon, Kintradwell Farmhouse, Brora, Sutherland, KW9 6LU.

Printed by The Northern Times, Sutherland Press House, Main Street, Golspie, Sutherland KW10 6RA
Print-run limited to 650.

Production and design by Trevor Preece: trevor@epic.gb.com

Contents

Foreword

To write a foreword to one's own book is never easy! The origin of this set of books was a monograph I had prepared on the subject of steam tram boiler explosions. Not only were the available Board of Trade and newspaper reports technically interesting, but to a transport-cum-social historian they throw a different light on the uneasy transition in day-to-day life that was taking place in these late Victorian days.

Although the railways had made available facilities for movements within the well-to-do population, nonetheless their great advantage lay (and lies) in medium to long distance journeys.

Later of course the availability of train services assisted (as an example) the great emigration from Ireland to America; many contemporary reports write of trains overloaded with young men leaving villages for Cork or Dublin, their girls weeping into their shawls knowing perhaps that these were all one way journeys.

On the mainland, aside from Thomas Cook-type excursions and the useage of trains to get to and from work, by and large 'heavy rail', to use today's parlance, had little impact on the working class populace of the cities: trains were just too expensive and too infrequent.

While urban-dweller Albert might (and might was the operative word) go down to the station and catch his workman's train at some unhealthy hour to go t'mill, Mrs Albert walked. And the Mrs Alberts of this world normally walked some quite remarkable distances due to Mr Albert's poor wages, shopping every day for the best bargains. After all, if you were buying second quality and often tainted meat long before the days of refrigerators, freezers, microwaves and the like, you cooked and ate it that day. And when you wanted to go to the market, perhaps two or three miles away, you walked or rode on the local carrier's cart. Horse buses and even the relatively tiny horse trams were too expensive for Mrs Albert, whereas when the steam trams arrived carrying 80 or 90 passengers with penny fares, the oyster of travel opened wide not only for Mrs Albert, but Mr Albert was no longer tied to his mill and could find better paid work, giving him a mobility previously unknown to the working classes. And this was the most important aspect of the brief twenty year period when steam trams ruled the streets.

This is also the story of the vicissitudes of tramway engineers trying to lay trackwork with a labour force that had no previous knowledge of this type of work, often in the most appalling weather conditions; with tools that were often at best minimalist, and with no attempt by the engineers or contractors to provide any facilities for the men to dry themselves out or to obtain hot food, particularly when out in the wastelands between urban centres. The enforced usage of ale-houses undoubtedly caused some appalling workmanship and accidents when the men came back – it was little use the engineer fulminating at the contractor when he or his foreman on-site in all probability had joined the men.

Many, many, mistakes were made in the choice of which patterns of rail to use; I counted over eighty patents covering this subject before I gave up, and yet most of these often strange combined rails (with interchangeable heads) were so designed to avoid or reduce to a minimum the need to rip up the road surface, and regarded solely as a rail capable of carrying a steam tram and its trailer with, probably, no more than four such trams passing along it every hour they were successful. But this was not the case as all the heavy iron-tyred springless carts ('lurries') found these new rails a far better surface to run on than the surrounding cobbles. This wreaked havoc on both rails and their fastenings, gauges becoming plus or minus an inch or two, and the hapless engineer having within months to go back to his directors and explain why any profit they hoped to make had just been buckled out of shape by the local iron-works traction engine and its overloaded trailers.

A few of the engineers were quite inefficient, weak, men, while others trained in horse-tram days found themselves hopelessly out of their depth faced with this new technology. Steam trams had a terrible press, and gloomily I must confess to some extent the companies brought this on themselves. Firstly they (or their contractors) ripped up the road surface then, seemingly, went away having run out of rails or fastenings or setts or concrete or even men, men that cost money in wages which the contractor, often a man in a small way of business had to pay while also paying out a guaranteed 4% or 5% to shareholders while the work was undertaken. Some companies suffered really dreadfully from continual sniping by their local councils, often made up of shopkeepers whose trade dwindled while access was blocked to Mrs Carriage Lady who could not be expected to walk anywhere. Indeed some Councils often quite irrationally turned their faces against the tramway and made life incredibly difficult for them; one Midlands Council Chairman W. Bassano, an Italian-Jewish colliery owner, was virulent in his hatred, why I do not know, but paying low wages perhaps he was afraid his men would be free to work elsewhere.

And yet the worst thing the steam trams did was to maim and kill children playing in the streets. These youngsters had nowhere else to play, and you cannot stop an inquisitive or forgetful three or four year old from running alongside or crossing in front of an engine. No-one living away from the railway in their insular city 'villages' in 1880 ever saw movement above that of a running man, or at most (rarely) a trotting horse, whereas the steam tram moved at eight miles an hour and distance perception just did not exist for these children. Incomprehensible to me, and Chapter 9 of this volume gives details of the belated action taken, was why the companies could not, or did not, realise this problem within months, and even more so why one of the steam tram engine builders (Green, Kitson, Wilkinson and the like) could not have invented a really efficient life-saver for fitting to the engines long before they were forced to. After all, the expense was trifling, and any competent designer could have produced something that was better than nothing. A child killed was relatively soon forgotten other than by the family, but a girl hopping along on crutches was held up to be an example of why young Johnny or Jeannie must not get too near the tram; a warning recorded time and time again and even heard by myself as late as 1960. Damaged boys could still gain employment and, of course, as they became teenagers they merged with war injured ex-soldiers and seamen, but a girl (even if her family avoided putting her in the dreaded 'Home') had little prospect of good employment or marriage as she grew up, thus she was even more so the living reminder of the danger. This omission of a basic lifeguard and its concomitant side effects, was to poison the whole history of steam trams, and indeed may well have carried over into electric days.

Later volumes will carry detailed accounts of some of the tramways I can trace, the good, the bad and the bankrupt, and similarly the men behind the tramway companies will be looked at, and there were some truly amazing characters among them – a manager supposed to have run off to France with the cash, a Director or two who were so crooked they made politicians (then and now!) look honest, a manager accused of rape, and another regarded by his workmen with 'great approbation' at the Company's Annual Dinner. Drivers and Guards all played their part, albeit too often they flit in front of us without any real three dimensional life – merely a name and an incident.

Boiler explosions will be a fascinating part of a later volume, as well as The End when the British Electric Traction Company took over many companies and introduced 'Sparklers', but the most successful of all steam tramway companies were among those subsequently municipalised. It cannot be entirely coincidental that the inhabitants of many of the towns and cities whose forbears had their streets graced by steam trams are among those now enjoying or about to enjoy modern electric cars.

It is the way of pioneers to be forgotten, but I hope these volumes will go some way to ensure the story of steam trams lives on.

An omission in this first volume is the acknowledgements due to many men, women and institutions who have helped in research – to avoid repetition all will be listed in the final volume.

David Gladwin, January 2004.

Introduction

Measurements

As a general principle 'Imperial' (feet/inches) measurements are used where they were the originals, and metric dimensions only where either manufacturers' specifications or drawings show them to be used initially – thus Die Lokomotivfabrik Krauss & Comp. of München referred to the gauge of the locomotives supplied to the Wolverton & Stony Stratford Tramways (Works nos. 1861-4) as 1067mm. Part of the reasoning behind this decision is based on my own experiences many years ago at coach-builders where the first instruction was to thoroughly sweep "Old Fred's Yard" and damp it down. As this was overtime on a Sunday the work was willingly carried out. At 9.00am on the Monday a girl brought down a roll of blue prints and took them into Fred's eyrie: a glass office suspended above the workshop floor. Promptly at 10.00am when most men (except us young 'uns) were having their snap, Fred, wearing his solemn expression, made his way down the steps and unfurled a sheaf of drawings. A while later the whole side of a coach was delineated in chalk, together with critical dimensions (in Imperial feet and inches) on the floor. The first timbers were cut to this outline and assembled, this set thereafter acting as a template, no more accuracy being required.

Inevitably humidity and ambient temperature variations meant some later bodies required a 'persuader', but were no less accurate than tramway wooden trailer bodies which, like garden sheds, dried out in summer and rarely went back to the same shape in winters' rains.

Even component parts of tram locomotives can give enormous difficulties. One of the Board of Trade Inspectors was fond of quoting B.W.G. – Birmingham Wire Gauge, commonly used in describing the wall thickness of boiler tubes made from seamless brass, seamless copper, seamless steel and aluminium. According to my engineering handbook of 1914 when BWG was 'obsolescent' the dimensions in the box show just some of 18 BWG's equivalent:

> Birmingham or Stub's Wire Gauge 0.1800
> American Wire or Brown & Sharpe Gauge 0.1443
> Steel Wire Gauge or Washburn and Moen or Roebling (U.S.) 0.1770
> British Standard Wire Gauge (Imperial Wire Gauge) 0.1760
> Music or Piano Wire Gauge 0.18
> Stub's Wire Gauge 0.199

All of these could then be amended by the use of 'Split Wire Gauges' involving ½ fractions!

The handbook adds: "All Dimensions are Approximate ... as all are rounded off ... in ordering material it is preferable to give exact dimensions *in decimal fractions of an inch*."

Within the American market measurements in feet and inches are still the norm, and in truth the majority of British subjects still instinctively think 'Imperial'. Some dimensional drawings are included for modellers' use, although whether you work on approximate sizes or not is a matter of conscience; given a boiler tube wall was 11/32nd of an inch, do you take it to be roughly 3/8" (9.525mm) or be a purist at 8.73125mm? As 7mm = 1 foot this is ... er ... 0.2187498mm. A final problem is that, realistically, there are dangers in transcription between calculator, word processor and printed result.

Horsepower

Throughout any book of this type, dealing with Victorian steam power, the notation 'HP' appears, be it in relation to railway locomotives, traction engines, road rollers, stationary engines (as used in collieries, mills and the like) or tram locomotives.

It is an abbreviation for 'horse-power', but bears very little resemblance to the power produced by the four-legged equine unit (or horse). For this reason the unit 'NHP' or nominal horse power can also be found.

The definition of 'horse-power' in the context of steam was first propounded by James Watt when he stated that one horse-power was equivalent to a weight of 33,000lb (14,969kg) being raised through one foot (0.3048m) in one minute. Therefore a 10HP engine ought to be able to raise 147.32 tons (149.69 tonnes) through one foot in one minute; or approximately 1 ton (1.016 tonnes) through 150 feet (45.72m) in one minute. Electrically one 'horse-power' may be said to develop 746 watts.

Early on in the railway steam age the dynamometer or friction brake was devised to

CONVERSION TABLE

Abbreviations: British thermal unit [BTU], centimetre [cm], chain [ch], decimetre [dm], foot [ft or '], gramme [g], hectare [hre], horse power [HP] hundredweight [cwt], inch [in or "], kilogramme [kg], kilometre [km], kilowatt [kW], litre [lt], metre [m], millimetre [mm], pound [lb], square [sq.]

One mile	Roughly 1½km	Exactly 1.6093km
One yard	Roughly 1m	Exactly 0.914399m
One foot	Roughly 300mm	Exactly 304.8mm
One inch	Roughly 2½cm	Exactly 25.4mm
One chain	Roughly 20m	Exactly 20.1168 m or 60'
One furlong	Roughly 200m	Exactly 201.168m or 1/8 mile
One square inch	Roughly 6½sq.cm	Exactly 6.4516sq.cm (cm^2)
One square foot	Roughly 0.1sq.m	Exactly 0.092903sq.m or 9.2903dm
One hundredweight	Roughly 50kg	Exactly 50.80kg
One ton (2240lb)	Roughly 1 tonne	Exactly 1.016 tonne
One pound	Roughly ½kg	Exactly 453.6g or 0.45359243kg
One stone	Roughly 6½kg	Exactly 6.35 kg or 14lb
One acre	Roughly ½hre	Exactly 0.40468hre
One square mile	Roughly 250hre	Exactly 259.00hre
One gallon	Roughly 4½lt	Exactly 4.5459631lt
One pint	Roughly ½lt	Exactly 0.568lt
One Horse power (at 33,000 ft/lb per minute)	Roughly ¾kW	Exactly 0.7457kW
One calorie	Roughly 4BTU	Exactly 3.968BTU
One kilojoule	Roughly 1BTU	Exactly 0.948BTU

apply a given load to an engine (mobile or stationary) which would give the effect of Watt's dictum without any actual lifting taking place; thus giving the 'horse-powers' a common factor, and giving rise to the more accurate and tested term 'BHP' or brake-horse-power rather than the older purely theoretical and nominal 'horse-power'.

Thus if we take a standard steam engine rated at 10HP, it should lift 330,000lb one foot (or, in theory, 45.625kg one metre); in one minute (609.6m/min) our engine should lift and hold 165lb or 74.84kg.

Various adjustments corrected this for frictional losses and in one of the largest testing houses built, at Rugby, a factor was proved on a dynamometer that engine-men always knew (whether on high speed or tram locomotives) that fully laden one was always teetering on the edge of slipping, i.e. reaching the point at which the traction of smooth steel tyres on smooth steel rails ceased to exist. This phenomenon carried the imposing title of 'the factor of adhesion' and can be reduced to a formula: (tractive force x 3.33 x 1.25), fine in a warm dry testing house, but in reality the whole problem of 'technical' as opposed to 'real' practice was found in 1965 when a new tug-boat entered service. The engine had according to the manual a nominal rating of 142 horse-power, a brake horse-power of 603, and yet after transmission losses was found to produce at least 350 'indicated' horse-power at the tail of the propeller shaft, i.e. in usable terms 2½ times the 'NHP' but only ⅗ths of the 'BHP'. We will not mention the losses due to cavitation, unequal stresses and rough seas!

In locomotive or tram engine terms this power at the shaft is classified as DHP – drawbar horse-power, i.e. the actual number of horses available to drag vehicles after the resistance of the engine is taken into account. Propelling vehicles is another kettle of fish entirely...

However, by retaining the manufacturers' ratings of tram engines throughout the book we have a theoretical comparative value: a combination of nominal size (8, 10, 12HP) wheel size (2' 0", 2' 2", 2' 4", 609, 660, 711mm) and weight (4, 6, 8, 10 tons). But so much always depended on the road (hilly or level), the weather (dry or wet) which critically affected adhesion, the fuel (good or sulphurous coke), the load being pulled (fresh or old grease in the axle-boxes of the trailer could vary the nominal weight or drag by a ton), the condition of the engine (leaky boiler and fittings, choked firebox, warped cylinders), and above all the abilities of the engineman and his experience (some were ex-railway main line, other 17 and 18 year old lads). All those factors mattered more than any nominal output.

Pre-decimal money. Younger readers may not be familiar with pounds (£) shillings (s) and pennies (d), which were replaced by decimal currency. One 'old' £ equalled 20s, and 1s equalled 12d. A guinea equalled 21s, and a farthing equalled ¼d. Because of the change in values, it has not been thought useful to add contemporary equivalent values.

Board of Trade

Ultimately the Board of Trade Inspector determined the fate of any steam tramway, for not only did their officers decide whether or not the line could be opened, but they could act as a form of arbiter between local Mayors (powerful people then) or Local Board Secretaries and tramway companies, and generally the threat of reference to the BoT led to a more conciliatory approach to whatever the problem was. In early railway days regulation was rather hit and miss, the BoT being a small Government department whose duties, logically enough, were to give advice to the Government on trade matters. In reality the body was miniscule, having only a President and a Vice-President together with a handful of clerks. Eventually, after the Regulation of Railways Act 1840, a specialist Railway Department was set up although this could not, initially, act autonomously, as the Board passed correspondence to the relevant specialist department (i.e. the Railway Department) who looked into the matter and passed it all back to the Board who then replied to the original correspondent accordingly.

The 1840 Act and its successors gave the Board the authority to appoint suitable persons as Inspectors of railways, and made it the duty of the Board of Trade to approve (or not!) railway and later tramway company bye-laws, to receive returns of traffic (the duty of providing them being placed on the company secretary), to receive advice of accidents and investigate them if desirable (particularly boiler explosions), to ensure workmens' trams were operated, and to enforce the proper observance of clauses in the company's Act of Parliament, but the primary duty of an Inspector (granted under the Conveyance of Troops Act 1842) was to prevent the opening of a tramway unless and until the Inspector was absolutely sure of the line's safety. And this was not a one-off, as the BoT licensed the use of steam so they could (and did) withdraw this licence at a later date if they believed that its operation was unsafe; and not only did this include the condition of the actual trams themselves, but the drivers and the physical state of the infrastructure, the condition of the rails, the 'pumping' of the track (whereby passing trams eventually turn the underlying roadbed to mud, weakening and fracturing the rails) and the state of the surrounding setts. Theoretically even the cleanliness or otherwise of the trailers could affect their judgement. One has to say though that the positive side of the BoT was apparent when companies were trying to ameliorate the strictness and vindictiveness shown by the police to drivers of steam trams in the early days, and towards the very end the Inspectors did their best to ensure safe operation of the remaining steamers even if only on a month-to-month basis.

Finally, readers will come across the name of Kinnear Clark, who wrote the classic book "Tramways – their construction and working". The second edition is the most comprehensive, published in 1894, 758 pages, and over 400 illustrations. It was reprinted in 1992 by Adam Gordon.

1. Steam car by Mr Brown, Winterthur. See page 130.

Chapter 1

PREAMBLE

Life in Britain 120 odd years ago bore little or no resemblance to the way we, in a civilised country, live today. This statement applies more perhaps to the 'working' classes than even clerical grades, but although 'Fat Cats' existed then as much as now, their lifestyles, however affluent, could not always buy them health, and their wealth was often built on fickle trade; many mill-owners for example were only too happy when wars broke out and orders for cloth poured in – which also benefited their operatives and as a knock-on, public transport. Nevil Shute in his 'Ruined City' tells how rearmament orders in the 1930s directly affecting one shipyard led to a whole town coming out of recession with even the trams' bells being heard again ... and Woolworth's 3d and 6d store re-opening. In the period of steam trams, loosely 1880-1905, we must remember that sick pay was hardly heard of, holidays limited to one day per year (more, however, if you forewent your pay and risked your job, St. Monday or St. Hangover was a commonly lost day, made up by working the next Saturday or Sunday), health provision outside clubs was entirely dependent upon charity from wealthy people, mainly landowners whose subscriptions kept hospitals, libraries and almshouses going until the National Health Service, following its Act of Parliament in 1946, arrived. Many of their hospitals are the ones now being sold off to developers with few of the foundation stones recording the benefactors' names being saved.

Crime was kept under control mainly by Draconian punishments, although the loss of Australia as a transportation point handicapped some magistrates. Conversely we must never forget there is in every country a brutish underclass that can and will wreck any soft approach; some modern schooling proves this today where teachers and lecturers alike can be forced to surrender any pretence at control.

Wages of course depended on where you were and what you did, but a Cheshire farm labourer saw his average pay climb from 9s.7d per week in 1850 to 17s. 6d. in 1880. The underlying cause was a shortage of agricultural labourers with many men emigrating or moving to factories in the cities.

Statistically we can get a better feel for the distribution of wages by drawing from one industry (almost gone) in a tram-fed city, Manchester. These statistics prepared for the Chamber of Commerce are surprisingly accurate. This increase in disposable income helped to improve tram industry wages as well. See table alongside.

Electricity was just beginning to make some headway – our local power station (now converted to flats) came on stream in 1894, but a better idea of commonplace work conditions can be gained from a paraphrase of an 1882 report.

The chief engineer of a brewery was involved in the repair of a refrigerating machine, and was on the Saturday trying to persuade a piston to free itself from the cylinder of an 'ether machine', struck it with a piece of wood which "had the effect of opening some of the valves of the machine", ether vapour escaped and came into contact *with a candle;* in the resulting explosion a lump of the machine then hit the engineer on the head. It was stated that the use of a candle near the machine was against the rules "although no other means of lighting was provided."

Even forty years ago, would-be employers queued up to offer employment to school leavers, and in tram days there was an incredible variety of trades available – in a steel works in Leeds when a boiler exploded those affected included many long lost occupations:

Tongs man at rolls	aged 32
Bogie man	aged 27
1st hooker at rolls	aged 24
Bar man at rolls	aged 27
Stocktaker	aged 40
Driver at hot shears	aged 28
Helper at rolls	aged 56
Forker at rolls	aged 22
Mill greaser	aged 27
Furnace fireman	aged 27
Mill craneman	aged 41
Mill timer	aged 29
1st hand rougher	aged 43
Hot sawman	aged 46

But finally, on a lighter note, 1890, Saturday in the Seven Bells, six rough tramway labourers were playing cards. But as the clock struck the hour of twelve, proclaiming the Lord's Day had come, with one accord they threw down the cards and left the taproom. They went across the street to see an organised dog fight!

Unlike farming there was no shortage of labour in industrialised South Wales, as Irish labour flooded in seeking better conditions, so much so that wages became depressed, causing a number of proposed tramways and railway branches to be put on hold; transport was always the first to suffer when money was short.

Following a meeting of tin plate workers from South Wales, Monmouthshire, Gloucestershire, Worcestershire and Staffordshire, it was resolved "to resist the reduction of wages determined upon by the masters ... of 20%". They wanted the masters to restrict output to 36 boxes per turn of twelve hours. Tin plate workers needed to maximise their earnings to assist their families; it was accepted that they would die at a relatively young age (45 was an old man) mostly as their lungs rotted.

A city could find its tramways in difficulty from emigration. Sheffield in 1879 reported an exodus of skilled engineers leaving for America, one firm owned by Mr Benjamin Eyre had lost twenty-two families "totalling 102 cutlers including child labour" and "there is a movement in the town for sending out large numbers more". At the same time in Sheffield law and order had in some ways long collapsed; mainly as the police officers were human and were vulnerable to attacks on their families. Much has been written about the "Nobility of labour, the long pedigree of toil" but there always has been a downside to the narrow clannish outlook within organised labour; intimidation of what were seen to be 'blacklegs' was commonplace and often violent.

During November 1879 the owners of Birley Colliery, the Sheffield Coal Company, wanted to change the method of working the pit. As the men saw it this would lead to a reduction in their wages of 15%, whereas the management claimed only 7½% was in dispute. Most of the eleven hundred men and boys employed went on strike, although a few, probably driven by financial necessity, worked on, including Walter Taylor and his father-in-law. At midnight on 26th November they were woken by a 'terrific explosion' and on going downstairs found a can of gunpowder had been exploded in the kitchen. Two men were caught but released and the perpetrators "were favoured by the usual immunity from police discovery", the colliers claiming Taylor after going upstairs to bed had walked down at midnight with the express intention of blowing himself up! Perhaps, added one report

1861-1881

	Average Increase of Wages	Total Number Employed
Cotton trade	40.70	523,754
Bleaching etc.	50.00	39,691
Calico printing	50.00	39,318
Fitters, turners etc.	10.30	78,828
Smiths	24.00	147,456
Carpenters and joiners	50.00	295,958
Bricklayers	46.00	129,966
Masons	34.00	131,476
Plasterers	31.00	34,662
Labourers	32.00	771,501
Mechanics	77.00	36,481
% Average increase	**40.00**	**2,220,091**

"to while away the monotony of these dull November days".

The other side of men's lives was reported in The Times during March 1886 when "several pitmen (who were on strike) with their wives and families were turned out of their cottages at South Medomsley (Durham) during a snow storm ... the Bailiffs were assisted at the eviction by the County Police".

Generally the greatest driving force that kept men at work was the very real fear of the workhouse. In exchange for basic food, clothing and protection against the weather you worked until you dropped. And if you absconded, as some did, you ended up deeper in the mire, although towards the end of our period one cheerful chap was "charged with absconding from Clitheroe Workhouse with clothes belonging to the Union. Henry Southworth, a merry old man, kept the Court in excellent humour during the hearing of the case. "Are the clothes marked?" inquired the clerk of the workhouse master. "Oh, yes" interposed Southworth, "they are all branded. No.1 is my number. They are valued at 20s. Cheap at half that price. There's not a lazy bone in my body." "But you've got the Union clothes on," said the Mayor, severely, "Well" returned the prisoner, "they have got mine, have they not?" "And you have only a halfpenny in your possession" went on his Worship. "True", said Southworth, "one halfpenny. It is enough for a start, my masters. More than I had when born."

The Stourbridge workhouse returns for 20 March 1884, when the Dudley & Stourbridge Steam Tramways was still only two years old and trade good, make sobering reading by comparison with today. In the preceding week twelve men and women were admitted, seven discharged, one pauper child was born, leaving a total of 583 inhabitants for this one workhouse in a small town. We also have a note of the constituents of their diet. Flour (seconds), oatmeal (best), bread (best seconds at 4d per 4lb loaf), tea (1/6d per pound), sugar, butter (9d), rice, pepper, starch, linseed meal, split peas, blue peas, beef and mutton (both 6d per pound) and ale. Other items included material (for uniforms), shoes and ... coffins.

Britain's last workhouse did not shut its doors until 1930, long after steam trams and many of their electric successors had closed. In 1928 a Bill to repeal the 1834 Poor Law Amendment Act was put forward; prior to this workhouses (or in Scotland, poorhouses) were the only legal source of poor relief. This Bill was enacted on 31 March, 1930.

Before this 'soup kitchens' and similar arrangements were the main source of social service; in 1895 a General Relief Fund was set up in Dudley with 400 people being fed each day "and many are sent empty away". Enormous attempts were made to supplement the rigid legal provisions, for example Watson's Green Football Club bought 20 'subscription tickets' and sent them to the local vicar, each representing a 4lb loaf, ¼lb of tea, 1lb of sugar and ½lb of bacon. Elsewhere children were especially looked after; a solicitor, A.G. Hooper, gave 140 dinners daily for the Kate's Hill School, and the King Street Wesleyan Church provided breakfast for 100 children daily; small wonder, though, when the Dudley & Stourbridge Steam Tramway wanted conductors, despite the hours and poor pay, some hundreds of men applied.

The fear of the 'wukkus' (as we knew it locally although by now it was converted to Almshouses) was very real; in Rose Street, Coseley, a tramway man kept his family together in one room. Himself, a daughter (aged 40), two sons (22 and 16), another daughter (14) plus five other children. Also there were a married daughter and her husband. Twelve bodies cooking, eating and sleeping in one room – that was the downside of 1897.

Education was a matter of luck as even a 'good' school did not mean good scholars, and not a few 'dull' boys moved up the ladder, particularly in the engineering trades. Then, as now, some children remained uneducated, while others, including an eight year old girl, Jane Crump, apparently died from stress, the verdict on little Jane in 1888 being "Death from natural causes, accelerated by overwork at a Board School." Against this councils and education officers made desperate attempts to use some part of the rate payers' money to 'ameliorate the condition of the children of the poor'.

Dudley, 14th January 1888 – "½d dinners for school children have commenced, and on Monday, Tuesday, Wednesday and Thursday no less than 1895 dinners were provided, nearly an average of 500 a day. Monday, Tuesday and Thursday a pint of good wholesome soup and a huge piece of bread and jam were supplied, and on Wednesday for a change cocoa took the place of soup, but there seemed a strong preference for the latter ... It is pleasing to see with (what) 'alacrity' teachers have supported the scheme ... and there are far too many pitiable looking children who 'went for' succulent soup and bread and jam in a manner unmistakeable".

But there were 'perks' for schoolchildren and we must not forget that in the disciplined age of Victoria, fun was gained wherever it could be found and not manufactured by Mr Sony. "Sunday School Demonstration at Netherton – The annual treat to the Sunday School scholars belonging to the church and chapels in the neighbourhood took place on Monday afternoon. The children numbering about 5,000 marched through the principal streets, carrying flags, banners and bowers of flowers. Shortly after three o'clock the whole of them met in the Market Place, when they sang a few appropriate hymns. As the weather was beautifully fine, a holiday was made of the occasion by the tradesmen, many of them closing their establishments. It is computed that 9,000 were assembled in the Market Place. Afterwards the children were paraded to the several schools where tea and cake were provided. The children belonging to the Church schools were marched to the cricket field, where a beautiful supply of cake, rolls and butter, and tea were awaiting them, provided by Mrs Hodgkiss, confectioner of Netherton. After tea, racing, cricket and other old English games were played with much zest. Sweets and money were freely 'scuffled' by the teachers and friends, but the most amusing of all events was a wheelbarrow race. In one of the races for females an accident of a serious nature happened to a girl named Mathews, who, it appears, in the heat of the race caught her foot in a furrow and fell, breaking her leg. She was at once carried home, where we are pleased to say, she is progressing favourably." The sting in the tail is that last phrase where the girl was carried home, but not to hospital.

May 1883, Louth, Lincolnshire, not far from the Alford & Sutton Tramway – "Ten farmers from the district were summoned for employing children under the age of 13 years". They all pleaded guilty and were fined one shilling each, plus costs of twelve shillings, effectively the minimum, the Chairman of the Magistrates remarking, "Whatever their private feelings were with reference to the Education Act, he was there to administer the law as it stood, but he must say that some cases that came before them seemed cruel..." The boys needed to work to help keep their families, although had this policy not been followed, perhaps wages would have risen. The same day it was reported that the cheap trip run on the railway from Boston to Grimsby for a performance of 'Iolanthe' (Gilbert & Sullivan) carried 120 passengers, including a number of children.

There was, however, a Victorian fairness in the handling of children, for when Robert Tweed, a small boy-cum-apprentice on a fishing boat was "punched and kicked in a shameful manner" by a deckhand, this man was sentenced to Hull gaol for six months.

But in reality life for children "of the lowest class" could be crude and short. One night in December 1881 it was foggy at Tipton when two cousins aged nine and seven were sent by a girl of twelve to get a tuppenny bag of coal. They fell in the canal, and although seen splashing about by "a young chap with a lamp", their cries were ignored until it was too late for one boy. The older boy was fished out by passers-by, and "Dr. Underhill having been sent for *he put hot coals on the boy's feet*", but he too died. The Coroner asked the mother why she had tried to send the girl (who had passed the job to the boys) out on such a bad night? The woman claimed she had not known it was so bad. "Oh, nonsense. Do you think [anyone] will believe you when you say you went out to the brewhouse just two minutes before?" The mother, who had lost five of her nine children, was called a liar by the jury ... but fourteen people were drowned in the Dudley area canals that night.

Life could be crude in the extreme; quite often there are comments that such was the uncleanliness of some passengers that it was better to travel in the reek of shag tobacco and the howling draughts upstairs, rather than down in the enclosed saloon.

In 1883 – only 120 years ago – the Sedgley Inspector of Nuisances was asked how many houses were in the district where the nightsoil (raw sewage) had to be carried through the house for removal, there being no back way, and was

DUDLEY UNION

NOTICE IS HEREBY GIVEN that there are several BOYS in the Dudley Union Workhouse ELIGIBLE for APPRENTICES. Application to be made to the Master of the Workhouse. By Order THOS. ALLEN, Clerk Board Room, Town Hall, Dudley, 30th December 1881.

told 47, to which the Chairman, after agreeing it was "a great nuisance", stated he knew properties in towns where the occupants paying £90 a year rental had to do the same thing. Curiously, at the same time the same council were trying to get the daily rate of their night soil men reduced to the same as the day rate from three shillings to two shillings and eight pence. This was agreed, as they "did not do half the work the road men did."

"To the Editor – Sir, Have we an Inspector of Nuisances in Stourbridge? I suppose we have, seeing that his salary is regularly paid out of the town rates. But where does he live, and does he ever walk down Enville Street? If so, I take it, it is either early in the morning or late at night – certainly not in the daytime, or he would have ere now discovered a great nuisance arising from the urinal there. This place of convenience was erected, I believe, one night in the dark, and consequently was not put upright, so the soakage drains across the footpath in the summer time to the detriment of health, and in the winter, when it freezes, the footpath is very dangerous. Now if our Inspector would attend to causes of this sort, instead of interfering so much with other things, it would be better for the town and ratepayers".

A curiosity of the mores of the time was that the captain of the Aston Fire Brigade, Mr A. Treadway, was also the Superintendent of the Aston Local Board's night soil department, but in his first uniform in 1888 he reckoned his 19 firemen could get their new steam appliance on the road in two minutes. Steam pump, but horse drawn of course.

One of the surprises of the late Victorian period was how men and women could work the hours they did in the conditions they endured on what must often have been an 'unbalanced' diet. Could it be that our ideas are wrong when we know a farm labourer would plough for a 12 hour day in heavy clay on a 'corner' (probably ½lb/227g) of bread, a lump of fatty bacon and cold tea? And do this year in year out, only varying the meat with beef garnished with whatever raw vegetables were in season, and yet living (in many cases) to good old age?

By contrast try the use of Tomlinson Co's Butter Powder – in 1883 it took away the taste of "Oil Cake, Turnips, Mangolds, Wild Garlic, Sour Grass etc." leaving the butter "Sweeter, Firmer and Better". Having got Tomlinson's you could then run an advertisement for "A strong girl for a farmhouse; one that can milk"! (Little Carlton 1883).

In Wainwright Street, Aston, Birmingham, near the Birmingham & Aston Steam Tramway on 15 December 1882 there was an extensive seizure of horse flesh. The firm concerned carried on a business of potted meat manufacture "and this horse flesh was intended for the food of man ... (there were) 352 pieces of putrid horse flesh, and we must say this was a most disgusting spectacle".

Even the simplest foodstuff could be adulterated. Had GM materials and their by-products been invented, no doubt they would have been used! In a Birmingham editorial during 1884 it was asked how anyone could make and sell "family plum jam" at 2d a pound wholesale using "honest fruit". And at the Southwark Police Court a Bermondsey jam maker was asked to explain his stock of tons of rotten figs. Magistrate: "What are they used for? I've never heard of fig jam". Sanitary Inspector: "They are used for making raspberry jam". Magistrate: "What? Raspberry jam? There is no resemblance". Sanitary Inspector: (One suspects rather pitying his dim pupil) "Any vegetable that will pulp forms the basis of the jam, which is coloured and flavoured with chemical extracts; and the fig seeds are used to represent the seeds of raspberries, without which the stuff could not be palmed off as real raspberry".

While admittedly jam might be considered a luxury, although always served on Sundays, bread was not, and the variations in prices during February 1894 must have affected wages to some extent.

Each loaf weighed 4lb (1.81kg), and the following were Cooperative Society prices:

Northern Counties	6d
Lancashire & Cheshire	4¾d
Yorkshire	4⅛d
Midland and Eastern Counties	3⅞d
Home Counties	4⅝d
South & South-Western Counties	4¼d
Scotland	4⅞d
Ireland	5¼d

There were variations within these figures, but the average price from the Societies was 4¾d.

Theoretically the underlying cause of high bread prices was the cost of the grain "but", asked an 1895 correspondent-cum-tramway official "why should we pay here in Birmingham 5d or 6d a loaf when it only costs 3½d or 4½d in Wolverhampton? When grain sold for 35-40 shillings a quarter (Quarter = 8 bushels = 10¼ cubic feet) bread cost 6d but now it has fallen to 24-26 shillings should we still pay 6d?" 1895 was one period when not surprisingly tramway men agitated for an increase in wages due to the rise in the cost of living.

Health statistics shed another light on the lives of our forebears; two examples show what they had to contend with. London in 1881 had a birth rate of 34.8 per thousand population, and a death rate of 21.2, while 13,811 (17%) of the deaths were due to zymotic (contagious) diseases. Smallpox took 2,371 lives, measles an unbelievable 2,533, with scarlet fever accounting for 2,108 – all diseases now wholly controlled. 2,988 people died of diarrhoea (mainly one suspects because of dodgy meat or adulterated food), and 1,961 from whooping cough, for which a common 'cure' was to take the child out to inhale the fumes of roadmenders' tar, or to the gas-works which, for the reasonably affluent, could be combined with a day at the seaside, where the breathing in of the ozone was believed to alleviate the condition. 96 died of typhus, probably rat-borne, 977 of enteric fever, 654 of diptheria (for which vaccine existed), and the rest of 'fevers'. However, in 1882 the medical officer was pleased to report a drop in infant mortality to 148 per 1,000 registered, down from an average of 158 in the previous decade.

By contrast Sedgley, in the Midlands, with a population of only 36,860, had 18 deaths in one month (September 1891), giving an annual death rate of 15.4 per thousand population. However, and they specified this, there were five deaths in the Workhouse, but they were not included in the total. There had been three deaths from zymotic disease, one from diarrhoea and two from typhoid fever. Notifiable illnesses included two cases of croup, and one of erysipelas (in Tudor Place where "the surroundings were in a very insanitary state, a foul open ditch being close to the houses"). The medical officer also reported that serious sanitary defects abounded. In Vale Street the well of drinking water was much too near a stagnant pool and a stable heap, and in the Square soap-suds and "other surface filth" also formed a stagnant pool, while in Kent Street the ash pits were uncovered and smelled badly and there was no water fit to drink, although a patient "seized with typhoid fever" had been obliged to continue to drink from the well, suffering a serious relapse brought on by the impure drinking water.

The regional death rate, as reported in 1884, was quite illogical, with the healthiest places being Brighton, Huddersfield, Norwich and Derby, at around 18-21 deaths per 1,000 population. The worst, in ascending order, were Halifax, Oldham, Manchester, Preston and Bolton (31-34).

Draconian punishments abounded – a Gainsborough pickpocket who stole the very precise sum of £16. 8s. 4¼d received six months hard labour in 1883; a drunken lout at Covenham was fined ten shillings plus eleven shillings and six pence costs a year later; a beggar at Utterby received 21 days hard labour; a farmer whose horse strayed paid up five shillings and two boys of 11 and 10 years who stole a duck (although probably more than one) received six and two strokes of a birch rod respectively at Wells. In 1886, for stealing half-a-crown a 13 year-old Black Country boy, Fred Evans, received twelve strokes with a birch rod. Another pickpocket, this time at Heywood, in 1905, received fourteen days goal for stealing four shillings and sixpence, while a man, Frank Robinson, said to be an old offender, received two months hard labour for breaking into a church in Manchester.

Handsworth, September 1890: "The stone-throwing season has set in with a vengeance, and has attacked the youth of Handsworth with particular virulence until now it is scarcely safe to walk through the streets. Handsworth seems to be the happy hunting ground too of juveniles from Birmingham, who want a little practice in the art of shying. Perhaps they know the policemen are rather scarce, and take advantage of this knowledge. However, the youthful delinquents are sometimes caught, and yesterday four of them were summoned at the police court and fined. We hope the cases will come as a warning to others similarly disposed." But even in 1904 after a "sodding match", 10 boys from Heap Bridge, Lancashire, decided to throw stones at a train. Each father was fined ten shillings for each of the boys concerned, and then the following rather zany conversation ensued: "How long have I to pay?". "Two weeks". "You will have to take mine down then. I have two of them and the missus is in the Infirmary". "You must do your best". "I have the missus in the Infirmary ... you will either have to take them or flog them or give me more time". "You must do your best". But ten shillings was half a week's wages.

How far these punishments worked we do not know, but in 1891 a chap had been fined five shillings plus costs for being 'offensive' on a tramcar near Wolverhampton. Defendant: "How much are the costs?" The Clerk: "Nineteen shillings". Defendant: "And how much in prison?" The Clerk: "Fourteen days". Defendant: "Down the hole I go".

Sharpshooter, fec.

London: Pub. by G. Humphrey, 24, St James's Street, August 28, 1829.

PAT'S COMMENT ON STEAM ENGINES.

By-and-bye a Man will go a hunting after breakfast upon his Tay-kettle.

2. Already in 1829 cartoonists worried about hunting!

THE TRAM. WANTAGE. 14099

3. The Wantage tramway survived until the end of the second World War, but by 1922 no attempt was made to conform to the Tramways Acts, although the trailer is a cut-down electric car built as an exhibition model by Hurst Nelson. The locomotive is Manning Wardle Works no.1057 new in 1888, but bought second hand in 1893 for £300.

Chapter 2

1870 AND ALL THAT

As a generality, British steam road tramways had their locomotives built by Beyer Peacock, Black Hawthorn, Falcon, Green, Kitson, or Merryweather, but in the very early days there were a number of men who built experimental engines. These and the designer-engineers of road steam vehicles were the precursors of those who produced the later successful engines.

First, though, it is as well to take a look at how the laws of Britain regarded steam vehicles of all sorts, particularly as it was to be our steam trams that led to the relative freedom enjoyed by today's motorists.

The majority of the population (including miners, farm workers and other people living outside boroughs, and those whose dwelling had a rateable value of less than £10 per annum), could not vote until the Third Reform Bill of 1884, and even later when they could, it was often 'sensible' to vote for he who paid you. For our purposes women can be discounted as they did not all get the vote until 1928.

Until 1872 'open' voting was normal, the theoretically secret box was first used in 1874.

The underlying premise behind the open dislike of steam on public roads was simple; the people who governed the country all owned or rented horses, often in profusion. All road transport involved horses, all canal boats were horse drawn, and the railways relied on them for cartage and local shunting. The army's elite rode horses and the commissariat, including the vital field kitchens, was hauled about by horses – in the first world war the French railways gave priority to horse-fodder over the squaddies' food. In civilian life horses required hostlers, stabling, grooms, vit'n'ries, saddlers, harness makers, blacksmiths, and horse-breakers, and often made a vast difference to a farmer's income; the horse manuring the field it ploughed to grow the corn, wheat, clover and beans to feed itself and other animals.

Into this world which had hardly changed in thousands of years dropped a smoking, rattling, stinking, cuckoo, which was not only faster than a horse, ate coal or coke rather than hay, and which it seemed could go for hours where a horse would founder, did not need all the plethora of trades that depended on the horse but instead, at most, involved only three bodies, the steersman (complete with top hat!), the mechanic and a boy to stoke the boiler.

Ranks closed, leading to the Locomotive Acts of 1861 and 1865, whose clauses virtually stifled the growth of steam road vehicles' use. The relatively benign 1861 Act specified the calculation of turnpike and bridge tolls, forced the use of coke to reduce smoke ('an engine must consume its own smoke' was the cry) and brought in a speed limit of 10mph (16kmph) in the country and 5mph in the town – not unreasonable, as there was a lot of country compared with towns!

The 1865 Act was the worst that could be dreamed up, and it was from this the infamous "red flag" rule came in. A three man crew had to be used on any road-going steam vehicle, be it bus, lorry, traction engine, or road roller; one of these men was totally unproductive, being required to precede any such machine on foot at not less than 60 yards (55m) distance, displaying a red flag, and whose duties included warning drivers and riders of horses that a locomotive was approaching, and then telling the engine-driver to stop while the horses passed. The warning whistle (oddly enough a compulsory fitting) was never to be used, neither must steam be emitted when a horse was about, while safety valves were never to lift or blow-off, even if it meant the engine ran below usable pressure, or the driver had to risk a boiler explosion. This latter happened on occasion when for some reason egress from a village was blocked and a poor minded constable was harassing the crew. If a horsed person raised his hand, the engine, wherever it was, going up hill or down dale, or whatever load was being hauled, had to stop immediately.

Speeds were reduced to 4mph (6.5kph) in the country and two in urban areas but, it was a big but, the authorities of any English or Welsh township with a population in excess of 5,000 (10,000 in Scotland) could make local byelaws governing the hours when the machines could be on the road, thus further restricting their speed. The word reasonable did not apply as one town could impose a dawn to dusk curfew with movement only in the dark, (streetlights being incredibly rare), and one three or four miles away the reverse; small wonder farmers' contractors often took chances on weak bridges and narrow roads to bypass the worst authorities.

The Tramways Act of 1870 appears to have been drawn up by members of Parliament without knowledge of the 1865 Act, and although horse traction was expected, steam was permitted if the Board of Trade so authorised. Strangely Irish tramways were allowed to work their lines by an 1871 Act; but the first instance of steam power on a roadside other than experimentally was to occur in England under regulations dated June 1875, the first Irish line in steam not being until the Dublin & Lucan opened in 1881.

The Wantage Tramway Company was eventually allowed to operate as high as 8mph, although the required automatic brake did not cut in until 10mph was reached, and the general parameters laid out were those which were to govern steam tramways throughout their lives. The Royal Assent to the Act allowing the use of steam on the Wantage line was received on 27 June 1876; although it was to be 20 years before the 'Red Flag' Act covering other steam-going road vehicles was repealed. For many long years before 1876 steam vehicles on the public highways had fought to be given at least the right to exist, but both early steam buses and lorries were regarded with equal parts of scorn, fear and dislike. Probably the first road steamer was that

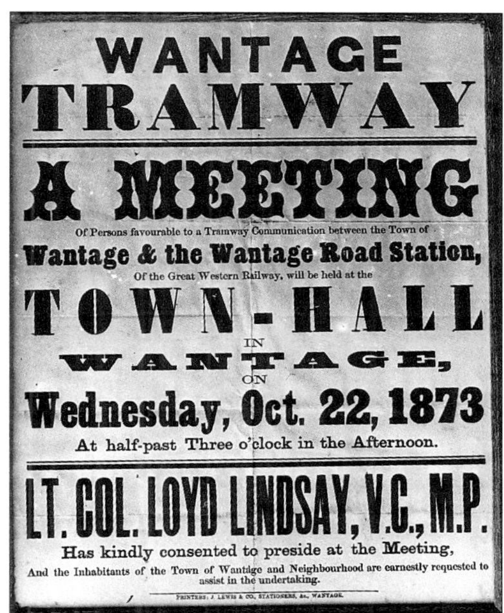
WANTAGE
TRAMWAY
A MEETING
Of Persons favourable to a Tramway Communication between the Town of
Wantage & the Wantage Road Station,
Of the Great Western Railway, will be held at the
TOWN-HALL
IN
WANTAGE,
ON
Wednesday, Oct. 22, 1873
At half-past Three o'clock in the Afternoon.
LT. COL. LOYD LINDSAY, V.C., M.P.
Has kindly consented to preside at the Meeting,
And the Inhabitants of the Town of Wantage and Neighbourhood are earnestly requested to assist in the undertaking.
PRINTERS: J. LEWIS & CO., STATIONERS, &c., WANTAGE.

4. Early proposals for the Wantage tramway.

5. Gurney's steam carriage.

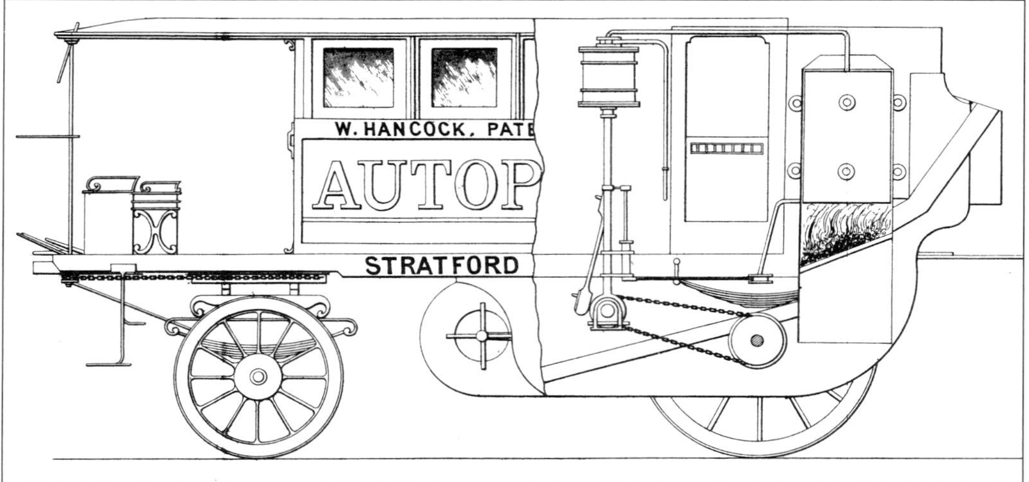

6. Hancock's Autopsy, 1833.

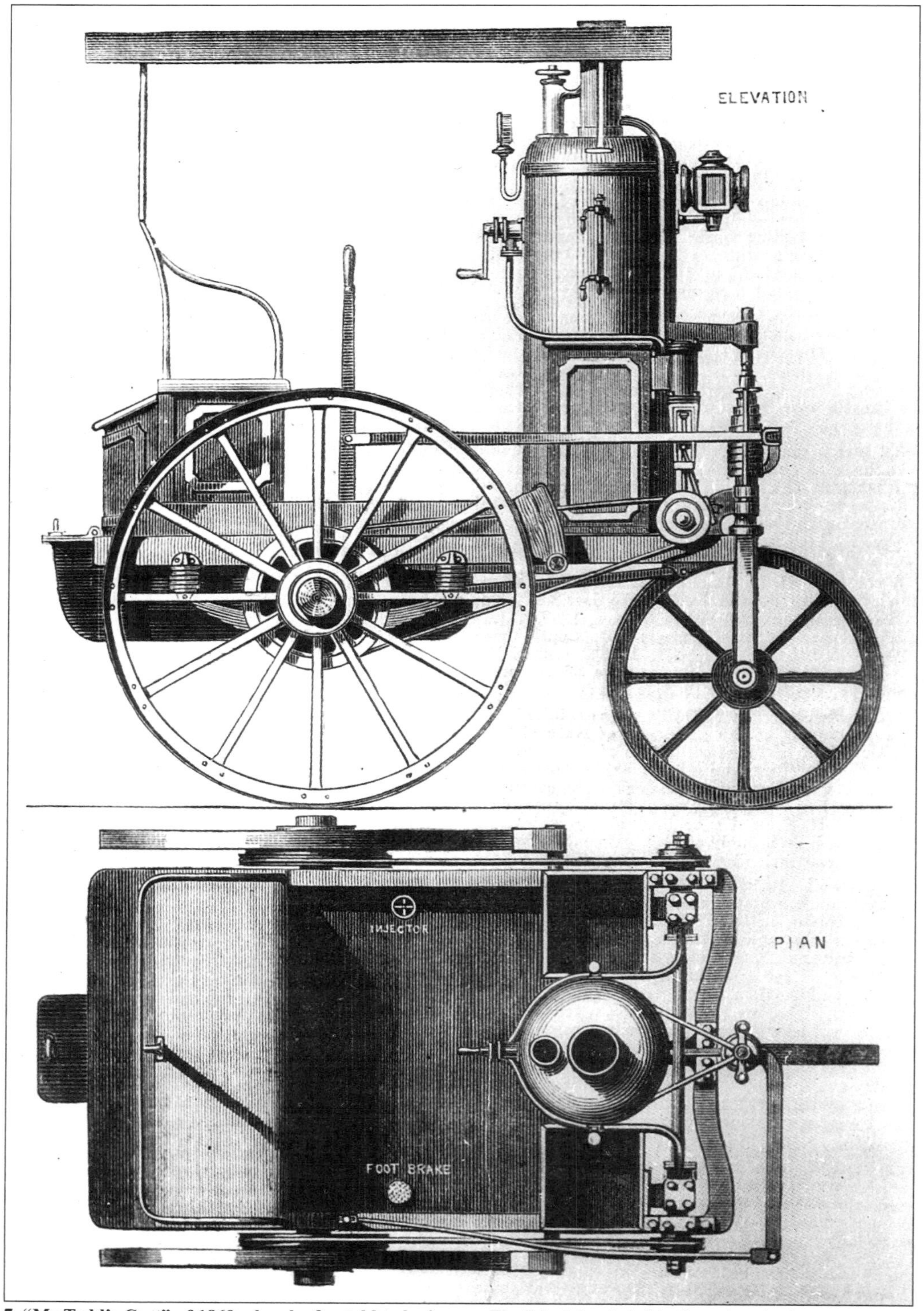

7. "Mr Todd's Cart" of 1869 when he foretold today's cars. Flexible drive (a belt) allowed springing.

clumsy brakeless gem of Cugnot which appeared in 1769, with next William Symington building a steam coach in 1786. The famous Captain Dick Trevithick, (whose name should be honoured as an English genius), is believed to have run a steam carriage (5½" cylinder, 50rpm) along Tottenham Court Road when the streets were cleared and the shops closed! In 1827, just 49 years before our steam trams, James Nasmyth built an 8-seater steam-car and ran it along the Queensferry Road. Probably not seeing any commercial use for it he broke it up, and used his fertile mind in other more profitable schemes. The same year another Scottish engineer, James Napier, ran a commercial 'bus between Kilmuir and Loch Ech, but boiler trouble saw the end of that. Goldsworthy Gurney now enters the scene, building successful steam coaches, one of which was by 1829 timed at nearly 17mph (27kph), while in 1831 Sir Charles Dance was running a commercial service between Cheltenham and Gloucester four times daily with Gurney vehicles at around 9-10mph; quite incredible given the truly appalling roads which all too often racked the boilers until the tubes twisted and blew; small wonder he used ex-naval stokers!

Walter Hancock was during his operating time (1831-1838) the most technically successful designer-engineer, but unlucky in his financial backers. He had certainly built ten separate steam buses, the largest seating 22 inside, although most were double deckers. Aside from a shortage of funds, a note relevant to steam trams came in a conversation, (reported forty years later at the Institution of Civil Engineers), between Sir Frederick Bramhall (later the adjudicator in a number of steam tramway tribunals), and Walter Hancock, when Hancock used to give him rides in his steamers. "You may be surprised to hear that the point in which I found most trouble is one that seems most simple: the tyres of the driving wheels, owing to their great wear".

In 1834 John Scott Russell built at least six coaches, running an hourly service between Glasgow and Paisley: 7 miles (11km) in 34 minutes. He had the foresight to lay in stocks of coke and water en route.

By the 1870s steam on public roads was at least known, with quite a few light steam 'gigs' or cars puffing about, (however ephemeral each may have been), and heavy road haulage passing more and more to the traction engine. In 1871 L.J. Todd ran a four wheel, 3 cylinder, 11-ton steam 'bus, 'The Pioneer', for four months between Edinburgh and Portobello, in all 952 trips at a profit of £8 per week. But then Mr Todd lost interest and, as we shall see, turned his attention to steam trams.

But all this was really too late, as now it was to be the era of railways when roads were passé, coaching hostelries fell derelict (many remained so until the 1950s), and roads received less and less care; it was also to be from 1842 the age of the traction engine. In the light of what was to happen to steam trams it is pertinent to note a comment of Thomas Aveling in 1861, made when one of his engines operated around Strood and Rochester drawing threshing machines, "A number of horses passed me but showed no sign of fear".

In 1876 steam tramways stood at a crossroads as they took their first tentative steps towards a future. Tramcars were running in Copenhagen, Paris, and a few other cities, albeit by and large unsuccessfully, but 1876 was also the year when the first real specification of a steam tramway and performance expected from its engines appeared in 'The Engineer'; no emotion, just science. Rarely, if ever, has such a definition of a steam tramroad appeared in print – a partial reprint follows, the whole may be found in the issue of this magazine dated 26 May 1876:

"It is worth notice that the present movement in favour of steam tram cars owes its success mainly to the labours of professional engineers ... an engineer takes a small railway locomotive, fits it with an apparatus for condensing steam, boxes it up to please the aesthetic tastes of horses, and achieves almost by a turn of his hand a very large measure of success. It is difficult, indeed, to see why steam should not be used successfully on a tramway; and the failure of an engineer thus to succeed might be regarded as abnormal. The mechanical difficulties involved are very trifling, and easily overcome; and we believe that nothing is wanted but a little energy and caution on the part of the mechanical engineers to render the adoption of steam tram cars almost universal. The things essential to success are that ample power should be provided to overcome the steepest gradients that may be encountered in all weathers, the prevention of noise, and the total suppression of all smoke and steam in a visible form. The danger of failure lies in underrating the resistance of a tram car, and in overestimating the power of its machinery; and we propose here to indicate the principles which should be observed by those who design and construct steam tram cars.

A tram road takes an intermediate position between a common paved or macadamised road and a railway. The resistance of a tram road in moderately good condition is less than that of the best common road, but much greater than that of good permanent way. On this last, at moderate speeds, and with wheels not less than 3ft high, the resistance is about 9lb to 10lb per ton – sometimes less, seldom more. On a fair common road the resistance is about 60lb per ton. Very few experiments have been made to test the resistance of street tramroads, but we have certain facts which bear on the subject which are available for use in an attempt to arrive approximately at the required information. The gross weight of a tram car carrying thirty passengers may be taken as four tons. This is easily drawn, and at a fair pace on a level, by two moderately good horses. The joint pull of these horses, under the conditions, will not exceed 150lb. This gives a tractive resistance of about 37lb per ton. It is possible that the resistance may be a little less than this, but it would be unwise to reckon on a smaller resistance than 40lb per ton. It may be asked how it is possible that such a difference exists between a tram road and a railway. The thing is easily explained. Tram car wheels are much smaller than those used on railways, and tram rails are never as clean as those traversed by an ordinary train. A little dirt on the rail will enormously increase its resistance to the rolling of a wheel on its surface. Inclines of 1 in 20 are met with on tram roads. The length of the incline may be very small, but a steam tram car may be stopped on it, and should be able to start again. This will add a resistance of 448lb. We have thus a total of, say, 600lb as the least tractive effort which it will be safe to provide for the haulage of a loaded tram car. A pair of horses are quite competent to exert this strain for a few yards if they have good foothold. It will not be wise to assume that an engine competent to draw a load of 4 tons under the conditions stated will itself weigh less than 4 tons with sufficient water for condensing purposes in the tanks. The car and engine together will thus weigh 8 tons, and require for the propulsion sufficient power to overcome a resistance of 1200lb. This does not represent the average work, but the maximum effort of which the engine should be capable. The whole weight of 4 tons of the locomotive being available for cohesion, we have 8960 (lb) over 1200 = 7.4 as the least possible coefficient of it that will suffice, which is probably enough, but certainly not too much. We believe that the figures on which our calculations are based are substantially accurate; and for this reason we are of opinion that, except for use on very level lines, no steam car is likely to succeed which has a smaller load than 4 tons on its driving wheels. Even on lines which are dead level it is important that a tram car should be able to start off rapidly, and to this end the tractive power must admit of being increased by four or five times over that which will suffice in ordinary work.

We can now estimate the horse-power which will be required. Let us assume that the average velocity is six miles an hour, or 528ft a minute, the resistance 350lb, the total weight moved being 8 tons. Then 350 × 528 over 33000 = 5.6 indicated horse power. This is probably over the mark, but the error is on the right side. Adding 1.4 horse power for engine friction, we have a total of 7 indicated horse-power. Such engines as will be used in tram cars will consume 50lb of steam per horse-power per hour. Thus 350lb of feed-water must be carried for an hour's run. The quantity of condensing water needed will amount to about eight times as much if its temperature is at no time to exceed 180 deg. Therefore, the engine tanks must hold 280 gallons, weighing nearly a ton and a quarter. We have assumed here that the gradients are compensating, so that although steam may be used at a much quicker rate than 350lb an hour at one time, it will be used less rapidly at another; but this cannot possibly hold good if the run is up hill almost continuously one way. Circumstances will seldom occur under which a tram car can carry less than an hour's supply of condensing water, and this fact should never be forgotten.

It would be impossible here to go into any minute details concerning the construction of the machinery of steam tram cars. It must suffice to state that a boiler of ample dimensions should always be adopted; that the fire-box, especially, should be very large, and that the rate of combustion should be moderate. Then the furnace will go without attention for at least half-an-hour at a time. Express trains are now run from London to Brighton with a single fire, no coal being put into the box between the two termini. If this is possible on a railway, it should be possible to traverse three miles on a tram road without firing up. If really good and *clean* coke is used, air being admitted above the burning fuel to consume the carbonic oxide evolved, no trace of smoke will issue from the funnel. If the steam is condensed rapidly enough no vapour will escape. To prevent the escape of smoke and steam is purely a matter of detail, easily settled by a competent engineer with a practical knowledge of his subject. We have said sufficient, we think, to prove that tram cars are not toys, and that toy engines cannot be employed to propel them. On occasions, indeed, the propelling machinery will have to exert as much as 20-horse power indicated, and the dimensions of all the working parts should be proportioned accordingly. If attention is paid to these matters, and the magnitude of the work to be done is not underrated, there is no reasonable doubt that steam tram cars will prove perfectly successful."

However one must note that at the end of this specification the editor of the magazine added a note of warning, which might have been better observed by some promoters and steam enthusiasts: "Whether, in the long term they (steam trams) will in this country prove much cheaper than horse-worked cars we shall not attempt to say."

The 1870 Tramways Act and Standing Order 171

To understand the variations in tramway ownership and operators it is necessary to go back to 1861 when the first, abortive, attempt was made to introduce a Bill into Parliament dealing generally with the regulation of tramways: mainly it is believed due to the activities of George Francis Train in London – his tramway operations starting a year earlier in Birkenhead were probably unnoticed by London politicians. In 1862 the Select Committee of 1861 was re-appointed but still with no result. Three times (1865, 1866 and successfully 1868) the Liverpool Tramways Bill

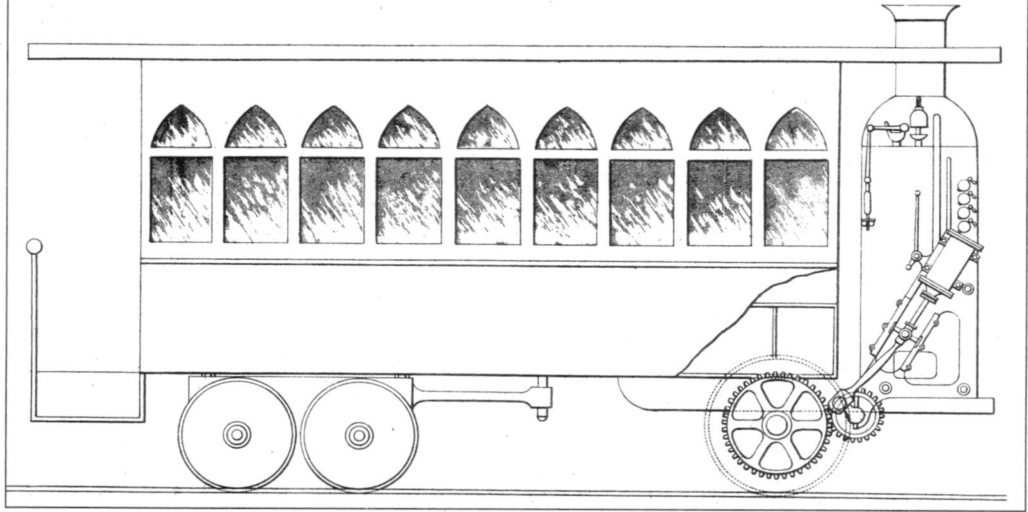

8. George Francis Train's steam carriage.

was brought forward. There was quite a furore repeated when the Glasgow Street Tramways Act was passed in 1870 for it was realised that within such a privately promoted Act any municipal authority could include a section (as in the Glasgow Act) whereby within a reasonable stipulated period, six months for Glasgow, the Corporation could step in, reimburse the original promoters their costs and become tramway operators.

This was totally contrary to any Victorian government's dream of fair trade – in effect, they said, we are giving any town or city the right to own the roads, dig them up, lay rails and then to run the trams at any rate they might propose.

Although not a steam tram operating city it is worth noting that by 1880 the Corporation of Liverpool had the local operators, the Liverpool United Tramways & Omnibus Company, over a barrel. The Company agreed to pay 10% on the cost of construction of new lines, older lines being let at 7½% of the purchase price paid by the Corporation to the Company for the Company's lines previously owned by (i.e. 7½% p.a. on £30,000, although the company lost £92,000 on the deal!). Outside the city the company had to pay 9% on the cost of construction. Bitterly shareholders attacked the Directors, for the Corporation could lay in new routes where they thought there might be traffic and the company had to pay 10% per annum on the cost even if no passengers presented themselves. Worse still the Corporation had no obligation to economise in construction, estimated in their own figures as £5,000 per mile, whereas their 1878 work rebuilding the old 1869 Inner Circle line had cost no more than £2,800 a mile. As a footnote by 1884 the Company was paying over £3,600 a year in rent for 6.3 miles of unused and unusable tramway branch lines. The Corporation it seemed, always won whatever the intentions of the Houses of Parliament!

Another quirk of Liverpool was that although the Liverpool Tramways Company promoted the original Bill a strange clause allowed any other operator to use the Company's rails subject to Liverpool Corporation licensing the vehicles; in which case a toll was payable.

In the case of Glasgow, the Corporation exerted their rights, laid the tracks but then leased them to an independent concern, the Glasgow Tramway & Omnibus Company for 23 years.

The 1870 Tramways Act allowed would-be operators, or at least tramway promoters, the facility of applying for a Provisional Order within a "general Act" which was far easier, cheaper and quicker than the concern having to get a specific Act. This procedure did, however, make it easier for Parliament to control all aspects of tramway life (although in reality this power was passed down to the Board of Trade) but in particular section 19 of the 1870 Tramways Act specifically forbade municipal authorities from operating tramways, even when they, rather than a private company, applied for their own Provisional Order.

Another clause, which grossly hampered the growth of steam tramways in Britain was Section 34 which stated: "All carriages used on any tramway shall be moved by the power prescribed by the Special Act, and where no such power is prescribed, by animal power only."

"Special Act" within this context was clarified in Section 23 as being any Act of Parliament or any Provisional Order authorising the building of tramways. Contrarily in Ireland (then governed by Britain) under the Tramways (Ireland) Act of 1871 any local authority could approve "any application ... to make and maintain a tramway to be worked by a locomotive engine ...".

Having satisfied Parliament that the proposed scheme was feasible and did not contain too much duplication of routes ("running powers" whereby two companies shared tracks was preferred) and having been issued with a Provisional Order the money had to be raised after, and the (surprisingly often) errors of the planners were eradicated when a 'portmanteau' Act could be issued which gathered up a number of Provisional Orders into one block – thus 44 & 45 Vict. Ch. clxiii Tramways Orders Confirmation (No.2) Act 1881 was "An Act to confirm certain Provisional Orders made by the Board of Trade under the Tramways Act 1879 relating to the Birmingham and Western Districts Tramways, Dudley and Tipton Tramways, Dudley, Stourbridge & Kingswinford Tramways, South Staffordshire Tramways and Wednesbury and West Bromwich Tramways".

The Promoters of these early Orders were rarely those who built them and were often office clerks and similar lowly beings given one share and told to "sign here, here and here". In the case of the Birmingham and Western Districts the bodies seem more solid – Herbert Wheeler, Railway Carriage Works, Oldbury; William Stableford, Oldbury; William Henry Dawes, Bromford Ironworks, West Bromwich; Alexander John Baylis, Redhill, Surrey (but Baylis was, and is, a quite common Midland name) and Richard Williams, Ironmaster, of Wednesbury.

Each "tramway" as we call it was divided up into a number of tramways (13 here) with single and double lines clearly defined, while "no passing place shall exceed three chains in length" was a typical clause. Inherent within the Standing Orders was a requirement that no Local Authority should object to a line (albeit "Not unreasonably" was a codicil) and many were the concessions made to obtain this permission (as well as beanfeasts for councillors!) The B & WD Order included the rights of, specifically, the Corporation of Birmingham to claim a deposit of £9,000 before work began.

Those of other local authorities were protected as was the right to free navigation by boats on the canals belonging to the "Company of Proprietors of the Birmingham Canal Navigations" – in this case the canal's interests always came first and the tramway company had to pay compensation for almost everything; today a canal or railway can be closed without bother (temporarily or permanently) as road works always take priority.

However, it is worth repeating part of clause 53 relating to the B & WD, but noting clause 54 defined the penalty for using steam "contrary to Order or regulations" and clause 55 confirmed the basic Board of Trade Byelaws.

"The carriages used on the tramways may, subject to the provisions of this Order, be moved by animal power, and during a period of seven years after the opening of the same for public traffic, and with the consent of the Board of Trade, during further periods of seven years as the said Board may from time to time specify in any order to be signed by a secretary or an Assistant Secretary of the said Board, by steam power or any mechanical power: Provided

THE TRAMWAYS ACT, 1870.

33 AND 34 VICT. CAP. 78.

An Act to facilitate the Construction and to regulate the Working of Tramways. [9th August 1870.]

BE it enacted by the Queen's most Excellent Majesty, by and with the advice and consent of the Lords Spiritual and Temporal, and Commons, in this present Parliament assembled, and by the authority of the same, as follows:

Preliminary.

1. This Act may be cited for all purposes as "The "Tramways Act, 1870." Short title.

2. This Act shall not extend to Ireland. Limitation of Act.

The Acts which are applicable to the subject of Tramways in Ireland are printed *post*, and are,
(1.) "The Tramways (Ireland) Act, 1860."
(2.) "The Tramways (Ireland) Amendment Act, 1861."
(3.) "An Act to amend the Tramways (Ireland) Acts, 1860 and 1861," 34 and 35 Vict. cap. 114.

3. For the purposes of this Act, the terms hereinafter mentioned shall have the meanings hereinafter assigned to them; that is to say, Interpretation of terms.

A

9. Commencement of The Tramways Act 1870 as reproduced on page 1 of Henry Sutton's "The Tramway Acts of the United Kingdom", 1874.

always, that the Promoters shall not use steam or any mechanical power upon so much of Tramway No.3 on the Bearwood Hill as lies between points distant respectively 57 and 70 chains from the commencement of the said tramway, until they shall have widened the roadway between the said points, so that a space of not less than nine feet six inches shall intervene between the footpath on either side of the road and the nearest rail of the said tramway: Provided also, that the Promoters shall not use steam or any mechanical power upon any tramways constructed within the borough of Birmingham without the consent of the Corporation of Birmingham; Provided also, that the exercise of the powers hereby conferred with respect to the use of steam or any mechanical power shall be subject ... to any regulations which may be added thereto or substituted therefor respectively by any order which the Board of Trade may, and which they are hereby empowered to make, from time to time as and when they may think fit for securing to the public all reasonable protection against danger in the exercise of the powers by this Order conferred with respect to the use of steam or any mechanical power on the tramways."

The Dudley and Tipton Tramways Order listed as one Promoter "William Wilkinson of Dudley House, Churchill near Kidderminster, Worcestershire, Ironmaster" ... not alas 'our' William Wilkinson! Others included a "coalmaster", a "merchant" and a couple of "gentlemen". Their Act included a clause covering "working over" or running powers:

"In the event of the South Staffordshire Tramways Order, 1881 (in this Order referred to as "the South Staffordshire Order"), being confirmed by Act of Parliament, passed before the 1st day of September 1881, the Promoters may run over and use with their horses, engines, and carriages, for the purposes of traffic of all kinds, so much of Tramway No.1 authorised by the South Staffordshire Order as lies between its junction with Tramway No.8 authorised by the Birmingham Order and the Dudley Railway Station situate in Tipton Road, when the said Tramway No.1 shall be completed and open for public traffic, but in the event of the said portion of Tramway No.1 not being constructed by the Promoters of the South Staffordshire Order within one year from the passing of the Act confirming this Order, then such portion of tramway may be constructed by the Promoters of this Order as though they were the promoters of the South Staffordshire Order, and from and after the completion and opening of the same for public traffic by the Promoters of this Order such portion of tramway shall be deemed to form and shall form part of Tramway No.1 by this Order authorised, and the Promoters of the South Staffordshire Order may run over and use with their horses, engines, and carriages for the purposes of traffic of all kinds such portion of tramway."

The South Staffordshire had, themselves, a number of more-or-less onerous clauses built into their Act, typically:

"Before the Promoters open or break up any road within the district of the Local Board of Coseley they shall deposit the sum of two hundred and fifty pounds in the Birmingham and Midland Bank, Limited, at Wednesbury, to a joint account in the names of the said Local Board and the Promoters. The sum so to be deposited shall from time to time during the progress of the works be paid out to the Promoters in the proportion of twenty-five pounds per centum on the value of the works in the said district, which at the time of making such payments respectively have been properly executed, such valuation to be ascertained by writing under the hand of the surveyor for the time being of the said Local Board. The sum of two hundred and fifty pounds so to be deposited shall, at the request of the Promoters, but at their risk, be invested in such securities as the said Local Board approve, and the interest thereon shall be payable to the Promoters."

The promoter of the Wednesbury and West Bromwich Tramways was just one man, Frederick Charles Winby, of 1 College Street, Nottingham, who turns up with regularity (whether as promoter, contractor, or patentee of a special rail section) throughout the early days of tramways.

All these tramways could use steam, were to be 3' 6" (1067 mm) gauge and to get this far would have cost £3,000-£4,000.

In 1871 the Vale of Clyde Tramways Act permitted the Glasgow and Paisley Corporations to hold similar powers to those in the 1870 Glasgow Act; Sheffield Tramways Company in their special Act (not Provisional Order but a full blown Act of Parliament) of 25 July 1872 incorporated a clause allowing the Corporation to construct the tramways if no suitable contractor came forward and to operate the tramways themselves if no suitable operator could be found.

The centre of Sheffield lies in a bowl with all roads out involving what were in 1870 severe gradients, taxing horses' strength to and beyond the limit. Cruelty to draught animals was endemic, not aided by the existence of a number of turnpike toll bars which in 1875 still remained among others on the Chesterfield, Langsett, Worksop and Meadow Hall roads. The initial nine miles of track cost £81,512 and the Company had to pay interest on the loans used to construct the trackwork plus £100 per mile per annum and furthermore they were to maintain the trackwork and road surfaces. Small wonder the Company tried to introduce steam in 1877/8 but on 24 January 1877 the Borough Council declined to support the Company in obtaining a Provisional Order authorising the use of steam.

One feasible reason could lie in that the Council had been thwarted in their own attempts to operate trams.

Parliament realised that the protective barrier within the 1870 Tramways Act was being breached by private Acts and adopted a new Standing Order, No.171 of 8 August 1872, sponsored by one of the more vitriolic enemies of tramways, Bonham Carter (Benjamin Hall, of 'Big Ben' fame was another). This Standing Order (and a similar one No.133 adopted by the House of Lords) expressly stated "No powers shall be given to any Municipal Corporation, Local Board, Improvement Commissioners, or any other Local Authority, to place or run carriages upon any tramway, and to demand and take tolls and charges in respect of the use of such carriages."

When a private Bill (in any form) came before Parliament it was scrutinised by a special committee who initially tested it against certain specified parameters – the Standing Orders – and for a number of reasons many, perhaps ill or hastily prepared, tramway schemes fell at this hurdle.

The effect of 171 and 133 was simply that no municipal authority (be it Birmingham or Burton-on-Trent, Halifax or Hull) could obtain powers to operate its own tramways. Lay the tracks and lease them out, yes, but place any car on them, no. But the best intentions can fail and it was Huddersfield that put the first crack in Parliament's edifice; and yet initially the Corporation had relied on Standing Orders, to defeat a scheme drawn up by the London Tramways and General Works Company to build and operate tramways in the town, simply by withholding their consent. In 1880 their own plans were passed and construction of the lines by the Corporation began the following year; by November 1882 ten miles had been laid.

An embarrassing situation then arose inasmuch as the ratepayers could see their paid-for rails rusting and no trams in sight. Simply, no company wanted anything to do with most of the network although they would have 'cherry picked' the best paying line, obviously this was not the intention that Parliament had so that when Huddersfield asked for powers to operate steam trams as one part of their 1882 Improvement Act this was granted albeit with a sting in the tail inherent in Section 17:

"If the Corporation are unable to demise the tramways upon such terms as in the opinion of the Board of Trade shall yield the Corporation an adequate rent, the Board of Trade may grant a license to the Corporation to work such tramways ... Provided that if at any time during such working by the Corporation any company makes the Corporation a tender in writing to work said tramways ... [for] ... seven years ... at such a rent ... the Corporation shall demise the said tramways to such company".

Only Plymouth and Blackpool (both 1892) joined Huddersfield as operators, although in July 1894 Glasgow made use of their powers granted in 1870 and began to operate their system. We could include Leeds in this arrangement as, following squabbles with the Leeds Tramways Company, they began to run their trams in 1894 albeit without official permission. It has been said that the Board of Trade were unaware of this change or that they turned a blind eye – difficult when many column inches in newspapers and magazines alike were full of Leeds' problems. Perhaps rather than cause problems to the millions of users and, possibly, difficulties in the council when re-election time came round some unofficial agreement may have been reached. Without this it is difficult to see how Leeds Corporation could have arranged insurance on the locomotives and trailers.

In the event after the failure of two private members' Bills in 1893 and February 1895 to ameliorate the effect of Standing Order 171 a third put down in May 1896 was withdrawn when on 4 May 1896 SO 171 was suspended for the remainder of that Parliamentary Session. Two Bills passing through Parliament benefited from this and in Sheffield the Corporation horse-drawn services took over from the Sheffield Tramways Company whose lease expired on 19 July 1896, another Act in 1897 permitting the electrification. Leeds, similarly, received unrestricted operating rights as shown in the mini-history later in this book.

On 12 August 1896 Standing Order 171 was effectively negated by the deletion of the clauses relating to municipal operation. The rest, as they say, is history!

10. The destination board shows the furthermost the Birmingham and Aston managed in their attempts to enter Sutton. Engine no. 24, an imposing Kitson product (T217), built and an unusually well sprung trailer – the inverted balancing leaf springs should damp out some shocks.

Chapter 3

TRAMS AND TRAPS

Or, as one might say, workers versus wealth.

The Birmingham & Aston Tramways Company operated a rather curious route from the Old Square, Birmingham, along the Aston Road to Aston Cross (Five Ways), where it bifurcated with one (single) line going via Park Road to Witton Lane at Aston Church. The other branch, also single, ran from the Cross via the Lichfield Road to rejoin its 'brother' at Aston Church.

Both lines were merged again into a single line (which caused problems in fog and snow) along Witton Lane to the junction with Witton Road, where the usual reversing 'wye' was installed. Eventually, the line along Wilton Road was extended to meet the Birmingham Central Tramways Company's line at Six Ways. The depot was (and is today as a museum) in Witton Lane.

The tram service commenced on 26 December 1882, but the agreements with the two authorities concerned, Birmingham Corporation and the Aston Manor Local Board, were dated from 1 January 1883. Although all track work was laid to Barker's system, Birmingham paid for their share to the city boundary, and leased the line out to the Birmingham & Aston for 21 years, while Aston Manor, after much debate in their Council Chamber, preferred to allow the Company to do the work, while being ready to take the line over after 21 years.

One of the major, if sporadic, traffics the company had was to the Aston Lower Grounds (the lines later effectively circling the area). Unfortunately the clientele who used the Aston Lower Grounds varied enormously from Sunday School parties (anything up to six trailers' full) to those who went to see glove, or even knuckle fights – and, worse, there were pickpockets, loose women and a "Ruffian Element". The Aston ruffian was not a pleasant sight fifty years ago, and in the 1880s must have been quite repugnant.

One Wednesday at the Aston Police Court during November 1883, cases included pick-pocketing (28 days hard labour); stealing half-a-crown (a nailer working 60 hours a week earned six shillings – 2½ times the amount stolen), for which the prisoner, a 13 year-old, received 12 strokes of the cane; a failed would-be suicide got seven days gaol; a chap who stole 12 roses to sell them on was adjudged insane; a drunk who had to be carried to the police station was fined five shillings, and a chap "loitering with intent to commit a felony" got 21 days hard labour. A year later a mob of striking colliers "behaved outrageously among themselves, and more than one in their drunken excitement got in the canal..."

But undoubtedly the bulk of the visitors were good-natured if noisy: "THE EASTER HOLIDAY AT ASTON [1883]. The Easter holidays brought a large number of visitors to Aston during the past week and the Park Lower Grounds and Aston Tavern have been numerously patronised. On the various places of waste ground adjoining Park Road there have been stationed swing boats, hobby horses, roundabouts etc., which have been well supported by the juvenile element. The Lower Grounds, during Easter Monday, were visited by upwards of 20,000 persons, all of whom appeared perfectly satisfied with what they saw. The programme which was published in our last issue was carried out in a highly satisfactory manner. The entertainment had been continued during the week and will conclude this Saturday evening." Let us not forget though how vital these 'green lungs' were, for in November 1882 the leader in the local paper was on the smoke nuisance in Aston. "Day after day, and week after week, our factory chimnies pour out clouds of dense unconsumed smoke, which joined with natural mists and winter fogs make a compound as nauseous and noxious as the worst London pea-souper".

It was not long before the Birmingham & Aston came under pressure to extend the line to Erdington, thus replacing an expensive, slow and not entirely reliable horse bus service. The opposition to this proposal brings out the dichotomy between two sub-divisions of the Victorian middle class. The factory, colliery and mechanical trades employers needed more labour to be made available, and therefore required greater mobility for their workforce. This labour had by now to include 'artisans' – carpenters, skilled machinists, engineers and their kind who would not consider living in the rookeries near the Works but wanted to move out (and up!) towards the suburbs. This meant transport, and although the railway was prepared to offer reasonably priced season tickets, for operational reasons they (and the LNWR was the prime player in Erdington) could not offer much better than one train an hour – more perhaps in the 'rush hour', but less in the day when Mrs Artisan (who, far from working, had one or more servants) was inclined to want to go to town for shopping or to visit friends in a suitable restaurant – probably Newbury's (later Lewis's) or Rackhams. And the labouring men and women who lived near the line of the tramway could look forward to dedicated 'Workman's Cars' albeit running at some unholy hour morning and night, but offering a return journey for the price of a single.

Elsewhere in the Birmingham/Black Country complex, tram companies had had a reasonable ride, with the exception of one planned through Rowley Regis; but different mores applied there – many of the Councillors who could say yea or nay were employers of labour and others were men like bankers, adept at trimming their sails to the breeze of progress.

But up in Erdington there lived Carriage Folk. And whatever we may think of them for their anti-tram activities, they had real fears. After all, they could read, and knew that colliers could riot and damage property and people alike, that nailmakers could and would upset the carriages of gentlefolk, and they thought they knew the rough element still went bull, bear, dog and cock fighting. Carriage folk also lived in dreadful fear of typhoid (if this killed Prince Albert, what chance had they?), diptheria, scarlet fever and erysipelas, all carried by the rougher classes who lived, bred and died in their foetid rooms. And they knew this because the newspapers (the only available source of information) said so. Reliable, solid, local newspapers whether Liberal or Tory, that carried matter-of-fact reports from local Medical Officers of Health, that printed in full (verbatim) reports of Council meetings, and discussed 'The Problem of The Distressed Poor'. And our carriage folk were frightened of what would happen when the hordes invaded Erdington: "Suddenly it is proposed to run steam trams to Erdington. It is well to note the origin of the requisition. It was certainly not the vent of a long-suppressed desire of Erdington itself – an expression of a great want, or even of a small one. No, the proposal emanated from the town. It was a magnanimous, disinterested (?) idea of the Tramway Company itself. It would be so easy and pleasant to glide up Gravelly Hill, and along the level stretch beyond up to the Swan with that insidious silent motion, which has such a fascination for horses; and to bring loads of the great unwashed, with their charming voices, to make a constant black line with the town, never possibly so palpable as upon a Sunday".

The truth is looking at Erdington today, one does wonder what all the fuss was about, until we find a note of November 1883 "Erdington retains many of its old world features; it can lay claim to a sylvan environment; its lungs still breathe fresh country air, unvitiated by poisonous manufacturing fumes; song-birds still gladden its life; its gardens can grow genuine country flowers; and its evenings are tranquil and its nights peaceful. It is, in a word, a healthy resort for the hard-worked business-man at the close of the busy day and week; possessing sufficient social and intellectual hum to save too much yawning and re-action. Its means of communication with Birmingham are ready and ample; trains and well-appointed buses ply backwards and forwards from early morning to late night for those of its inhabitants who cannot afford the gratification of a journey by road in their own conveyance".

In a further article the writer brings forward yet another fear, all too real, of that which we now call 'infill' or 'ribbon development', surely the greatest destroyer of cherished privacy. The writer put it thus: "Trams to Erdington mean, in a short space of time, their continuation to Sutton. And then the jerry builder will fill up all the gaps upon the country road with his abominations, to be rented by fried-fish vendors and very general grocers. It needs no prophetic mantle to predict that a tram to Erdington would be a relentless iron-arm and hand that would certainly and rapidly draw our rural district into the clutches of one of the least agreeable parts of the town". And of course he was right, for when the electric tram inexorably spread its tentacles, so ribbon development equally inexorably followed; and it was a common enough occurrence throughout most of Europe that the once beautiful suburbs eventually became overrun (one thinks of the unlovely tower blocks in every city from Worcester to Sheffield; in both cases today's 'carriage folk' have long since fled) and so families move out or are swamped; the great mill owners of the north eventually built their mansions miles from the towns that gave them wealth, and by doing so and becoming insulated from reality, lost control of their destinies.

Although aware of this hostility, at an Extraordinary General Meeting on 22 September 1883, the B & A agreed to apply for further powers to serve Gravelly Hill and Erdington, the chairman mentioning that it was a good road to Erdington and "it would enable the company to increase their traffic returns without increasing their expenses". It also seemed they were overstocked with engines "which are paid for" as in quiet times they were not all needed. One director, E.H. Carter, drew attention to the fact that originally anyway the B & A was supposed to go further on to Sutton Coldfield. Another thought was that the very heavy rental they paid to run trams was a fixed amount, and the more mileage they ran the better this would be amortised.

Their provisional order of 16th November 1883 included lengths in the hamlet of Erdington as well as the parish of Aston and the County of Warwick, and seems to have polarised matters with letters for, against, and fence-warming, flying in all directions:

"THE EXTENSION OF THE TRAMWAYS TO ERDINGTON.
To the Editor. Sir, Being an advocate for the extension of the tramway, I hope soon to see lines at least as far as the foot of Gravelly Hill, if the opposition is too great to allow it to approach nearer the renowned village of Erdington. It will be a great boon to the immediate locality, as we are a long way from either railway station, and the omnibuses, which are gradually becoming a thing of the past, are generally full inside before they pass our line of road, so that our accommodation is, I consider, very poor for a growing district. The extension of the tramways would be a great saving of time, and a convenience to those engaged, like myself, in daily occupation, and I hope we shall soon see the 'monster' at Erdington. I enclose my card, and hoping the promoters of the tramways will meet with success, I am dear sir, Yours faithfully."

In the issues of the local papers the company and its opponents carried on the battle at a higher level.

The fact was that however well thought out these arguments were, the fears they tried to address were real, and this relatively inoffensive notice in The Birmingham & Aston Chronicle, of Friday, 20 November 1883, unleashed a bliz-

BIRMINGHAM AND ASTON TRAMWAYS PROPOSED EXTENSION OF THE TRAMWAYS TO ERDINGTON

TEN REASONS FOR VOTING FOR THE TRAMWAYS:

1. The proposed Tramways to Erdington will be a GREAT PUBLIC CONVENIENCE as is admitted even by opponents.
2. The present Railway and Omnibus services quite fail to meet the growing requirements of the district.
3. The Tram Car will pick up the inhabitants of Erdington at their own doors and will convey them comfortably and cheaply to and from Aston and Birmingham.
4. The fares to be charged will be very low, to suit the working classes, and the cars will be elegant and comfortable.
5. The Tramway Company will pay all the cost of laying the lines, and ALL THE EXPENSES connected therewith, and will also become heavy ratepayers.
6. The Tramway Company will pay nearly half the cost of keeping the road in repair and will thus SAVE the RATEPAYERS of Erdington some hundreds of pounds yearly.
7. The lines will be laid in the best and most substantial manner with steel rails, and the mode of laying will have to be approved both by the Board of Trade and the Road Surveyor.
8. The rails will be so laid as not to interfere with the wheels of carriages; the width of the groove being less than 1 inch.
9. The road between Aston and Erdington is capitally suited for Tramways being wide and straight, with plenty of room for the Tramways and for the ordinary traffic of the road.
10. The Tramways will be very convenient for every inhabitant of Erdington who does not keep a carriage, and will afford a cheap, pleasant and easy mode of travelling.

RATEPAYERS, now is the time to show by your Votes that you are determined to secure this great public advantage, notwithstanding the selfish opposition of a few Carriage Owners.

URGENT!

EVERY MAN MUST THIS DAY DO HIS DUTY – VIZ.,
Vote Himself Against STEAM TRAMS
AND SEND ALL HE CAN TO DO LIKEWISE.

"STOP THE "MONSTER" WHILST YOU MAY,
OR WHEN YOU WILL YOU SHALL HAVE NAY."
POLL: PUBLIC HALL (THIS DAY) TUESDAY, 10 TILL 4.

Now or never! Do not let a little personal inconvenience hinder you and afterwards grumble. Not a vote must be lost. Our canvassers are volunteers; help all you can.

DECEMBER 4, 1883.

zard of paper, some of which has survived and is reproduced.

At a vestry meeting of the parish held on 28th November a proposal to the effect that "this meeting of the Highway Ratepayers desire their Surveyor not to give his sanction to the proposed line of tramways through the hamlet of Erdington," on the grounds that the available means of transport were quite sufficient (in plain English carriages and an occasional omnibus), was passed by a vote of 40 to 9. However, the minority demanded a poll which it was agreed would be held on Tuesday 4 December, between the hours of ten and four. One would hesitate to say this was rigged, but those who were most to benefit – the working classes, including ratepayers like our artisans and most clerical staff – would be conveniently out of the way at work.

RATEPAYERS OF ERDINGTON

VOTE AGAINST the STEAM TRAMS spoiling the neighbourhood and bringing the noise and turmoil of the town to our doors.

VOTE AGAINST an INCREASE OF RATES for Lighting, Guttering, and Kerbing the Tram Road ONLY.

Give your VOTES at the Erdington Institute on TUESDAY December 4th. 1883 between 10 a.m and 4 p.m

Proposed Tramways to Erdington
TEN REASONS WHY WE SHOULD NOT HAVE THE ABOVE TRAMWAYS.

1. The proposed Tramways to Erdington will be a PUBLIC NUISANCE, as is admitted even by their apologists.
2. The present Railway and Omnibus accommodation are more than adequate to the requirements of the district.
3. The Houses along the line of route will be subject to continual annoyance from the Noise, Steam, Smoke, Grit and Sulphur made by the Tramcars passing.
4. No reduction of Fares from the present Railway and Omnibus service can be expected.
5. The Public will either directly or indirectly have to bear the cost of repairing the carriages, carts, and other vehicles which travel along the road, as they will be constantly out of repair; for wherever rails are laid down the vehicular traffic is found to suffer.
6. The Highway will always be out of repair, as is invariably the case with roads composed partly of macadam and partly of granite.
7. On whatever system the rails may be laid, if a rail is placed on granite, macadam or wood, the setting will wear or fall away from the iron or steel rail, and although the groove in the rail may be narrow, it is the groove made between the road and rail that causes the damage to vehicle.
8. In case steam becomes adopted the danger to life and limb and property will be so great that no one will be safe. Accidents of a serious nature are already of daily occurrence on the Aston Road, some of which have resulted fatally.
9. The tramways are not being promoted by residents, but by speculators who care nothing for the comfort of the residents, or preserving the beauty of the neighbourhood, and whose only object is to get all they can out of the scheme.
10. Tramways are not a success. Take Birmingham for example. The first Birmingham Tramway Company's undertaking was purchased by the present Company for £110,000 less than it cost. Steam has already had to be discontinued in the streets of Paris, Sunderland, Nottingham, &c., on account of the danger to passengers and vehicular traffic resulting from the pace Steamcars travel, and the smoke and sulphur emitted.

RATEPAYERS OF ERDINGTON

attend early on TUESDAY NEXT, December 4th, and vote against your beautiful road being turned into a Railway Track.

And it all got quite dirty, a Birmingham solicitor, R. Fowler & Sons of 19 Bennett's Hill, sent out a batch of telegrams receiving the following replies on 29 November 1883. Note that they were all hand picked to suit the carriage folks' wishes.

From the Town Clerk, Wolverhampton:
"Steam tram licence expired and Council did not consent to renewal as General Purposes & Streets Committee considered the use of steam as then used was not in the best interest of the public. Write tonight."

From the Town Clerk, Newcastle on Tyne:
"Steam trams tried experimentally on a small portion of line a few years ago, no regular steam service yet established".

From the Town Clerk, Bristol:
"Steam trams were used in Bristol for year under licence from Board of Trade which was not renewed".

From the Town Clerk, Edinburgh:
"Steam tram cars have never been used on public streets here except between the city and Portobello abandoned because local authority withdrew consent".

And immediately after receipt of these replies an anonymous leaflet was circulated in Erdington:

STEAM TRAMWAYS

Steam Tramways have been **abandoned** after **Trial** at BRISTOL, EDINBURGH, NEWCASTLE-ON-TYNE, WOLVERHAMPTON, PARIS, &C.

Why, therefore, should **Erdington Ratepayers** be inconvenienced and their Roads experimented upon by **Speculators** who show such a sudden anxiety for our welfare?

Show by your Votes that what the Promoters call our "Insignificant few Carriage Holders"! is an **overwhelming Majority of Ratepayers without Carriages**, who are naturally more anxious for the Welfare of their Village than any Tram Company.

Both sides had resorted to a bare-knuckle contest, for the gentlemen made their carriages and traps available for use by the anti-tram committee, while the Birmingham & Aston Tramways Company made "plentiful provision ... for the conveyance of their supporters free of charge ... Churchmen and Conservatives declared their intention of voting for 'trams and progress' while some ardent and avowed Radicals were all the other way..."

BIRMINGHAM AND ASTON TRAMWAYS PROPOSED EXTENSION TO ERDINGTON

What the Opponents say.	What the Tramway Company say.
1. – That the roads are not wide enough.	1. – That a Single Line only will be laid with passing places, and that there will be sufficient width for any vehicle to pass the Tramcars and Engines on either side.
2. – That the Railway and Omnibus Services are sufficient for the District.	2. – That there are only 15 Trains by railway during the day, (or an average of one an hour) and one small omnibus each hour to supply the requirements of the large and rapidly-increasing districts of Erdington and Birmingham.
3. – That the Omnibuses should be supported and Tramways opposed.	3. – That Omnibus traffic destroys the roads, and Omnibus proprietors do not contribute towards the maintenance of the same. That the Tramway **make and maintain more than half the road at their own expense**, and, in addition, contribute to the rates on the value of their lines and building in each district. That omnibuses are noisy, badly-lighted and ventilated, and are regular "bone-shakers." That Tramway Cars are easy, commodious, well-lighted, and ventilated.
4. – That the Tramway Engines frighten horses, and make much noise and smell.	4. – That horses quickly become reconciled to the engines and cars, and take no notice of them. That a conspicuous few of the drivers and owners of vehicles on the route will never get reconciled. That neither railway trains or omnibuses are moved without noise and smell, and that the Steam Tramways will compare favourably, in this respect, with any means of locomotion.
5. – That roads are not lighted with gas, and, therefore, are unsafe for Tramways.	5. – That the saving in the rates by sanctioning the Tramways will far more than pay for lighting your streets with gas.
6. – That the Promoters benefit by the Tramways at the inconvenience of the Public who use the roads.	6. – That the large receipts from the Tramways prove their popularity and usefulness. That they, undoubtedly, benefit an enormous majority of the inhabitants at the smallest amount of inconvenience to the **fortunate few who possess carriages of their own.**

RATEPAYERS OF ERDINGTON.

A POLL is demanded on the above question, show by your votes that you believe Omnibuses are as much out of date as "Noah's Ark."

Give your Votes early for the Tramways, and show that you are in favour of progress and improvement in the introduction of cheap, easy and popular travelling.

The Poll will be taken on TUESDAY, December 4th, 1883, at the Public Hall, High Street, between the hours of 10 a.m. and 4 p.m.

Voting at the poll on 4th December was rather less democratic than might be expected: "The election was conducted by means of slips of paper, on which was printed the resolution proposed by Dr Machin, and passed at the recent vestry meeting, the terms of which were as follows: 'That this meeting of highway ratepayers desire their Surveyor not to give his sanction to the proposed line of tramways through the hamlet of Erdington, inasmuch as the travelling requirements on this road are quite sufficient'. One of these slips was handed to each ratepayer on his arriving at the table and rendering the necessary evidence of his having paid his rates, without which qualification no one was permitted to vote. He then wrote the word for or against across a blank space left for the purpose in a form of declaration, also printed on the slip, and, having subscribed his name at the foot, handed his paper to the clerk, and the record was complete."

And even during this 'confidential' process, a Mr Bibby, the collector of rates for the hamlet of Erdington got rather carried away, causing a semi-official complaint to be made, which rumbled on for a while to the detriment of Mr 'Bumble' Bibby. The contretemps was reported in the local newspaper in the forms of a letter:

"On several respectable ratepayers presenting themselves at the Public Hall for the purpose of recording their votes, their demand for voting papers was met by the official in question in the following terms – 'Can't have it; haven't paid your rates', and this in a sufficiently loud tone of voice to be heard by most of the bystanders, who were very numerous at the time; your correspondent being amongst the number. Now, Mr Editor, apart from the fact as to whether people who had not paid their rates (which is not a very easy matter just now in the hamlet, seeing that they have so largely increased of late) ought to have been excluded from the privilege of voting, and of which I cannot offer an opinion, I do think that no ratepayer, however humble he may have been (and in the case in question the ratepayer to whom I have alluded is a gentleman well known and highly respected in the hamlet) ought to have been treated in such an offensive manner by a person who is a servant of the ratepayers: and for what? For inadvertently omitting to pay his rates three or four months before the close of the year for which they are levied. I never in my life saw a gentleman subjected to such humiliation at the hands of an official, in public, as it was my painful duty to be a witness of yesterday, and I do trust that the attention of the Aston Board of Guardians, whose servant I believe Mr Bibby is, will be called to the matter, in order that the officer may receive such a rebuke as will prevent a repetition of such disgraceful and high-handed

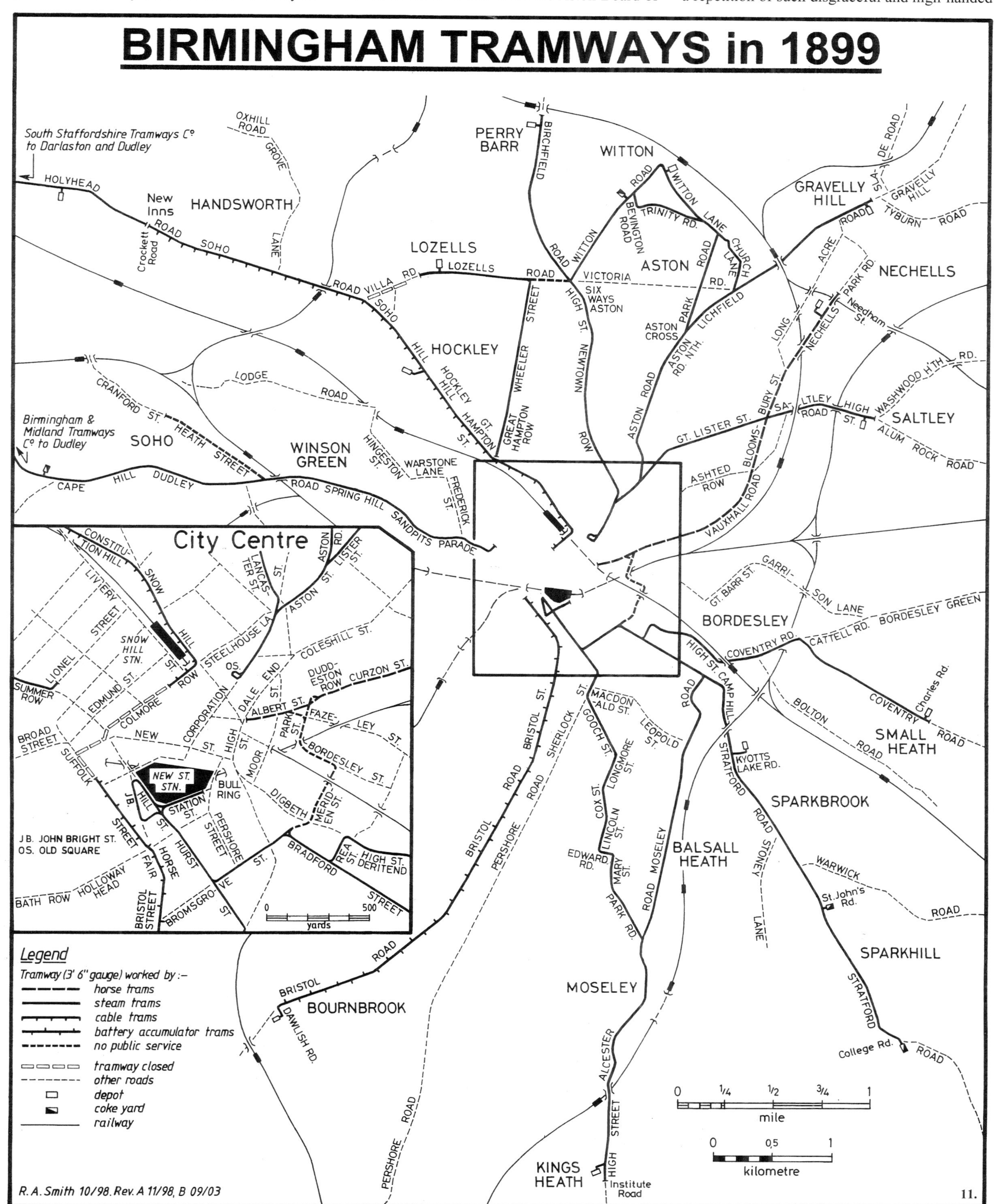

conduct in the future, and at the same time cause him to treat the ratepayers generally in a more courteous and considerate manner than it is his practice to do. I need not say that I am in possession of the names of several gentlemen who were treated as I have described. I am, Sir, your obedient servant, AN INDIGNANT RATEPAYER, Erdington, 5th December, 1883."

Surprisingly perhaps a mildly anti-tram newspaper, the Sutton News in its issue of 15 December, expressed disquiet not only in the manner in which the poll was arranged but drew attention to another aspect of Erdington life; "Since the declaration of the poll at Erdington last Friday night, matters in relation to the proposed introduction of the trams appear to have assumed a somewhat different aspect. In our report of the proceedings on Tuesday last week, we sufficiently indicated that the voting could hardly be taken as a test of the general feeling of the inhabitants, since, out of a constituency of some 1,500 only 228 recorded their opinion at the Public Hall ... After the declaration of the poll on Friday, a somewhat irregular public meeting was held, when a memorial, which had been refused by the chairman of the legal gathering, was presented, to which were attached the signatures of over 800 inhabitants each and all in favour of the Tramway Company's proposal. There appears then to have been either a considerable revulsion of public feeling, or the voting test was at the first unfair or untrue, and upon one or other of the horns of this dilemma the opposers of the tramways must undoubtedly find themselves impaled! It is worth while, for a moment, to consider of what sort the opposition is. It will be found on enquiry that it naturally resolves itself into two classes – the first, the gentry and private residents, who fear that the trams will bring people into the place; and secondly, the shopkeepers, who fear that people will be taken out of it. An inconsistent combination this, surely! ... The cost of the railway season ticket between Witton and Birmingham, before the trams began to run, was £5; after their introduction the railway authorities reduced it to £3, which, it will be admitted, is a very considerable concession, and the probability that a like state of things will result from the laying of the trams to Erdington ought surely to have its due influence with those who oppose the proposal for purely selfish reasons. The case of the shopkeepers requires to be more tenderly dealt with; but we are utterly unable to understand what injury can possibly accrue to their business if the proposal be adopted. For a score who may be taken out by the tramways, probably five hundred may come in, and the result will be a direct accession of wealth to some, and the indirect diffusion of it to all."

Whatever may have been the rights and wrongs of the matter – and one can see both sides had a valid argument – the fact is that in the B & A Act of 1884 only two small tramways and another reversing 'wye' were agreed, the lines to Erdington being rejected; but from 23 February 1885 the service to Gravelly Hill, or rather Salford Bridge, although the company always referred to the terminus as Gravelly Hill, was commenced with a horse bus service outward to Erdington. Notoriously overcrowded on occasion, and always somewhat erratic, this horse bus service remained unloved by the company even into the days of the Birmingham & Midland Tramways Joint Working Committee (which included the relevant councils) when the manager of the Erdington Omnibus Department, after mentioning that the cost of forage had risen from the 8 shillings and 11.704 pence per horse in 1905 to 9 shillings and 0.68 pence on 27 January 1906, said that "owing to the fact the price of forage was excessive, the feed scale was reduced on 22nd September last, one pound of hay being substituted for one pound of barley, and on 20th November, a further pound of hay was included in place of a pound of beans. Later a pound of oats was taken off and a pound of hay added, so that commencing on 27th November the feed scale was as follows:

Straw	2 lb
Hay	14 lb
Maize	8 lb
Barley	4 lb
Oats	2 lb
Beans	1 lb
Total	31 lb

This scale did not contain so much muscle forming element, but the bulk was increased, and taking everything into consideration, the condition of the horses did not suffer. Although a few of them are leaner at the present time, it is due in the main to the wet and mild, enervating, weather we are experiencing. If we could get a good spell of cold, dry weather, the condition of the stud would speedily improve.

No deaths. Mare bought for £25. Gelding bought for £34. Horses 62 and 74 were sold on 20th December as they were unfit for further omnibus work."

Where was the humanity of the carriage trade then?

Postscript – From Herepath's Railway (And Commercial) Journal, 24 November 1883

STEAM *versus* ELECTRICAL POWER FOR TRAMWAYS

Mr Editor, – The time is not far distant when either one or other of the above will supersede horse power on tramways. But it becomes a question which shareholders should carefully consider, before they sanction a change that may involved an outlay ruinous to many apparently fair speculations in tramway undertakings. Directors in such concerns cannot at the present stage decide as to the eventual cost for wear and tear of engines. Granted that the immediate saving may be as stated, 15 per cent, or even 30 as foreshadowed, still I challenge any man to say how long a tram engine will last, or what it will cost for renewal as it gets older. They have not been long enough on the roads yet to test this all important point. The Wilkinson engine so far has proved the best for such purposes, but even this is a clumsy affair, and must ere long be superseded by a neater appliance. Surely for the 3 or 4 horse power required to move cars it should not require such unsightly and cumbersome machines as those which have so far been introduced upon tramways? Electrical power is making slow but steady progress, and will doubtless ere long come to the front as a motive power for small engines. I think, therefore, it behoves those who have the disposal of Shareholders' money to act with caution, be content with horseflesh and small dividends till such time as these problems have been fully solved. Inventors will only be too glad to place their engines at the disposal of tramway Companies, for the sake of test and advertisement. By adopting even the Wilkinson engine, each of which costs about £850, a large outlay may soon be made. Eventually, as I doubt not, a much less costly, neater, and effective machine will be invented to supersede horses. When that day comes what a hue and cry there will be over the spilt milk and the too great haste with which Directors have rushed into steam, before the proper time has arrived for either this or electricity to be developed in a more economical form? My advice to Shareholders is, either to steer clear of tramway shares altogether where Directors are employing steam or be content or put their money into tramways having level roads, with a 1 or 2 horse car, till the day has come for making the all important change.

Yours obedient Servant, INVESTOR.

Chapter 4

PRO'S AND CONS – AND EARLY DAYS...

There are a number of viewpoints on exactly why urban steam tram companies were, in the main, unsuccessful or, at least, just viable. The majority of concerns were undercapitalised to the extent that there was little spare cash to buy new locomotives; the ground-level managers were far too busy just running the lines day-to-day to be able to evaluate any improved models the steam tram manufacturers offered (and they were precious few); many had half an eye on the forthcoming electrical systems, and those which might have done well found themselves lumbered with either 'wrong' engines, trade slumps, or faced such incredible and articulate vituperation that the steam tram protagonists deliberately stayed low-key, just collecting their meagre dividends. Finally there was the inescapable difficulty that licences for steam trams were always issued for short periods, giving little security.

If we take an individual and relatively successful company, the Birmingham & Aston Tramways Company, the problems can be encapsulated. They never built their promised extensions but bought 27 engines, three in 1882, nine in 1883, four in 1885, and twelve in 1886. Twenty four were by Kitson and quite orthodox, two by Wilkinson were regarded as scrap after seven or eight years, and their one experiment, no.27 of 1886, a Kitson compound, was regarded with disfavour: "The engine is rarely in service, the ordinary engine preferred". Although repaired, their bogie trailers (built 1882-86) were only noticeable inasmuch as four of them were made from eight four wheelers, and two – the most advanced design – were single-ended. But nothing in their fleet was less than sixteen years old when the B & A was sold out to Aston Manor UDC. And yet this tramway had started with such high hopes and many good wishes from influential people.

In this context it is worth quoting from an editorial leader in the Birmingham and Aston Chronicle, Nechells Gazette, and Saltley Courier of Saturday, 30 December 1882, which occupied virtually the whole of one page.

The article began with stating "Now that this long-promised addition to the means of a communication between Birmingham and Aston has been fully and successfully effected, it seems desirable to place on record some account of the successive steps in the execution of such an important scheme; by so doing we feel that we shall add greatly to the interest with which our readers must naturally regard the latest of our public improvements." Rhetorically, the editor asked why steam trams "which, as waggonways or tramroads were the precursors of railways" had not arrived sooner, and answered himself that engines would consume vast amounts of fuel "dragging heavy loads up the steep gradients of many high roads", and just as importantly there were not then the "thickly populated suburban districts round most of our great towns" which would make tramways "exceedingly lucrative". In the intervening 50 years (i.e. since 1832) towns had expanded as labour moved from country to city, locomotive engines had advanced and, says our Editor, "it seems impossible to place any limit upon the advantages which may eventually be enjoyed throughout the length and breadth of the land when tramways come to be universally adopted."

12. A typical Birmingham and Aston entourage photographed in 1900 towards the end of its days as an independently run concern. No. 19 engine is heavy, and more than capable of hauling the top covered trailer with its 66 passengers. Kitson T207, 1886 built.

He was, sadly, both right and wrong, for electric trams proved to be the means adopted to expand "throughout the length and breadth of the land". He admitted there were objections to tramways – "Objectors by the score may be found" – but shot them down one by one. One claim was that they injured the road, "nonsense" was his robust answer. "Now whatever may be alleged by unreasonable grumblers, there can be no fear that the lines of the Birmingham and Aston Tramway Company will tend to deteriorate the roads on which they are laid. On the contrary, in Aston, the Company is actually bound under the regulations of the Tramways Act to keep a large portion of the road in thorough repair, and in this manner the ratepayers are relieved very considerably at the expense of the company".

"In some cases, it must be admitted the lighter and fancier classes of carriages" could get damaged owing to their narrow tyres dropping into the slot of the tram rails, but the Birmingham & Aston "has shown all reasonable forethought by adopting an unusually narrow groove." It was true that as new the slot was narrow at seven-eighths of an inch (22.225mm) but the points or switches were ever a problem.

The company had even turned a disadvantage into a pat-on-the-back. Where there was not sufficient road width to allow double track they had either to use single or interlaced lines, or operate on a one-way system, but "As the cars ran on lines carefully laid for the purpose, there is an immense decrease in the friction encountered by the wheels as compared with those of a vehicle running upon the ordinary surface of the road. As a result of this ... it also follows that less power is required to move any given weight on the tram-cars, than would be necessary to move the same weight upon the road".

The mechanics of 'friction' were covered mentioning for readers to whom this was a new concept, that the rolling resistance of a wheel on steel rails must always be less than that of an iron tyred wheel on cobbles or other road surfaces. "Another point in which the superiority of tramways is incontestably established is the easy and quiet motion by which a tramway journey is pleasantly distinguished from the rough and tumble jogging inseparable from travelling by omnibus or even carriage, and in these days of high pressure and nervous exhaustion, such a consideration should by no means be lost sight of." The pre-history of the line took up a column or so, giving the passage of the Tramways Act through Parliament, mileage, and the agreement with the two relevant councils, the Corporation of Birmingham and the Local Board of Aston, later Aston UDC (in passing having just two councils to deal with was a great advantage – other companies were bedevilled with difficulties and local rivalries. If council A liked it, council B would always say no!). There was some degree of pride in the announcement that the sleepers and fixings were manufactured by the Smethwick Patent Nut and Bolt Company, and the rails were of course British, being rolled by the Darlington Iron Company in best Bessemer steel.

The company then had to decide which form of motive power to use, and it is worth quoting the whole of the relevant paragraph in order to contrast the relative ease with which they passed various hurdles, without the shenanigans practised elsewhere. "Meanwhile there had been much discussion as to whether the Company should be permitted to use Steam Power on the tramways instead of horses. ...Mr Chamberlain's Bill had rendered this possible, but it was still necessary to obtain the consent of both the Local Authorities through whose district the tramway passed. The question came before the Birmingham Town Council in July, and before the Aston Local Board in August, 1882; the usual arguments were adduced, to the effect that steam engines would be dangerous because they would frighten horses, and also be difficult to stop: the usual irrefutable replies were made, that on the one hand many horses are never frightened by the engines, while almost all would become accustomed to them, and on the other the engines can by means of strong brakes be pulled up with far greater ease than vehicles drawn by horses. To these reasons may be added the not unimportant fact that the use of engines prevents a large amount of unavoidable cruelty incurred in starting and stopping heavily-laden tram cars ... Fortunately both for the Company and the public, the Local Authorities very liberally gave their permission and the Company, anxious to procure the best engines, resolved to order them from two of the best-known makers, Messrs Kitson and Co. of Leeds and Messrs Wilkinson and Co. of Wigan."

Everything being ready, Major-General Hutchinson, the appointed Inspector, arrived on Friday 22 December 1883 (roughly four years after the application for a Provisional Order to build the tramway was announced) and he made a "thorough and searching" inspection of the whole route. "Many gentlemen interested in tramway enterprises were present, among others being the Mayor of Birmingham and Councillors ... Mr Orford Smith (Town Clerk), Mr Till (Borough Surveyor), Mr Farndale (Chief of Police), ... Mr Joesbury (Chairman of the Handsworth Local Board), Messrs Millward, Reading, Wragg, Bloor, Darrall and Nightingale (members of the Aston Local Board), Mr Broughton (Chairman of the Tramway Company) and Messrs Pritchard Southall, T. Smith, H.G. Smith and Wilson (directors), Mr C.A. Edge (engineer) and Mr E. Harold Carter".

We presume that around this time the menfolk (and the omission of ladies is noticeable compared with electric tramways twenty years later when some Lady Mayoresses actually drove the first cars with great aplomb) had some refreshment as then "About half-past twelve o'clock, a tramcar containing fifty passengers, and drawn by one of Kitson's engines, started from the Old Square. General Hutchinson however walked as far as Aston Cross, and subjected the line to a close examination; it will be enough to point out that the only points on which any anxiety could possibly be felt were as to the behaviour of the engines at sharp corners and upon steep gradients, and accordingly the severest tests were applied at every possible place of difficulty. The engines were driven at a high speed round several of the most formidable curves, up and down the steep gradients in Park-road, and in the course of their descent at high speed, were checked almost instantaneously by the powerful brakes. The quiet working of the engines, the smoothness of their motion, and the freedom from steam and smoke were especially noticeable and appeared to satisfy the requirements of the engineers who witnessed the trial and of General Hutchinson the Inspector."

13. Birmingham and Aston again in the leafy surroundings of Aston Lower Grounds after, presumably, bringing picnickers and the like for a day out. Rare to see such open land and even more so a matching pair. Locomotive no. 21 (Kitson T214/1886) and trailer no.21 (Metropolitan, Saltley 1886) and bags of coke on the trailer's platform ... make it all rather human.

Described as three miles two furlongs and seven chains long, the steepest gradients were noted by the Inspector as being 1:11 and 1:23 in Park Road, Aston, where compulsory stops were to be made at the top! There were regrettably no fixed stops as we know them today, drivers having to stop when and where required. The sharpest curve was of forty feet radius, the gauge of the rails "from the outer edges of the grooves" was the later-to-be Birmingham standard of 3' 6" (1067mm) while (and as this is mentioned three times one feels there was still some element of doubt) the groove was only seven-eighths of an inch against a bearing surface of three inches width.

The trailers (or 'carriages') were tiddlers, weighing two tons three cwt each, carrying forty-four passengers. It was claimed the engines (a mere eleven feet long and six feet wide) and the trailers were fitted with steam brakes (although no trailers were known to be so fitted) and lighting was by 'Müllers patent gas'. "With the express sanction of General Hutchinson, the Company were allowed to begin running their cars on Boxing Day, and to judge by the crowds, who have since then availed themselves of the new means of locomotion, there can be little doubt that a prosperous and useful existence is before the new undertaking, and that both the public and the shareholders will look back with complete satisfaction to the Birminghan and Aston Tramways Company in the Christmastide of the year eighteen hundred and eighty-two."

Mechanical problems reared their heads very quickly, but failings in both trackwork and the actual performance of the rolling stock could have been overcome. It is, however, an inescapable fact that the very existence of steam trams running on public roads left them open to attack. People today, other than those directly affected, are seemingly quite blasé when details of another accident killing two, three, four or five people is read out in the course of a television news bulletin. How does it go? Blah, blah, "two people, a boy and girl killed", blah, blah, "when their car was hit by a lorry", blah, blah, "lorry driver taken to hospital with bruises", blah, blah, "today's total of dead on the roads twenty-two" blah, blah, and then we watch the weather forecast.

But it was not like that in the 1880s. There was no TV, no radio, just newspapers which appealed primarily to the middle class ratepayers – the people who voted for, and stood for, the local council; the people who could, would, and did, influence the success of a tramway. Some councillors hated tramways with virulence that is difficult now to comprehend, while others took every opportunity to disparage them.

We have a cameo of this in November 1884. "The Surveyor (of the Rowley Regis Local Board of Health) reported that the Birmingham Western Districts Tramways Company were posting notices to apply for a provisional order for the construction of a line from Oldbury boundary to Blackheath, thence through the village of Rowley, and along the Rowley Road to the Dudley boundary at Dixon's Green.

The Chairman: "I have to ask what is your proposition with regard to the proposed line?"

Mr Taylor: "I should say dead against it."

Mr Barker: "I should keep them out of the parish."

Mr Taylor: "They ought not to be allowed."

The Chairman said he was very strongly prejudiced against the tramways when he saw how they were coming into the roads in all directions, and endangering people's lives and limbs. But before saying anything about it at the Board he felt disposed to call a parish meeting and see whether the inhabitants wished for the tramways or not.

Mr Taylor: "If the tramways come through Blackheath there will be one killed every day."

The Chairman: "I must confess I am dead against all tramways. I hate them, they're the ruin of our roads."

Mr Round: "Are the roads sufficiently wide for them?"

The Chairman: "Nothing like sufficiently wide..." Continuing, he said it was no joke to drive up Dudley Street with that beastly thing (the tramcar) elbowing one up. If his horse had not been staunch on a recent occasion he should have been knocked over, as there was not six inches of room all the way up. Mr Round considered the tramways should not be allowed where the roads were not wide enough.

If this wasn't enough, further discussion then ensued in which the Chairman expressed his regret that they could only oppose the tramways after calling a public meeting, but the Clerk informed him that as it was only a Provisional Order the Board could decide against it without the sanction of the ratepayers. It was fairly obvious from the reports, if not expressly said, "Whoopee" and "Hurrahs" were in the air at the thought of being able to hinder progress.

"If the Board were unanimously of opinion that they ought to oppose the obtaining of the Order they might do so at once, and he had no doubt that the mere show of opposition would make the promoters do as was done in a previous instance, (and) withdraw the application at once. He [the Chairman] moved that the application for a Provisional Order for the extension of the tramway system to Rowley be opposed by the Board. Mr Taylor seconded, and the motion was unanimously carried."

Did the members of the Local Board ever guess the furore they were to cause? The local, very influential newspaper (not one to wholly back tramways) inveighed against them. "Dudley Herald, Saturday, November 20th, 1884: We much regret the necessity for again adverting to the policy pursued by the Rowley Local Board of Health with reference to tramways projects; and we do so now because we believe that their policy, if successful, must necessarily be most injurious to the interests of those the Board profess to represent ... Tramways have become as essential to the prosperity of populous places as railways; and those districts whose governing bodies take an enlightened view of their duties will do all they can to encourage the formation of steam tramways, which cannot fail to be beneficial to the traders, inhabitants and property owners, and to be a great convenience to the public. Those, on the contrary, who opposed tramway schemes show that they are not alive to the value of the progress which is going on around them; their districts will decline and prosperity vanish, and soon the value of the property and the number of inhabitants, which are now sufficient to constitute a guarantee of success to a tramway project, will have become so reduced as to render such an undertaking impracticable."

The Birmingham Western Districts Tramways Company proposed to make this new line from the main line at Oldbury, through the heart of the old manufacturing area of the Black Country, thus going via Blackheath and Rowley Regis to Dixon's Green, Dudley. "The Rowley Board appear to be inclined to oppose this scheme, as they did the one to connect Cradley and Netherton with Dudley; and one member of the Board expressed himself as 'dead' against tramways generally. In his representative capacity he should remember that it is possible in being 'dead' against this particular scheme, to be acting 'dead' against the interests of his constituents, whose welfare he is bound to make his first consideration. The pleas about danger to the public is scarcely worth noticing, in view of the fact that steam tramways have proved to be less dangerous than the same amount of traffic conducted by ordinary vehicles. The tramcars take up a less width of road than an ordinary wagon, are far more under control, and are always in care of responsible men. The feeling of the Rowley Board is in strong contrast with that of Sedgley who, after the tramway had been in operation for some time, stated publicly, that 'it had conferred a boon on the parish', and had given to its inhabitants 'the greatest benefit the Sedgley people had ever had'. A public meeting of the ratepayers and inhabitants of the parish of Rowley would probably very much alter the views of their representatives as to tramway enterprise.

The minutes of the prosaically named Streets & Gas Committee, whose members were drawn from the Dudley Borough Council General Purposes Committee, followed an (almost) neutral stance until 3 January 1883 when "The ex-Mayor reported that owing to the action taken by the Rowley Local Authorities, the Promoters of the above Tramways had decided not to proceed further in their application for a Provisional Order for the construction of these tramways."

Nearby Brierley Hill was another relatively small area but lay athwart the line of the Dudley & Stourbridge Steam Tramway; at meeting after meeting the Local Board scritched and scratched at the subject; it does seem a fact that if only some truth was spoken the tramway company brought many of their problems on themselves. In a typical example reported on 10 April 1886, "The Chairman said he had several complaints about the smoke and steam issuing from the tramway engines. Mr Roberts, of Church Hill, said it was a very great nuisance to his house. The Tramway Company were of course under certain regulations which they were bound to obey. Mr Fereday said that if there was extra smoke it should be allowed to emit before the populous places were reached. Mr Grove said he had been struck with the want of facility to get in and out of the tramcars. Twelve months ago he understood the Company applied to the Board for leave to enlarge the cars and engines six inches. If that six inches additional had been made to the cars, travelling would be much more convenient. The Chairman said the increased width only applied to the engines, and only one he believed had yet been enlarged. The directors of the Tramway Company however were not very obliging in other ways. Several gentlemen, himself included, having sons who went to the Stourbridge Grammar School, had applied for season tickets for them between Brierley Hill and Stourbridge. He had himself written two or three times, and the only answer he could get was that if the boys wanted season tickets they must pay the full price of one between Dudley and Stourbridge – nearly £4 a year. The directors said that was cheap enough, and as low as they could afford it. He however did not see why Dudley should have an advantage over Brierley Hill. He had offered £2 for a season ticket for his son – that being half the price of a ticket from Dudley to Stourbridge – and thought it a fair sum, seeing that it was only 2d. from Brierley Hill to Stourbridge, and 3d. from Brierley Hill to Dudley. The company however refused to do anything of the sort." The railway, for the same journey, allowed Grammar School children a season ticket at the cost of £1.17s.6d. but "The Tramway Company would not take £2 for the same distance (interjection – Oh!). He considered the Company had treated him in a rather cavalier spirit. It was not for him to tell them how to conduct their business, but his opinion was that they were not looking after their own interests."

Another councillor (Mr Guest) said he had approached the chairman of the Tramways Company to ask to help "but he positively refused ... with respect to the inconveniences of travelling, Mr Guest thought the Board had only to ask for better accommodation – more regular-

14. The smoke and fumes you can see from the Kitson engine running on the Dudley and Stourbridge Steam Tramways Co.'s line is, of course, an illusion. Both the tram engine (No.5, Kitson T91/1884) and the trailer (No.8 Midland Railway Carriage and Wagon Works 1884) are recovering from their 5¼ mile (8.45km) trip from Dudley. The crew, also relaxing, have presumably just watered and made up the fire.

ity in starting and stopping – to get it. It would be for the benefit of the shareholders and of the public who used the trams."

After some further discussion Mr Guest then seems to have got carried away, declaring "The times kept by the trams were bad, the convenience was bad, and the conduct of the conductors was very reprehensible and careless." One in three of the trams passing "the lamp in the centre of High Street" did not stop at all, with the conductors looking neither right nor left. He agreed the engines had slackened their speed, "but the wheels never ceased revolving." He then seems to have back-tracked and admitted, "No doubt the public are somewhat to blame, as people sometimes stood twenty yards on either side of the proper stopping point, and caused the tram to stop sometimes by Mr Marsh's shop, and again at the Horse Shoe Market. That was a cause of complaint for the company."

After a discussion over whether the track should be doubled to make matters better ... (it should, but a Mr Freeth added that a double set of rails would serve but to block the way) ... the Chairman added that the steam and smoke alluded to earlier (Mr Freeth, again, "he had frequently seen as much emitted between Round Oak and the Level as would come from a railway engine") could be avoided if the engine ran more regularly. "Owing to prolonged stoppages, and the consequent loss of time, the drivers sometimes exceeded the speed allowed by the Act of Parliament. Were the speed uniform the smoke and steam would not be emitted."

And then the Chairman stated his Board should have received better treatment "...at Oldbury, Moseley, and Balsall Heath he found the tramway companies had to pay a large sum of money to the Boards for the privileges of laying down the lines ... The Brierley Hill Board had pressed for no such payment."

Even when it was obvious that steam tramways could be perceived as a problem many councils fully understood that both the employers and (in the main) employees were doing their best to operate as well as they could. Birmingham Council set its face against steam and tried to bully all the local area councils to support them in "Suppressing the Steam Tram Nuisance."

Early in May 1888 the Town Clerk of Dudley read a communication from his opposite number in Birmingham stating that a conference of local authorities was to be held in Birmingham "to consider the best means to abate the nuisance arising out of the emission of steam from tram engines..." The council members agreed that the Town Clerk might attend but, and it was a big but, "they might agree to do something to abate the nuisance, but they must not countenance anything that would have a tendency to interfere

15. On a clear day and with an awful lot of imagination, this part of the Alcester Road, Moseley, can still, just, be recognised. What is different apart from the people, shops, air and quietness, is the condition of the road. This is exactly why the tram was so vital a means of urban transport.

with the public convenience which tramways undoubtedly gave. They may be a great nuisance and danger, but the beneficial element predominated, and, therefore, they must not do anything likely to check their usefulness – (hear, hear)." The Tipton Local Board agreed with Dudley but made an away-day of it, sending three councillors plus the Chairman!

The end result of the conference was, inevitably, a fudge, and worth quoting to show how attitudes could vary from town to town. "A conference of representatives from local bodies of the district to consider what steps may be taken to prevent the nuisance arising from steam trams was held on Wednesday at Birmingham – Mr Weekes (Clerk to the Aston Local Board) read a resolution as follows: "That this conference of representatives of local authorities of districts through which the tramways of the Central Company, the Aston Company, and Midland Company pass, is of opinion that the use of steam as a motor ought to be abolished unless the dangers and nuisance arising therefrom in the shape of smoke, steam, and offensive odours are minimised so as to cease to be a cause of reasonable ground of complaint by passengers or the public. And inasmuch as the law for breaches of the Board of Trade regulations in these respects cannot be enforced against the real offenders – namely the tramway directors and managers of the companies, but only against engine drivers, whose stereotyped defence is that they are entrusted with defective engines – there is no alternative for the local authorities but to make the further use of steam absolutely dependent on their own regulations being complied with. And the members present undertake to respectively recommend their authorities, when the existing licenses for steam-user expire, to regrant them for a limited period only (say twelve months), with the understanding that they will not be renewed unless in the meantime the escape of smoke and steam is brought within proper control, and the foul stenches prevented by the use of suitable 'fuel' ". The Mayor said he would accept that resolution, but not for adoption by the conference. Mr E.M. Warmington (Town Clerk of Dudley) said if the companies would only meet the objectors in the matter of the fuel they used, the consent to burn North-country coke, the bye-laws of the Board of Trade were sufficient to keep down all the other evils complained of; and if the companies would remedy that one matter, they should not attempt to hamper the carrying on of the tramways, which were undoubtedly "a great public convenience." Mr Wright (Rowley Regis) and Dr Underhill (Tipton Local Board) expressed sympathy with the objects of the conference, and the latter gentleman drew attention to the fact that "the engines of the South Staffordshire Company in his district travelled at a highly dangerous rate, and not only emitted steam and sulphur, but also fire, which at night was a grave source of danger to the drivers of horses." A lengthy discussion took place on the matter, but no real action was taken."

Chapter 5

TRAVAILS OF A TRAM ENGINE

"The Fire-box is of copper, the tubes are brass, wheels of wrought iron, tyres of best crucible steel, axles, crank-pins, piston rods, motion bars, crosshead pins, and excentric sheaves of best forged steel. The axle-boxes are of gun metal". *BLACK HAWTHORN 1883.*

The basic components of a street tramway are the track, the locomotives, and the trailers. Initially, at least with orthodox track and new engines, there is no doubt the ride was quite good, despite the poor springing and apparent top heaviness of the trailers. The underlying problems found in laying orthodox trackwork are covered in chapter 8, but finance was always a major difficulty; the temptation to use a light (say 40lb/yard 20kg/metre) rail section must have been great as to an unskilled eye there was little apparent difference to a rail 25% heavier (and 25% dearer, as rails were sold by the ton) whereas an engineer would be aware that not only was the foot (base) wider, giving a better bearing surface, but the vertical section (web) was meatier and less likely to bow or twist. Finally, the head was of larger section, giving longer life. The contractor, however, would merely regard a heavier rail as a nuisance, requiring more labour to handle it. Furthermore, heavier rail required heavier and more expensive foundations.

A curiosity of any well laid railway is that theoretically the wheel flange is superfluous on straight lengths of trackwork, as assuming the rails are laid to the correct cant, and the tyres are in good condition, the natural coning effect will prevent derailments, the flange existing basically to prevent the wheels riding over the rails on a curve.

In 1882 a variant on this philosophy was tried in France with The Engineer allowing some correspondence: "Sir, I have never seen mentioned in THE ENGINEER particulars about the tramways of the Compagnie Générale des Omnibus de Paris. Some prominent features are: First, the wheels which have flanges only on one side, while the rails are grooved each side so as to allow the cars to run either way. From experiments that were made by M. Tresoa, the saving in the power needed for traction amounts to 10 to 12 per cent, against wheels with two flanges. This difference comes from the impossibility of keeping the two rails on common roads always exactly the same distance, so that it brings a strain and resistance on the flanges of the wheels. Small stones and mud in the rails will have the same effect. It gives also facilities for turning curves and still the cars keep the metals as well as other vehicles. They use no switches or points for sidings, which are necessary with other cars. ... F. Gougy, Boulevard Mont Parnasse, 6th February."

"Sir, It may be stated generally that practice obtains, at least with the public, a greater favour than theory, although the practice may be doubtful and even faulty, which is not the case with theory. Good practice may be said to be that built on theory, properly so-called ... The trailing of rolling-plant on railways has been already more or less discussed, and for special purposes the adoption of a central rail proposed. There is no startling novelty to be considered ... in regard to the control exercised by the rails on railways, if the proximity of the contact surfaces be preserved, we arrive at the consideration of a single flange wheel, and a corresponding single grooved rail, as the essential requirements of present practice in 'trailing' rolling-plant on railways. The tramway rail and car wheel illustrate the practice. From this it may be seen by a little consideration that, whatever danger or inconvenience there may be to the public by the construction of tramways in public thoroughfares, such are intensified by the existing practice of grooving both rails, when as may be seen, only one groove rails is necessary for the efficient trailing of the car. The road-surface of the second or plain head rail might be considerably diminished, to the advantage of the public and economy in traction power. J. SMITH, Kenningtongrove, Lambeth, 11th September."

(Mr Smith's exposition was long and complex, involving regarding a wheel as a cylinder whose bearing surface could be reduced "to vanishing point".)

"Sir, The theory which your correspondent, Mr J. Smith, wishes to uphold is carried out in actual practice in Paris at the present time, where some of the tramways are worked with American horse cars which only have flanged wheels on one side. The only time I rode on one it left the metals at the first sharp curve. The flanged wheels were nearest to the radius of the curve. ROBT. ED. PHILLIPS, 32 Selby-road, Anerley, Sept. 18th."

The combination of flanged tram wheels and grooved rail has, as said, many disadvantages, some of which are shown in the drawings.

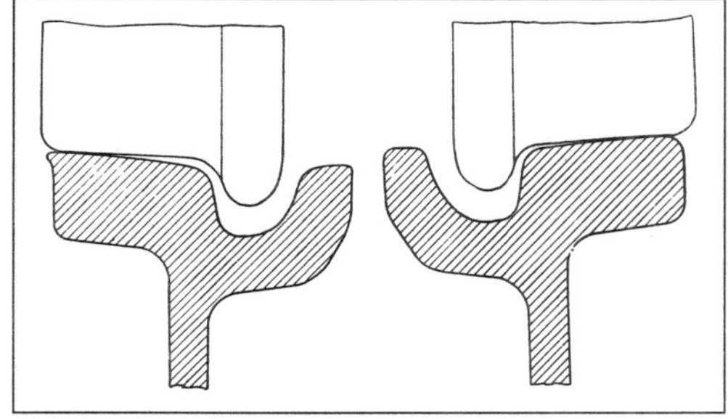

16. **New tyres on old rails.**

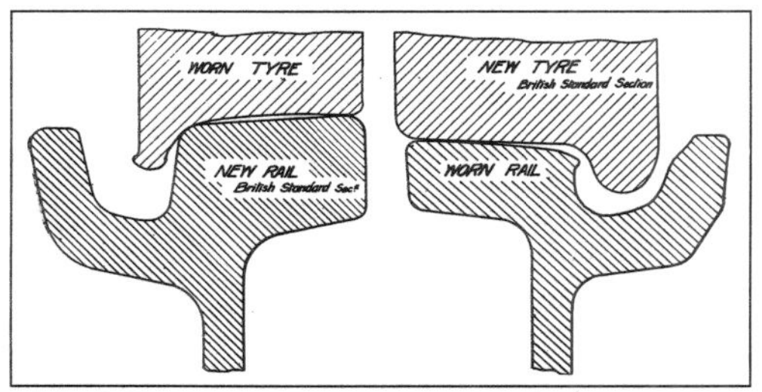

17. Left: Faulty contact between new rail and worn tyre. Right: Faulty contact between new tyre and worn rail.

For a number of reasons (primarily the design of the rolls in the steelworks) most tram rails are flat topped on delivery, but within 48 hours of use they become abraided by the tyres, taking up a convex form, and in a year or so slope towards the groove at an angle of 1 in 20. Looking at the camber of most roads it is obvious why engineers preferred to occupy the crown of the road, but when they run nearer the gutter, the angle of the wheel to the rails is altered – the drawing shows this clearly.

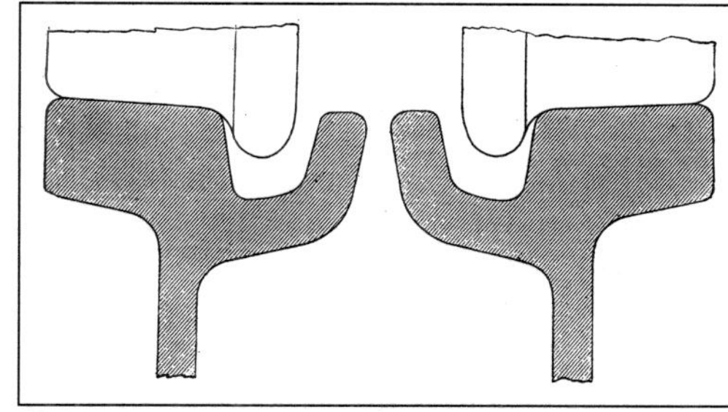

18. New tyres and rails at rest on straight track.

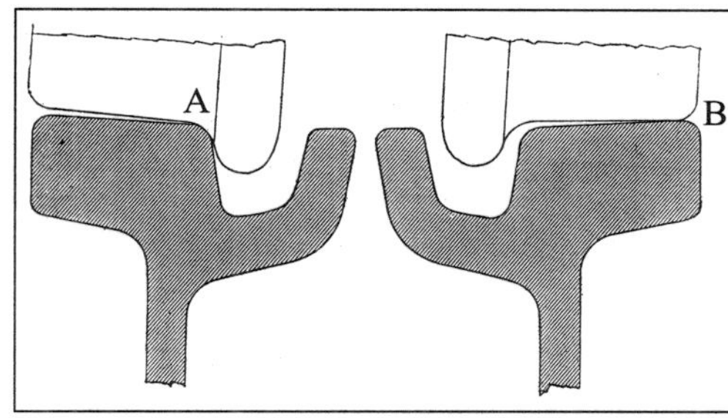

19. New tyres and and rails in motion on straight track.

In effect the tram is trying to stay upright, the result is that the wheel nearest the kerb (A) rides on its largest diameter while the higher wheel (B) rides on its outer edge. No problem until wheel (A) covering the ground more quickly outpaces its mate on the axle and pushes the tram uphill. The tyre of the wheel (B) then hits the flange of the rail and pushes the whole tram downhill again. This oscillation and pounding going on day after day eventually bends light rail to such an extent that the line can go out of gauge. At radial joints a remarkable twisting effect could be observed with any looseness on the fishplates allowing the 'waggling' movement to become even more exaggerated.

In steam tram days this could lead to the rail flange sheering off; a number of councillors mention picking up pieces of rail and either taking them to the tramway company's office, or thumping them down on the table at a council meeting. Partly at least this could be due to poor metal being used in the manufacture of the rails or their having cooled excessively during the rolling; the resulting 'chattering' causing parts of the rail to become crystalline. But when excessive wear on the head of the rails occurred

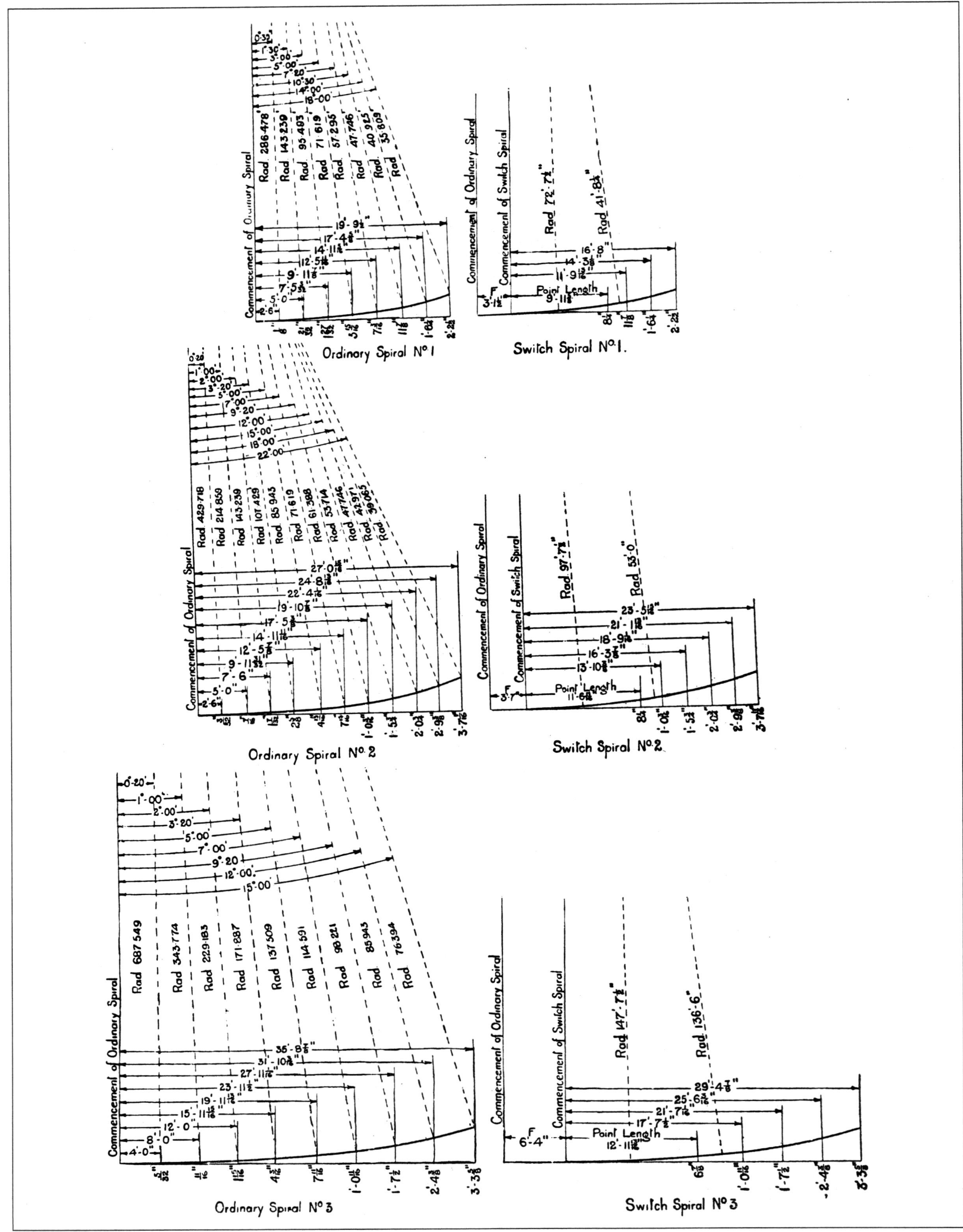

20. Detail of Lorain ordinary and switch spirals Nos. 1, 2 and 3.

whether caused by the trams themselves or by the normal traffic of the road (and in the days of steel tyres on unsprung carts and wagons this could be very heavy), and new tyres were fitted to the wheels the flanges could run along the bottom of the groove, thus attacking the rail at its weakest point.

21. Shows loss of metal in rail head due to six years' wear of street traffic, not having been in service.

The greatest difficulty with steam tram engines was that they were, as built, inherently unsuitable for the work they were given.

Comparatively speaking, on a normal railway even suburban steam services had clear stretches of track, giving wheels, axles, springs and framing a chance to straighten up; although recently (2003) different problems have been highlighted as although modern vehicles do not 'hunt' as did tram engines, they do tend to wear the rails in the same place at all times; even the underground trains in London, Glasgow, Paris or elsewhere, generally face curves of a reasonable radius, although some indication of the wear between rails and wheels could be found a few years ago when the 'Bubble Cars' (single unit railcars) used on the Stourbridge Town shuttle (more or less a permanent left hand turn) were rotated onto the Leamington-Stratford-upon-Avon service to try to even out excessively high wear on the wheel flanges. The Permanent Way is covered in detail in Chapter 9.

But trams habitually were forced around unbelievably tight radii, with as little as 27 feet (8.23m) to complete a 90° curve. Tables existed to show how the lead in and out should form a spiral with the entry and departure points laid out for the engineer; even a relatively easy 35' (10.67m) radius corner occupied 41 feet (12.5m) in each direction to reduce the strain on a tramcar's components. See page 28.

The manufacturers of steam tram engines were faced with an almost impossible task, for on the one hand they were constrained by the Board of Trade approved bye-laws, even the relatively lenient one of 1884 "Every engine shall be free from noise produced by blast or clatter of machinery, and the machinery shall be concealed from view ... No steam or smoke shall be emitted from the engine so as to constitute any reasonable ground of complaint to passengers or to the public ... A governor (which cannot be tampered with by the driver) shall be attached to each engine, and shall be so arranged that at any time when the engine exceeds a speed of [normally ten] miles an hour it shall cause the steam to be shut off and the brake applied."

But to meet these requirements the manufacturers had to work within tight dimensional limits, and had to keep weight as low as possible.

While the noise requirement was reasonable, in later years it is apparent that the casings hiding the machinery wore loose and caused an infernal racket, especially when the old wood and iron bodies supplied with most locomotives were replaced with steel sheeting. While on the face of it the governor was a very reasonable requirement, in reality it either broke or was disconnected at the works for a very simple reason still sometimes found in the autumn. Trains of my day tended to have problems with leaves, slipping to a halt and having to (very gingerly) re-start, often many times, losing time on each occasion. A sharpish incline could defeat the best tram driver at 5.30am on a 'soft' October day with the rails covered by an amalgam of horse-muck, leaves, market refuse, night soil from a leaking cart and other noxious waste. Sand the rails as he might, eventually the weight of the trailer (4 tons, perhaps) will overcome what little adhesion he has. The obvious way to clear the rails is to juggle the regulator and blast his way up so that although the wheels are slipping, nonetheless forward motion is maintained. But mechanical governors cannot judge the actual speed of the tram engine and react to the speed of the wheels instead; as they slip, the message reaches the governor that the equivalent of 10mph (16kph) has been reached, although in reality the true speed is only perhaps 2mph; steam is cut off and the brake applied. The ensemble stops, and the driver faces having to feather his regulator to avoid slipping (and re-awakening the governor) while also holding his brakes on to prevent his losing rather than gaining ground. And lose ground they could; passengers were prone to jumping out and getting damaged when it seemed that the car and trailer were running away backwards whereas in reality setting back and taking a run at the hill was probably the driver's only hope. And we must not forget if our unfortunate 18 year-old driver should make a puff of smoke or emit a wisp of steam his fine in court would exceed his week's wages.

It is recorded that in Wigan on one occasion no less than three engines and trailers were trying to surmount a hill and in turn each failed. Eventually the driver of the third engine unhooked his trailer, and pushed the entire entourage up the bank, then returning for his own passengers. Drake Street, Rochdale, was a famous hill, passengers actually leaving trams and walking up, rather than risk being on a runaway car; it was almost a daily occurrence for the trailers to drag the enfeebled little Wilkinson engines backwards; the local paper helpfully commenting that "it would not be a remote possibility if one day an engine, car, and passengers were not deposited in the River Roche."

On the Manchester, Bury, Rochdale & Oldham Steam Tramway Company's lines another twist lay in the failure of drivers to stop their Wilkinson-type locomotives (mainly those built by Green's of Leeds) at the Board of Trade compulsory stops, which were normally insisted on for safety reasons, as having stopped at the foot of hills they were quite unable to restart. In Rochdale town centre there were eight compulsory stops, missing even one would cost the luckless driver not only the loss of a day's pay but a fine equivalent to a further two.

Unfortunately even when they were working properly, mechanical speed governors on tram locomotives could be 'iffy', as tyre wear could reduce the real diameter of a nominally 2' 4" (711mm) driving wheel by 3" (76mm) in two years or less. N. Scott Russell, the engineer at Falcon's, partially resolved the problem by using a fifth wheel which bore directly on the track, thus being unaffected by any happenings to the driving wheels, but really the whole idea when applied to the unique conditions found on street tramways was a snare and a delusion, although as late as 1885 Merryweather & Sons were very proud of their brake whereby "a powerful centrifugal governor is driven from the driving axle by gear direct, without chains or belts. The governor operates on a throttle valve which closes when the speed reaches eight miles per hour (North London Tramway requirement), should the speed not then be checked, as for instance descending an incline, a small steam valve is opened giving steam to the brake cylinders and applying the brake. This acts automatically and ceases to act when the speed has been reduced below the given limit". These particular engines were large for Merryweather's, having cylinders 7½" x 12" (190 x 305mm), being delivered in 1884/5 at which time smaller (7" x

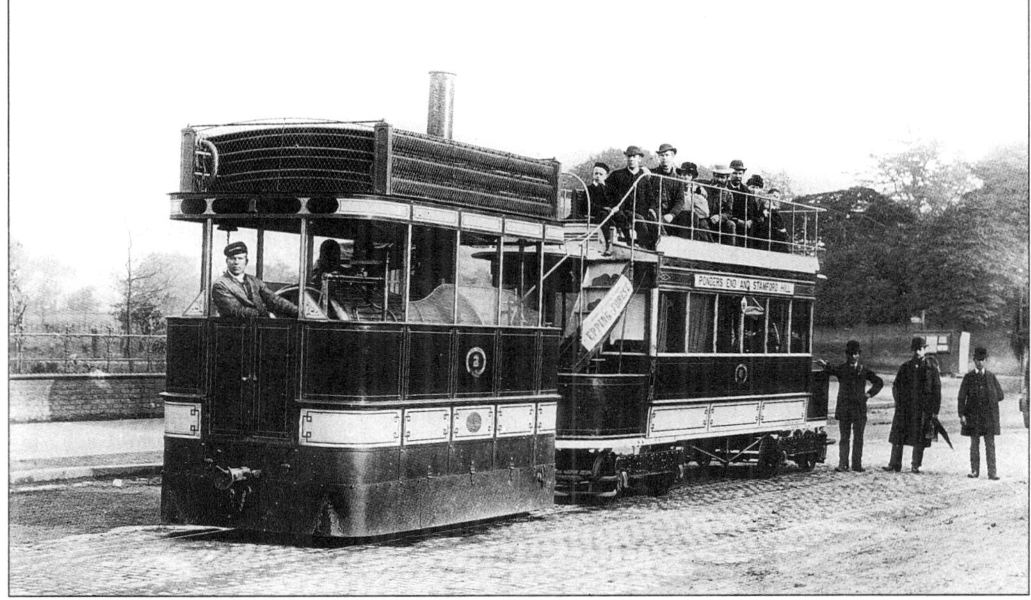

22. A North London Tramways Merryweather engine in quite new condition, together with open topped trailer; the muck from the chimney cannot have helped its acceptance!

Stockton and Darlington Steam Tramways Company Limited, Cost of Repairs and Running of Engines for Six Months, from 1 January to 30 June, 1885.

Number of miles run = 55,286

	£. s. d.	Per mile d.
Drivers' steam raiser and cleaners' wages	330. 7. 0d	1.43
Renewals	185. 11. 6.	.80
Fuel, coke and coal	154. 3. 0.	.66
Oil, waste and other stores	35. 5. 6.	.15
Water and gas	22. 6. 4	.09
Total	727. 13. 4	3.13

Consumption of coke per mile = 9.52 lb
Total mileage from commencing to run = 356,340

11") machines on the Stockton & Darlington Steam Tramway Company cost nearer 3d. per mile to run (see above).

The Engineer was always keen to report on new mechanical devices of any type of interest to engineers and steam trams which came within their view, but not only did they review machines but studied their running some years afterwards. In 1887 (28 October) "we can do no more than broadly indicate some of the peculiarities connected with this type of machinery. The gauge being usually narrow – 3ft. 6in. – there is considerable crowding of parts, augmented by the extreme shortness of the wheel base – 4ft. 6in. to 5ft. Wear and tear of tires takes place to an extraordinary extent; very few tires last two years. In Birmingham tires are now being tried no less than 3½in. thick in the tread ... The peculiar action set up in going round curves wears out axles and axleboxes endwise, in a way unknown on railways. Crank shafts have their outer webs worn down in a few months half an inch by rubbing against the axle brasses. The mud and dust in the bearings difficulty has to a great extent been got over, but it still operates in some degree. The necessity for providing an air pump, or more accurately, a drain pump, for the condenser; a jet condenser, and two sets of tanks, to say nothing of a speed indicator; a governor, and powerful steam brakes – all to be carried in a very small space – greatly cramps the machinery, and serious trouble can only be avoided by a very skilful designer. On the Birmingham central lines, there is now an engine which reminds us strongly of a story told concerning a locomotive for a narrow gauge railway, designed and built by a man long since dead. This engine was delivered, and a month subsequently the firm received a letter from the foreman of the running shed to the effect that he "wanted to know how he was to take down the big ends". There were only two methods open to him, so far as he could see; one was to turn the engine upside down, for which work he had no suitable crane; and the other was to take the boiler off the frame, "which would cause much delay." The tram locomotive to which we refer is not quite so bad as this. If, however, the pistons have to be drawn, they can be got out of the cylinders either at the back or the front – at the back by taking down the whole of the valve motion, guide bars, etc.; if at the front, by taking down a tank, an air pump, and breaking half a dozen joints or so. It is three clear days' work for a clever mechanic to get at the slide valves and rejoint the covers."

The drawing on page 31 shows just how the casings of steam trams hid some monstrous complexity of machinery. Clearly shown are the short wheelbase (4' 6"/1.37m), the inclined cylinders (8" x 14"/203/356mm), the fifth wheel governor, condensor and myriad of small components providing the motive power. The weight was 9 tons (a far cry from the 2 tons quoted by makers as adequate six years before) the driving wheels relatively large at 2' 6"/762mm and the air condenser which relied too much perhaps on the cleanliness of the steam entering it consisted of "250 very thin copper tubes, fixed in thin cast brass chambers". From the condenser any uncondensed steam was in cold or damp weather passed into a water tank at the front end of the engine. Normally the steam was diverted into the smokebox (the valve is visible in the main drawing) and "being superheated there, does not show before it is dissipated in the air". Unfortunately this was not always so, as although the steam was invisible immediately above the chimney if it struck cold air (on, say, a Spring morning) it would appear as a series of clouds suspended a few feet above the chimney. Jolly, but not quite as expected, and of course the driver busy about his various tasks had no way of seeing this phenomenon from his cab until the officer of the law descended. This particular engine was destined for the Burnley & District Tramways Company to run the three miles (4.8km) between Burnley and Padiham. This road climbs 250 feet/76m to the Tim Bobbin* public house in 2 miles with a maximum gradient of 1:17 (6%) and then descends 150 feet (45.7m) with a 1:20 (5%) bank en route.

* *Tim Bobbin was the nickname of John Collier, the Rochdale poet.*

23. This imposing Burrell compound locomotive for Birmingham Central Tramways was popular with the drivers, for the power available, expensive to run for the Directors owing to its "heavy track-destroying weight (12 tons)", and hated by the fitters for the complexity of machinery. The lack of a lifeguard at this late date (1886) is surprising.

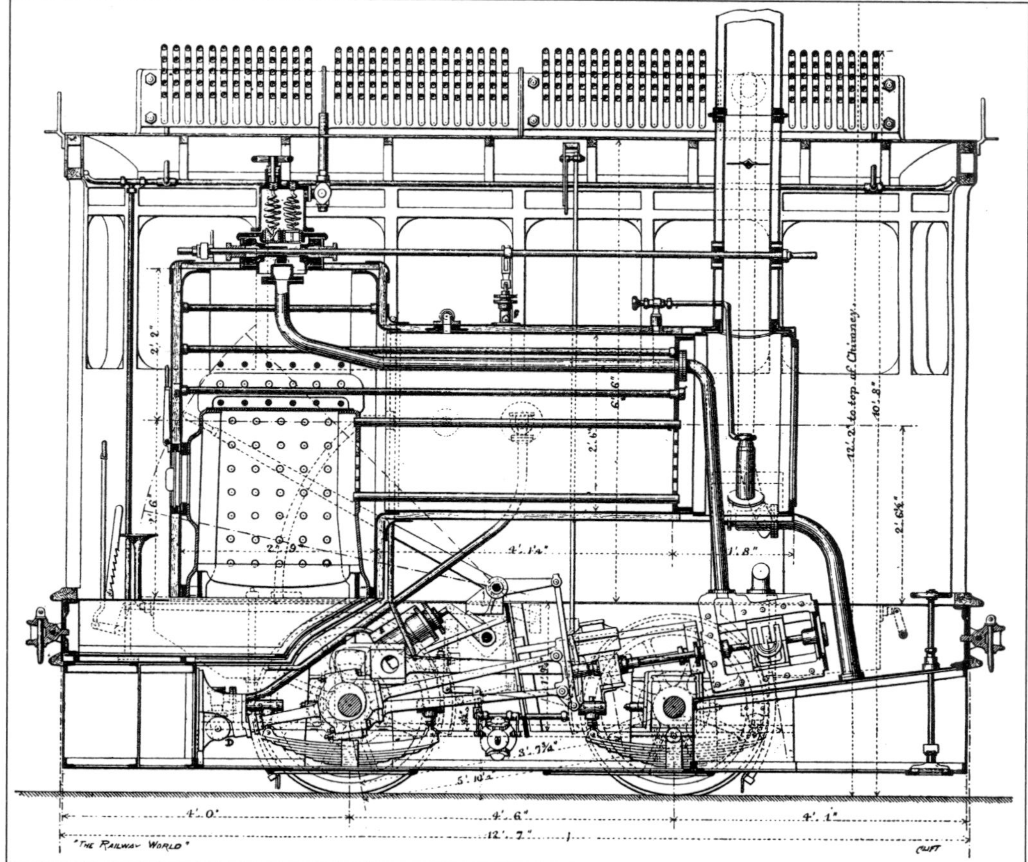

24. Longitudinal section – Falcon Engine Works Tramway Locomotive.

25. Burnley and District Tramways Co. operated just over 7 miles of steam tramway from Padiham via Burnley and Brierfield to Nelson, a 'rough' road but one with great traffic potential. After five Kitson engines, they seem to have taken a liking to the Norman Scott Russell-designed Falcon engines, buying twelve between 1883 and 1897. This is no.13, with an 1884-built Starbuck trailer. The lamp halfway down the open top of the trailer is the sole 'outside' illumination. The scenery was typical of the area until recently, but was the boy in the centre of the engine a son or stoker or quite what?

Single small 46 seat trailers were used although experimentally two carrying 73 passengers were hauled "with ease". Fuel consumption was comparable with Merryweather's at 8½ to 9 lb coke per mile (roughly 2½kg/km), Burnley must have liked them as their fleet totalled five Kitson products and 12 Falcon engines (out of the 85 or so Scott Russell-designed-products built).

But no matter how cleverly designed, these engines would pitch up and down badly, although the weight of the trailer could nullify this to some extent, hunt, unavoidable with the push-pull motion of the pistons driving the wheels coupled to a short wheelbase, and as very often reported, they rolled; by nature top heavy the condensers mounted on the roof were in exactly the wrong place for stability. Combine

26. This is a genuine Kitson tram engine (T111, built 1884), but the purchasers, the West Lancashire Railway, only kept the three they bought (T109-111, No. 10 Hesketh Park, 11 Crossens, and 12 Churchtown) for a short time from 1884, as in 1886 they were back at Kitson for overhaul and resale. After that it all gets complicated, but as late as 3 May 1956 T111 was photographed by the late Jim Peden at Rea Ltd. premises. Technically T111 was an 0-4-0 well-tank engine with 3' 0" (914mm) driving wheels, and 8" x 12" (203 x 305mm) cylinders. I wonder how much was original by 1956, but there it is – an undressed tram engine.

these three characteristics, add worn components (worn quickly simply because the underlying railway was bad) and you have a mobile track destroyer.

It was suggested with regularity both in the press and by some engineers that cheaper industrial engines could be modified to suit rather than purpose-built tram engines, and it is true that there was some crossover with Kitson "T" (tram) classified engines entering service in commercial works, particularly where the emission of smoke and sparks was very undesirable. But if we exclude the Wilkinson-pattern vertical boilered tram engines, only Kitson and T. Green built industrials and trams simultaneously; although in Ireland where roadside running rather than urban was the norm, 'standard' engine building companies including Hunslet (Cambria on the Dublin & Blessington was a standard contractor's locomotive), Beyer Peacock (Castlederg & Victoria Bridge line), Hudswell Clarke (C & VB), Sharp Stewart (Clogher Valley), supplied the motive power. Even Stephen Lewin down in Poole, Dorset, managed to sell one of his rather agricultural engines to the Guernsey Steam Tramways Company. Clearly the tramways on these islands, far from the beady eye of the Board of

27. The Wolverton and Stony Stratford tramway became a far more efficiently run line when tram engines were abandoned, and this barely modified Bagnall engine (WB 2153/1921) was used. The chimney, though, shows just how unaesthetic designers had become!

Temperature of feed water entering the injector. Deg. F.	50°	60°	70°	80°	90°	100°	110°	120°	125°	130°
Percentage diminution of delivery	0%	1½%	3%	5%	7½%	10½%	13½%	19½%	24%	100%

Trade, were a law unto themselves, Irish engines often being photographed running around without their skirts, and in many cases, condensers, even if they existed at one time, were removed. Barrow-in-Furness Steam Tramway Company cars were treated in the same way although contemporary records seem to indicate their condensers (and many other parts including governors) fell off. One exception to all rules was the Wolverton & Stony Stratford who used a barely modified conventional W.G. Bagnell Ltd. of Stafford saddle tank engine which with its large 2' 9½" (851mm) wheels, 10" x 15" (254 x 381mm) cylinders and lack of condenser could do everything true tram engines tried, but too often failed to do: to perform adequately.

The difficulty with having to condense or (as Victorian writers rather picturesquely put it) "eat" one's own steam is that if the condenser is efficient, and later ones at least were, all the water that has been drawn from the water tanks, converted to steam, and then returned again to water has to go somewhere, and one wonders who first thought of utilising it in a form of perpetual motion water turns to steam to water to steam etc., whoever, they were quickly disillusioned as this water has to enter the boiler with sufficient force to overcome the average 120 pounds pressure per square inch of the existing steam. Steam travels in the boiler at a measured velocity of 2850 feet per second (868m/sec) so that even with efficient nozzles the injector(s) pumping up the water from the tanks has or have to provide a theoretical velocity of 183feet/sec (133 to overcome this extant boiler pressure plus 50 to overcome frictional losses etc). The nearest simile is when I once tried to refill my wife's hot steam iron by injecting cold water into the refill nozzle with a plastic squirter. The resulting steam/water volcano was interesting and a fine example of velocity! However, nature has a nasty trick up her sleeve. The contemporary table above shows the diminution of capacity in injectors caused by the use of hot feed water.

The figures refer to an injector fixed non-lifting and working with and against a boiler pressure of 100lb* per square inch.

In practice drivers, when variable valves were fitted, diverted some of the condensed water into the feedwater tanks and ran the balance into holding tanks, often fitted transversely fore and aft of the locomotive, representing up to a half ton of excess weight sloshing about. Ideally this was then discharged at the end of each round trip, although traffic jams could cause the engine to be taken short! Cold fresh water was taken on from a hydrant in the road or lay-by.

Sometimes there were problems with these hydrants, to some extent the irritation to other road users is understandable as the frost would freeze the pools of water, and horses by slipping could be seriously hurt or have to be destroyed. "There are" said one councillor in Coventry, "enough natural hazards without incontinent tramcars."

The County Express as late as March 1897 carried details of the discussion which took place at a meeting of the Brierley Hill Urban District Council – obviously there the problem was very serious indeed. "A very proper complaint was brought before their notice as to the way in which the Dudley and Stourbridge Tramway Company took in water near to Level Street. The taking of water here by the engines had become a great public nuisance to residents there, and also to others who crossed the road and had to wade through pools of water. He proposed that the clerk write to the Tramway Company complaining of this nuisance, and also stating that unless it was remedied the Council would take steps to prevent them taking water in the town. The Chairman said he had no objection to the letter being sent, but he saw the manager of the trams recently and called his attention to the nuisance, and he promised to give attention to the matter ... Mr E.W. Pearson thought a letter should be sent forbidding the company taking water at all in the town. Dudley and Stourbridge would not permit it, and he failed to see why Brierley Hill should have the nuisance. Mr Guest said the road was frequently covered with water owing to the carelessness of the tramway company's servants ... Though the trams were certainly very useful, yet they must see that the company gave them [the public] the consideration they were entitled to."

Clearly where hard water was used, the scale coupled to the various impurities (red lead, tallow, coke grit) could block both the condenser and the injector or pump inlets. We have an example of this on the Birmingham & Aston line in 1884 when James Fligh was charged with making steam. The constable stated, "The steam was coming from the tubes on top of the engine." A rather unjust fine of five shillings (a day's pay) plus costs was imposed.

Copper and brass elements within the condenser, pump, or the injector were cleaned by immersing them in a 10% solution of hydrochloric acid, nitric acid although commonly used, was not recommended as it attacked and pitted brass and copper; gloomily scientists advised the other alternative, dilute sulphuric acid, while excellent for dissolving and cleaning sludge, did not entirely remove hard scale. If the injector or pump elements were small enough to handle easily, it was suggested an apprentice could gently heat them in a 'Bunsen' (gas jet) flame and then drop them in a 'bosh' (or even a bucket) of cold water, on the basis that the sudden contraction would crack the film of scale which the luckless apprentice using "utmost care and blunt tools" could scrape off.

Some tramway companies employed a consultant chemist when the question of testing water hardness arose. Clearly the tishy little tubes of a tram's locomotive type boiler would become almost uselessly bad conductors of heat when they were encrusted with scale as indeed are immersion heater, electric kettle, washing machine and dishwasher elements today in hard water districts; the principle is exactly the same.

The cause of this scale is the presence of lime and magnesia salts in the water; a little can easily be flushed out of a boiler with a jet of water and a mild solution of calcium carbonate (say five grains to a gallon of water – one to a litre), otherwise softening equipment had to be installed or, in many cases, a new well dug – this item appears regularly in tramway company accounts. In a later chapter the account of the accident at Huddersfield clearly demonstrates the problems of hard water.

One failure of tramways, mainly due to non-co-operation between the companies, was their lack of a research establishment; neither from surviving correspondence is there much trace of co-operation in metallurgical studies. The great railway companies were surprisingly open over the advantages to be gained from, say, better rails, and published many of their findings for their colleagues to study. It is true that from time to time a member of the Mechanical or Civil Engineering Institutions would have a 'paper', and the ensuing discussion published in the relevant journal, but whether this had any impact on hard-pressed managers is hard to know. A few classic examples of railway research had results which applied to street railways as much as the Great Western thundering down to Bristol. Steel was used in axles, tyres, boiler, frame plates and springs – its quality and hardness varied according to use; some tramways remained wed to chilled iron tyres on their engines long after these were superseded on railways, but even then quality control was vital if money was not to be wasted.

Tyres whether for heavy rail or tramway were often obtained from the Patent Shaft and Axletree Company's works at Wednesbury, Staffordshire, and a description of the process used to produce steel tyres appeared in The Railway Magazine during 1898 and is worth repeating: "The production of a tyre is probably as interesting as any operation on the works. The ingot, re-heated to a white heat, is quickly placed under an eight-ton steam-hammer, under the blows from which the mass is reduced to the form of a cheese. Next, a hole is punched in the middle, and what looks like a red-hot mill wheel goes, after being weighed, to a "becking" hammer, which beats up the flanges. The red glow has become somewhat dull by this time, and the steel has to undergo a slight reheating called a "wash heat", after which it passes to one of the two vertical rolling mills, under which operation it is rolled out to the full diameter and exact section required."

The specifications for wheels and tyres for an early batch of electric tramcars has survived; curiously they were ordered from Germany, presumably price/delivery affected this. The tyres were to be "of the very best Siemens Martin Basic Steel made from the best qualities of haematite and Swedish iron with a small proportion of scrap steel ... 0.5 to 0.55 per cent of carbon ... and to be capable of standing a tensile strain of 45 to 50 tons per square inch, with an elongation of 15% in a length of 2 inches. Tyres to be 2½" thick."

The axles were of a lesser quality ("milder in temper") containing 0.2 to 0.3 per cent of

* *At the above boiler pressure the injector ceases to work reliably when the feed water reaches it at over 120° F.*

carbon. "One axle to be tested under blows of a ton weight falling from a height of 12ft on the centre of the axle, which is to be supported on bearings 3ft 6 in. apart, and reversed under each blow. The axles to be machined and polished and cold rolled on the bearing surfaces". The comment on the wrought iron wheel centres was that the carbon was not to exceed 0.25 to 0.35 per cent.

Just before 6am on 20 March 1889 a trailer overturned at the Saddle Inn, Newtown, on the Lamberhead line of the Wigan Tramways Company. Classed as a "workman's tram", a female workperson, Alice Ann Heaton, died from her injuries. This car (No.9, a Starbuck 4-wheeler of 1882) had a nominal capacity of 42 but probably (and quite usually) held in excess of 100 passengers, including one riding on the coupling between engine and trailer, and although apparently running at normal speed around the curve prior to reaching the Inn, both tram and the trailer then left the rails.

At the inquest it was stated that both axles of the trailer were broken, curiously one was of steel and the other wrought iron; they showed evidence of old cracks ("of some standing") although these could not have been detected in the course of normal maintenance. The actual overloading of the car was irrelevant insofar as the cause of the accident was concerned; the primary cause was the sharp curves on the line (itself, here and there, out-of-gauge) had weakened the axles by the continual twisting they suffered; the binding of the inner wheels on the curves was described as "a continuous screaming". Presumably baffled, the jury returned a verdict of "Accidental Death" and could only suggest the impossible: curves should be eased, track kept in better repair, and steps taken to prevent the overcrowding!

Rails similarly should only be made within a very tight envelope; although as late as 1907 very eminent engineers stated categorically that a universal specification could not be reached. "The varying conditions, such as ore available, processes of manufacture, weight of rails ... differ to a great extent in every case..." surely a bad admission. The ideal aimed at, and clearly in our period not often achieved, was for steel made by the acid or basic Bessemer processes to conform to the following limits:

Carbon	0.40 to 0.55 per cent
Manganese	0.70 to 1.00 per cent
Silicon	not to exceed 0.1 per cent
Sulphur	not to exceed 0.08 per cent
Phosphorus	not to exceed 0.08 per cent

In Bradford around the turn of the century a piece of rail made by the older open hearth method was recovered and tested and was found to contain:

Carbon	0.50 per cent
Manganese	0.75 per cent
Silicon	0.04 per cent
Sulphur	0.041 per cent
Phosphorus	0.005 per cent

While theoretically meeting the 'ideal', the problem was that the metal was often poorly mixed with carbon blocks clearly visible.

A curious side effect of modernisation found by the tram companies who retained steam until a relatively late period (the 20th century), was

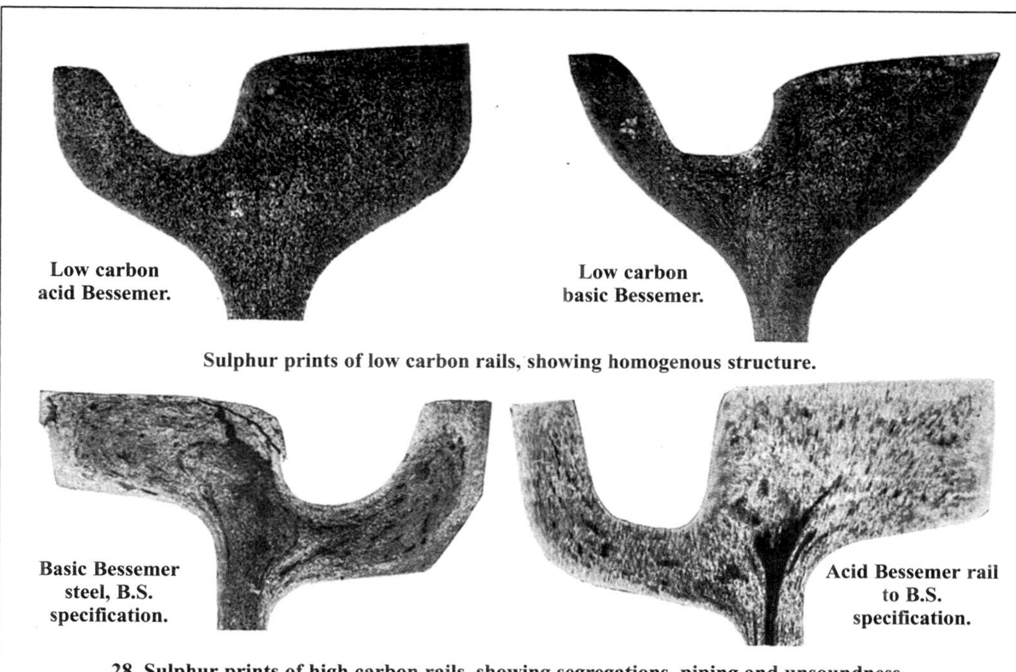

28. Sulphur prints of high carbon rails, showing segregations, piping and unsoundness.

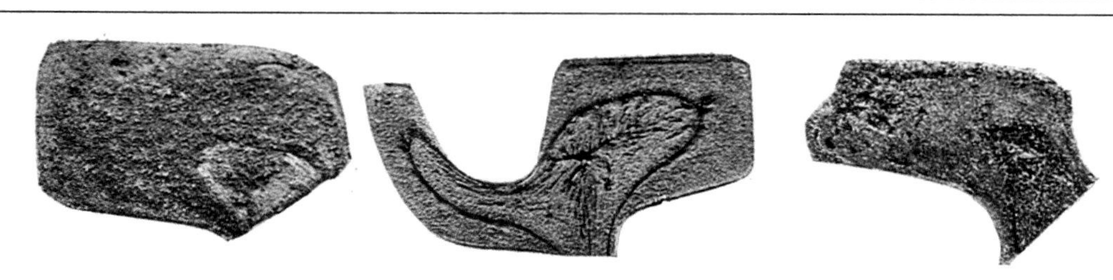

29. Etched specimens high carbon basic Bessemer rails showing much segregation and unsoundness.

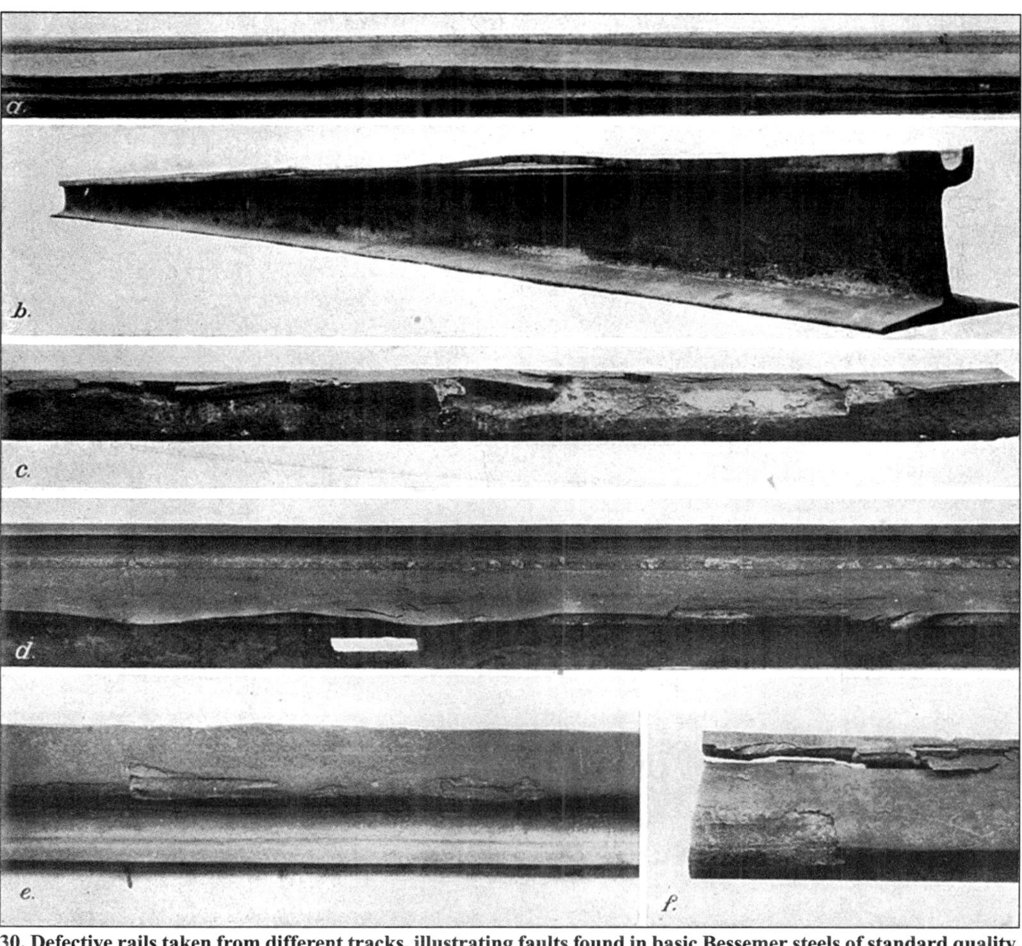

30. Defective rails taken from different tracks, illustrating faults found in basic Bessemer steels of standard quality. (a) and (b) show the entire stripping of the head of 20ft 0in., due to being made from a badly-piped ingot. (c) and (d), (f) show the battering, extrusion, exfoliation and total collapse of the heads of two rails; in (c) the presence of slag is easily detected. (e) shows a case of scabbing which is very common.

that the copper tubes used in boilers were being eroded by grit carried in the blast at a faster rate; this phenomenon was then found to be affecting railways in a greater degree – the cause on analysis turned out to be that copper was being manufactured to a pure quality to meet the requirements of the nascent and expanding electrical industry; arsenic, lead and bismuth together with other impurities had slowed down wear.

Even today the use of a cheap oil instead of the (vastly more expensive) manufacturers' product can affect the performance and engine life of a car. Years ago it was the practice of those who could only afford very old, oil burning, cars, to buy reconstituted oil at (I think) 1s. per gallon (4½ litres); this was re-claimed oil, mostly from buses, which was centrifuged until it was about right! However, this compound was still better than anything that was available to the night mechanic on steam tramways. He had two choices: an oil-based on animal or vegetable sources, or very primitive (and expensive) mineral oils. Most vegetable or animal oils contain "free" fatty acids which left alone quietly chomp their way into a bearing. The odd thing is that having eroded the bearing, the fatty acid combines with the metal to form a 'soap' which very protectively covers the bearing, thus preventing any lubrication; usually reported in axle boxes as 'hot box', the give-away being stinking smoke and a red hot bearing. Here even 40 years ago tallow could be the culprit, the worsted packing in the box igniting.

Oil lamps both for the engine and to provide a dim smelly, flickering light in the trailer were rarely superseded by electric, and the quality of the oil used (rape oil or paraffin) was variable and prone to blocking the pipes and burners – cleaning them out was a horrible job often carelessly done. As few, if any, tramway companies had the equipment to test the quality of oil provided they had to rely upon (unreliable) merchants who in turn relied upon (unreliable) supplies from wholesalers. Incidentally, W.B. Dick of Alford & Sutton Steam Tramway Company fame made his money importing oil in casks, his railway trucks (lettered W.B. Dick & Co.,) being recorded with regularity as they traversed various company lines. When in 1886 Dick (the individual) decided to turn himself into a limited liability company, the company's businesses were said to be "an Oil Merchant and Dealer in Tallow and other Fatty Substances; an Oil Refiner, Crusher and Exporter; a Commission and General Merchant; a Manufacturer of and Dealer in Paint, Varnish, and kindred substances; a Contractor for Public and other Works; a Money Lender and Money and General Dealer.", presumably in order of priority. The company's capital was to be £250,000 in £10 shares; 10,000 of them being given to William Bruce Dick in lieu of cash.

Painting of locomotives and trailers almost followed a ritual, although some cars were never repainted in their lifetime, only additional coats of varnish being added. It was to be hoped that the initial preparation for the final colours was well carried out in the manufacturers' workshops. As today, the painting of the basic metal parts had to be carried out as soon as possible, badly rusted and pitted faces were almost impossible to cure. Wood too needed priming, the paint used being almost invariably made from white lead mixed with common varnish, boiled linseed oil, turpentine and terebene driers. This was followed with 'stopping' (4 parts of dry white lead to one of ochre mixed with gold size until it formed a sticky 'goo') which was applied with flat trowels.

After drying, some unlucky youths had the job of rubbing down. A good foreman ensured they used wet rags over their mouths, as although the long term effect of white lead could be ignored, in the short term replacing boys meant more training by the firm. The job was simple, screamingly boring and destructive on the skin as all that was required was for the boy(s) to take up a soaking wet hand sized piece of pumice stone, rub it with a circular motion over the panel not pressing hard (otherwise the stone will follow the ridges and furrows left by the trowels) until the stone got dulled or clogged up. It was then swished around in the water to wash off the sludge and restore its cutting ability. When the first couple of square feet are done, one faces the next ... and the next ... and the next, almost to eternity. After thorough drying, another coat of primer restored the surface and then two coats, or up to five, of gloss were brushed on, and rubbed down.

Finally at least three coats of copal (a resin derived from tropical trees) varnish were applied; the first being again rubbed or 'flatted' down by our youths, only this time finely ground pumice stone creamed with water is used, applied by a tuft of horsehair or similar material.

Ultimately the wearing ability of the paint was decided by the permissible downtime (time out of service) – two weeks was suggested for an overhaul and paint job. The engines of urban tramways mainly became sadder and sadder to look at, a combination of economy, acid horse manure splashes, acrid fumes from factory and/or mill chimneys, and indifferent cleaning taking effect. As befits the LNWR when they owned the Wolverton & Stony Stratford tramway, the engines and carriages were smart; the cleaning time for their engines including scouring the handrails and other polished items was six hours each. Typically in 1924 the materials to be issued per locomotive were formalised at two or three pints of cleaning oil (basically paraffin), two or three pounds of cleaning 'composition' (apparently based on petroleum with some form of scouring element added) plus ¼lb of petroleum jelly if required. Twelve washed cloths or one pound of cotton waste were to be issued per locomotive, although more were available on request – washed cloths were still normal issue to drivers and guards in the 1980s due to the muck on handrails of locomotives, barely cleaned at all by then.

The cleaning materials were on the basis of a two man gang who, if the engine was to be 'bulled-up' were allowed six hours. If brasswork was present (and most tram engines had brass name and manufacturers plates, etc.) two ounces (57g) of powdered bath brick (or 'whitening') would be an extra issue.

The vexed argument between engineers over the size of locomotive driving wheels (and from this the size/weight of other parts) continued as long as there were steam engines to argue over. Tram engines had little choice as the whole mass of working parts had to be concentrated in as short a wheelbase as possible (normally 4ft 6in./1371mm). Generally, the larger the wheel the more economic the working, partly because the wheel covers more ground on each revolution, and partly because thermal losses caused by radiation from the cylinder walls are reduced. Our tram unit, as we know, was not allowed to make noise from 'blast', while at the same time the tortuous path the steam had to take to the condenser undoubtedly caused back pressure thus choking the whole engine. And with small wheels, faster, shorter, movements occurred in the working parts causing greatly increased friction of journals, crank pins, cross-head slides and the pistons themselves; allied to poor lubrication it is a wonder they did not fail in service more often.

The dream of every tramway engineer was to have at his disposal a fleet of locomotives that could run a round trip on the main line service, enter the siding, have ashes, clinkers etc., cleaned, be watered and then be capable of the same again *without the driver having to touch the fire.* While he was trying to stoke the fire, or clean out some of the clinker which always forms when using coke, he could not give all his attention to the road ahead. Not so much a problem in Ireland where 'stokers' were habitually employed, but then their journeys were generally longer.

A Mr W. Higgins who, unusually, gave his full address (41 Bank St., Brierley Hill) wrote to the editor of the Birmingham Post on 22nd October 1884 with what was probably a legitimate grumble, but probably with some exaggeration as it would seem the tram had a firebox full of nothing but clinker. "Sir, Would you kindly allow me, as a member of the public of this neighbourhood, to beware of the situation on the Dudley and Stourbridge line, and also to call attention of the directors to the dangerous practice carried on by their servants. About ten minutes to three this afternoon I passed an engine and car which was standing at the bottom of Brettell Lane, waiting for the return tram from Stourbridge. When a little distance off I saw the driver (without looking where it was going) throw out a large red-hot clinker, which fell as near as possible on the middle of the footpath on which I was walking. When opposite the engine I was startled by a second, weighing, I should think, some 8lb or 9lb, falling at my feet. Comment is unnecessary; the thoughtlessness, and the probable results of this practice will be seen at once."

Merryweather for some time so believed in the abilities of their engines that they used sideways mounted firebox doors; when steam failed, the luckless driver had to fire up his boiler from the kerbside – one can imagine the comments of the public!

The fuel used in the fireboxes of tram engines was coke, although from time to time various 'Patent' fuels were tried, including petroleum blocks where waste oil was combined with coal dust giving, it was claimed, up to six-and-a-half times the calorific value; but alas, under the heat of usage the oil melted and the coal dust flowed through the firebars into the ashpan, doing no good to that, and being almost impossible to clean in the yard. But there were problems with coke which by its nature varied according to the type of coal originally supplied, and the efficiency or otherwise of the Gas Company who processed it. As a fuel coke was used in many and varied trades: forges and hearths preferred it as there were no smoke impurities, and no carbon to find its way into the metals being forged, and some industrial locomotives used it inside factories for the same reason as tram engines, and of course that vital albeit humble night-watchman's brazier was always coke fired. Good coke once lit (and lighting often had to be assisted by coal) gave a high degree of heat which theoretically was both smokeless and fumeless. But it was not, particularly when the firebox door had to be wedged open to provide a draught. An editor in 1899 used his column to report some unhappiness; he was normally pro-tram so this must have been a bad engine: "We do not believe in unnecessary fault finding, and are always loathe to cast opprobrium upon anyone. We must say, however, that the sulphur fumes emitted from the Steam Tram leaving Handsworth for West Bromwich, on Monday morning last, about a quarter to ten, were so horrible that during the whole journey to the Beeches we had to keep our handkerchiefs over mouth and nose to avoid swallowing any more of these noxious vapours than possible. It really was a disgrace to the company, and we could not refrain from speaking to the Inspector about it when we alighted from the tram, at the Beeches. What we should like to know is if a passenger has power to protest in a case of this kind. If so, we should feel inclined on philanthropic grounds to take the case before the bench in the event of a recurrence."

At one works where coke-burners were used I was mildly surprised to see a driver adding a shovelful of coal to the firebox; it appeared this Hunslet engine was a bad raiser of steam due to the brick arch in the firebox being 'clagged'; one wonders if in fact the drivers concerned in the following report were assisting the fires in their Wilkinson-type engines, alternatively the coal may have been imperfectly processed at the gasworks, and unless the driver looked behind he would not be aware of the smoke being emitted; these 1887 prosecutions were malicious acts by the "Ban the Tram Association" as evidenced by a quaint denial "he (the witness) had not been on watch six weeks in order to get a case against the company." It is worth reiterating that the drivers not only lost at least one day's pay (five shillings or more) attending court, but had to pay the fines and costs.

"EMITTING SMOKE. Wm. Gubbins and Samuel Cotterill, both of Wattville Street, Handsworth, engine-drivers in the employ of the Birmingham and South Staffordshire Tramways Company were charged with permitting smoke to escape from their engines on the 25th. Mr H. Jackson prosecuted, and Mr Elliott (Walsall), solicitor to the Tramway Company, defended. Wm Jefferies, of Handsworth, deposed to waiting for the trams which were driven by the two defendants on the date named. As soon as the tram neared him, black smoke was allowed to escape, and that was continued for a distance of one hundred yards. At eight o'clock the same night he was also watching, and he saw the car of which Gubbins was in charge. It emitted smoke at Highland Lane, which continued down to Wattville Street. Cross-examined: He had not been on watch six weeks in order to get a case against the company. Frank Stokes deposed to being in company with the last witness, and at two o'clock he saw a tram engine emitting smoke. Cotterill was the driver of the car. He was also there at 8pm and he saw a car on which Gubbins was the driver emitting steam from a distance. The smoke and sulphur fumes were very offensive. Cotterill, who had been previously charged, was fined 10s. and costs, and Gubbins was fined 5s. and costs." Cotterill must have been a loyal man as he re-appeared in 1890 being defended by the South Staffs solicitor; and then being fined £2 plus costs (1½ weeks pay).

One task a driver had was to apply sand to the rails, thus hopefully giving enough grip to provide forward motion or at least stop the whole ensemble sliding backwards. Despite the primitive apparatus provided (basically a hopper and a pipe near to the wheels) the proper use of sand is quite a skilled job, as coupling rods, crank pins and even crank axles, can be broken by the improper and reckless use of sand. Theoretically as soon as the driving wheels slip, the regulator (or throttle) should be closed before the sand ("clean sharp sand, properly dried and screened") is poured on the rails. If starting away on a hill it was found that slipping was continual, the engine should be balanced on the regulator as sand was applied – but of course that little demon of a governor would cut in! Too much sand and it gets carried by the wheels to be caught by the axleboxes owing to oil or tallow seeping past ill-fitting joints and becoming mixed up with all other available muck. Many tram engines only had provision to sand one side, thus putting great strain on the axles; a windy day could nullify any benefit from the dropped sand. Most depots had sand driers, and sack or wagon loads were left at each terminus. In electric tram days special sand carriers ran daily from the drying sheds to depots.

Accustomed as we are now to relatively long-lived axleboxes and bearings, it is difficult to remember just how skilled a job fitting these was in steam tram days. One manual of good enginemanship reiterated time and time again: "Owing to the importance of good fitting and the impossibility of easy running without such, the axleboxes should never be allowed to go 'near enough'; if other parts of a locomotive have to be hurried, these should never be passed until correctly finished."

The basic structure of a bearing incorporated a brass 'sleeve' inserted into the ironwork, this then being faced with white metal or having white metal inserts. A manual of the 1890s alludes to a method of working (presumably commonplace): "Some fitters have a practice, and it gives good results, of cutting away with a file or scraper the brass separating the white metal inserts after the face has been found, and leaving the white metal to stand up a little and take the first wear; the brass then comes down to the journal more gradually. It is a rule to apply white metal to the face of the bearing of axleboxes, as it gives excellent results in wear and also acts as a lubricant, melting as it does at a much lower temperature than brass, and preventing the latter seizing."

When the boxes were new they were 'trued-up' at the works and it was normal practice for an apprentice to paint the bearing surfaces with 'engineers blue', then scrape away high spots by hand (applying more blue as required) until a mirror-finish surface was achieved; but with age not the least of axlebox problems could be that of uneven wear, particularly exaggerated by the weakening of the spring on the gutter-side of the engine, as it carried the greater part of the machine's weight. This in turn threw an extra burden on the axle bearings on that side. Effectively it meant that rebuilding of each box and its bearings had to be carried out individually rather than in bulk; labour intensive work of course, especially when the finished product had to be accurate to 1/64th of an inch (0.4mm). "After fitting, the box and journal are wiped clean of 'marking', which is used in bedding down, and filings, chips, etc., then smeared with oil or grease. The keeps are preferably filled with Laycock's packing, consisting of curled horse-hair and wool, this, being elastic, keeps the journal moistened with oil, which finds its way from the oil chamber at the top of the box."

We were advised it was the duty of the engineman to put "a little oil on each face of the hornblocks and also the sides and flanges", in addition to all his other (manifold) duties. In the filthy conditions steam trams worked under it would be surprising if they could see the hornblock ... but where axleboxes become loose in the hornblocks (which carry them), the wheels will actually and quite visibly move in the frames, which can be quite interesting!

'Hot boxes' were always an anathema and a very real problem. The 1887 cure was "to put a lump of tallow in the centre of the end of the axle, or on the outside of the boss of the wheel, or better still, take an oil feeder full of melted tallow and run a line of it from the spout of the feeder across the boss of the wheel and end of the axle, when it will at once congeal on striking the cold metal and set into a fine line of tallow. This will melt and run, if the box runs warm and heats the axle at all, and it can then easily be seen from the foot-plate with the engine moving slowly or standing. If a box heats, a thick lubricant, such as tallow, soap or black lead, should be mixed with the oil to aid in reducing heat." The alternative was crude but if out in the country miles from anywhere, and a hot box was found if the available tea from cans didn't cool it, men had (usually) access to a supply of liquid which worked well enough to stagger (in our case) to the nearest signalbox; I have no doubt steam tram drivers knew and used similar methods.

THE WILKINSON TRAMWAY LOCOMOTIVE.

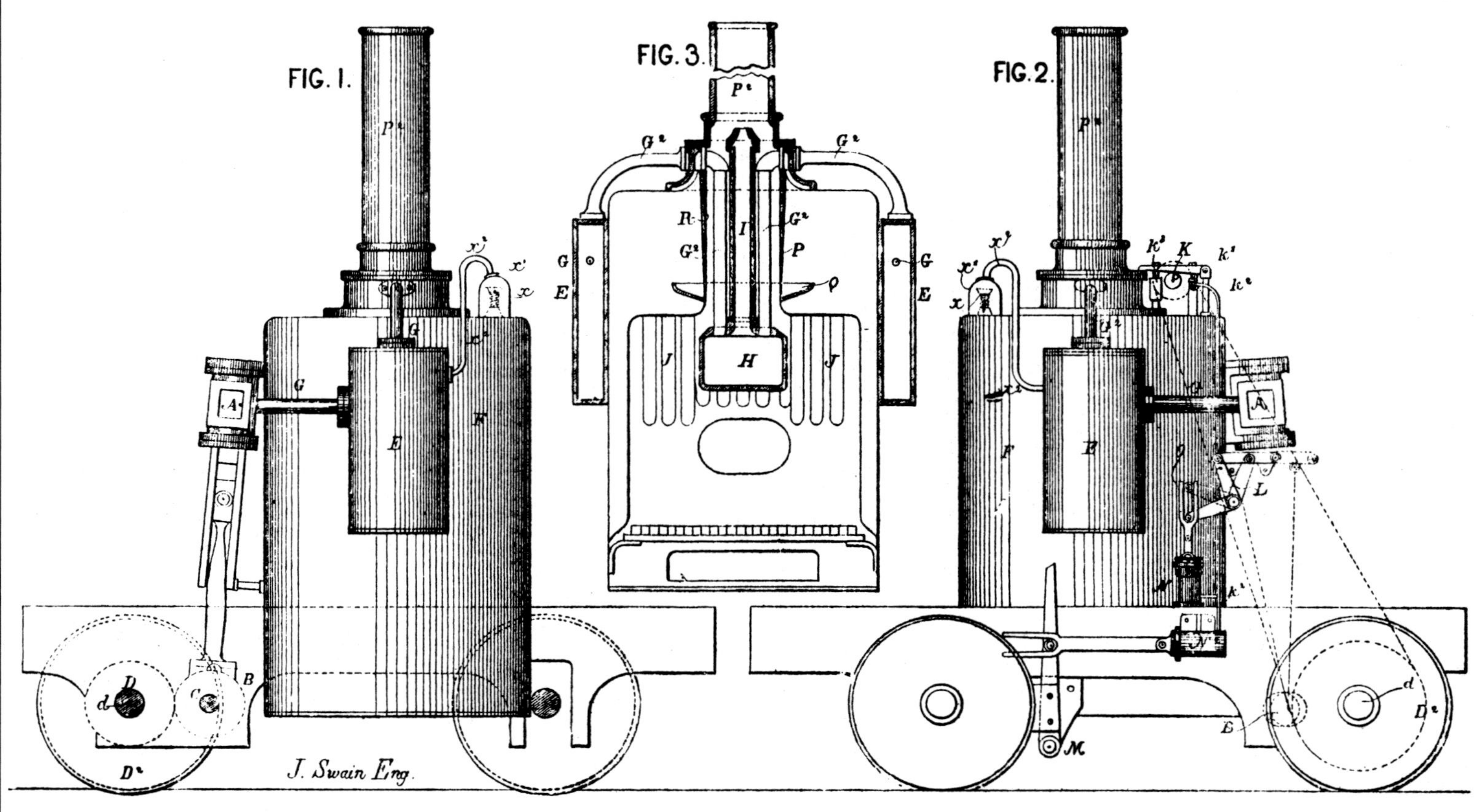

31. The Wilkinson tramway locomotive as shown in The Engineer 2 March 1883. The basic principle of the geared drive is shown on the left, the governor linkage (and cause of many drivers' problems) is the pecked line on the right from a pulley on the driving wheel to the "Allen's Paddle Governor" which reverses the valve gear of the engine, no other brake force being available.

Chapter 6

MANUFACTURERS

(THE PRINCIPAL PLAYERS)

Wilkinson v. The Rest

The evolution of the steam tramway engine was briefly disturbed by the arrival of Mr Wilkinson's engines. The story of these vertical boilered trams can never be wholly told – for example we know very little of the men who maintained them, or even the men who built them. There were companies who ordered and re-ordered this pattern of engine – each batch a little cheaper or perhaps the engineer had had or read good reports, and yet cast them aside after quite short lives, preferring something more orthodox, stronger, or more capable of true development. The battles between the various manufacturers and ultimately how the non-Wilkinson Patent builders 'ganged-up' on Wilkinson is best told in the columns of newspapers and journals of the day. Clearly these latter have had to be greatly reduced in length, but hopefully I have retained the wonderful flavour of Victorian letter writing.

First of all an editorial of 28 March 1879 in praise of Merryweather by the Minister of Public Works in Rouen: "The locomotives having fulfilled with great regularity all the conditions necessary for security, the engineers consider that it is desirable to authorise the city of Rouen to continue mechanical traction, and as the trial of the train of two cars has also presented the most complete success, it is proposed to continue it and extend it even to three cars."

By 9 September 1882 the magazine *Money* was clearly smitten by the Wilkinson engine's performance. The article may well have been written by Messrs Marple & Co. who were Mr Wilkinson's agents and sole proprietors of the foreign patent ... but the battle lines are being drawn. "We learn that the eminent firm of locomotive builders Messrs Black, Hawthorn and Co., of Gateshead-on-Tyne, have commenced to make the new patent tram locomotive known as the 'Wilkinson' type. This engine has obtained a striking success since its introduction. The first tramway company that adopted it (viz. that at Wigan, where the patentee resides) has effected a saving of over 40 per cent, and, working on gradients of 16, 20, and a long one of 22, this little engine only weighing six tons loaded, is drawing cars, loaded inside and out, with the greatest ease. As a consequence of this economical traction, the tramway company have been able to reduce the fares, which the public are showing by their patronage is fully appreciated ... This engine is the only one that conforms to the regulations of the Board of Trade. The question of steam versus horse traction is now settled, although up to the introduction of this engine steam traction on tramways has been a failure, some engines after only running 3,000 miles having to go to the sheds for repairs. The first Wilkinson engine made has run over 15,000 miles and does not exhibit a trace of wear except that the tyres are slightly worn by the rail. It is simple in construction, all the working parts are protected underneath from dust; it is noiseless and steamless, and has none of the unsteady jerky motion that accompanies other types of tramway locomotives."

However, the correspondent of *Engineering* on 17 November 1882 saw the other side of the coin: "At the commencement of this month the Corporation of Huddersfield purchased a steam tram motor and car from Mr Wilkinson. This engine is provided with the 'Field' type of vertical boiler, and fitted with a 'steam burning' apparatus, and spark catcher, as applied by Messrs Merryweather to their boilers so long ago as 1861. The car is unlike those used in London as, although it has seats for outside passengers, it is fitted with a sort of glass framework for the purpose of protecting the travellers from the smoke, &c., issuing from the funnel of the engine. How far this conforms to the Board of Trade requirements has not, at present, been ascertained, as General Hutchinson has not inspected this tramway. The first trial of the engine took place at half-past eleven at night, but it did not prove so satisfactory as was anticipated, the escape of steam and fire from the chimney being, we are informed, excessive. The engine ran off the metals on going through the square in front of the railway station, but was ultimately reinstated on the line. There was, however, considerable difficulty experienced in driving the locomotive to the summit of the steepest gradient, owing to the wheels slipping. Since the trial, the road makers have been busily engaged, taking up the setts, and pulling the rails to pieces. We are afraid the good people of Huddersfield will not be very well satisfied with the results of the experiment."

In fact they were slightly out-of-date as on 16 November Major-General C.S. Hutchinson had inspected the completed lines using engine No.1 (7¼" x 11", 184 x 279mm cylinders, 27½", 699mm diameter wheels) weighing 8¼ tons, and trailer No. 1 built by the Ashbury Railway Carriage & Iron Company, a rather small 38-seater. The Huddersfield Examiner, 18 November: "When opposite Buxton Road Chapel, the Inspector ordered the engine to be stopped so that he might test its capacity to restart from that point with a load...", it could not until 25 passengers were unloaded but the Mayor, thinking on his feet, explained they did not intend to stop there anyway... "[later] it was discovered that the brake had been on the car since it left the Lockwood Terminus..." Flats on the wheels and all they tried again with success. More Wilkinson engines were bought (nos. 1-6), three from Black Hawthorn (7-9) but by 1890 Kitsons (10-18) had arrived and the Wilkinson engines went in part exchange for new Green's locomotives a year later.

Kitson & Co., 29 January 1883: "...we have constructed over eighty of these [tram] engines, and after three years' working at home and a longer period abroad, we are more than ever convinced that steam on tramways is able to hold its own against any other form of mechanical power, and is also capable of leaving the horse far in the background where the traffic is sufficiently heavy or the gradients severe ... On the Vale of Clyde railways there are eight engines constructed by us, which are run at intervals of from five to seven minutes throughout the day. The traffic is very heavy which is proved by the receipts, being 21d. per mile, and in order to accommodate this traffic the engines and cars are continually stopped and started to take up and set down passengers ... maintenance of the engines and cars the previous half-year amounted to 5¼d. per mile run, and that the last half-year it had been reduced to 5⅛ ... To the Blackburn and Over Darwen Tramways Company we have supplied seven engines ... These engines, during the year ending the 30th June, 1882, ran a distance of 151,000 miles, and worked at the rate of 5.55d. per mile, including all working expenses and maintenance ... we think that what we have said will be sufficient to show your readers that where engines are properly designed and worked by competent engineers they will prove themselves vastly superior to horses, and anything but a disastrous failure."

Initially rather than be too confrontational Marple & Co. (on behalf of Wm. Wilkinson) preferred the "here are the figures" approach, offering: "...a statement as made up and signed by the manager and secretary of the Wigan Tramway Co., showing actual working expenses of four of the Wilkinson locomotives, which have been running on their lines, which by the way are not of the best to work, as there are gradients of 1 in 16, 1 in 19, and 1 in 21, with scarcely any level parts in the entire length. Total distance run during nine months, ending October 31st, 1882, 37,564 miles.

	£	s.	d.
Cost of maintenance, including fitters' wages, one new set of wheel tires and returning old ones, &c., or equal to 0.42d. per mile run	65	1	10
Working Expenses for One Week of No.3 Engine			
Miles run in seven days, 410.			
Driver's wages	1	10	0
Cleaners wages (half) one man to two engines		12	0
Coke, 32½ cwt. (common furnace) at 13s.	1	1	1½
Water, 2000 gallons at 1s. per 1000		2	0
Oil, seven pints at 3s. 6d. per gallon		3	0¾
Tallow, 6lb. at 6d. per lb.		3	0
Waste for cleaning, 10 lb. at 2d. per lb.		1	8
Depreciation at the rate of 15 per cent. on first cost of engine at 5s. 9d. per day (being 5 per cent on first cost, and 10 per cent. depreciation)	2	0	3
	£5	13	1¼
Repairs on 410 miles at 0.42d. per mile (or say 3.75 per car mile run)		14	4¼

(Signed) J. Y. MAWSON

Wigan Manager and Secretary

P.S. No repairs of any kind have been required to be done to the boiler up to date, and from all appearances none will be required for a long time."

Marple & Co. then listed the dozen companies who had adopted the Wilkinson engine; most, although not all, were City of London Contract Corporation concerns.

A London "Director", presumably of a horsing livery wrote to the Engineer on 14 February 1883 regarding the Wilkinson engine, "The steam tram-cars first tried in Paris gave way principally in the journals and axle-boxes. Those next put on failed by the cracking of the fire-boxes, which almost invariably gave way, after a few weeks, near the right-hand corner. These engines were succeeded by those of Brown of Winterthur. I have often ridden on these engines from Paris to Courbevoie, and I at first thought that they had solved the problem; but a month was all that was needed to convert these engines into rickety rattletraps. Hitherto steam tram-engines have been killed by the cost of repairs. I want Mr Wilkinson, or Messrs Marple, to tell me in what respect his engine differs from those which have gone before. Has he special appliances for keeping dust, and dirt, and road grit out of his slide bars, crank pin bearings, and valve gear? Has he better springs than are commonly met with in such engines? Has a boiler which is better than any other boiler? In one word, why is Mr Wilkinson's engine better than those made by Merryweather, Brown, Kitson, Hughes, and others? We have the word of Mr Wilkinson, at all events, that it is better; but I want to know why."

Perhaps one of the most fascinating parts of these correspondence exchanges lies in the way relatively 'ordinary' men wrote in to what were and are serious journals; so many Victorians used their education to advance themselves by reading – were it so today! "A.B" complained of the steam emitted by engines and mentioned the number of drivers being fined by magistrates. Marple & Co. responded rather like a vixen guarding her litter: "It is only right and proper, if the Wigan Tramways Company are careless and inattentive in the use of their engines, that the local authorities should intervene to wake them up to a proper sense of their duty. As regards the emission of steam, we may remark that it is quite possible at the termini where the engines have to wait twenty minutes that steam may be apparent. The driver has to keep a black fire during the interval to keep steam down, and this necessarily interferes with the superheating arrangements; but it is simply an impossibility that during the journey, with proper attention to the fire, there should be the slightest appearance of steam. Coke is used alone, so that no smoke can possibly be seen."

Wilkinson himself wrote on 12 February, quite clearly rattled by previous letters and aspersions. Henry Hughes, once the leading manufacturer of tramway engines queried the cost of running Wilkinson engines; the reply is included not only for the general information contained therein but the note shown in bold type – this is Wigan and most unusual indeed. "The statement of working expenses – 3.75d per mile run – is more than correct, inasmuch that, instead of any items in the account being understated, in anticipation of criticism, the reverse is the case – viz.: engine drivers and cleaners on the line referred to are paid less than 30s. and 24s. per week respectively; oil and tallow are bought at less than 3s. 6d. per gallon and 6d. per lb; the water used is under 2000 gallons, and the price paid for it under 1s. per thousand; **the repairs to the engines have been done by a local firm – the Tramway Company not having any fitters of their own – and therefore must necessarily cover "files, tools, &c."** We have the best reason possible for stating that the whole cost of working this line of heavy gradients – 1 in 21, 1 in 19, and 1 in 16 – including all administrative expenses, is a very small fraction over 6d. per car mile run, since the introduction of steam, as against 9¾d. before that event. In reference to the engines being driven by 'other than well skilled and intelligent men' the fact of them – the engines – being under such complete control, and so easy to manage by the 'unskilled and non-intelligent' men who now drive them, after having run upwards of 75,000 miles with only one accident to life or limb – viz: that of a child running from behind another vehicle going in an opposite direction right in front of the engine, speaks well for both engines and men in charge of them. We would remark also that during the above time there have been no less than four lives lost in the borough of Wigan by slow moving carts, lurries &c."

William Wilkinson then decided to have a field day with "A.B" and I have to add that Wilkinson's works were in Wigan so his attack was really a bit unusual by any standards! "In reference to the letter signed "A.B" ... we beg to say, for the information of readers interested in steam tramways, that Pemberton is a straggling township outside the borough of Wigan, that refused to avail itself of the advantages of a free library, and that the opposition to steam on the tramway emanates from two or three fossil members of the local board, who happened to be in that happy position of being able to drive to Wigan behind their own and other people's horses, and who are so narrow-minded in their views, and opposed to progress generally, that we believe they would hail with delight the abolition of railways, steamships, telegraphs, and the postal service, and would monopolise the highways for their own exclusive use, without any consideration whatever for the comfort and convenience of the public at large. As proof of what we say, we have before us at this moment a letter from the chief constable of this borough, saying that he has not had a single complaint about the engines; also letters from an ex-mayor, a member of the Streets Committee of the Corporation, a surgeon, and a magistrate of the borough, all speaking well for the working of the engines inside the town ... I hope you will insert the above in justice to ourselves, and that "A.B" may have the courage and honesty that Mr Henry Hughes has, to sign his real name when next he writes a letter to the public papers."

On 27 February Henry Hughes re-entered the fray with an absolute stinker of a letter, published in *The Engineer*, a far cry from earlier exchanges: "Mr Wilkinson still thinks 3¾d. per mile the correct cost of working, but he tells us he employs "unskilled and unintelligent men" at 3½d. per hour, and only manages to kill one child in nine months with four engines. He will find in the end that the public will not allow him to do this, and he will then have to increase the cost of labour by ¾d. per mile, and with ½d. per mile for management we arrive at my estimate of 5d. One of your correspondents desires to know the difference between the Wilkinson engines and those of other makers. I will tell him. The Wilkinson engine is an exact copy of the old Coffee Pot locomotives, made by Messrs Chaplin for the last twenty-five years,* but with the addition of an iron box placed inside the firebox and over the fire to receive the exhaust steam and superheat it before passing into the chimney. The intention of this is that the steam may be invisible when it arrives in the atmosphere, which depends entirely upon the state of the fire and the state of the weather. The Kitson engine is an ordinary locomotive provided with an air condenser, consisting of copper tubes exposed to the atmosphere, and through which one half of the exhaust steam is conducted and disposed of, the other half passing away through the chimney at a high temperature, so that in ordinary weather no steam is perceptible; but should there be too much steam to be disposed of in this way a valve is lifted and the exhaust passed into a tank of water and condensed. This principle is certain in its action. The engines of other makers are but copies of these, and it is not, therefore, necessary to describe them. Foundry-square, Leicester."

One "Jno. S. Batchelor" entered the fray at this point with rather rambling letters, although in fairness he did see trams 'on the hoof' at Leeds – some correspondents seem not to be really sure of what they did see. Jno. S. tries mostly to attack H. Conradi, one-time manager of a couple of German tramways where he regarded Merryweathers products as the finest of all. Conradi seems to have made a curious mistake regarding the "shortness of wheel-base necessary for the existing [tramways] sharp curves" by recommending Wilkinson and/or Hughes engines as having short wheelbases: not so writes Jno. S.: "It must be noted that the reverse is the fact, the Wilkinson engines having a wheel-base of 5ft. 6in. whereas the Merryweather engines are 12in. less, and none of the Kitson engines, of which some eighty have been built exceed 4ft. 6in. With curves frequently not exceeding 40ft radius, the latter dimension has everything to recommend it, as regards freedom of working, power of starting on curves, freedom from derailment, absence of wear on tire flanges and damage to points and crossings. Indeed, with the longer spread of wheels, the flange wear will involve renewal of tires before any reasonable lifetime has been secured from the tread, and this indicates with sufficient clearness a measure of injury to permanent way that should not be tolerated."

[A minor digression relates to the spelling of 'tire'; it was not American, many words of the period had greater affinity with those of our ex-Colony than they have today; the impact later of electric trams from the U.S. led to many

**Alexander Chaplin and Company, Cranstonhill Engine Works, Port Street, Anderson, Glasgow – established 1849 for their locomotives used vertical boilers of a pattern patented by Chaplin and quite a different internal design to Wilkinson's. Drive to the engine etc. was via connecting rods rather than Wilkinson's gears. Capable of being fired with small coal, wood or peat, no attempt was made to reduce noise or smoke. The first 'coffee pot' was built in 1860, the last 40 years later with a total production in excess of 150.*

32. North Staffs no.7, Manning Wardle works no. 828 of 1882, 4' 0" cylinders. Heavy with a water condenser mounted on the roof. Unusual inasmuch as initially both driver and stoker were carried. Driven from a side position giving an enormous blind spot. For other details of Manning Wardle locomotives see page 74.

Americanisms in tramcar language but oddly we never adopted their 'streetcar']

Mr Batchelor then tackled water or air condensation against superheating. Water was, he says, a feature of Hughes engines "but exists at present in none but the Manning and Wardle, 13 to 15 ton locomotives, **rather misnamed tram engines**. The Kitson engines have always had air condensation, and of late years the Merryweather also..." His attacks on the Wilkinson superheater were measured and brought out at least one point that must have made Mr Wilkinson wince. To produce the heat to vapourise (superheat) the steam there was "an increase of not less than 50 per cent in the weight of fuel burnt, not for the generation of steam, but for supplying the requisite volume of hot air..."

The content of a letter from Wm. Wilkinson & Co. Limited (per Wm. Wilkinson) was quite remarkable to the extent that the Editor of *The Engineer* in the issue dated 16 March 1883 issued a sort-of disclaimer. "We publish Mr Wilkinson's letter in accordance with his request, though after some hesitation. It is not courteous to attribute unworthy motives to scientific opponents, and certainly it is not wise, for readers are apt, not unreasonably, to consider abuse a mere substitute for argument. However, Mr Wilkinson's letter is before our readers. We may inform him that we ourselves published the illustration of his tramway engine with the simple motive of enabling our readers to form their own opinion of it. When Mr Wilkinson's improvements are perfected we shall do the same for them."

It is clearly impossible to reproduce a letter of some 1,250 words here although for its interest it will appear in the Appendices (Volume 4); but one paragraph proves incontravertibly that 'dirty tricks' are nothing new. It read: "...in reference to our allusion to the evidence given by Professor Thorp at the Leeds Town Hall, we would call the attention of the tramway interest to one fact, viz. that five summonses were taken out by a Mr Edison, a solicitor, of Leeds, against one of our engines, and, on being placed in the witness-box, he – Mr Edison – admitted that his brother was partner in a firm of Leeds engineers who had brought out a tramway locomotive, which he also admitted had so far not been a success. Consequently, under the circumstances, we think we are justified in asserting that this prosecution, like many others before and since, savours somewhat more of selfish vindictiveness and interested motives than of pure philanthropy..."

A chap named Chas. Crowden of Wandsworth-common, London S.W. had his two-pennorth claiming that he could not see Wilkinson "has the least pretension to be termed an inventor", claiming Merryweather had tried and abandoned the Field boiler with superheater "some years ago". But Wilkinson's claim as an inventor of his engine-design was backed by the Patent Office and his geared drive was the vital ingredient.

I think perhaps living in Aston near Birmingham must have had its good points in 1883, for an anonymous writer covering both Kitson and Wilkinson trams alludes to the former as "not having the full benefit of the exhaust from the cylinders, are obliged to use the steam jet to assist the draught when ascending hills, the noise of which I have heard over a quarter of a mile distant; **the consequence is the chimney resembles a huge rocket at night** ... [and] as to the [Wilkinson] engine being a copy of Messrs Chaplin's, of Glasgow, coffee-pot locomotive, I think that is something in its favour, as from my experience Messrs Chaplin's is a capital engine for what it is intended to do, viz., contractors' work and the like. I have also noticed how easily the Wilkinson ascends the long hill at Aston with two cars and one hundred passengers with 120lb of steam, whereas it is with difficulty the Kitson ascends with 175lb, although they have cylinders 1in. larger in diameter than the Wilkinson engine, but the last named has the advantage of being geared about 3 to 2."

Leeds, 20 March. J.D. Harte writes: "Permit me, as one having a little experience, to say that the getting rid of steam by superheating it has two objections. The first is, that although no steam issues directly from the funnel of the engine, yet in cold or damp weather condensation takes place the moment the steam gets out of the influence of the furnace gas, and thus a cloud of steam will accompany an engine, and yet be apparently disconnected from it by two or three feet. This result ensues with the Wilkinson engine used in this town, and very recently one of the drivers was fined 10s. by Mr Bruce [a very anti-tram magistrate] for this very thing ... The second point is that superheating the steam runs away with a great deal of fuel; in fact, visible steam is practically water, and to render this invisible is must be evaporated all over again."

This point was re-iterated the same day by Henry Hughes if anything more forcefully. "Messrs Wilkinson say that their engine is economical in fuel. Surely this cannot be the case, seeing that they get up steam twice – once to drive the engines, and again to render the steam invisible; and as to sparks being emitted, I saw both blue flames and sparks issuing from their chimneys in Leeds only a fortnight ago."

I do wonder exactly who Mr Harte was; there seems no trace of his name in connection with Thomas Green, and it may well be he was an interested professional engineer. But one has to laugh at his phraseology: "Mr Wilkinson is now going through what I call the first stage of tramway experience. Nearly all makers have been through it – Messrs Merryweather, Mr Hughes, Mr Brown, of Winterthur, &c. It is known as the sanguine stage. In about six months he will begin to learn that all is not gold that glitters."

My best friend (because he was writing letters to newspapers for at least 200 years) is "Pro Bono Publico". Here he is quoting from the *Leeds Mercury*. "These [Wilkinson] engines, jangling, wheezing, and flaring along the road day and night, seem to me, apart from any question of horses, to add another curse to existence. This superheated steam, in fact, would frighten horses more speedily than any white steam shown by a locomotive."

Merryweather and Son decided on 27 March that it was time for them to join in; it sounds as though they were niggled by various letters from Henry Hughes, including one where he stated: "Messrs Merryweather, I am sure, will be the first to admit that they copied my water condenser, and have also made use of Messrs Kitson's air condenser. If engineers do not copy other people's ideas, it will be the worse for them in the end."

"Referring to a letter from Mr Hughes in your last issue, we notice one sentence which requires contradiction at our hands. We therefore beg to say that we have not 'copied Mr Hughes' water condenser, and made use of Messrs Kitson's air condenser'. Our water condenser is totally different in construction to any we have seen described of Mr Hughes', and was specially designed to obtain the best possible condensing effect with a limited supply of water. Our air condenser, although somewhat resembling that of Messrs Kitson's and others in mere outside appearance, is constructed in a different, and, as far as we know, novel manner, while the means taken to bring the steam into contact with the cooling surfaces are the result of experiments extending over several years." They also confirmed they had tried vertical boilers and superheated exhaust steam and were quite dismissive of the whole idea as being "quite unsuitable for heavy work".

33. On 27 March 1876 a trial run of a Hughes tram engine was tried in Leicester. Horse tram no.10 (normally requiring two animals) is seen behind the engine in the depot yard. A 'tatty' photograph, but probably unique.

Part of a letter from Henry Hughes makes, perhaps, rather sad reading for so inventive a man: "I am not a maker of or dealer in tramway locomotives, but only an examiner for tramway companies, in which capacity I am pretty well able to judge of their respective merits. A few years ago I was a maker, and lost a large sum of money by the venture".

A fortnight separated two letters – it is difficult even now not to feel that Marple & Co were, to put it mildly, set up – despite Mr Kitson's rather snide remark, they were a reputable firm. This mini-episode began with a letter from Marple & Co to *The Engineer* datelined London, March 14th 1883: "We may mention that a few days since one of Kitson's engines came to a standstill on a gradient at Birmingham, and it was not until the arrival of a Wilkinson engine with loaded cars attached, which pushed the Kitson engine and car to the top of the hill, that it could resume its journey. This, we think, speaks volumes as to the superiority of the Wilkinson engine, as all the engines used by the Birmingham and Aston Tramways Company have to work under the same conditions as to load, &c.; moreover, the Wilkinson locomotives, besides being very much lighter and more compact than the Kitson, has a considerably smaller cylinder."

Kitson and Co wrote back from Airedale Foundry, Leeds, on 28 March and despite the restrained tone of their letter, only part of which is given below, one suspects they were absolutely hopping mad. "We are not acquainted with Messrs Marple and Co., and are also ignorant as to the source of their information – which they publish with the ostensible object of damaging the reputation of our engines. We can only hear of one instance when one of our engines failed to mount the long incline at Aston. During the heavy fall of snow about three weeks ago, the manager sent one of our engines, with a car attached, thinking it would be best able to force its way up the incline, and clear the line for traffic. After mounting for a considerable distance it came to a stand-still, owing to the heavy accumulation of snow in front of it. One of Messrs Wilkinson's, which happened to be the engine to run the next trip, having a clear rail came up behind, and assisted the first engine to mount to the top of the incline. We shall not comment upon the above statement but leave the matter in the hands of your readers to decide in favour of which engine the above facts 'speak volumes' ".

We should, perhaps, allow William Wilkinson almost the last word in a letter dated 3 July 1883. The point to note in this is the habitual towing not of one car, but two, or even three when circumstances demanded. "Our largest class of engine, now on the Manchester and Bury Tramway, drawing two cars, each carrying forty to sixty passengers, and each weighing $3\frac{1}{4}$ tons empty, on gradients of 1 in 120, is working at a cost of under 5.5d. per mile run. On one occasion one of the above engines drew three cars, each $3\frac{1}{4}$ tons, and carrying 299 school children and 20 adult passengers from Berry [presumably Bury] to Blackford Bridge up a gradient of 1 in 20, stopping and starting on same, witnessed by the Mayor of Bury and other gentlemen. WM. WILKINSON AND CO., Limited. Holme House Foundry, Wigan, July 3rd."

The furore did not really die down until a few years later, and in passing one must add that not only did many operators abandon Wilkinsons superheaters but changed to roof mounted condensers, and in many cases the vertical boilered trams were 'laid aside' in favour of locomotive-styled cars. But the survivors in the UK that are capable of running are both 'coffee-pots' made by Beyer Peacock.

34. Seven engines were tried in Bristol. No.6, named after Hughes' works, is attached to a rather hastily top-covered horse tram. The chimney can hardly have helped the machine's ability to make steam. Built in 1879/1880 the seven Hughes locomotives, plus Fox, Walker no.8, ran on the routes from Horsefair Junction to Horfield (Egerton Road) and from the Old Market to Redland.

A mini-history of each of the main

manufacturers follows. Some companies that manufactured, at most, a handful of tram engines in Britain appear in the next chapter. The histories of '3 Brits' – makers that dared to be different, will feature in Volume 4.

As the records of very many tram engine builders were lost when companies amalgamated, or destroyed as the makers saw no further demand for spares, or as in Merryweather's case due to wartime bombing, to some extent I have had to rely on secondary sources, including contemporary journals, (The Engineer, Engineering, Society Proceedings, etc.) and newspapers (be it the London Times or the Rochdale Observer), but where possible these have been double checked.

Works Lists

It has not proved possible to provide 100% accurate works lists of all the main manufacturers. The problems are manifold especially where they went out of business probably a hundred years ago and there were few archivists to gather up their paperwork. Those we do have are:

1. Beyer Peacock & Co. Extracted from Dr. R.L. Hills' original work in the Transactions of the Newcomen Society, Vol.40 1967-8, and reproduced with his and their permission. This has been checked for steam tram content and updated by Joe Lloyd, to whom I extend my thanks. This list is as accurate as can be.

2. Black Hawthorn & Co. Extracted from Allan C. Baker's Works List (including Chapman & Furneaux) which was published by the Industrial Locomotive Society and is reproduced with his and their permission. Apart from a couple of insoluble queries this list is as accurate as can be.

3. Thomas Green & Son. These lists are those compiled by John Pollard and published in Tramway Review, the Historical Journal of the Light Rail Transit Association, Nos.166 and 167 1996.
They are reproduced by permission of John Pollard and the Editor, Richard Wiseman and are as accurate as can be.

4. Kitson & Co. Extracted from Reg Carter's Works List, drawn up from works records held by the Stephenson Locomotive Society and reproduced with his and their permission. With the exception of a few early machines, especially those which formed Rowan cars and/or went to Colonies (whose details are corrected in the text from information given to me by Ron Grant of New Zealand) this list is as accurate as can be.

5. Merryweather & Co. Owing to the apparent loss of all records during the bombing of London 1941 any list must necessarily be hypothetical. This works list is based on that produced by Nick Kelly and reproduced with his permission. It has a high degree of provable accuracy.

6. W.Wilkinson & Co. This list is based on the researches of the late Dr. H.A. Whitcombe, updated by the late E.K. Stretch and incorporating further work by Nick Kelly and myself. Apart from three queries as shown it has a high degree of provable accuracy.

35/36. One survivor of the Beyer Peacock built Wilkinson engines is no.2464 of 1885 now kept at the National Tramway Museum, Crich, seen (above) on 3 October 1965, and (below) by 1 September 1968 she was back in steam towing Oporto car 9. The steam wreathing the machine and chimney smoke is very authentic!

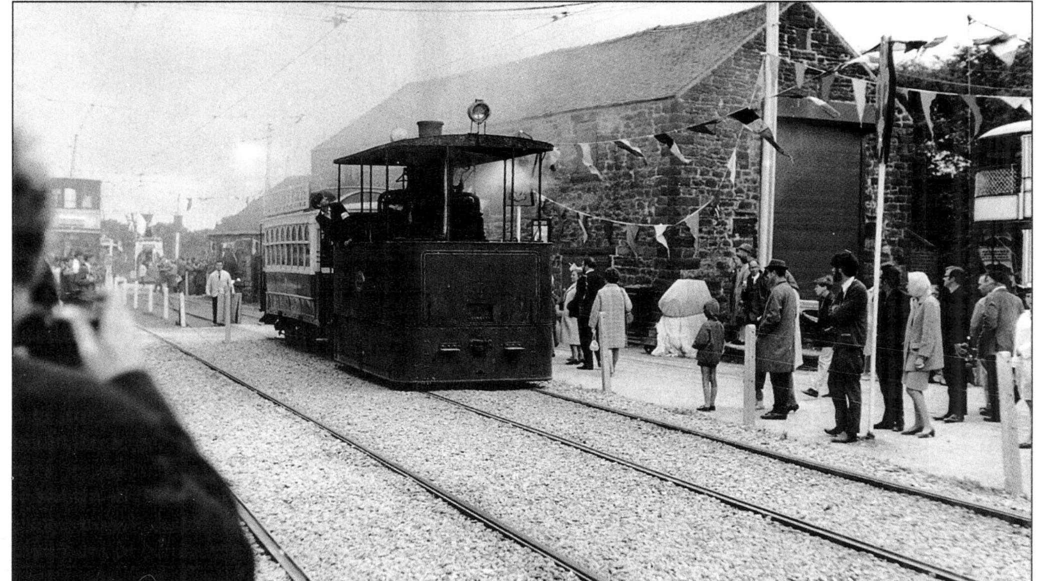

It has not been possible to construct an accurate Hughes/Falcon/Brush list but it is hoped George Toms, the Falcon/Brush historian will be able to provide a suitable document later in this series.

Standard notations are used as far as possible.
Works numbers are those used on the shop floor and were probably cross-referred to drawings, pattern numbers etc.

In the case of Kitson only the "T" works numbers are known to be accurate; the 4-digit 'works numbers' are an attempt to correlate the normal production numbers with T-registers.

Progressive numbers are a minefield. The theory was that where an order number included more than one engine each engine would have a progressive number. Thus order no.100 for five engines would take up the next five available progressive numbers (say 150-4). This works well in theory but at one works where I was employed as a production engineer we found when drawing stock material from the stores the storeman only wanted one number. Similarly the workman cutting plates drew all his material en bloc and only wanted a docket for, say, "5 off part E42". By the time an extremely urgent order had borrowed "one off E42" (probably without a chit) and a number of other bits from here and there, our progressive numbers were almost valueless, and emergency chits would be issued under the original number (100) to make up shortfalls in parts.

Order numbers. Different companies used different nomenclature, in many cases works numbers and order numbers appear to be interchangeable. For spare parts the normal requirement was for the manufacturer's order number to be quoted, particularly where no works number was quoted on the locomotive or trailer bogie builder's plates. In our period Beyer Peacock rarely quoted numbers on their plates (other than the 'Wilkinson Patent' progressive numbers); Black Hawthorn always marked a works number on theirs; Kitson varied (but no "T" number plate appears to have survived), and the most beautiful plates of all came from Sentinel. Measuring 5⅛ x 9⅞" (130 x 251mm) they not only carried their trademark logo, a knight in armour, but quite clearly "Loco No. xxxx".

Order date: The date shown in the order book. However, where parts or even whole trams were built for stock the sequence of date/works number can be skewed.

Delivery promised. Just that. Can be a period of time or a fixed date.
Type. Normal Whyte notation is used; the wheel configuration reading from the locomotive's smokebox (chimney) end. Most trams, but not all, were 0-4-0, having only 4 wheels, all driven. By their nature 'pure' tram engines were "T" for tank, i.e. they carried their own water and fuel supplies and no tender was utilised.
Gauge. Std = 4' 8½" (1435 mm). Others as shown.
Cylinders. All dimensions in inches, giving diameter of piston x stroke. Theoretically the larger the cylinders the more powerful the engine. Where possible the position of the cylinders is indicated by either i.c. (inside the frames of the engine) or o.c. (outside). As a generality most tram engines had cylinders outside the frames, but where overall width was restricted by a Board of Trade ruling due to narrow streets, cylinders could be inside the frames, leading to impossible contortions in the cramped space for fitters.
Driving Wheels (DW). Exterior dimension in feet and inches of the tyres when new. These could alter materially from wear on the rails and from the action of the brake blocks, in some cases the wheel dimensions were altered to give better acceleration or economy.
Name or number. All tram engines in the U.K. had to carry their fleet number clearly displayed, it was always believed primarily to assist police officers and members of the public when they wanted to cause trouble for drivers! The sequence of works numbers did not necessarily correspond to the fleet numbering. A few Irish and Scottish tram locomotives were named.
Customer. This is always as shown in the order book, but not necessarily the company to whom delivery was made. In some cases the order, and presumably the invoice, was made out to an agency (for example City of London Contract Corporation or Whittell or Wilsons) with delivery to a specific tramway or ship.

Beyer Peacock & Co.

Three men of widely disparate character and origins were to come together to form the partnership known as Beyer Peacock & Co. in 1854, and which was to commence operations on 1 January 1855.

Charles Frederick Beyer was born in 1813 at Plauen in Saxony, although he was to receive his higher education in Dresden. As a weaver's son it was not altogether illogical that when he received a travel grant it was used to study textile machinery in England, then, surely, the most advanced country in most forms of engineering. His first employment on his later return to England was with Sharp Roberts & Co of Manchester, and in 1843 he became Chief Engineer of their railway locomotive department.

Richard Peacock, seven years younger than Beyer, had a meteoric career on the railways, as indeed did a few other men who hitched a ride on this ascending star, although he had left school (Leeds Grammar) at 14; after completion of his apprenticeship at the locomotive builders Fenton, Murray & Jackson, he became locomotive superintendent of the Leeds & Selby Railway at 18 years old – although this work was not quite so grandiloquent as it sounds, for not only did he have the responsibility for the running of the company's locomotives, but it was not uncommon for such men to have to work alongside fitters through the night preparing recalcitrant lumps of ironwork to run at all, let alone properly. After a year (1840-1) with Daniel Gooch on the Great Western Railway (which was to stand the new company well later) at 21 he was appointed as "No. 1 Engineman", although he soon assumed control of the locomotive department of the Sheffield, Ashton-under-Lyne & Manchester Railway – his primary task being to build their locomotive and running sheds on a green field site at Gorton. Thirteen years later, older but seemingly still restless, he entered partnership with Charles Beyer.

A third partner, Henry Robertson, of a similar age to the other two (Beyer was 41, Peacock 34, Robertson 38 when the partnership began) was an engineer who had graduated from Aberdeen University, had worked in collieries and as a surveyor on railways both in Scotland and on the English/Welsh borders. The viaduct at Ceiriog near Chirk, clearly visible from the neighbouring Telford canal aquaduct, was designed by him, as was the 19 arch viaduct over the Dee near Ruabon. Curious that two Scotsmen, quite unlike in their training and manner should have left their marks in such close proximity.

The firm of Beyer Peacock were to prove that from their Gorton Works they could, and would, send out all the necessary machinery and expert fitters to set up complete railway workshops (especially in the Indian sub-continent), provided of course their engines were ordered. Beyer Peacock lathes, turners, millers and similar machine tools still remained in use in the 1950s, many of those I saw were proudly shown as being "Many, many years old but most, most excellent."

Small wonder then that not only did the partners design their new works, but oversaw the manufacture of the machine tools used to build the first engine, a 2-2-2 tender locomotive to Daniel Gooch's design for the Great Western Railway which rolled out on 21 July 1855. Beyer Peacock never claimed to be cheap, this engine, one of eight ordered, had a contract price of £2,660, and the order was made at quite a heavy loss. Costing the company in all £23,373, against £21,280 received, the quality and finish was there right from the beginning to the end – a quality which served them well in the export markets.

In 1861 Charles Beyer invited a fellow countryman, Hermann Ludwig Lange, a 24 year-old engineer to join the firm and he chose well, for in 1865 Lange became the Chief Draughtsman (and on Beyer's death in 1876 then became Chief Engineer and Joint Manager), the collaboration between the Saxons leading to the design of a batch of 4-4-0 condensing coke-burning tank engines for the Metropolitan Railway (then and now part of the 'Underground' London network) in 1864; one of which is preserved in the London Transport Museum; but it is said that the difficulties of persuading these engines "to consume their own smoke" was why the firm never built orthodox tram engines in sufficient quantities for the UK market to rival Kitson's or Green's. More prosaically it might as well be that they were so busy with export orders in the 1880s to such diverse places as Australia, Java, Spain, Argentina and Japan that they could not release the design staff or the experimental shop to prepare for such a radically different type of locomotive without, perhaps, any guarantee of sales.

Whatever the cause, their first attempt (order number 3986, works no. 2059) a combined Grantham-type car for the North Staffs Tramways Company delivered in 1881 of 4' 0" (1219mm) gauge was a disastrous failure.

It is unclear exactly why this car was built and even less obvious why the North Staffs company should go to Beyer Peacock for it. In November 1880 at a meeting of the shareholders, the steam tramways chairman stated that the rolling stock was on order – two engines from Manning Wardle & Co., two from Merryweather & Sons, plus the 'combined car' from Beyer Peacock. Tried in steam at the works on 1 February 1881 as a bodyless engine and chassis, after the bodywork was added (built by the Ashbury Railway Carriage & Iron Company) it finally arrived on the tramway on 29 June 1881. The engineer of the North Staffs was Henry Vignoles and he must have been mortified to read in the Chairman's report: "We have also a combined engine and car specially designed by our engineer, which at present is not answering the expectations formed of it, and may in fact be considered a failure as many of the public object to ride on it ... As to the combined engine and car which is at work, I have told you that we considered it a failure but our engineer thinks that be some expenditure he can so alter it as to work as a detached engine instead of a combined engine. The public object to ride on these combined cars. The heat is so great from the engine that it makes the passengers uncomfortable.

Vignoles, aware of the hilly terrain to be worked by the tramway company showed a logical preference for large cylindered engines, but this combined car (no. 5 in the fleet) does seem to have been a galumphing great thing which probably really did frighten the horses. Double-decked it was 30' 5" (9.27m) long, and measured 13' 5" (4.089m) from the railhead to the top of its zinc covered roof. Apparently the zinc was added (and made the machine even more top heavy) after some difficulties with hot coke particles raining down on the traditional painted canvas-on-wood roof. Loading must have been interesting as although the rear had a traditional horse-tram appearance, the forward entrance led to a corridor along one side of the saloon and a staircase to the top deck. The locomotive-type boiler was on the other side of the corridor; the pungent smell of blistering paintwork accompanied the machine's movements – probably the "great heat" referred to.

It appears that the vehicle was sold to the North Staffs at well below cost (£957.5s.6d. against £1680.16s.0d. although whether this included the bodywork is unclear) but its 11+ tons empty weight to carry only 60 passengers could hardly be viable – certainly its great length (for 1881) was destructive of the trackwork.

Strangely enough, given Vignoles' choice of 9" x 14" (229 x 356mm) cylinders on the Manning Wardle engines and 10" x 15" (254 x 381mm) for Merryweather's products towing 50-seat trailers, he settled for 8" x 12" (203 x 305mm) for the combined car, despite its inherently greater rolling resistance. We have to assume that space prohibited anything larger.

As there is no record of the disposal of this engine (although it might have gone back to Beyer Peacock in part exchange for the later Wilkinson-pattern engines) the late H.G. Dibdin

37. Rather a rough, gritty photograph (perhaps most suited to steam trams) this shows King's Heath depot of Birmingham Central Tramways in 1886, when fleet no.64 (BP 2748) was new. The trailers are Falcon built in 1884-5. The boy cleaners were probably pleased to have the job.

38. After repatriation from Australia works no.2464 was used as a works shunter in Beyer Peacock's Gorton works. The casings were modified and the skirts removed while railway-type drawgear and buffers were fitted.

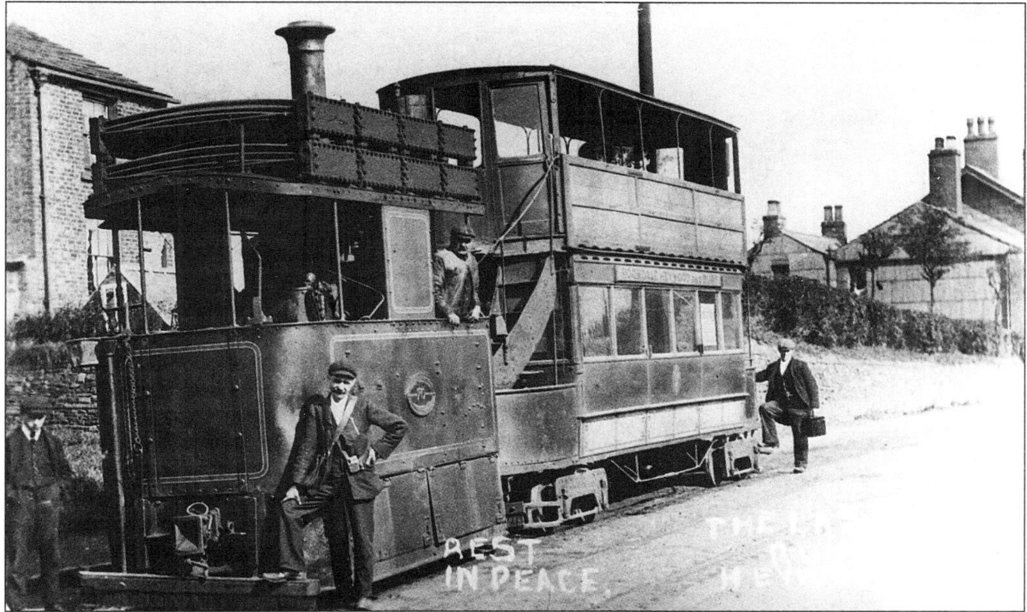

39. In 1886 twenty narrow gauge engines were built by Beyer Peacock (order 6736 works nos. 2713-32) for the Manchester, Bury, Rochdale and Oldham Steam Tramways Company's network. In 1904, Heywood Corporation, bereft of trams, bought 13 engines in order to run a shuttle service, pending electrification. No. 70 was one of these.

suggested (Tramway Review no.26, 1959) the 'coach' portion may have been converted to a single deck trailer.

Despite this failure the firm had a new erecting shop built for this class of work, known as the 'Tram Shop' it retained this cognomen long after steam trams had left the roads.

One of Beyer Peacock's characteristics was the neatness of their manufacturer's brass nameplates fitted to locomotives and in 1883 (order no. 6336) works nos. 2377-2382 were supplied between 23 April and 2 May to the Manchester, Bury, Rochdale & Oldham Steam Tramways Company bearing in addition to 'Beyer Peacock & Co. Ltd., Manchester' the magic letters "Wilkinsons Patent" with or without the Patent Authority numbers (in this case serials 1-6) and the purchasing company's fleet numbers (21-26). The second batch of engines (order 6326, works nos. 2383-92) for the South Staffs Company followed between 22 June and 22 October 1883. Order no. 6413, dated 14 October 1884, to be supplied to the New South Wales Government Tramways should have been workmanlike enough with 9½" x 12" (241 x 305 m)) cylinders and 150psi boiler but as sent out (works no. 2464, Wilkinson Patent No. 47) on 20 April 1885 seems to have been a failure, after some vicissitudes ending up as Beyer Peacock's "No. 2 Yard Engine" where it was used from 1890 as a "temporary" machine until 1959. It is now (2003) at the National Tramway Museum, as their "John Bull".

The fee for each Wilkinson engine built under Wilkinson's Patents was £20 – not an amount to make a fortune for the inventor. Basically the Wilkinson patent involved the use of vertical boilers with 'Field' type tubes (later the cause of many tramway boiler explosions as will be shown in Volume 3 of this series), normally 3' 6" (1067 mm) in diameter and between 5 and 7 feet high which produced adequate steam to serve a vertical launch type engine with cylinders of varying dimensions from 6" x 7" (152 x 178 mm) to 7½" x 12" (191 x 305 mm) according to the perceived traffic requirements. This then operated the geared drive to one axle, the two axles (all were of 0-4-0 configuration) being coupled by side rods. The gear ratio was either 2 or 2½:1 with wheelbases normally between 5' 6" and 5' 8" (1.676-1.727 m) making for a neat and compact locomotive around 12' (3.659 m) long, 5' 6½" to 6' 8" (1.675-203 m) wide as permitted by the Board of Trade to any specific line, and overall some 9' 0" (2.74 m) high. Weight for early models, at under 6 tons was not really adequate, but the 8-tonners provided by Beyer Peacock proved to be more than capable of restarting the engine and trailer on gradients in excess of 1:12 (8%) even on a greasy rail with a full load.

Its Achilles heel lay in difficulty of concealing or dispersing steam emitted from the chimney; a form of superheater in the fire box was far from satisfactory, a roof mounted condenser being really the only answer. By now a queue of would-be buyers was forming and the North Staffs having ordered 20 were probably aggrieved when Beyer Peacock advised them that due to new Board of Trade regulations delivery would be delayed, their first not arriving until 6 December 1883 (works no. 2393) and the last (works no. 2429) 2 July 1884.

That these tram engines which cost from £900-£1,000 each were a small part of the

40. No.77, based and seen at Oldham, was built in 1886 for £890 and sold during 1904 for around £40. Typical of all late Wilkinson-type engines built by Beyer Peacock, a roof mounted condenser supplemented the superheater as a means of reducing steam.

company's output can be gauged by their total production in excess of 200 other engines in the period 1883-4. In all 86 'pure' tram engines (70 to Wilkinson Patent design and 16 with loco-type boilers) were to be supplied to the UK market, the last, a replacement for one scrapped by the MBRO, was built as works no. 2799 and left Gorton in 1887. Numbered 91 in the MBRO standard gauge fleet it was, unusually, a compound with 9" x 14" (229 x 356 mm) high pressure cylinders and 14" x 14" low pressure and is said to have been sold to a tea plantation in Rangoon during 1900. Weighing 13 tons ready for service, and measuring 13' 0" (3.96m) long by 5' 10¾" (1.8m) wide, it seems to have done little work in Manchester despite or perhaps because of a high boiler pressure (180psi). It also had a voracious appetite for coke, and it would, I feel, be too complex and cramped a machine to maintain on a day-to-day basis, but as a generality it was said that the Beyer Peacock variant on the Wilkinson design was the strongest and the best quality product. The Glyn Valley under w/nos. 2969-70 were to receive two hybrid steam trams, in October 1888, No.1 "Sir Theodore", and in April 1889 No.2 "Dennis", and three years later a third (works no. 3500) "Glyn" (May 1892). Coke-fired and initially fitted with short-lived exhaust steam condensers (with steam passing into the side tanks and grossly overheating them) they also had both whistles and bells and were governed down to 10mph (1.6kph) but although the motion, boiler etc. were enclosed, a cab was only fitted at one end. Cylinders measured 10½" x 16" (267 x 406mm) giving a tractive effort of 6,620lb at 75% boiler pressure, driving wheels were 2' 6" (762mm) and these engines were heavy enough at 12¾ ton unladen to require a pair of pony wheels giving conventionally an 0-4-2 configuration.

A curious mistake by the estimator occurred when order no. 6741 for two locomotive boilered steam trams was received from the Manchester, Bury, Rochdale & Oldham company (works nos. 2737/8), delivered on 2 and 6 November 1886) as their fleet nos. 87 & 88. Beyer Peacock quoted (and were obliged to charge) only £890 each, whereas they cost £1,207 to actually build. Presumably vacancies would occur when the truth came out!

We must not overlook the importance of the export trade of steam trams to Beyer Peacock, not only for keeping the works busy but greatly adding to their profits. In all ninety-seven horizontally-boilered, four wheel, tram engines incorporating several different designs were sent to Java; typical prices were quoted by R.L. Hills and D. Patrick in their superb Beyer Peacock history as in the table below.

Charles Beyer had died in 1876, Richard Peacock in 1889 and Henry Robertson in 1888. This only left Hermann Lange, the Chief Engineer, of the men who had driven Beyer Peacock to success, and he died on 14 January 1892, not however before he oversaw the building of an immense variety of machinery, from the company's first compound locomotive (a 4-4-0 under works no. 2792 with 16" diameter H.P cylinder, LP 23½", stroke 24") for the Buenos Ayres & Rosario Railway in 1887 – to 5' 6" (1676 mm) gauge incidentally; a number of patented rack engines using toothed wheels to engage into a special serrated track, separate from the running rails, and in 1890 in conjunction with Mather & Platt the first electric tube engines in the world were built for the City & South London Railway.

Ten years after the death of Lange, Ralph Peacock, son of Richard, decided the time was correct to turn Beyer Peacock & Co. into a public company – he had become Managing Director in 1889 and was the last link with the old families, although remaining on the Board of Directors until 1905.

With the steam railway engine market in some decline it was axiomatic that the firm would seek other outlets, partly to keep the works busy and hence pay dividends and partly, I suspect, as the new company still had some men with ingenious minds. After contemplating and discounting internal combustion engines (the cost of reorganising the works was, in 1905, far too high) they began building a series of steam lorries, the first being shown at the Liverpool Motor Show in February 1906. The link with steam trams lay in the boiler which contained familiar 'Field' tubes and was of generally similar design to those used on Wilkinson-type engines, albeit the chimney was offset to one side. The horizontal engine produced 40bhp when running at 430rpm from its 3¾" x 5" (95.25 x 127mm) duplex cylinders.

Date	Order	Cost	Sold for	Profit	No of trams
1882	6176	£861	£962	11.62%	9
1883	6373	£789	£962	21.92%	2
1884	6508	£854	£960	12.25%	3
1885	6614	£792	£950	19.87%	2

A total profit for the sixteen trams of £1,889 or £118 each.

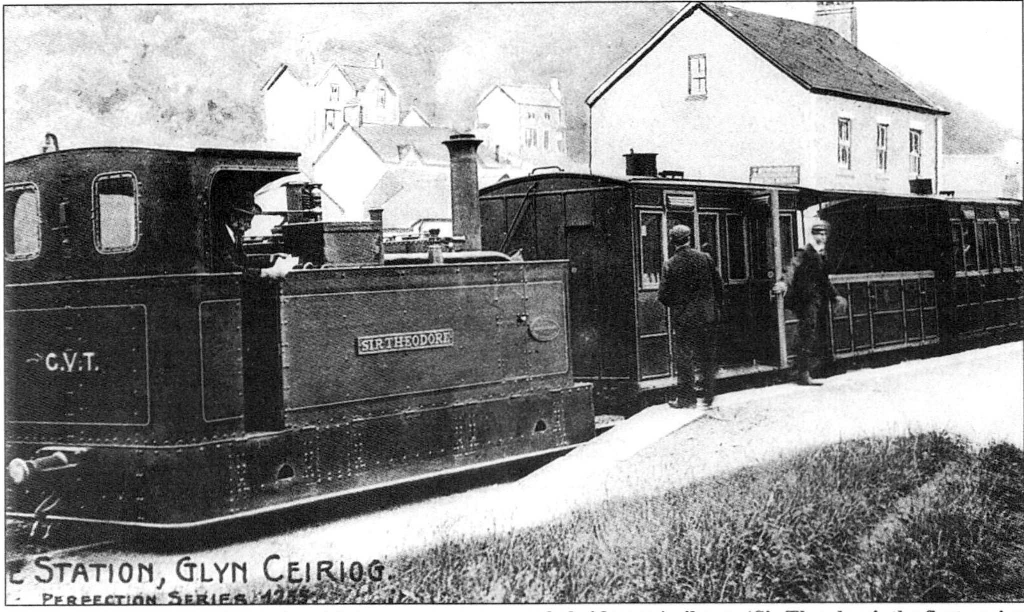

41. Much used by modellers who wish to run narrow gauge hybrid tram/railways 'Sir Theodore', the first engine delivered to the Glyn Valley Tramways proudly shows her brass maker's plate at the smokebox end of her water tank. Photographed in 1903 (works no.2969 of October 1888).

Beyer Peacock & Co.

Order No.	Progressive No.	Qty Built	Wheel Arrangement	Date	Gauge ft.	in.	Name of Railway
3986	2059	1	0-4-0 tram & car	1881	4	0	North Staffs Twys Co
6176	2237-41 2291-4	9	0-4-0 tram	1882	3	6	Samarang-Joana, Java
6326	2383-92	10	0-4-0 tram	1883	3	6	South Staffordshire & Birmingham District Steam Tramways
6336	2377	6	0-4-0 tram	1883	3	6	Manchester, Bury, Rochdale & Oldham Steam Tramway
6347	2393, 2411-29	20	0-4-0 tram	1883-4	4	0	North Staffordshire Tramways Co
6373	2405-7	3	0-4-0 tram	1887	3	6	Samarang-Joana, Java
6373	2409-10	2	0-4-0 tram	1883	3	6	W.Petchell & Co., Java
6413	2464	1	0-4-0 tram	1885	4	8½	New South Wales, Australia
6508	2576-8	3	0-4-0 tram	1884	3	6	Samarang-Joana, Java
6526	2593-4	2	0-4-0 tram	1884	3	6	Coventry Tramways
6526	2595-2600, 2609-10	8	0-4-0 tram	1884	3	6	South Staffordshire & Birmingham Tramways
6614	2653	2	0-4-0 tram	1885	3	6	Samarang-Joana, Java
6679	2742-54	13	0-4-0 tram	1886	3	6	Birmingham Central Tramways
6736	2713-32	20	0-4-0 tram	1886	3	6	Manchester, Bury, Rochdale & Oldham Steam Tramway, 3' 6" gauge for Bury
6737	2733-6	4	0-4-0 tram	1886	4	8½	Manchester, Bury, Rochdale & Oldham Steam Tramway
6741	2737-8	2	0-4-0 tram	1886	4	8½	Ditto
6754	2799	1	0-4-0 tram	1887	4	8½	Ditto
6882	2821	1	0-4-0 tram	1887	3	6	Samarang-Joana, Java
7050	2969-70	2	0-4-2 tram	1888-9	2	4½	Glyn Valley
7061	2976-78	3	0-4-0 tram	1888	3	6	Samarang-Joana, Java
7129	3016	1	0-4-0 tram	1889	3	6	Samarang-Joana, Java
7170	3057	1	0-4-0 tram	1889	2	9	A.L.Elder & Company
7463	3386-9	4	0-4-0 tram	1891	3	6	East Java Tram
7563	3500	1	0-4-2 tram	1892	2	4½	Glyn Valley
7670	3540-3	4	0-4-0 tram	1893	3	6	Samarang-Joana, Java
7875	3654-61	8	0-6-0 tram	1895	3	6	Serajoedal Tramway, Java
7902	3669-70, 3675-6	4	0-4-0 tram	1895	3	6	Samarang-Joana, Java
7903	3671-2	2	0-4-0 tram	1895	3	6	East Java Tramway
8005	3775-94	20	0-4-0 tram	1895-6	3	6	Samarang-Cheribon Tramway, Java
8083	3859-60	2	0-4-0 tram	1896	3	6	East Java Tram
8243	3963-6	4	0-4-0 tram	1898	3	6	Samarang-Joana, Java
8297	4056-8	3	0-4-0 tram	1898	3	6	East Java Tramway
8455	4090-1	2	0-4-0 tram	1899	3	6	Samarang-Joana, Java
8470	4103-4	2	0-6-0 tram	1899	3	6	Serajoedal Steam Tram, Java
8481	4122-5	4	0-4-0 tram	1899	3	6	Samarang-Cheribon Tramway, Java
8634	4246-7	2	0-4-0 tram	1900	3	6	East Java Tram
8648	4260-1	2	0-4-0 tram	1900	3	6	Samarang-Cheribon Tramway, Java
8679	4299-4304	6	0-4-0 tram	1901	3	6	Samarang-Cheribon Tramway, Java
8732	4313-6	4	0-4-0 tram	1901	3	6	Samarang-Joana, Java
9268	4634-6	3	0-4-0 tram	1905	3	6	Samarang-Joana, Java
9372	4717-8	2	0-4-0 tram	1905	3	6	Samarang-Joana, Java
9565	4938-40	3	0-4-0 tram	1907	3	6	Samarang-Cheribon Tramway, Java
9840	5179-80	2	0-6-0 tram	1908	3	6	Serajoedal Tramway, Java
097	5378-9	2	0-4-0 tram	1910	3	6	East Java Tramway
0101	5380-1	2	0-6-0 tram	1910	3	6	Serajoedal Tramway, Java

Payload was, apparently, five tons or so, and half a dozen 'road engines' were built to this design, plus a number to a later, improved design with a 'high speed' boiler which contained both vertical and slanted tubes with "a locomotive type of firebox ... (allowing) ... for plugging of a tube on the road ... the whole of the tube ends in the firebox can be seen through the firehole, enabling any leak to be instantly discovered". If only our trams could have had such a facility!

Eventually it was a design of articulated locomotive by H.W. Garratt that brought more success to Beyer Peacock, although their last steam *tender* engine, one of a set of three (order 1569, works no. 7777-9) of 2-8-0 configuration was delivered to the Cerro de Pasco Copper Corporation, Peru, in 1957, the design being based on the Peruvian Corporation's "Andes" class of which 49 were built by BP. 1935-1953, the Copper Corporation having had five others in 1953, with the final *Beyer-Garratts* being an order for seven 24" (610 mm) gauge 2-6-2 + 2-6-2 locomotives delivered in 1958 (order 11188, works nos. 7862-8) that had been ordered by the Tsumeb Corporation and were almost the same as those previously-built to the NG/G16 design for the South African Railways. In the event they were delivered to the S.A.R as the Corporation's lines had been re-gauged between the order being placed and the locomotives' delivery. The last *Tank Engines* had been built in 1949, although not delivered until 1951, under a hire purchase arrangement as the Irish railway company that had ordered them could not afford to pay for them! Gorton Foundry finally closed in 1966.

Joe Lloyd has provided the definitive summary of steam tram-type locomotives built by Beyer-Peacock. (see table overleaf.)

Tailcorn:

Dr H.A.Whitcombe, in his original talk to the Institute of Locomotive Engineers on 6 January 1937, after stating "the practical perfection in steam tramway locomotives was ultimately reached by the labours of Messrs Kitson and Co" added that Wilkinson engines "especially in the hands of Messrs Beyer, Peacock, proved a very serviceable machine ... The finest of the series was the last consignment by Beyer, Peacock to the M.B.R & O ... They were magnificent

0-4-0 configuration

8 standard gauge	4 vertical boilered MBRO 1 vertical boilered NSW Govt. Tramways 3 horizontal boilered MBRO
156 3' 6" (1067mm) gauge	46 vertical boilered all for UK companies 13 horizontal for Birmingham Central Tramways 97 horizontal boilered for Java
20 4' 0" (1219mm) gauge	All vertical boilered for North Staffs

All these were enclosed in box shaped bodies.

0-6-0 configuration

Fourteen 3' 6" (1067 mm) gauge which were spread over four orders from the Serajoedal steam tramway, Java, the last two trams (works nos. 5380-1) being delivered as late as 1910. Although having the appearance of orthodox side tank locomotives, ten had skirts or curtains over the motion.
This gives a total of 198 to which might be added the three Glyn Valley Tramway engines.

engines and continued to run with the fullest satisfaction until the electrification of the system was completed in 1905..."

On 21 September 1883 patent No. 4526 was granted to Ralph Peacock and Hermann Ludwig Lange of Gorton Foundry relating to "Improvements in Tramway or Other Road Engines". Two items were covered, one to dispose of the exhaust and waste steam from cylinders, brake cylinders and safety valves. A pot was placed over the vertical Field-type boiler with a built-in annular chamber; cylinder exhaust steam (through the pipe); safety valves, and brake cylinders all enter this chamber "and from being in close contact with hot boiler top on which it rests ... the exhaust and waste steam is dried and heated before it escapes into another super-heater placed inside the fire-box [this as in normal Wilkinson type engines] on its way to the chimney".

The second part covered the much improved automatic brake which passed the eagle eyes of the Board of Trade Inspector. Attention to such detail was that which made Beyer Peacock such a great manufacturer.

Black, Hawthorn & Co. Ltd.

In 1839 John Coulthard an 'Engineer' left the service of Losh, Wilson & Bell at the Walker Iron Works on the Tyneside to set up business on his own account; a year later John Coulthard & Co. were soliciting for work at their new manufactory, established within Quarry Field, Gateshead. Although never in any way a major manufacturer of locomotive engines (Allan C. Baker gives an outside figure of 30 in 24 years) nonetheless John together with his brother Ralph, one-time engineer to the Brandling Junction Railway, expanded steadily into the marine and general engineering trade, so that by 1858 the Works, by now known as Quarry Field Iron Works, covered quite an extensive area embracing boiler and machine shops, as well as the usual fitting and turning shops, forge and assembly shed. A saw mill was adjacent, and on the east side were the Gateshead Coke Ovens ensuring an easy supply of fuel for the forges. A branch of the North Eastern Railway entered the works with the two internal lines of rails running in and out of the Workshops.

However, John Coulthard had died in 1853, leaving Ralph in sole charge – twelve years later he was glad enough to retire and sell out to Thomas Hawthorn and William Black. The former, perhaps surprisingly, was the son of a local doctor, but preferring iron works to iron tablets had served his apprenticeship at the world famous works of Robert Stephenson & Co. in Newcastle, and after satisfactory completion of his indentures was employed as an engineer at the new dock and harbour works in Marseilles. His partner William Black was a Scot from Airdrie who had followed his father to Newcastle, joining the Jarrow Alkali Company where he worked for five or so years; he left when he found the dust and fumes were affecting his health. Whether a change of air in the reek of a foundry was much of an improvement is a matter of opinion, from caustic soda and lime to coke fumes and the acid reek of nitric

42. No.8 locomotive of Gateshead was supplied by Black Hawthorn on 5 March 1884 (works no.777) and is shown attached to a later, probably Lancaster-built, trailer. A note on the back of the original explains the driver's expression "This is a true photo as my brother-in-law was the driver" M.J. Tweedy. Difficult in this cynical age to imagine a man would be proud of being a driver of any public service vehicle, let alone a steam tram.

acid seems little different, but happily his years of experience, especially in the production of heavy marine castings, were to be of inestimable value to the new company. By 1865, the date Black, Hawthorn began their partnership, he was 42, Thomas Hawthorn being ten or so years his junior.

Inevitably there were a number of other partners in the business, presumably to provide the necessary finance for their rapid expansion, whereby the main core of the business was moved across Quarryfield Road giving rise eventually to not only boiler and tank shops, but a fully fledged rail served erecting shop. It would seem Black, Hawthorn & Co. (Limited from 1892) decided railway locomotive building as well as their other marine work, was the way ahead.

Unfortunately, just at a time (August 1880) when one would have hoped they would whole heartedly have entered the tram engine business, Thomas Hawthorn died following a climbing accident, and they contented themselves primarily with building 'Wilkinson Patent' engines under licence. Orders were obviously being sought quite actively from 1879, although perhaps they could not compete with Kitsons and the like in the production of 'orthodox' (locomotive boilered design) tram engines.

Their changing emphasis in manufacture is obvious from lists of other machinery supplied – from 1865 to 1879 the primary trade was winding gear and engines for collieries, not only locally but as far as Cannock in the Midland seams. After this date marine engines and their ancilliaries filled the works, including a 70hp "screw condensing machine" (works no. 178, ordered 14 February 1871) for the little 576 ton tramp s.s. *'Terlings'*, owner John Blumer and Co., Sunderland. At the other end of the scale was a 150hp compound engine (32" x 62" x 40" cylinders) to order no. 505 for the ship s.s. *'Irthington'*. One unusual engine ordered under works no. 532, delivered probably (if completed) in 1879, was a Patent 4 cylinder rotary engine to the design of the Hon. C.A. Parsons of Newcastle. The objective was economy in fuel, but whether the technology of 1879 could produce a satisfactory rotary for marine use is perhaps doubtful. But Black Hawthorn also included in their lists four sets of engines for paddle boats plus the necessary paddles and floats. Extremely slow running this special order (works nos. 809, 811, 812, 813 ordered 24 March 1884) had cylinders measuring 30 + 54 x 51 inch and was for use in the Andrew Leslie & Co of Hebburn's ships nos. 253-256, the *Para E Amazonas, Oyapock, Acara and Araguay*, each of 400 gross registered tonnage ... and destined for the Amazon! Not, however, before 253 had carried Prince Albert down the Tyne from Newcastle to North Shields to name the then new Albert Edward Dock.

But this type of manufacturing was being constricted as more and more shipbuilding yards laid down their own engine building works – more than one (Doxford for example) having their engines in as great demand as their yard work.

With the formation of the Limited Company, 23 March 1892, we find the works including work in progress, stock-in-trade, debts and investments plus the nebulous entity, 'Goodwill', were worth, nominally at least, £110,000, five partners (really seven, but one family held their share 'in common') having

43. Presumably in the last year of its existence, Alford and Sutton No.1 (Black Hawthorn 735 of 1883); the tenth 'Wilkinson Patent' engine built by this company) is standing near the shed at Alford. The wagon behind, which to judge by the clinker is only in use for rubbish, reads "GREA..." on the left hand side; presumably Great Northern Tramways Company. The general area is unkempt and it is by no means certain the engine is even in steam.

one-fifth or £22,000 worth of shares each, including William Black. A stocktake carried out at the time threw up an anomaly inasmuch as four tram engines (works numbers 624, 625, 842, 855) were still lying around, plus a lonely marine works no. 673 built 1882 as a compound (29" x 55" x 36" cylinders) for Hodgson & Soulsby of Blyth's ship no. 50. Ships nos. 49 & 50 appear to have been two steam hoppers built for the Russian Government. One might speculate that perhaps there were problems with payment, but the almost valueless tram engines represented a lot of effort with no return, 624 and 625 being particularly mysterious. They were ordered February 1881, for 3 months delivery, 4' 0" (1219 mm) gauge, cylinders 10" x 15" (254 x 381mm) and 36" (914mm) driving wheels for the North Staffordshire Tramways Company, per W. Lyster Holt of London, who appears to have been an agent, although the Holt name also appears among other directorships.

The dates (delivery April 1881) make sense as the North Staffs company were in the throes of opening their main line, utilising two Manning Wardle and two Merryweather engines. The two Manning engines were turned down flat by the Board of Trade Inspector. In the upshot the two Merryweather engines proved to be too light, but heavier ones were "put in hand". The Manning engines were clumsy beasts as using a water condenser they weighed 15 tons in working order.

The most probable suggestion from John Pollard (Tramway Review no.187, Autumn 2001), is that if the Black Hawthorn engines were delivered it was on hire between June 1881 and February 1882. Were this so it is surprising that the Board of Trade missed inspecting them, particularly as these were not Wilkinson pattern engines but boxed-in industrial type tanks. But why were they still hanging about ten years later as a wasted asset? Although 4' 0" gauge (which matches North Staffs Lines) they could have been adapted for some contractor's works.

842 was a standard gauge 'show' engine put in hand 31 March 1885 and ex-works May 1885 with tiny 6½" x 9" (165 x 229 mm) cylinders and 2' 3½" (698 mm) wheels. A Wilkinson-type she appeared at the Antwerp Exhibition, but then returned to the works and gathered dust. It is worth noting that symptomatic of the apparent chaos in the works they could have as easily built a similar Wilkinson-type engine to works no. 835/5, these being completed for Huddersfield in January 1885 and for which they must have retained the drawings, patterns, cores and casting boxes. These at least were decent sized engines with 7¼" x 11" (184 x 279 mm) cylinders...

We may never know all the details behind works no. 855, a solid standard gauge compound tram engine with 8" x 14" x 12" (203 x 356 x 305mm) cylinders which was built some time in 1885, apparently 'on spec'. It is true that this was a period when various manufacturers were trying different experimental designs, but it was not to achieve much for Black, Hawthorn as they were only to complete two more true tram engines, (works nos. 964/5) in 1889 for their local operator, Gateshead & District Tramways Co., although they did provide nos. 1 & 2 of the Swansea & Mumbles Company Ltd's fleet (works nos. 1072/3, August 1892) which were really orthodox tank engines albeit fitted with condensing gear.

In 1896 William Black (by now 73 years old) decided to retire, the firm being offered for sale on 12 May by auction, although as the reserve price (£40,000) was not reached, the sale was withdrawn. In October a new partnership of Abel and Henry Chapman, plus John Furneaux, purchased the whole concern for £15,000. However, Chapman & Furneaux for reasons for their own – perhaps they were under capitalised – refused to carry on the marine work, and neither did they carry on the work in hand. In January 1897 there was an auction sale including among the various marine and locomotive engines "the property of the [Black Hawthorn] liquidator" were two tram engines, the compound (855) which fetched £135, and one other, perhaps the Antwerp engine which was only worth its scrap value – £75. But Chapman

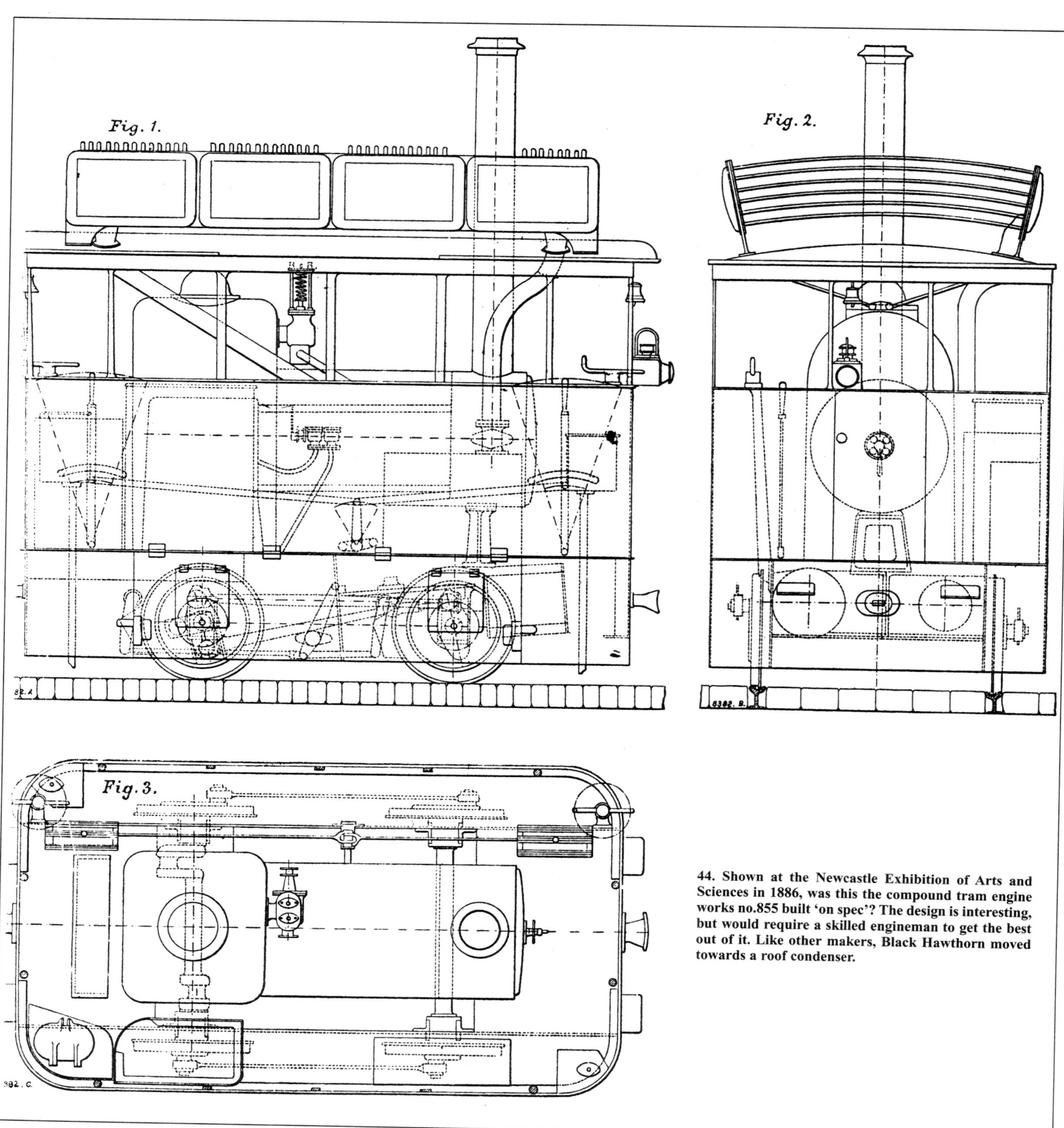

44. Shown at the Newcastle Exhibition of Arts and Sciences in 1886, was this the compound tram engine works no.855 built 'on spec'? The design is interesting, but would require a skilled engineman to get the best out of it. Like other makers, Black Hawthorn moved towards a roof condenser.

& Furneaux was, quite literally, to be a short-lived partnership, Abel Chapman dying in 1902 after a long illness, and John Furneaux, who seems to have been the king-pin of the company, was seriously ill for some time. The works proffered for sale on 8 April 1902, but unsuccessfully; sales of equipment and various engines (built for stock prior to orders being received) took place during 1902 and 1903. In October 1904 the works were sold, and Black Hawthorn & Co ceased to exist even as a ghost, although the goodwill, patterns and drawings of Chapman & Furneaux (including presumably some Black Hawthorn material) passed to R. & W. Hawthorn Leslie & Co. Ltd. – quirkily as well known for their shipbuilding as their locomotive engines. Their last orders were completed by Hudswell Clarke, although these (alas) were not for tram engines. A final note to clarify the gaps in Black Hawthorn works numbers lies in their strange refusal to use numbers ending in "O".

THE MYSTERY TRAM:

Black Hawthorn works no. 506 was put in hand 14 June 1879 for "C. LUND of Newcastle". The following comprehensive report appeared in The Engineer dated 7 November 1879 but was drawn from the Newcastle Daily Journal. The question is where did this tram engine end up? As far as I can check it does not appear in any British tram company's fleet lists, so was it therefore exported? If so, why was it necessary for this machine to meet Board of Trade requirements; curious, too, that there is no record of its gauge.

"**NEW TRAMWAY LOCOMOTIVE.** On Monday, the 27th ult a large company of gentlemen, including the Mayors and members and principal officials of the Corporations of Newcastle, Gateshead, Tynemouth, South Shields, and Sunderland, assembled at the engine works of Messrs Black, Hawthorn, and

Black, Hawthorn & Co. Ltd.

Works No	Order date	Delivery Promised	Type	Gauge ft./in.	Cylinders (inches)	Driving Wheels ft./in.	Name/ no.	Customer
506	14.6.79		0-4-0 tram	?	7 & 11 x 11	2-0		C. Lund, Newcastle
522	31.10.79		0-4-0 tram	Std	2-2			(Not sure if built) compound loco – no customer shown
579	6.80	6 weeks	0-4-0 tram	Std	10x15 ic	3-6		F.C. Winby, Nottingham for Tynemouth Tramways
581	6.80	6 weeks	0-4-0 tram	Std	10x15 ic	3-6		As above
582	6.80	6 weeks	0-4-0 tram	Std	10x15 ic	3-6		As above
589	14.10.80	6/7 weeks	0-4-0 ST	3-3?	7x12	2-4	(Conde)	Hugh Wilson, London for export
624	2.81	3 mos	0-4-0 tram	4-0	10x15	3-0		North Staffordshire Tramways Co per W.Lyster Holt, London
625	2.81	3 mos	0-4-0 tram	4-0	10x15	3-0		As above
707	26.10.82	12 wks	0-4-0 tram	Std	6¾x10	2-3½	(1)	Gateshead & District Tramways (Wilkinson type loco)
708	26.10.82	14 wks	0-4-0 tram	Std	6¾x10	2-3½	(2)	As above
709	26.10.82	16 wks	0-4-0 tram	Std	6¾x10	2-3½	(3)	As above
711	26.10.82	18 wks	0-4-0 tram	Std	6¾x10	2-3½	(4)	As above
712	26.10.82	20 wks	0-4-0 tram	Std	6¾x10	2-3½	(5)	As above
713	26.10.82	22 wks	0-4-0 tram	Std	6¾x10	2-3½	(6)	As above
717	16.10.82	3 mos	0-4-0 tram	3-0	6½x9	2-3½		North Shields District Tramway Co (Wilkinson type loco)
718	16.10.82	3 mos	0-4-0 tram	3-0	6½x9	2-3½		As above
719	16.10.82	Apr 83	0-4-0 tram	3-0	6½x9	2-3½		As above
735	9.1.83	3 mos	0-4-0 tram	2-6	7¼x11	2-3½	(1)	W.B. Dick & Co for Alford & Sutton Steam Tramway
776	26.11.83	12 wks	0-4-0 tram	Std	7¼x11	2-3½	(7)	Gateshead & District Tramways per City of London Cont.Corp.
777	26.11.83	5.3.84	0-4-0 tram	Std	7¼x11	2-3½	(8)	As above
783	28.11.83	2.5.84	0-4-0 tram	Std	7¼x11	2-3½	(9)	As above
784	28.12.83	16.5.84	0-4-0 tram	Std	7¼x11	2-3½	(10)	As above
785	28.12.83	30.5.84	0-4-0 tram	Std	7¼x11	2-3½	(11)	As above
786	28.12.83	13.6.84	0-4-0 tram	Std	7¼x11	2-3½	(12)	As above
815	30.4.84	4 mos	0-4-0 tram	3-6	7¼x11	2-3½	42	Manchester Bury Rochdale & Oldham Steam Tramways Co
816	30.4.84	4 mos	0-4-0 tram	3-6	7¼x11	2-3½	43	As above
817	30.4.84	5 mos	0-4-0 tram	3-6	7¼x11	2-3½	44	As above
818	30.4.84	5 mos	0-4-0 tram	3-6	7¼x11	2-3½	45	As above
819	30.4.84	6 mos	0-4-0 tram	3-6	7¼x11	2-3½	46	As above
821	30.4.84	6 mos	0-4-0 tram	3-6	7¼x11	2-3½	47	As above
822	30.4.84	7 mos	0-4-0 tram	3-6	7¼x11	2-3½	48	As above
823	30.4.84	7 mos	0-4-0 tram	3-6	7¼x11	2-3½	49	As above
824	30.4.84	8 mos	0-4-0 tram	3-6	7¼x11	2-3½	50	As above
825	30.4.84	8 mos	0-4-0 tram	3-6	7¼x11	2-3½	51	As above
827	12.8.84		0-4-0 tram	Std	7¼x11	2-3½	No.13	Gateshead & District Tramways Co
835	15.1.85	8 wks	0-4-0 tram	4-7¾	7¼x11	2-3½	(7)	Corporation of Huddersfield Tramways
836	17.1.85	1.5.85	0-4-0 tram	4.7¾	7¼x11	2-3½	(9)	Corporation of Huddersfield (after South Kensington Exhibition)
842	31.3.85	5.85	0-4-0 tram	Std	6½x9	2-3½		Antwerp Exhibition – no later customer shown (Wilkinson type)
849	12.5.85	10 wks	0-4-0 tram	4.7¾	7¼x11	2-3½	(8)	Huddersfield Corporation Tramways (Wilkinson type loco)
855	.85		0-4-0 tram	Std	8+14x12	2-4		No customer shown in order book
964	11.1.89	8 wks	0-4-0 tram	Std	7½x11	2-3½	(14)	Gateshead & District Tramways Co
965	11.1.89	12 wks	0-4-0 tram	Std	7½x11	2-3½	(15)	As above
1072	8.8.92	10 wks	0-4-0 ST	Std	12x18	2-11	(1)	Swansea & Mumbles Railway Co. Ltd (with condensing gear)
1073	8.8.92	16 wks	0-4-0 ST	Std	12x18	2-11	(2)	As above

Additional notes

506 – Customer not shown in order book; compound loco with condenser. Press report suggest cylinder dimensions were 7+12x11.

735, 776-777, 783-786, 815-825, 827, 835-836 = Wilkinson type locomotives. Tram locomotives shown as Wilkinson type were built to that firm's patent, and had vertical boilers, and cylinders were geared.

Company, Gateshead, for the purpose of witnessing the trial of a tramway locomotive engine designed and manufactured by that firm. A tramway car was attached to the engine which was run on a long line of rails in the yard of the works. Recently, Messrs R. and W. Hawthorn, of Newcastle imported a tramway engine – Browne's patent – which has been at work on the Continent, and which is to be tried on the lines on the North-road, Newcastle, and now Messrs Black, Hawthorn and Co. have built an engine which possessed the qualities insisted upon by the Board of Trade. The compound system has been adopted, and a special feature in the engine is a surface condenser, in which the same condensing water is used over and over again continuously, thus obviating the necessity for frequently taking in new supplies. The cylinders are placed between the frames, and are 7in. and 12in. diameter respectively, with a piston stroke of 11in. The engine is direct-acting, thus differing from Browne's, and has four 24in. coupled wheels. The boiler is of the locomotive type, having copper fire-box and brass tubes, with a working pressure of 150 lb per square inch. The engine was tried in steam for four consecutive hours. There was no appearance of steam nor smoke, and the engine was practically noiseless during the whole trial. The engine is short and compact, and runs very smoothly and steadily. It can be worked from either end, the driver sitting in front, having an unobstructed view before him. The engine is fitted with a steam brake, which can also be worked by hand, and is capable of bringing the engine to rest in a distance equal to its own length, or 10ft, when travelling at a speed of six or seven miles an hour. All the working parts of the engine are hidden from view, and protected from dust and dirt. It is estimated to take two loaded tram-cars up a gradient of 1 to 20."

45. Thomas Green himself in his 80s.

Thomas Green & Son

Thomas Green was just 24 when he opened his first works in Lower Headrow (Eastgate) Leeds. He did not initially specialise taking any work that came to hand, although when he moved to his new Smithfield Ironworks, North Street, in 1848, the Company became well known for quality wire work, including wire weaving and galvanising. The jump to lawnmowers for which they became best known took place in, roughly, 1856-8 by which time it is obvious they had all the necessary machinery and forges – and, more importantly, skills – to undertake such ironwork.

In due course the plant was to produce not only steam engines and locomotives, boilers, road rollers, food preparation machinery ("their celebrated sausage chopping and mincing machines"), horse-stable metalwork, equipment for tennis courts (including not only the posts, but as a derivation of their original activities the wire netting to surround the courts), ornamental gates and railings, plus – and these fetch vast sums in antique markets – foot scrapers.

Interestingly, at least until relatively modern times (certainly the 1950s) lawn mowers were always the main product and items like steam rollers were only made in slack periods, although about 50 'portable' i.e. non-self propelled engines all with massive dynamos for electric lighting, powering rides etc. were made between 1895 and 1901, mainly for showmen, both in Great Britain and Germany – this was of course the great era of fairs, menageries and 'bioscope' shows.

One problem to bedevil the works in later days and historians today was that internal paper work was kept to a minimum, giving rise to problems in the provision of spares.

The firm of Thomas Green & Son became a Limited Liability Company in 1879. Thomas Green Senior, who very late on moved back to his home town of Carlton-on-Trent, died in 1892 at the age of 81.

In the 1940s the late George Alliez, a perspicacious transport historian, collected a number of letters written in 1936 by C.V. Clark of Thomas Green & Son. These copies in turn passed into the library of the Industrial Locomotive Society and are preserved for posterity.

One of the most interesting extracts relates to the actual assembly of their tram engines: "Do you remember me showing you the engine shop down that back street? Well, the engine boiler motion and wheels were put together on the ground floor. The body made of mild steel-plate was completed on the top floor of the building, say 50 feet or more up, then two large trap-doors were opened, and the job was lowered on to the business end of the affair and it only remained to be bolted to the frames and get steam up. If Leeds were taking delivery, a lot of flat plates were laid down the street during the night, and by brute force and cuss words the engine was run up under its own steam, then slewed round and dropped on the tram-lines. So much for that. Another method was to lift them bodily, drop them on a special bogey made for the purpose and haul them to their destination. We supplied a number of towns in Lancashire as well as other counties, and it was not so long ago I came across a picture of a steam-tram taken from a photograph that came from Birmingham. It is very evident they did useful work there. I should be glad if the old firm were doing the business now they did in those days."

Another locomotive historian of the period, the late W.P. Riley, put on file in 1947 that he had been told that those engines built for the Accrington Corporation Tramways Company in 1885 were delivered by rail on the old Lancashire & Yorkshire Railway, and were taken down from the railway station to the tramshed behind the Corporation's Aveling & Porter 1884 steam roller and then slewed onto the rails. The racket over cobbles must have been impressive and one wonders what damage was done to the relatively fine wheel flanges of the engines.

It is not clear exactly how Thomas Green got involved in building batches of Wilkinson-type locomotives as they were only to produce these from 1883 to 1885, thereafter supplying their own locomotive-boilered tram engines. The only real clue lies in the fact that the company held shares in most of the tramway concerns they supplied; but of course no-one would suggest nepotism in Victorian days ... but in connection with their 'home' system one director of the (horse-drawn) Leeds Tramway Company, Alderman Mason, had to resign in 1877 when, as a director, he had been found to be selling corn to the company! Corn to coke is not much of a jump, particularly when we take into consideration that among other connections William Turton, who operated the Blackburn & Over Darwen and Bradford Tramway & Omnibus companies (in conjunction with Daniel Busby)

GREEN'S PATENT "SILENS MESSOR,"
OR NOISELESS
LAWN MOWING, ROLLING, & COLLECTING MACHINES,
PATRONIZED BY
HER MOST GRACIOUS MAJESTY THE QUEEN
(ON 68 DIFFERENT OCCASIONS,)

H.R.H. THE PRINCE OF WALES. THE KING OF THE BELGIANS. THE EMPEROR OF THE FRENCH. THE EMPEROR OF RUSSIA. And most of the Nobility, Clergy, and Gentry of the United Kingdom.

THE extraordinary success of GREEN'S PATENT LAWN MOWERS is an established fact; during the last five years the demand has been unprecedented, which alone is a proof of their superiority over all others.

The following are their characteristic features :—

1st.—Simplicity of construction, every part being free of access.
2nd.—They are worked with far greater ease than any other Lawn Mower.
3rd—They are the least liable to get out of order.

NOTE.—The above machines have proved to be the best, and have carried off every Prize that has been given in all cases of competition. Every machine is warranted to give entire satisfaction, and if not approved of can be returned at once unconditionally.

Illustrated Price Lists which include free delivery to all the principal Railway Stations in the United Kingdom, on application to THOMAS GREEN & SON, Smithfield Iron Works, Leeds, and 54, & 55, Blackfriars Road, London.

46.

47. I have credited this engine to Thomas Green & Son with some trepediation. Dr Whitcombe shows "North Shields & Tynemouth District Tramways Ltd ... 4/5 Wilkinson (Green) 1883. It is a Wilkinson-type engine, it is no.4, and NS&T were the only concern (as far as I am aware) to operate strange single-deck combination cars, but John Pollard (the Thomas Green historian) does not show any TG tram engines going to NS&T. One hypothesis is that it was Thos Green works no.12 diverted from Coventry to Tynemouth.

Thomas Green & Son

Wilkinson Patent, Vertical Boiler Engines. Works Numbers 1 to 12.

Wk. Num.	Pat. Num.	Customer	Gauge	Delivery Date	Ref.
1	-	Leeds Tramway Company	4ft. 8½in.	unknown	1
2	-	Leeds Tramway Company	4ft. 8½in.	unknown	1
3	3	Manchester Bury Rochdale & Oldham	4ft. 8½in.	9 May 1884	2
	2	Manchester Bury Rochdale & Oldham	4ft. 8½in.	30 Jul 1884	
	1	Manchester Bury Rochdale & Oldham	4ft. 8½in.	24 Nov 1884	
	4	Manchester Bury Rochdale & Oldham	4ft. 8½in.	14 Feb 1885	
4	-	Bradford Tramways & Omnibus Company	4ft. 0in.	14 Jun 1883	3
5	-	Manchester Bury Rochdale & Oldham	4ft. 8½in.	9 Apr 1883	4
	-	Manchester Bury Rochdale & Oldham	4ft. 8½in.	unknown	
	-	Manchester Bury Rochdale & Oldham	4ft. 8½in.	11 May 1883	
6	-	William Wilkinson & Son, Wigan	3ft. 0in.	26 Jun 1883	5
	-	William Wilkinson & Son, Wigan	3ft. 0in.	10 Jul 1883	
7		Blank			
8	13	South Staffordshire Tramways Company	3ft. 6in.	1 Nov 1883	6
	14	South Staffordshire Tramways Company	3ft. 6in.	26 Nov 1883	
	15	South Staffordshire Tramways Company	3ft. 6in.	22 Dec 1883	
	16	South Staffordshire Tramways Company	3ft. 6in.	unknown	
9	17	Manchester Bury Rochdale & Oldham	3ft. 6in.	4 Apr 1884	7
	18	Manchester Bury Rochdale & Oldham	3ft. 6in.	24 Apr 1884	
	19	Manchester Bury Rochdale & Oldham	3ft. 6in.	17 May 1884	
	20	Manchester Bury Rochdale & Oldham	3ft. 6in.	29 May 1884	
	21	Manchester Bury Rochdale & Oldham	3ft. 6in.	17 Jun 1884	
	22	Manchester Bury Rochdale & Oldham	3ft. 6in.	2 Jul 1884	
	25	Manchester Bury Rochdale & Oldham	3ft. 6in.	4 Oct 1884	
	26	Manchester Bury Rochdale & Oldham	3ft. 6in.	15 Oct 1884	
10	27	South Staffordshire Tramways Company	3ft. 6in.	17 Dec 1884	8
	28	South Staffordshire Tramways Company	3ft. 6in.	19 Dec 1884	
	37	South Staffordshire Tramways Company	3ft. 6in.	3 Jan 1885	
	29	South Staffordshire Tramways Company	3ft. 6in.	9 Feb 1885	
	38	South Staffordshire Tramways Company	3ft. 6in.	26 Mar 1885	
	31	South Staffordshire Tramways Company	3ft. 6in.	4 Apr 1885	
	30	South Staffordshire Tramways Company	3ft. 6in.	23 Apr 1885	
	32	South Staffordshire Tramways Company	3ft. 6in.	1 1 Jun 1885	
11	33	Bradford & Shelf Tramways Company	4ft. 0in.	25 Aug 1884	9
	34	Bradford & Shelf Tramways Company	4ft. 0in.	28 Aug 1884	
	35	Bradford & Shelf Tramways Company	4ft. 0in.	4 Sep 1884	
	36	Bradford & Shelf Tramways Company	4ft. 0in.	24 Sep 1884	
12	23	Coventry & District Tramways Company	3ft. 6in.	23 Jul 1884	10
	24	Coventry & District Tramways Company	3ft. 6in.	10 Sep 1884	

References to Vertical Boiler Engines Works Nos. 1-12

1. In December 1882 the first Greens tramway engine was used for a Board of Trade inspection in Leeds, public service commenced in January 1883. It is assumed that these two engines were Leeds Tramway Company numbers 5 and 6.

2. The index of drawings states "Four engines for Leeds. Alterations for Nos. 1, 2, 3 and 4. Sold to M.B. & Rochdale Company, February 1884". The date of the order is 6 November 1883. The gauge is given in both the order book and index of drawings as 4ft. 8½in., the order book shows the size of the cylinders being altered from 7.75in. by 11in. to 6.875in. by 9in. Dr. Whitcombe gives these engines fleet numbers 9 to 12.

3. It is assumed that this engine was Bradford Tramways & Omnibus Company number 7, where it had a short life. A replacement number 7 (works number 15) was supplied in 1885.

4. On 5 December 1882, when the Board of Trade inspection took place a visit was made to Smithfield Works where three engines were in various stages of construction. As these three engines were the first order in the order book, date 16 December 1882, and the first to be delivered it is thought they were the ones inspected, despite being works number 5. Dr. Whitcombe gives these engines fleet numbers 1 to 3.

5. This order is in the name of William Wilkinson & Son, Wigan, dated 2 March 1883. Both the order book and the index of drawings state the engines were "supplied to Dublin". The index of drawings states the customer as North Shields & District Tramways where it is assumed they were numbers 4 and 5.

6. It is assumed that these engines were South Staffordshire Tramways numbers 13 to 16.

7. The order book shows these engines as 3ft. 6in. gauge, the index of drawings gives them as 4ft. 8½in. gauge altered to 3ft. 6in. gauge. It is assumed that they were Manchester, Bury, Rochdale and Oldham Tramways numbers 27 to 34, the fleet numbers given by Dr. Whitcombe.

8. There is an error in the order book as two engines are shown with Wilkinson Patent number 35 whilst Patent number 31 is omitted. The author believes that the error is in works number 10 and has therefore substituted number 31 for 35. It is assumed that the engines were South Staffordshire Tramways 30 to 37. The order book gives the order as c/o City of London Contract Corporation.

9. It is assumed that these engines were Bradford & Shelf Tramways numbers 1 to **4.** The order was originally for five Wilkinson Patent type engines but was changed to four Wilkinson type and one horizontal boiler type (Works Number 13).

10. It is assumed that these engines were Coventry & District Tramways Company numbers 3 and 4. The order book gives the order as c/o City of London Contract Corporation.

was also the Chairman of the Board of Thomas Green & Son Ltd, while the Green family were represented on the board of directors of the Accrington and Rossendale steam tram companies.

The Wortley line in Leeds had been operated entirely by steam using hired Kitson locomotives since 1881, and after relaying in 1882 the Headingley line was passed for steam use and it is at this point that the first two Green tram engines enter the stage. Carrying works nos. 1 and 2, and, probably, Leeds nos. 5 and 6, these were built to Wilkinson patents with vertical boilers and geared drive, although unusually no patent (Wilkinson) numbers seem to have been allocated. When tested on 2 December 1882, with the Board of Trade inspector on board the trailer as well as sundry council and tramway officials plus "Mr Thomas Green and Mr Baxter, vice Chairman of Thomas Green & Son", they had a number of serious problems which were accounted for variously by the wet state of the rails, the greasy condition of the wheels, and "the wetness of the sand on the line, which should have been dry". With hindsight we know the truth of the matter was that these two first engines from Greens were with their 6" x 7" (152 x 178mm) cylinders just too tishy to do their job – proven perhaps by a letter in the Yorkshire Post, 18 January 1883: "Up Cookridge Street and Woodhouse Lane, the engine did not send an odd spark or two out of the chimney, but one continuous stream of sparks 10 or 12 feet high, and covering passengers on the top with pieces of cinder insomuch that some put up their umbrellas to protect themselves. How horses will be got to face such an infernal machine goodness only knows."

Another complaint following their entry into regular service on New Years Day 1884 was that although these engines were non-condensing, using instead a superheater to 'dry' the steam, at the Oak Public House, Headingley, they took in water from a hydrant and "discharged vast quantities of steam" to the distress of the locals, and their horses.

In Huddersfield a fatal accident (seven people were killed and 28 seriously injured) caused the Board of Trade to take a long hard look at the braking systems used on (specifically) Wilkinson-type locomotives and generally all engines, its having been proved the automatic brake designed to both cut off steam and stop the engine and trailer, as designed by Wilkinson did not always function.

Francis William Webb, the locomotive superintendant was called in by the operators, Huddersfield Corporation, as the undeniable expert to ascertain the cause of the accident. He laid the blame fairly at the feet of William Wilkinson, "the designer and patentee of the engine involved" (No.2, Wilkinson 1882 w/no. 6) because he had designed a locomotive that totally ignored the Board of Trade ruling that tram engines used on the highway had to have two independent braking systems. The worm drive system was such that it could only be used as a brake by reversing the engine. In this case as the driver used his reversing lever the relatively flimsy valve gear disintegrated "the slide valve of the right-hand cylinder had moved on its spindle, [then] the piston of the same cylinder was smashed to pieces and the piston rod bent, while some of the fragments had been carried through the ports into the exhaust box". It was made very clear that there was no other way of stopping the tram once the engine failed. "Reversing is effected by a lever which has only two positions, either up or down, there being no intermediate notches between the ends of the quadrant. Connected with this lever is the piston of a cylinder to the lower part of which steam is admitted by the governor whenever the speed exceeds eight miles an hour, whereupon the lever is pushed up and the engine reversed. This same lever is also employed in stopping and starting the engine, there being no other means at the disposal of the driver, except the regulator, of arresting its speed. Besides reversing the engine the governor also applies a steam brake to the wheels, and had it been in good working order it ought at least to have prevented the speed rising to a dangerous point. The engine was reversed, whether by the man or the governor does not appear, but the one cylinder had not power to hold the tram, and the driver had no more resources at his command."

Green's worked hard to modify this equipment and to add a handbrake, completing the fitment of these alterations by 3 August 1883. On 5 August the 5.20 p.m. steam tram was ten minutes late leaving Boar Lane for Headingley and was followed close behind by the 5.30 horse tram. According to the newspapers, at Cookridge Street the engine failed and both it and the trailer

48. Although a few years old when this photograph was taken, Birmingham & Midland Tramways loco no.24 (works no.42 of July 1886) still looks immaculate and the trailer, Oldbury built, is still straight and true. Colours at this time were dark green and cream.

49. Blackburn and Over Darwen's tram engine no.8 is assumed to be works no.19, delivered 9 June 1885, and is shown coupled to one of this company's rather oddly-specified trailers; effectively a cross between a horse tram and a covered-top steam trailer; it was, however, purpose built together with seven others by Ashbury during 1881-2.

399

THOMAS GREEN & SON,

LIMITED,

Smithfield Iron Works, Leeds

AND

SURREY WORKS,

BLACKFRIARS ROAD, LONDON, S.E.

ENGINEERS AND MANUFACTURERS OF

GREEN'S IMPROVED LOCO-TYPE TRAMWAY ENGINES

With either Inside or Outside Cylinders,

HIGH PRESSURE OR COMPOUND PATTERN.

ALSO TANK LOCOMOTIVES & LIGHT RAILWAY ENGINES AND VAUX'S PATENT TRAMWAY COUPLINGS.

These Engines may be seen at work on the following Tramway Companies' Lines, viz:—

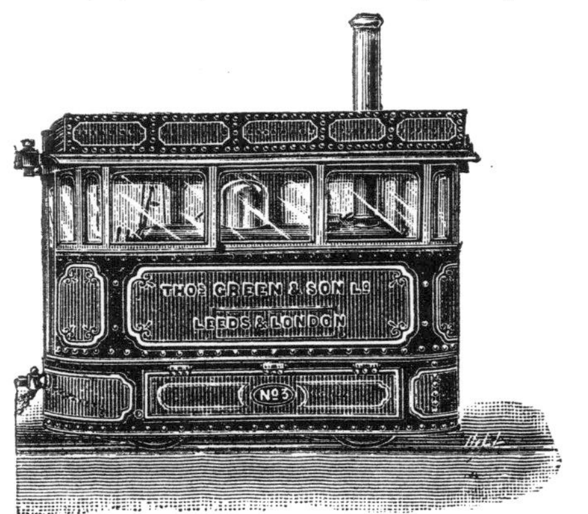

The Bradford & Shelf,
The Dundee & District,
The Bradford Tram and Omnibus,
The Blackburn and Over Darwen,
The Leeds,
The Accrington Corporation,
The Birmingham and Midland,
The Blackburn Corporation,
The Rossendale Valley,
The Drypool and Marfleet, Hull,
The Wolverton and Stony Stratford,
St. Helen's,
AND OTHERS.

PATENT LIFT FOR TRAMWAY ENGINES,

TOOLS AND FITTINGS FOR TRAM-ENGINE SHEDS.

OVERHEAD TRAVELLERS, HAND-POWER AND STEAM CRANES.

PATENT STEAM ROAD ROLLERS, TRACTION, STATIONARY, AND VERTICAL ENGINES AND BOILERS COMBINED.

STEAM WINCHES, PUMPS, &c.

Specifications, Price Lists, and References on Application.

50.

began to drift backwards. Incredibly the male passengers aided by bystanders were able to stop both vehicles running into the following three-horse tram.

The Kitson engines were by February 1884 costing 6d. per car mile and Green's 6½d. compared with horses at 9⅛d. per car mile run, but at the end of May 1884 the Green engines were ousted and replaced by a number of Kitson products. Presumably they were returned and dismantled.

Numerically the next batch of Wilkinson-type engines were built under works number 3, Patent nos. 1-4 and comprised four engines, originally intended for Leeds but wisely diverted to the Manchester, Bury, Rochdale & Oldham Steam Tramway Company and delivered between 9 May 1884 and February 1885, after conversion of various items to suit, not least the cylinders which were reduced from 7¾" x 11" to 6⅞" x 9" (197 x 279 to 175 x 229mm), and although designed as being of standard gauge they may have been altered to narrow gauge (3' 6", 1067 mm) the M.B.R & O operating trams in both sizes, although it is difficult to see how this could have been carried out economically. Whatever the event, there is no doubt orders 5 (3 trams) and 9 (8) were supplied during 1883 and 1884, together with 12 for the South Staffordshire Tramways Company, four for Bradford & Shelf Tramways Company to 4' 0" (1219 mm) gauge and two for Coventry where apparently they were found to be useless on the climb out of the city centre often requiring the service of a 'banker' to push them up! The two missing out of a total of 38 were destined for "William Wilkinson & Son of Wigan" but to an odd gauge of 3' 0" (914 mm). Precisely who these were destined for is in some doubt, as both the North Shields & Tynemouth and Giant's Causeway companies ran on 3' 0" gauge and both used Wilkinson-pattern engines, the N S & T having, according to Dr. Whitcombe (History of the Steam Tram, reprinted Adam Gordon) two, Nos. 4-5 of 1883, and the Giant's Causeway Nos. 1-2 of 1883, No.3 in 1886 and finally No.4 in 1896. This late and lonely engine No.4, 'Brian Boroimhe' was thought at one time to have been built by Wilkinson out of spare parts, one query being why they would want to subcontract such an order to Thomas Green. The truth may well lie in the fact of Wilkinson's company liquidation coming at this time – in all probability the Receiver was unwilling to allow work other than completion of orders in hand. Incidentally the Irish engines were once described as having "the general air of a couple of old ladies in crinolines" due to their panelling and, for the earliest machines at least, the fact they were "half as broad as they were long". Marvellous!

Thomas Green & Son's horizontal boilered engines were far more of a success, with 178 being delivered between the first, 1885 works number 13, Bradford & Shelf Tramways Company, No.5 and the last, really rather a pseudo-tram, was w/no. 267 Dublin & Blessington Steam Tramways Company's no.10 (ex No.2) of 1906. The last true tram engine delivered in the UK works no. 230, Accrington Corporation Tramways Company No.6, was supplied in 1898 as a replacement for a scrapped 1885 example.

The letter from Mr C.V. Clark, alluded to earlier, shows the pride of a loyal 'company' man, and one who was interested in the products of Thomas Green & Son. "The engine a 0-4-0 steam tram was one of a batch supplied to Leeds and built by my firm. They did quite a big trade in this line years ago, and it was often the case that six or eight of these locos would be in hand at once. As far as I know the last engines made were sent out to Kimberley, S.A. round about 1900, but for some considerable time after that spare parts were often called for, and these were sent to towns in this country. I have been told that the South African batch never arrived as the ship went down! ... This particular machine, No.12, was compounded, and the running costs were very low indeed. The driver told me (he is alive today by the way) that engineers from various places were greatly interested, and used to marvel at the work she did. You will notice the nest of pipes on the roof of the body. These were for condensing the exhaust steam and were the patent of the late Mr G.W. Blackburn who was our manager, and the father of the present Robt.

51. Clearly showing her nest of tubes, the 'Blackburn' condenser, no.9 of the St. Helens & District Tramways Company, works no.168 of 1861 looks very smart in deep red and broken white, together with the accompanying Milnes-built trailer.

52. The plate on the side of Leeds no. 12 reads:

T. Green & Son Ld.
Makers 1885
Leeds & London

It was, in fact, initially a lonely 'one-off' as works no.26. The packages visible through the cab apertures are bags of coke. Both the retro-fitted Blackburn patent condenser and the life guard are clearly visible. The trailer, no.26, was built by Milnes in 1890 and supplied to Leeds Tramways Company at a cost of £245. Although seating 66 (28 saloon, 38 outside), it was useless in electric days and scrapped in 1902.

Blackburn of the Blackburn Aeroplane Co.Ltd ... I very well remember these things running about 1902 or 3 when they were taken off the streets and can see them now tearing up Briggate, sending out steam and sparks. By means of flap valve the driver was able to exhaust to atmosphere without condensing. A bell was suspended at each end (they could be so driven) and a lanyard fixed to the clapper. You can well imagine what a dickens of a row was made if other traffic did not offer a clear road. The fuel was coke, and no doubt you will notice several bags of this just above the driver's head. This man, and another shared No.12 between them and got a bonus for economical running. The coke was weighed out to them daily and the other drivers finding they were not able to share in the spoils took the law in their own hands and ditched the weighing machine in the River Aire, with what results to themselves I do not know."

Engines could be provided with either inside or outside cylinders as required by the operators but in general 'simple' engines had cylinders 9" x 14", and compounds 9½" for the High Pressure side exhausting in to a 15" Low Pressure cylinder still with a 14" stroke (HP 241mm LP 381 mm x 356mm). Boilers generally measured 2' 8" (813mm) in diameter, the Ramsbottom safety valves blowing at 150psi. Driving wheels were, ideally, 2' 6" diameter (762mm) although they varied, braking on the later engines was either by vacuum or by a foot pedal operating a steam cylinder measuring 4" bore x 5" stroke (102 x 127mm) supplemented by a hand (screw) brake. The trailer car cable operated brakes were designed to be applied before the engine brakes by being wound onto drums, the speed governed by the steam cylinder. Curious how much more efficient steam tram brakes were in later days than even in the 1950s when we were still instructed to use the tram's hand brake before any electrical or air systems. Overall dimensions, which naturally varied to suit local conditions, were, taking Accrington as typical, some 12' 6" (3.81m) long 6' 0" (1.83m) wide and 9' 2" (2.79m) to the top of the condenser tubes.

Every year it was proper practice for the

References to Horizontal Boiler Engines: Works Nos. 13-367

1. The Order book states "sent on approval, returned 3 May 1886". Following its return this engine became works number 57, Dundee & District Tramways Company number 8.

2. Assumed to be Blackburn & Over Darwen Tramways Company number 8.

3. Works numbers 20 to 22 are assumed to be Bradford Tramways & Omnibus Company numbers 9 to 11.

4. The original Bradford & Shelf Tramways Company number 5 (Greens works number 13) was badly damaged in an accident in September 1885. Following repairs the original number 5 re-entered service. Either the old or new number 5 are assumed to have been renumbered to 8.

5. The orders for works numbers 49, 52 to 55, 59, 60, 64 and 66 to 76 were in the name of Contract Construction Ltd.

6. The index of drawings gives works number 56 as a third engine for Wolverton & Stoney Stratford Tramways, in addition to works numbers 43 and 51, but no fleet number is given. The order books states only two engines were supplied as do published histories of the tramway.

7. This engine was originally works number 18, North London Tramways Company. (See above, note 1).

8. The order for works numbers 80, 82 to 87 and 92 to 93 was initially in the name of Charles Courtney Crump but changed to Contract Construction Company. The first engine for Rossendale Valley Tramways Company is shown in Greens order book as fleet number 15, following on from engines of Blackburn Corporation Tramways Company.
It is assumed that this was re-numbered to Rossendale Valley Tramways Company number 8 but it has been claimed that Blackburn Corporation Tramways Company did have a number 15, built by Greens. No such engine is shown in Greens records, perhaps this engine was at one time BCTC number 15 before becoming RVTC number 8.

9. The order book states "in part exchange for Wilkinson engine".

10. The order for works numbers 138 to 144 was in the name of John Waugh, Sunbridge Chambers, Bradford.

11. The index of drawings states "later to Skipton Rock Company".

12. Works number 169 is blank in both the order book and the index of drawings. However the order book shows "Dundee & District Tramways, boiler for tram engine" immediately after the order for St. Helens & District Tramway Company which became works number 168. If new boilers were given works numbers in the same series as engines this could explain some of the blank numbers.

13. No operator of this name has been traced. However H. Fayle, Narrow Gauge Railways of Ireland, states that works number 169 was Dublin & Lucan Tramway 7, an engine not traced in Greens records. Works number 170 is described as a three foot gauge, side tank engine with a five foot wheelbase, a description which fits Dublin & Lucan Tramway 7. It is assumed that McDonnell was an agent who supplied Dublin & Lucan 7 and that Fayle quoted the wrong works number.

14. The order book states that six old Wilkinson engines were taken in part exchange for the engines supplied as works numbers 181 to 188.

15. If this engine was built and kept in stock it may eventually have become Rossendale Valley Tramways Company number 11.

16. No gauge is given for these two engines, the only instance of this in the index of drawings.

17. It is assumed that two out of works numbers 221. 222 and 226 were Blackburn & Over Darwen Tramways Company numbers 13 and 14.

18. The index of drawing gives these four engines as both Kimberley Tram Company and Victoria Tramway Company, presumably one was a subsidiary of the other.
It has been stated that these four engines were rebuilt from earlier Greens engines, previously supplied to either the Bradford & Shelf Tramways Company or the Bradford Tramways & Omnibus Company. There is nothing in Greens records to suggest this, neither has the authors research into the history of the two Bradford companies produced any evidence of earlier Greens engines being withdrawn and subsequently rebuilt.

Thomas Green & Son

Horizontal Boiler Engines. Works Numbers 13 to 367.

Wk. Num.	Customer	Gauge	Delivery Date	Ref.
13	Bradford & Shelf Tramways Company 5	4ft. 0in.	29 Jan 1885	
14	Bradford & Shelf Tramways Company 6	4ft. 0in.	12 Feb 1885	
15	Bradford & Shelf Tramways Company 7	4ft. 0in.	1 Apr 1885	
16	Dundee & District Tramways Company 1	4ft. 8½in.	22 Feb 1885	
17	Dundee & District Tramways Company 2	4ft. 8½in.	9 Jun 1885	
18	North London Tramways Company	4ft. 8½in.	8 Jan 1886	1
19	Blackburn & Over Darwen Tramways Co.	4ft. 0in.	9 Jun 1885	2
20	Bradford Tramways & Omnibus Company	4ft. 0in.	20 Jun 1885	3
21	Bradford Tramways & Omnibus Company	4ft. 0in.	6 Jul 1885	3
22	Bradford Tramways & Omnibus Company	4ft. 0in.	31 Jul 1885	3
23	Accrington Corporation Steam Tramway Co. 1	4ft. 0in.	12 Mar 1886	
24	Bradford & Shelf Tramways Company 7	4ft. 0in.	22 Sep 1885	
25	Dundee & District Tramways Company 3	4ft. 8½in.	10 Jul 1885	
26	Leeds Tramways Company 12	4ft. 8½in.	25 Aug 1885	
27	Dundee & District Tramways Company 4	4ft. 8½in.	16 Oct 1885	
28	Dundee & District Tramways Company 5	4ft. 8½in.	14 Apr 1886	
29	Birmingham & Midland Tramways 13	3ft. 6in.	17 Nov 1885	
30	Birmingham & Midland Tramways 20	3ft. 6in.	4 Jun 1886	
31	Birmingham & Midland Tramways 21	3ft. 6in.	11 Jun 1886	
32	Accrington Corporation Steam Tramway Co. 2	4ft. 0in.	20 Mar 1886	
33	Accrington Corporation Steam Tramway Co. 3	4ft. 0in.	15 Apr 1886	
34	Accrington Corporation Steam Tramway Co. 4	4ft. 0in.	26 May 1886	
35	Accrington Corporation Steam Tramway Co. 5	4ft. 0in.	4 Jun 1886	
36	Accrington Corporation Steam Tramway Co. 6	4ft. 0in.	23 Jul 1886	
37	Accrington Corporation Steam Tramway Co. 7	4ft. 0in.	20 Aug 1886	
38	Accrington Corporation Steam Tramway Co. 8	4ft. 0in.	12 Feb 1887	
39	Accrington Corporation Steam Tramway Co. 9	4ft. 0in.	23 Mar 1887	
40	Birmingham & Midland Tramways 22	3ft. 6in.	22 Jun 1886	
41	Birmingham & Midland Tramways 23	3ft. 6in.	7 Jul 1886	
42	Birmingham & Midland Tramways 24	3ft. 6in.	30 Jul 1886	
43	Wolverton & Stoney Stratford Tramway 1	3ft. 6in.	29 Jul 1887	
44	Bradford & Shelf Tramways Company 5	4ft. 0in.	10 Jun 1886	4
45	Dundee & District Tramways Company 6	4ft. 8½in.	23 Jul 1886	
46	Bradford & Shelf Tramways Company 9	4ft. 6in.	23 Aug 1886	
47	Bradford & Shelf Tramways Company 10	4ft. 0in.	17 Sep 1886	
48	Bradford & Shelf Tramways Company 3	4ft. 0in.	unknown	
49	Blackburn Corporation Tramways Company 1	4ft. 0in.	9 May 1887	5
50	Dundee & District Tramways Company 7	4ft. 8½in.	8 Oct 1886	
51	Wolverton & Stoney Stratford Tramway 2	3ft. 6in.	14 Oct 1887	
52	Blackburn Corporation Tramways Company 2	4ft. 0in.	9 May 1887	5
53	Blackburn Corporation Tramways Company 3	4ft. 0in.	17 May 1887	5
54	Blackburn Corporation Tramways Company 4	4ft. 0in.	17 May 1887	5
55	Blackburn Corporation Tramways Company 5	4ft. 0in.	28 May 1887	5
56	Blank			6
57	Dundee & District Tramways Company 8	4ft. 8½in.	27 Jan 1887	7
58	Bradford & Shelf Tramways Company 4	4ft. 0in.	26 May 1887	
59	Blackburn Corporation Tramways Company 6	4ft. 0in.	27 Jun 1887	5
60	Blackburn Corporation Tramways Company 7	4ft. 0in.	13 Jul 1887	5
61	Dundee & District Tramways Company 9	4ft. 8½in.	29 Oct 1888	
62	Dundee & District Tramways Company 10	4ft. 8½in.	24 Dec 1888	
63	Blackburn & Over Darwen Tramways Co. 9	4ft. 0in.	25 May 1887	
64	Blackburn Corporation Tramways Company 8	4ft. 0in.	4 Aug 1887	5
65	Bradford & Shelf Tramways Company 1	4ft. 0in.	30 Jul 1887	
66	Accrington Corporation Steam Tramway Co. 10	4ft. 0in.	24 Aug 1887	5
67	Accrington Corporation Steam Tramway Co. 11	4ft. 0in.	31 Aug 1887	5
68	Accrington Corporation Steam Tramway Co. 12	4ft. 0in.	14 Sep 1887	5
69	Accrington Corporation Steam Tramway Co. 13	4ft. 0in.	5 Oct 1887	5
70	Blackburn Corporation Tramways Company 9	4ft. 0in.	21 Oct 1887	5
71	Blackburn Corporation Tramways Company 10	4ft. 0in.	1 Nov 1887	5
72	Blackburn Corporation Tramways Company 11	4ft. 0in.	5 Nov 1887	5
73	Accrington Corporation Steam Tramway Co. 14	4ft. 0in.	30 Nov 1887	5
74	Blackburn Corporation Tramways Company 12	4ft. 0in.	21 Dec 1887	5
75	Blackburn Corporation Tramways Company 13	4ft. 0in.	20 Jan 1888	5
76	Blackburn Corporation Tramways Company 14	4ft. 0in.	9 Mar 1888	5
77	Bradford Tramways & Omnibus Company 12	4ft. 0in.	28 Oct 1887	

tramway manager to report to his company's shareholders. Where the Council's money was being used to run the tramways control was, if anything, stricter, although it was also true that Councils always employed the best men available for the job. In electric days local government owned tramways were regarded partly as a social service and were expected to contribute to the rates thus keeping the total down. By draining profits in the good days precious little money was left for maintenance so when profits no longer occurred the Councillors were quick to close the lines. The County Borough of Huddersfield was one of a tiny number of councils allowed to operate their own tramways – in their case having built the lines no one wanted to run the cars. J. Pogson, M.I.M.E., the Manager, reporting on the year ending 31 March 1896: "The Rolling Stock at present consists of 26 engines, viz: 13 Kitson's type, 10 Green's type, and 3 Black Hawthorn (Wilkinson) type, also 24 bogie cars made by Messrs G.F. Milnes and Co., Birkenhead. The engines made by Messrs T. Green and Sons were of the compound type and a considerable amount of difficulty was experienced in starting after a stoppage on the severe gradients; six of these have been altered to high pressure, and the same charged to Revenue. The remaining four will be dealt with as speedily as possible. The engines as altered are working in a satisfactory manner. The total number running daily are 15, with two extra on Tuesdays and four extra on Saturdays, also two engines under steam in reserve at the Depot daily. ... The length of line open for traffic is – double track 1 mile 37 chains, single track 18 miles 31 chains. Total street miles – 19 miles, 68 chains, or 21 miles 25 chains of single track. ... The number of miles run are 398,448 an increase of 7,095 over last year. The number of passengers carried (allowing 1½d. as an average fare per passenger) amount to 4,308,289, an increase of 294,658. ... The receipts per mile (passenger fares only) are 16.22 pence. The total working expenditure under the heads of locomotive power, traffic, maintenance of ways and works, repairs to engines and cars, management, rents, rates, and taxes, miscellaneous, and the sum set apart for compensation amounts to £17,383.16s.3d. or 10.47d per mile. ... In comparing the undertaking here with the Tramway undertakings in other towns it should be remembered that there is no other instance with such an extensive Tramway system compared to population. It is the only system where two sets of drivers and conductors are employed, and further, there is no Sunday service. During the year additional Waiting Rooms have been erected at various points on the Tramway system. The number of Waiting Rooms at present in use are two large ones in St. George's Square at a rental of £50 a year each (to one of these a ladies lavatory is attached), and 17 others have been fixed or rented at the various termini and important junctions along the line of route, and two others are in course of construction. These are found to be a great convenience, and there is no doubt but they are a source of revenue. ... The total number of employees in the Department, exclusive of the office staff, are 136, and the total wages paid during the year amounts to £9,280.3s.9d."

One problem with trying to clarify exactly how many steam locomotives were built by Thomas Green & Son lies in the early works numbers including steam rollers and probably

Wk. Num.	Customer	Gauge	Delivery Date	Ref.
78	Bradford Tramways & Omnibus Company 13	4ft. 0in.	24 Feb 1888	
79	Bradford Tramways & Omnibus Company 14	4ft. 0in.	24 Apr 1888	
80	Rossendale Valley Tramways Company 15	4ft. 0in.	27 Oct 1888	8
81	Blackburn & Over Darwen Tramways Co. 10	4ft. 0in.	10 May 1888	
82	Rossendale Valley Tramways Company 1	4ft. 0in.	24 Nov 1888	8
83	Rossendale Valley Tramways Company 2	4ft. 0in.	8 Dec 1888	8
84	Rossendale Valley Tramways Company 3	4ft. 0in.	17 Dec 1888	8
85	Rossendale Valley Tramways Company 4	4ft. 0in.	14 Jun 1889	8
86	Rossendale Valley Tramways Company 5	4ft. 0in.	28 Jun 1889	8
87	Rossendale Valley Tramways Company 6	4ft. 0in.	17 Jul 1889	8
88	Bradford Tramways & Omnibus Company 15	4ft. 0in.	14 Sep 1888	
89	Bradford Tramways & Omnibus Company 16	4ft. 0in.	21 Sep 1888	
90	Bradford Tramways & Omnibus Company 17	4ft. 0in.	13 Oct 1888	
91	Bradford Tramways & Omnibus Company 18	4ft. 0in.	21 Oct 1888	
92	Rossendale Valley Tramways Company 7	4ft. 0in.	29 Jul 1889	8
93	Rossendale Valley Tramways Company 8	4ft. 0in.	7 Sep 1889	8
94	Bradford & Shelf Tramways Company 11	4ft. 0in.	unknown	
95	Bradford & Shelf Tramways Company 12	4ft. 0in.	18 Jan 1893	
96	Bradford & Shelf Tramways Company 2	4ft. 0in.	27 Feb 1890	9
97	Bradford Tramways & Omnibus Company 19	4ft. 0in.	17 Nov 1888	
98	Bradford Tramways & Omnibus Company 20	4ft. 0in.	1 Dec 1888	
99	Bradford Tramways & Omnibus Company 21	4ft. 0in.	13 Dec 1888	
100	Bradford Tramways & Omnibus Company 22	4ft. 0in.	20 Dec 1888	
101-27	Not used, see main text			
128	Drypool & Marfleet Steam Tramways Co. 1	4ft. 8½in.	26 Mar 1889	
129	Drypool & Marfleet Steam Tramways Co. 2	4ft. 8½in.	25 Mar 1889	
130	Drypool & Marfleet Steam Tramways Co. 3	4ft. 8½in.	11 Apr 1889	
131	Drypool & Marfleet Steam Tramways Co. 4	4ft. 8½in.	12 Apr 1889	
132	Railway Locomotive			
133	Bradford Tramways & Omnibus Company 23	4ft. 0in.	14 Apr 1889	
134	Bradford Tramways & Omnibus Company 24	4ft. 0in.	3 Aug 1889	
135	Leeds Tramway Company 19	4ft. 8½in.	13 May 1889	
136	Leeds Tramway Company 20	4ft. 8½in.	4 Jun 1889	
137	Drypool & Marfleet Steam Tramways Co. 5	4ft. 8½in.	1 Oct 1889	
138	St. Helens & District Tramways Company 1	4ft. 8½in.	6 Jan 1890	10
139	St. Helens & District Tramways Company 2	4ft. 8½in.	8 Jan 1890	10
140	St. Helens & District Tramways Company 3	4ft. 8½in.	22 Jan 1890	10
141	St. Helens & District Tramways Company 4	4ft. 8½in.	31 Jan 1890	10
142	St. Helens & District Tramways Company 5	4ft. 8½in.	14 Mar 1890	10
143	St. Helens & District Tramways Company 6	4ft. 8½in.	21 Mar 1890	10
144	St. Helens & District Tramways Company 7	4ft. 8½in.	24 May 1890	10
145	Leeds Tramway Company 21	4ft. 8½in.	23 Sep 1889	
146	Leeds Tramway Company 22	4ft. 8½in.	11 Nov 1889	
147	Leeds Tramway Company 23	4ft. 8½in.	29 Nov 1889	
148	Drypool & Marfleet Steam Tramways Co. 6	4ft. 8½in.	14 Dec 1889	
149	Drypool & Marfleet Steam Tramways Co. 7	4ft. 8½in.	24 Dec 1889	
150	Leeds Tramway Company 24	4ft. 8½in.	4 Apr 1890	11
151	Leeds Tramway Company 25	4ft. 8½in.	2 May 1890	
152	Leeds Tramway Company 26	4ft. 8½in.	24 May 1890	
153	Leeds Tramway Company 27	4ft. 8½in.	20 Aug 1890	
154	Leeds Tramway Company 28	4ft. 8½in.	5 Nov 1890	
155	Bradford Tramways & Omnibus Company 25	4ft. 0in.	30 Jun 1890	
156	Bradford Tramways & Omnibus Company 26	4ft. 0in.	2 Aug 1890	
157	Blackburn & Over Darwen Tramways Co. 11	4ft. 0in.	3 Dec 1890	
158	St. Helens & District Tramways Company 8	4ft. 8½in.	4 Mar 1891	
159	Huddersfield Corporation 19	4ft. 8½in.	17 Jul 1891	
160	Huddersfield Corporation 20	4ft. 8½in.	10 Sep 1891	
161	Railway Locomotive			
162	Accrington Corporation Steam Tramway Co. 15	4ft. 0in.	14 May 1891	
163	Accrington Corporation Steam Tramway Co. 16	4ft. 0in.	11 Jun 1891	
164	Blackburn & Over Darwen Tramways Co. 12	4ft. 0in.	7 Jul 1892	
165	Bradford Tramways & Omnibus Company 27	4ft. 0in.	1 Aug 1891	
166	Compania de Tramvias, Valencia 1	1 metre	10 Jun 1892	
167	Compania General de Tramvias, Valencia 5	1 metre	21 Jan 1892	
168	St. Helens & District Tramways Company 10	4ft. 8½in.	28 Nov 1891	
169	Blank	-		12
170	Martin McDonnell, Dunmore, Co. Galway 0 1	3ft. 0in.	19 Sep 1892	13
171	Compania General de Tramvias, Valencia 1	1 metre	12 Dec 1891	

portable or stationary engines in the sequence. The totals as far as can be ascertained are:

Tram engines:	
Wilkinson Patent, Vertical boiler	38
Horizontal boiler UK	161
Foreign	17
Sub-total	**216**
Railway engines:	
(orthodox, but counting w/nos. 179, 218 and 267 as trams)	35
Total	**251**

The first Wilkinson Patent tram engines, Works No.1, was delivered before December 1882, and the last, Works No.10, 10th September 1884; each batch of Wilkinson-pattern engines being given one works number, regardless of how many were built.

The first horizontal boilered engine, w/no. 13, was delivered on 29 January 1885, at their peak (1887) Green & Son were to supply no less than 26 tram engines in the one year, the delivery rate of one a fortnight probably being the maximum possible, given all their other work; and the last w/no. 367 in April 1906.

This last was a far cry from the relatively puny Wilkinson engines (W/no.1 for example had 6" x 7"/152 x 178mm cylinders) with 12" x 18"/305 x 457 mm cylinders, coupled wheels 3'.03/8th" (924mm) and the leading and trailing wheels of her 2-4-2 configuration 2' 0" (610 mm) in diameter. The boiler was 3' 0" (914 mm) diameter, with 92 tubes of 1б" (44.45 mm) and a generous 373sq.ft of heating surface. This engine (as No.10) survived in service on the Dublin & Blessington until closure in 1932.

The low works numbers of engines built should not belie the company's output as several sequences were in use at any one time. For example w/no. 1439 was a steam roller supplied to the Saffron Walden Borough Council in 1899 in which area it was employed on road laying duties for many years.

Although Thomas Green & Son had an excellent reputation they could occasionally nod. In October 1902 South Clare Railway engine no.7 (Dubs w/no. 2892 of 1892) was sent to Green's for overhaul involving a new boiler, with girder stayed firebox, the earlier crown rivets having sprung and distorted the shell, and the wheels were to be re-tyred. For no reason known to me it was mid 1904 before the work was finished and even then there were problems with the injectors resulting in the Railway's hard pressed fitting staff having to withdraw 15 boiler tubes in the rectification process – Greens apparently paying £9 for this work. Possibly as a result of the rebuilding by 1911 a new firebox was again required – it did not come from Thomas Green.

Prior to this (and making the above events even more surprising) in August 1896 the West Clare had invited tenders to build a new 2-6-2T engine which eventually had 15" x 20" cylinders, 3' 6" driving wheels, a fixed wheelbase of 9' 3" and 743.5sq.in. of heating surface. All-up weight including 900 gallons of water was 36.5 tons and tractive effort at 85%, 13,607lb. Quotations were received from Beyer Peacock £2,990, Neilson £2,775, Falcon Foundry £2,473, Robert Stephenson £2,395, Sharp Stewart £2,270, Kitson £2,220 and finally Thomas Green & Son of Leeds for £1,790 in cash or £1,948 in six six-monthly instalments. The wild disparity in prices between the companies is noticeable – clearly you got more value or strength from a Beyer engine at £2,990 than a Green-built job for £1,200 less, but the hire purchase terms decided it! Greens were offering monthly or quarterly payments.

The order was placed in April 1897 (w/no. 229) delivery being promised in September, but in the event this urgently needed locomotive (No.9) did not arrive until November 1898. The delay was, in part, due to a strike at Green's for although they had the reputation throughout their tram-building days as a 'family' firm, wages were kept low and conditions even in 1900 were rather archaic. No.9 must have given satisfaction – although the price and credit arrangements no doubt helped – and two more engines (w/no. 234/1900 and 236/1901) were supplied in September 1900 at £2,168 and June 1901 at £2,225, prices still lower than those quoted by rivals in 1897.

In the meantime Green & Son had not forgotten where their real strengths lay and continued, following the Locomotive Act of 1896, to develop and supply steam rollers, the last in 1931; but also found an unusual market for rollers inasmuch as these were wanted both by the gentry for their country estates and by sports clubs. By fitting state-of-the-art petrol engines they adapted their hand and horse-drawn rollers to fill these needs; apart from any other aspect this pre-1914 era was one of lawn tennis, cricket and football – all needing ground that had to be rolled. One neat arrangement was that a light roller for use in Spring or Autumn could be made heavier by filling the four rolls with up to 2 tons of water.

Another marketing opening eventually, but far too late, taken up by T. Green & Son, was for a steam lawnmower which appeared in 1902, whereon the driver sat in front of the boiler and steered the thing by means of an additional small roller. It weighed something over a ton and cut 30" (762 mm) swathes of grass; fuel was petrol or paraffin but the quick firing boiler only took 10 minutes to be ready for work, about the same as many modern motor mowers in the Spring! However the following year (1903) they also introduced a 42" (1067 mm) cut water-cooled petrol engined model ... which also weighed a ton! and was regarded as "an infernal machine and a dangerous freak". But one with 24" (610 mm) cutting blades was far lighter and more acceptable at 5cwt even with a water cooled engine, and by 1929 their 'new' 20" (508 mm) machine with a 2½hp engine cost £52 but only weighed 2cwt. However any resemblance to a modern Hayter or mower of that ilk is remote; chains and sprockets, all unguarded, were waiting for fingers or feet. T. Green & Son's lawnmower side was sold off in the 1960s, although Reekie of Arbroath still manufacture Green's pattern wheel-propelled and hydraulically-controlled gang units for cutting mass grass areas, but 1975 saw the end of this once-famous tram engine manufacturer.

The Yorkshire Evening Post 14 November 1975: "In a few week's time, the old established firm of Thomas Green and Son Ltd – the firm where aviation pioneer Robert Blackburn served his apprenticeship – will sever its 140-year link with Leeds. As announced exclusively in the Evening Post on Wednesday 'Tommy Greens' have sold their road roller business to

Wk. Num.	Customer	Gauge	Delivery Date	Ref.
172	Compania General de Tramvias, Valencia 2	1 metre	14 Dec 1891	
173	Compania General de Tramvias, Valencia 3	1 metre	19 Jan 1892	
174	Compania General de Tramvias, Valencia 4	1 metre	19 Jan 1892	
175	Compania General de Tramvias, Valencia 6	1 metre	18 Feb 1892	
176	Compania General de Tramvias, Valencia 7	1 metre	18 Feb 1892	
177	Compania General de Tramvias, Valencia 8	1 metre	2 Mar 1892	
178	Compania de Tramvias, Valencia 2	1 metre	14 Jun 1892	
179	Dublin & Blessington Steam Tramway Co. 7	5ft. 3in	unknown	
180	Railway Locomotive			
181	Huddersfield Corporation 23	4ft. 8½in.	31 Mar 1892	14
182	Huddersfield Corporation 24	4ft. 8½in.	14 Apr 1892	14
183	Huddersfield Corporation 25	4ft. 8½in.	13 May 1892	14
184	Huddersfield Corporation 26	4ft. 8½in.	3 Jun 1892	14
185	Huddersfield Corporation 27	4ft. 8½in.	28 Jul 1892	14
186	Huddersfield Corporation 28	4ft. 8½in.	8 Sep 1892	14
187	Huddersfield Corporation 29	4ft. 8½in.	6 Oct 1892	14
188	Huddersfield Corporation 30	4ft. 8½in.	19 Nov 1892	14
189	Compania General de Tramvias, Valencia 9	1 metre	16 Dec 1892	
190	Compania General de Tramvias, Valencia 10	1 metre	7 Feb 1893	
191	Compania de Tramvias, Valencia 3	1 metre	8 Dec 1892	
192	Railway Locomotive			
193	Bradford & Shelf Tramways Company 13	4ft. 0in.	25 Apr 1893	
194	Rossendale Valley Tramways Company 10	4ft. 0in.	19 Jun 1893	
195	Bradford Tramways & Omnibus Company 28	4ft. 0in.	29 Apr 1893	
196	Bradford Tramways & Omnibus Company 29	4ft. 0in.	20 May 1893	
197	Bradford Tramways & Omnibus Company 30	4ft. 0in.	19 Jul 1893	
198	Bradford Tramways & Omnibus Company 31	4ft. 0in.	1 Aug 1893	
199	Bradford Tramways & Omnibus Company 32	4ft. 0in.	30 Aug 1893	
200	Railway Locomotive			
201	Railway Locomotive			
202	Bradford Tramways & Omnibus Company 33	4ft. 0in.	30 Aug 1893	
203	Bradford Tramways & Omnibus Company 34	4ft. 0in.	18 Nov 1893	
204	Accrington Corporation Steam Tramway Co. 17	4ft. 0in.	11 May 1894	
205	Bradford Tramways & Omnibus Company 35	4ft. 0in.	6 Jul 1894	
206	Bradford & Shelf Tramways Company 14	4ft. 0in.	23 Dec 1893	
207	Built for stock			15
208	Dundee & District Tramways Company 11	4ft. 8½in.	10 Apr 1894	
209	Dundee & District Tramways Company 12	4ft. 8½in.	24 Jul 1894	
210	Leeds Corporation 29	4ft. 8½in.	unknown	
211	Blackburn & Over Darwen Tramways Co. 6	4ft. 0in.	22 Sep 1894	
212	Dundee & District Tramways Company 13	4ft. 8½in.	20 Dec 1894	
213	Leeds Corporation 30	4ft. 8½in.	unknown	
214	Railway Locomotive			
215	Dublin & Blessington Steam Tramway Co. 8	5ft. 3in.	unknown	
216	Railway Locomotive			
217	Railway Locomotive			
218	Blank			
219	Railway Locomotive			
220	Railway Locomotive			
221	Blackburn & Over Darwen Tramways Co.	–	unknown	16
222	Blackburn & Over Darwen Tramways Co.	–	unknown	16
223	Railway Locomotive			
224	Railway Locomotive			
225	Accrington Corporation Steam Tramway Co. 18	4ft. 0in.	unknown	
226	Blackburn & Over Darwen Tramways Co.	4ft. 0in.	unknown	17
227	Railway Locomotive			
228	Railway Locomotive			
229	Railway Locomotive			
230	Accrington Corporation Steam Tramway Co. 6	4ft. 0in.	unknown	
231	Kimberley Tram Company 1, "Kimberley"	3ft. 6in.	unknown	18
232	Kimberley Tram Company 2, "Beaconsfield"	3ft. 6in.	unknown	18
233	Kimberley Tram Company 3, "Premier"	3ft. 6in.	unknown	18
234	Railway Locomotive			
235	Kimberley Tram Company 4, "Kimberley"	3ft. 6in.	unknown	18
236 to 366	Either railway locomotives or blank			
367	Dublin & Blessington Steam Tramway Co. 2	5ft. 3in.	unknown	

Atkinsons, of Clitheroe Ltd. The decision to sell up and move out of the Bridge Street premises caused heartache and sadness among old and loyal employees. Inevitably, there were redundancies. But the cold, harsh fact was that in recent years the company was just not able to make a profit. ... Thomas Green and Son Ltd., founded by the son of a Nottingham verger, is the kind of company where everybody is on first name terms. Over the years, sons have followed fathers in their chosen trade frequently working side by side turning out a variety of products ranging from mowing machines to road rollers, from sausage making machines to hand grenades. For many of them Tommy Green's was their only employer. Just 18 short months ago, the company had 400 on its pay roll. Now only a fraction remain in Leeds to carry on the tradition of fine workmanship."

The following letter was sent from Accrington to the Editor of the Locomotion News & Railway Contractor on 20 January 1922 by Reginald H. Coe, appearing in the issue dated 25 February. Headed "Old Steam Tram Engines" it reads: "Sir, It might interest some of your readers to know that the East Lancashire towns of Haslingden (near Accrington) and Rawtenstall (near Rochdale) each still preserve an old steam tram engine, which they use for the purpose of keeping the electric tramways clear during heavy snow falls. The Haslingden engine is No.1 of the now defunct Accrington & District Steam Tramways Co. It was built by Green & Co of Leeds in 1887, and is an 0.4.0 well tank completely enclosed, of course, for working through the streets. The Rawtenstall machine was No.8 of the old Rossendale Valley Tramways (now owned by Rochdale & Rawtenstall Corporation) and was also built by Green & Co in 1887. During the recent heavy snowfall, which even for East Lancashire was a record one, these two fine old locomotives kept their respective tramway systems open, when many other tramway systems in the district were entirely blocked, which thus once more demonstrates the superiority of steam over electricity."

The sad part of this is that a few years later the Rawtenstall engine was offered for a very nominal sum to anyone who would like to have it – in effect an early attempt at preservation. The time (and perhaps place) was wrong and No.8 duly went to the scrapman. But this letter wasn't a bad epitaph for T. Green & Son's tram engines.

The Hughes/Falcon/Brush Story

The Falcon Engine Works was established c.1853 by Messrs Capper and Moon, on a small site between the Derby Road and Loughborough Navigation, near to the terminus of the latter. It is presumed that it produced small engines of most types. Moon seems to have departed fairly soon. Around 1855 Henry Hughes (b. 12.6.1833, London) was taken on as an engineer, and upon the retirement of Capper around 1859 he took over the business with the help of funding from his aunt. By now the business included timber and its sawing, and dealing in agricultural & railway contracting equipment and selling locomotives – the latter activity dating from 1861/2. The concern had a London office or agent in 1861.

By 1863 the Falcon Works site was becoming too cramped, and land adjacent to the east of the Midland Railway line near Loughborough station was acquired, and a new works established. Gradual transfer to the new site spanned the years from 1864 to 1866. The locomotive erecting shop consisted of two bays fronting the Midland Railway. In this new venture Hughes' old foreman, Huram Coltman, became his partner, with investment ⅔ Hughes, ⅓ Coltman.

The early/mid 1860s saw Hughes advertise his tank engine, a small basic 'no-frills' 0-4-0 saddle tank design, which by 1867 had been adapted into an 0-6-0 saddle tank. Most production was based on the two types, and it was the former that was exhibited in the Paris Exposition in 1867. It is upon this simple design that Hughes is believed to have based his first tramway engine, although a Hughes variant without saddle tank is preserved in Sweden and may thus indicate that the basic design could be easily adapted.

The first tramway engine built by Hughes however was to the design and order of John Downes, and the first Hughes engine proper appeared soon afterwards in 1876. It set off a legal quarrel which lasted almost ten years, viz. the following (and see volume 3):

From *The Engineer*, 18 September 1885:
"STEAM TRAMWAY ENGINE MANUFACTURE – A point of much interest to the manufacturers of steam tramway engines has just come before Mr Justice Day, sitting at the Birmingham Assizes. It was an action which occupied the closing three days of the assizes, and was brought by Mr Jno. Downes, of Birmingham, formerly the proprietor of large works at Liverpool and Stockport, to recover £20,000 damages from the Falcon Engine and Car Works, Loughborough, for alleged infringement of patent. The facts were unusually instructive. In 1870 Mr Downes, observing the severe labour of the tram-car horses in Birmingham, conceived the notion of a noiseless and steamless engine to be used upon the road, and four years afterwards he entered into negotiations with Messrs Hughes, of Loughborough, for the construction of such a locomotive. The engine was built at a cost of £600, and early in 1876 it was publicly tried in Birmingham. The trial turned out to be a complete success. Two or three months afterwards Messrs Hughes conducted a public trial at Birmingham of a second engine which they had made, and which proved equally successful. Mr Downes claimed that this second engine was a usurpation of his patent rights; but Messrs Hughes ignored the claim, and [in 1877] floated a limited liability company [Hughes' Locomotive and Tramway Engine Works Ltd. "HLTEW"], with a capital of over £71,000, to manufacture the locomotive. That company went into liquidation, and the concern was purchased by the Falcon Engine and Car Works, which has since carried on the production. The Falcon Company denied the infringement, and called Sir Frederick Bramwell. Sir Frederick gave it as his opinion that the plaintiff's notion for constructing a noiseless engine was entirely that of water condensation, while the defendants' was that of air condensation. There were many noiseless engines in use before plaintiff's patent was taken out. Mr Justice Day concurred, and entered a verdict for the defendants. Mr Downes has intimated that he will appeal."

HLTEW had been set up on 13 June 1877 with a capital of £92,000 in fully paid up £10 shares. In 1877-8 a 6% dividend was paid, and 1878-9 4½%.

> **HUGHES LOCOMOTIVE AND TRAMWAY ENGINE WORKS**
>
> The Directors invite applications for £20,000 lst mortgage debentures bearing 6 per cent per annum interest, payable half yearly. The object of this issue is to provide additional working capital, a large portion of it having been absorbed in extending the works, &c. The debentures will be a first charge on the whole property, and otherwise specially secured as the prospectus points out.
>
> *Herepath's Railway (and Commercial) Journal 29 May 1880*

Hughes lost a lot of money in a business in Derby in which he was a sleeping partner and in which he did not keep an eye on the non-sleeping partner's activities. He was liable for its fail-

54/55. In March 1877 a steam tram engine arrived at Wantage on trial. Unfortunately it proved incapable of hauling two 10 ton trucks along the line, but after modifications at Loughborough passenger work was within its capacity and it was purchased as Wantage No.4 in September 1877 for £600. Overhauled in 1895 by the Great Western Railway, poor maintenance during the First World War led to its withdrawal after 42 years service in 1919.

ings, and there is some suggestion that he borrowed funds from HLTEW to finance the problem. For HLTEW this added to the financial burdens of producing tram engines for hire and extending the works.

There is no doubt that Hughes built a good tram engine (his first) for Mr Downes [the full story will be given in a future volume]. There is little doubt that it inspired Hughes, and doubtless the condensing arrangement would have affected his own prototype, but it is debateable whether or not he copied it outright. Some believe it was an adaptation of his own locomotive and Downes' condensing – Hughes would not have required information on building a locomotive, but he would be quick to adapt the condensing arrangement and hide it away within the dummy tramcar body!

The claim by Downes took so long to come to fruition that both Hughes and his design were out of the running, and Falcon could not be pinned down as successor to the business and hence its liabilities because the new company dropped the design(s) in favour of the so-called Scott Russell design. The claim in the newspaper report above that Hughes floated the new company to promote the steam tramway engine is only partly true. Tramcars were also part of the new business intention, as an American-built horse car was bought indirectly, stripped and copied for production purposes! What motivated Hughes to float the company was that his partner wished to sell out to set up his own business in Loughborough, but Hughes did not have the ready funds to buy him out. The HLTEW company promoters were keen to promote the tramway side, and Hughes was keen to do this using his design of engine. It is doubtful if he could have funded many steam tramway engines anyway, as legislation limited running of mechanical power on street tramways to specified short periods, so hiring out was the order of the day, with the owner bearing substantial costs in maintaining an imperfect world of condensing steam (and dealing with all the impurities it introduced into the boiler thereafter).

While Hughes incurred considerable costs and eventually losses building his version of tram engines, the twist lies in the fact that his works, under the Brush name, made vast quantities of electric trams and, later, British Railway locomotives, when most of the later tram engine builders had failed.

It is not clear how many pioneer Hughes engines were produced in 1876 because the reports suggest that it was one engine that worked at Leicester, Govan and Dublin. This may be correct, but it must have been expensive for one engine to continue the round by returning to the works to be re-gauged for service in Ireland and then shipped back for re-conversion. It is thought that maybe two or three did the rounds, each claiming to be "the Hughes engine".

His first two trial engines ended up at Govan followed by four in 1877 where they ran on hire including the driver, fuel etc. at 5½d. per mile run. Another of 1877 went to the Wantage Tramway as their No.4, being purchased in September for £600. This had the benefit of no condensing equipment, and was basically a Hughes locomotive within a tramcar enclosure. The records show that this early engine was worked hard, making eight return trips a day hauling 6½ tons deadweight in passenger rolling stock (including, curiously, a couple of ex-horse trams!) at an average speed of 9.4mph (15kph) and using coal rather than coke consumed 300lb (136kg) on her daily working.

Rebuilt by the Great Western Railway in Swindon in 1895 only the postwar rundown in passenger traffic saw No.4 scrapped in 1920; back in 1877 it was proved that the engine was incapable of hauling two 10-ton goods wagons at the required 6mph (10kph) and it was retained solely for passenger work, generally running with the drive wheels uncoupled (notation 2-2-0, rather than 0-4-0). Other engines went to the Swansea & Mumbles, starting with one of 'Hughes' Patent Tramways Engines' in August 1877, where it hauled a pair of particularly cumbrous trams, but later including an esoteric mixture of locomotives, not all approved of by the Board of Trade.

Further deliveries up to the Falcon take-over included more to the Vale of Clyde, and twelve each to Lille and Paris. Despite Hughes not using works numbers for his 'normal' locomotives he seems to have built in excess of 35 plus 42 trams between 1864 and 1882. The Paris 12, similar to those for the Vale of Clyde, were constructed for use on the Bastille-Charenton line of the Southern Tramways of Paris. The contract payment for the engine service commenced in August 1879 and finished in February 1880, when horse power resumed traction. It appears that the finishing of the contract was due to the breaking down of engines by "lodgment of a compound of grease and lime on the walls of the fire-boxes – the grease derived from the condensed steam and the lime from the water – by which the fire-boxes became overheated and bulged inwards, and the flue-tubes leaked and broke."

Hughes always claimed he had built fifteen engines for use in Lille, but it is thought (although not proven) three of these were ex-Paris.

Four of the ex-Paris engines were those worked by the Guernsey Railway Company from October 1882; although it has been suggested they were hired, nonetheless three were offered to a scrapman (Ward of Sheffield) for £75 – the three, not one! – which was agreed to in 1889, when they were only ten years old, although an offer for the fourth of £12. 10s. wasn't. The Guernsey Railway Company wanted £25!

It seems, however, that when the Falcon works were taken over, a mixture of ex-Vale of Clyde, Lille and Paris engines were tucked away in various corners, and one at least formed the basis of the works shunting locomotive, w/no 283 of 1899, a neat 0-4-0 saddle tank, with inside cylinders named "SPRITE".

By 1878 Hughes' engines were in use on the Vale of Clyde tramways seemingly more or less successfully, although his water condensing system seems to have been a cause of his failure in tackling the line between Edinburgh and Portobello. "The condensing chamber is situated between the water supply tank and the water receiving tank and communicates with both these and with the exhaust. In the pipes of communication are fitted valves, the action of which is such that on the exhaust steam forcing open the valve in the exhaust communication at the end of every stroke the valve in the supply communication is simultaneously opened, and water is discharged into the condensing chamber on the incoming steam". On a level track this system, which involved a 400 gallon (1820lt) saddle tank filled with cold water and weighing about 1.8 tons plus two low level tanks fore and aft beneath the footplates, holding about 200 gallons each, worked well other than causing some noise due to the "intermittent pulsation of the exhaust".

The line from Waterloo Place to Portobello was very different from the level Vale route, including the equivalent of one mile at 1:22 (5%), and it was obvious the "occasional" failure of the engine to manage a return trip was due to condensing problems – it becoming apparent that 30-40 gallons (135-180 litres) of water to cool the steam were required for each mile run plus sufficient for the boiler's feed, and this for an engine with 7" x 12" (178 x 305 mm) cylinders, 30" wheels and a laden weight of $7\frac{1}{4}$ tons.

Theoretically with the absence of a blast pipe, natural draught only being used, and a large (19.5sq.ft heating surface) firebox, not only would there be little sound, but if the fire was made up at each end of a trip there was no need for the driver to do any more stoking or even carry any coke – "the driver thus having nothing to do with making the supply of steam, but only having to use it." The boiler, the powerhouse of any tram engine, measured $27\frac{3}{4}$" (705 mm) in diameter, contained 62 $1\frac{1}{2}$" (38 mm) o.d. brass tubes $63\frac{7}{8}$" (1622.4 mm) long between tube-plates.

Dunedin (New Zealand) trams were a private venture by David Proudfoot, a civil engineering contractor, who instructed Hugh A. Macneil from the importing firm of Arthur Briscoe & Co. to purchase the best tram equipment (rails, plant, locomotives and rolling stock) available in Europe. At the 1878 Exhibition in Paris, the Gold Medal winner for tram engines went to one of Henry Hughes' products, destined for Paris. As a result four locomotives, Hughes w/nos 326-9 arrived in Dunedin in March 1879. These were really quite conventional 0-4-0 outside-cylinder saddle-tanks enclosed in wooden cabs with all controls brought to the right-hand side, thus giving the driver a good view forward. The condensing arrangements were quite different to the Paris trams, with the exhaust steam cascading through tubes mounted on the cab sides and entering low level tanks at each end of the engines. This condensate was not re-circulated into the boiler, but instead was discharged as (rather hot) waste water into a specially built sump at the city terminus, where the saddle tanks were refilled. The engines were quiet enough but back pressure absorbed a lot of power. After an arson attack and depot fire in December 1880, the three repairable engines had their condensers blanked off to the relief of the parboiled enginemen; the engines were found to "bark" but were much more powerful.

Seven of the engines retrieved from Paris were worked on the Horfield section of Bristol, 1.43 miles long. To quote from Kinnear Clark, "It is a severe line to work, being up-hill for four-fifths of the length in one direction – towards Horfield; and downhill for the remaining fifth. The prevailing gradients are from 1 in 24 to 1 in 68. The line runs through a very populous district. The work was done under a contract for 12 months ... by means of four engines in steam daily. During the week 1,717 miles were run, of which $261\frac{5}{8}$ miles were run each week-day, averaging $65\frac{1}{2}$ miles per engine; and $147\frac{1}{2}$ miles on Sunday. In these engines the steam was not condensed. The weight was taken at 7 tons each in working order. One car only was allowed to be hauled by an engine; the car weighing, with passengers, 4 tons. The gross weight of engine and car was thus 11 tons. The fuel (coke) consumed was $12\frac{1}{2}$ tons per week, or at the rate of 16.31lb per mile run, or 1.48lb per ton-gross per mile." Here again the Hughes engines work at a disadvantage, since, besides working up steep gradients in one direction, they were braked for most of the way back, and, to the extent of brakeage necessary, lost the advantage of the aid of gravitation. The contract-price paid by the Tramway Company for steam-haulage was 7d. per car-mile run.

Norman Scott Russell first appeared on the scene when he was called in by HLTEW to investigate the indifferent working of the engines at Bristol. His findings were, to say the least of it, scathing, but his involvement brought him into the HLTEW and Falcon companies. He was the son of the great naval engineer John Scott Russell, who sent his son to Russia to "give him something to do as an engineer", but he mysteriously re-appeared in England c.1880. Later he became very prominent in the later Falcon company but operated somewhat at arms length for the Brush company in the 1890s and beyond.

On 4 April 1882 control passed to, effectively, Norman Scott Russell, initially the Chief, and later the General Manager of a new company, the Falcon Engine and Car Works Limited. With only one director, J.M. Gillies, in common with the old company, the new one had a written-down capital of £36,646 in fully paid up preference £1 shares, and £7,500 in fully paid £1 ordinary shares. The preference share holders were in (to use modern parlance) a win-win situation, for not only were they entitled to a cumulative preferential dividend of 7% per annum (quite remarkably high with 3-5% being the norm) but "had preference as regards the principal in the event of a distribution of assets". Following his removal from the HLTFW, Hughes tried working as an engineer and patent agent in Leicester and then emigrated to New Zealand, where he worked for a mining firm on the west coast of South Island and re-established himself running a patent agency.

He died in 1896 and was buried in Wellington (North Island). He might have been ironically amused when, later, the cemetery was removed to allow a new by-pass road to be built. After re-interment his grave's stone surround and headstone were preserved nearby.

Apart from tram engines Falcon produced a

56. This scene on the City of Birmingham Tramways Company's route from King's Heath to Sparkbrook, is at Moat Row around 1890, when both the engine and trailer (no.45) were still relatively new. Both were Falcon products, the details of the trailer's rear staircase is intriguing; small wonder modest ladies were unwilling to climb up.

57. A magnificent scene with all the detail of a well-run tramway and marvellous advertisements – signwritten then, of course. The engine is Birmingham Central Tramways Co.'s no.38 of 1885, and visible is the gate at the leading end of the trailer to try to prevent small children boarding unseen. The patent coupling and lifeguards are also visible. McDougall's flour can still be bought, Oakeys I saw a few years ago, and Davenports, towards their end, were famous for their 'Beer at Home' slogan, making deliveries once by cart and later by lorry.

good number of orthodox railway locomotives; it is believed they commenced production of these following a sub-contract offer from Kerr Stuart & Co. then of Glasgow. Falcon not only continued to build to Hughes' designs, but also improved them. From FE 45 or thereabouts works numbers of a new, but definitely Falcon series, started to appear on works plates. It included steam tramway engines. Some locomotives and tramway engines cannot be identified as they bear the earlier un-numbered Falcon plates. Kerr Stuart, having no facilities for building locomotives, when they were awarded contracts for this class of work, had no option but to sub-contract to other builders. The late John Price always quoted the number as 30 odd; they certainly included a great variety, from CORLEONE, a 2-4-0 tank engine with 14" x 22" (356 x 559mm) cylinders of 1885 to the appositely named MIDGE (their own works shunter) an 0-4-2 tank with 7" x 12" (178 x 305mm) cylinders in 1887. Apart from contractors' engines most were exported, although works no. 283 of 1899 was destined for the Brush Electrical Engineering Company, and 284 was a solid tank engine for the Dublin & Blessington Steam Tramway (their No. 9), a curious looking beast with a 'proper' cab at the normal end and a half-cab at the leading (chimney) end. Earlier the Dublin & Blessington had had some real tram engines from Falcon. On these the cabs apart from windscreens were soon de-glazed and the skirts over the motion were either lost or fell off. Six of this pattern with 9" x 14" (229 x 356mm) cylinders, 30" (762mm) driving wheels, works nos. 125-130 were provided in 1888, number one (No.3 works no. 127) lasted until 1927 and number six (works no. 130) albeit rebuilt, as late as 1932.

The Falcon steam tram engine design was afforded the "Norman Scott Russell-designed" tag (in the manner of the Gresley A4s or Stanier 8Fs). Falcon was quick off the mark in introducing a prototype and advertising it in the engineering journals. This (apparently one-off) engine was prominently shown off at Burnley and probably became the system's No.1. It should be noted that whereas the Hughes companies built and hired out most of their productions, Falcon did not (other than active Hughes examples that were probably initially hired and then sold).

Among the first batches of Scott Russell tram engines were some delivered to Burnley & District Tramways as their nos. 6-9 in 1883. No. 10 in 1884, and to prove their satisfaction 11-13 in 1885. In 1889 Burnley came back again for their number 14, and again for number 15 in 1896, and perhaps surprisingly two more (16-17) in 1897. In the later years trailers were also supplied. Two trams went to Barcelona in 1883, but an order the following year for three narrow (3' 6"/1067mm) gauge engines for the Manchester Bury Rochdale & Oldham Steam Tram Company was only followed with an order for five standard gauge engines in 1885, all with 9" x 14" (229 x 356mm) cylinders, but it seemed 'Wilkinson' type designs were favoured as out of a fleet total of 91 only 14 were 'orthodox' engines, although Falcon did built 36 out of 81 trailers. The narrow gauge engines Nos. 39-41 were neat enough at 13' 4" (4.06 m) long, a width of 6' 0" (1.83 m) and a weight of 9½ tons in running order. Their 9" x 14" cylinders were fed by a boiler 4' 6" (1372 mm) long, and 2' 6" (762mm) in diameter. Perhaps to reduce weight the cabs were wooden, the condenser designed by Scott Russell had 250 copper tubes arching across the roof with collector boxes (again in brass) on each side, draining down to tanks, fore and aft.

Falcon's largest order was from Birmingham Central Tramways Company who took 28 in total between 1885 and 1886.

Described as "somewhat similar to Kitson engines", cylinders for the first batches were 8" diameter x 14" stroke (203 x 356mm) with larger (30½"/775mm) diameter wheels and the governor was attached directly to a shaft which carried a "fifth" wheel located between the driving wheels on one side. This operated a speed indicator in the cab, and more importantly if overspeeding occurred the steam brake was applied and the regulator closed by a small valve. It main use for drivers was when running downhill this governor would check the speed, making for a very smooth run. As an independent system it was totally unaffected by the drive wheels slipping on re-starting with a loaded trailer.

By 1888 Falcon were already in trouble, being unable to pay the entire preference share dividends – 1882-3, 3%, 1883-4, 3%, 1884-5, 7% plus possibly the arrears, 1885-6, at a time when orders were not only in hand but being paid for, 7%, but 1886-7, only 2% was possible. Nothing was ever paid to the ordinary shareholders, although in its last year of independence Falcon paid 5% on that preference capital of £150,000.

The Brush Electrical Engineering Company Limited was a reconstruction of the Anglo-American Brush Electric Light Corporation Ltd. and first registered on 10 August 1889 at which time Falcon, too, was swallowed up. The Brush capital by contrast to Falcon was no less than £750,000, a fantastic sum for 1889. The mutual benefit was that Falcon found an electrical company to apply its products to Falcon trams, and Brush found a tramcar producer to apply its electrical equipment to its tramcars. The added benefit that Brush gained was to obtain a green field site with plenty of scope for expansion and with lower wage costs than found in London.

Truth to tell, the Falcon Company was really worth very little, Brush acquiring the whole concern for £22,000 in shares + £500 in cash to satisfy small debts. After 1898 when all tram engines (except the Wolverton one) were completed, the works changed beyond recogni-

58. The last locomotive supplied to the Wolverton and Stony Stratford tramway. A Brush/Falcon product, this little engine is seen dwarfed by the trailer. Photographed in 1904, the LNWR ownership ensured the paintwork was in good condition.

tion – the new 'sparklers' and the American way of working had ousted reliable if mucky old man steam. The last tram car of the Falcon 'family' was delivered after the Brush takeover. This was supplied to the Wolverton & Stony Stratford Tramway in 1900, but seems to have been a surprisingly weak engine. It must have been well-loaded with workmen at peak times; with little resort to refuelling en route, it may have been short winded at times. With cylinders 7½" x 12" (191 x 305mm) which were less than those of the Krauss engines supplied in 1886/7, and withdrawn as inadequate, contemporary reports seem to indicate the Brush/Falcon engine was only just able to haul the workmans trains (2 x 44'/13.41 mm long, 100-seater trailers,) on the 2-mile route, and it suffered greatly and frequently – once twice in one day – from suspension spring breakages; after a year in service serious and life threatening bulges appeared in the firebox in the stayless areas. Rectified at considerable expense this seems an odd failure for a company with their experience, although the old Hughes/Falcon system where a two-man gang built the complete tram including all its components and taking three or four weeks to do so may already have been phased out. It has been claimed that the main reason for its failure was gross overloading, but who sold the machine to the tramway? Was it in fact an engine that had been built 'on spec', although by 1904 the new electric age was at full strength? The tram engines were produced in the locomotive erecting shop, but this was demolished during redevelopment works c.1898. Following the large building programme of Beira 4-4-0s, Brush locomotive production tailed off. The BR locos would be among the last to be made in the loco erecting shop, and as the accent was on electrical goods and electric tramcars, locomotives appear to have been made where there was space. Brush in modernising the plant increased output from 250 vehicles of all types a year to 750 electrically operated cars, and eliminated the older craft working so that each man made specific components mostly on machines – true factory working.

Unfortunately for historians, the bulk of the Hughes records were probably lost in a fire, probably during 1882. Wartime salvage operations and ruthless clearouts in 1971 saw further losses of archive material, though fortunately the Leicestershire Record Office rescued some important material which now forms the basis of its Brush Collection. George Toms of Loughborough has made a worthy contribution to the rescuing, care and documentation of material.

Any attempt to produce a works list at this juncture (2003) would be to exist in fantasy-land, but it is hoped that a verifiable list of Hughes, Falcon and Brush tram engines will appear as an appendix in Volume 4.

Kitson of Leeds

James Kitson, the son of the Brunswick Tavern's licensee was only 28 when he established the Airedale Foundry, Hunslet, Leeds: the name of the works first appeared in an 1839 Directory. Properly (in the old sense of the word) educated in "a little school run by a clever old lady", although working almost anywhere to keep his widowed mother and younger children he found the time to both join and take advantage of the Mechanics' Institution and Literary Society. Here he found a book, Nicholas Wood's "A Practical Treatise on Railroads", which was said to have "inspired within him an admiration for the Locomotive Engine". Married when he was just 21, on 13 September 1828, perhaps this gave him the incentive to change from employee to employer. To put the whole gamble into context when in 1838 his first engine rolled out of the works only 490 miles (783km) of railway (much of it disconnected) existed in England and Wales, while the first crossing of the Atlantic under steam had just taken place. Clearly though James Kitson had a need for expertise which he obtained by entering into partnership with Charles Todd who had gained a good insight into the art and skill of locomotive building by having been an apprentice with the famous Matthew Murray at the Round Foundry; most of these partnerships tended to be short-lived, as many of the men involved seem to have been rather volatile.

Another partner arrived on the scene in 1837/8, David Laird, a Scottish landowner who in exchange for hard cash expected a good return. On the 2 October 1837 the firm of Todd, Kitson & Laird contracted with the Liverpool and Manchester Railway's Board to provide "Ten Locomotive Engines" including "2 Luggage Engines, 11 inch cylinder, 20 inch stroke, to be delivered 30 April 1838, at £1,100 each" – one being the "Lion", happily and surprisingly preserved to take part in that happy fairy tale of a film, the "Titfield Thunderbolt".

It seems as though Todd was unwilling to cut corners and although the firm was still being called Todd, Kitson & Co. on 6 February 1838, and Todd, Kitson & Laird in April, by 19 May we have two new partnerships, Shepherd & Todd of the Railway Foundry, Hunslet, and Laird, Kitson & Co. of the Airedale Foundry. By 1843, when Laird had withdrawn but Isaac Thompson and William Hewitson had replaced him, new orders were completed by Kitson, Thompson & Hewitson. Thompson left in 1858, when he seems to have retired, but Hewitson remained with Kitson until his death in 1863.

One problem that has always plagued historians is the total number of locomotives built under the various partnerships, and as an early form of creative accountancy from around 1850 the firm allocated one works number to a tender and another to the motive unit – thus a pair of tank engines would carry works numbers 13 and 14, two tender locomotives would be allocated numbers 15, 16, 17 and 18. In 1875 they seem to have normalised their numbering but like many companies when an order was cancelled the works numbers were left blank and unfilled. To add a further twist when a batch of four-wheel steam plough agricultural engines were built for John Fowler in 1860 they were allocated numbers 737-760, although not all numbers were used; a further batch later in the year, albeit with shaft rather than chain drive, carried work numbers 797-802. As with so many British firms in those far off days export trade developed on the back of quality and keen pricing, thus in 1873/5 locomotives went out to Russia, Argentina, Spain, Japan, Germany, Australia, Ceylon, Trinidad and South Africa, as well as to the main and local railway companies in the UK.

But Kitsons always claimed to be general engineers including among their output an iron lighthouse for Ceylon, heavy factory tools, cranes and pumping engines (plus all the ironwork used in these 'working cathedrals').

In 1876 there came the first unit in a new "T" series of numbers which were used for Tramway locomotives, Rowan (combined) cars and a number of light tank locomotives, which latter were to all intents and purposes undressed tramway engines.

However, there are problems with cross referencing the "T" numbers to normal works numbers and I cannot do better than to quote the relevant paragraph in the Kitson Works List compiled by Reg Carter, Hon. Librarian of the Stephenson Locomotive Society:

> "The 'T' numbers are for Tramway Locomotives, Rowan Cars and Light Tank Locomotives.
>
> PLEASE NOTE THAT THE 'T' NUMBERS ARE RECORDED IN THE KITSON RECORDS BUT THERE IS NO REFERENCE TO THE ALLOCATION OF WORKS NUMBERS FROM THE MAIN LIST.
>
> The works numbers I have used for these are shown in various sources as being for tram locomotives. There is no other record for any other use of these works numbers. These works numbers are blanks in the Kitson Trials Book, the 'T' numbers being recorded in a separate ledger. I have included the 'T' numbers in this list to complete the record.
>
> PLEASE DO NOT TAKE THE ALLOCATION OF WORKS NUMBER TO 'T' NUMBERS AS BEING ACCURATE."

In all 302 'T' numbers were allocated, the last being an 0-4-0 tram for the Portstewart Tramway, their no.3, with 2' 3¾" (730mm) wheels and 9.5" x 12" (241 x 294mm) cylinders.

Some part of the story of Rowan cars will be found elsewhere in this series of books, but the mechanical portion of the Kitson design was a 'Chinese' copy of the power bogie built by Merryweather for the first Rowan cars of 1875. The Kitson car, a much larger double-decked railcar, was first steamed at Hunslet in August 1876 and resulted from an agreement beween Kitson & Co and the Scandia Company, whose proprietor was W.R.Rowan, the patentee of this design. Retrospectively numbered T1 by Kitson (but definitely works no 678), the motive power unit, or 'steam bogie', had 6" (152mm) diameter x 10" (254mm) stroke cylinders, with 24" wheels. A vertical 'Field' type boiler was used with the pair of vertical cylinders mounted singly on each side of the boiler, thus providing a compact, balanced, design. Drive was via an intermediate shaft and gearing. Of orthodox 0-4-0 configuration only one axle was directly driven, adhesion being gained by the use of external coupling rods. Extensively tested with 1,000 miles or more running, although a technical success (unlike many combined cars it at least worked), this combination of a quite small engine and a 62-seater saloon proved to be underpowered and with an all-up weight of 14 tons almost impossible to stop. One successful arrangement, foreshadowing diesel railcars of later days, was that the air condenser and water tanks were carried underneath the car, with an arrangement that the hot water could be turned through pipes to warm the saloon.

A problem recorded was that the very short bogies, designed to allow its use on very tight

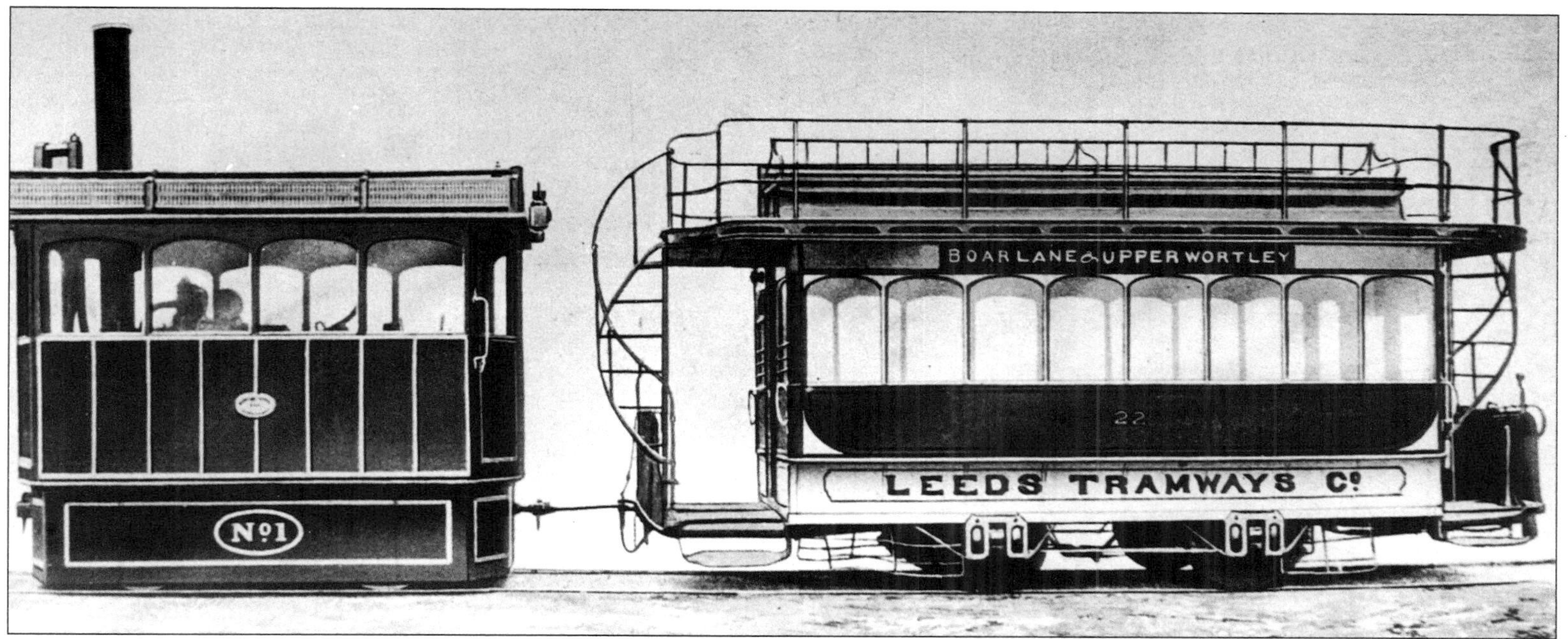

59. Leeds No.1 was built as Kitson T15 in 1880, with 7" x 12" cylinders, in which guise it proved capable of pulling its Starbuck-built horse trailer, but was withdrawn during 1890. The trailer, no.22, dating back to 1873, was rather longer lived, not being struck off strength until 1899.

radii corners, coupled to an overall length of 33' 4" (10.16m) made for great unsteadiness at anything approaching the machine's designed 10mph (16kph).

Foreseeing the future has always been difficult, but James Kitson had two independent engines ((T2 (1876) and T3 (1877)) mechanically identical to the Rowan cars' bogie built as an experiment, T2 running on the lines of the Hamburger Pferdeeisenbahn in 1878, together with Hughes engine w/no.11 and Krauss w/no. 865. In the event SLM Winterthur engines were chosen, 21 being delivered between 1878 and 1892. Prior to this T2 had been run for a day (15 November 1876) on the lines of the Dewsbury, Batley and Birstall Tramway Company. T3, incorporating improvements, had a more adventurous life, being tried initially in Leeds (October-November 1877) and again in January 1878, then moving to the Dewsbury, Batley and Birstall for two months, March-April 1878 – these movements, presumably at least in part by ponderous horse carriage, seem to have evaded local photographers but could they have been other than exciting?

During the earlier trial in Leeds, when "Mr James Kitson Junior [was] travelling in the engine-car" a joint in one of the pipes burst but the delay was only of two or three minutes duration – good Yorkshire plumbing joints perhaps? Water was taken on "by means of an ordinary india-rubber tube connected with a tap in the depot, and a pipe underneath the engine-car, whence it was pumped into the boiler" – an exercise immortalised in film and seen on the video "One Hundred Years of British Trams" (Midland Publishing 1999). "Altogether" added the Yorkshire Post, 25 October 1877, "the trial passed off very satisfactory with the exception of the discomfort caused to outside [i.e. riding on the open top deck] passengers by the emission of fumes and grit from the funnel; but we understand this can easily be obviated". Ah! That it could have been so.

In the case of the Dewsbury company Kitson were unsuccessful but in Leeds they were to share the proceeds with the other local company, Thomas Green & Son; the first three tram engines T15 (7" x 12") cylinders, T17 and T26 (7¼" x 12") being on hire until 20 January 1883 when they were purchased at £506 each – presumably the price made some allowance for the rental (about £110 a month for three engines) as the next batch, fleet nos. 4-10, T102, T112-116, cost £702 each in 1884 and T117 £720 in 1885. Eventually T3 ended up with Palmer Harding as part of the fleet of the Tramways Company of France in Rouen, where it ran in company with various Merryweather, Fox Walker and Fives Lille tram engines; although Lille reverted to horse traction in 1884.

T4 was built in 1878 as an improved T3 for the Great Eastern Railway (their fleet no. 230) intended for use on the Millwall Extension Railway in London's dockland, which duty it performed well enough until various ricketty bridges and poor trackwork could be improved. Laid aside, unlike its half-sisters it did not go for scrap but found a new life as a semi-mobile engine. The G.E.R had their main carriage shops at Stratford (East London) and in order to move the new carriages from workshop to workshop or indeed running lines they built a traverser covering nine 'roads' or lines of rail. The pit measured 171' long, 25' 7" wide and was 14" deep. Our T4 (or most of it) was fitted to a table which in turn was mounted on wheels with 7' 1½" centres. In addition to the normal 4' 8½" lines there were also rails for a narrow (18") gauge materials tramway – which utilised hand propelled 'trolleys'. Originally horse powered the traverser was converted to steam by the G.E.R locomotive superintendent. A new boiler was required for T4 but the vertical format was maintained with cross rather than 'Field' tubes and operating at 90psi. Attached to the engine was a winding drum, enabling the coaches to be pulled onto the traverser although they were restricted to a 30' 6" wheelbase. Vacuum brakes could be tested by means of a vacuum ejector fitted to the boiler (strangely, most operators shied away from vacuum brakes on steam tramways and yet T4 was so fitted!). A new cab was built for our tram, the lower part in steel and the top in wood with proper glazing, the machine ending up 12' 6" long by 4' 9" wide. Said to have been painted black but properly lined out by the shedmen T4 seems to have survived into the 1920s. In 1903 it was described as "very useful to the carriage shops, and at the same time a neat and compact piece of mechanism".

T5 was to have an entirely different life. It all began well enough with an order for a Rowan car running on 5' 3" (1,600mm) gauge rails which was ordered by the Glenelg & South Coast Tramways, near Adelaide, Australia. The order, probably gained by the activities of Captain F.C. Rowan, dated 7 August 1878, was rather unfortunately (although normal practice) supplied on hire purchase. Sent out in January 1879 the tram began a sort of service in May 1879 from Glenelg* through a wasteland of sand dunes to Somerton – the idea was that in conjunction with the railway, a connecting service from Adelaide to Somerton could be run thus opening up what could be a dormitory suburb of Adelaide.

In the event the sand dunes regularly blocked the light trackwork and not even the enlarged 6½ x 12" (165 x 305mm) cylinders of T5 could propel the machine through. With this new dimension came a complete relocation of the cylinders by the designer, the Honourable Richard C. Parsons, to very nearly a horizontal position, driving directly onto the wheels. More efficient, but more exposed to road muck, dust ... and sand.

However, a Parliamentary Commission appointed to report on public works in what was then (1880) the colony of South Australia not only inspected this Rowan car but travelled several miles on it – some parts of their contemporary report make interesting and unusual reading.

"ROWAN'S COMBINED CAR AND MOTOR – A formal trial of the steam-car imported by Captain Rowan for the Glenelg and South Coast Railway Company took place on Thursday, at the request and in the presence of Mr Clerke, the manager of the line ... The following were the tests to which the Company's manager required that the motor should be put: (1) To run a distance of six miles without stoking

**There cannot be many palendromic place names!*

or replenishing the fire with fresh fuel. (2) To run eight miles without replenishing water-tank. ... To run for a spurt at the rate of twenty miles an hour. On the first test being applied, the motor accomplished the six-mile journey with ease in 31 minutes 15 seconds, and without stoking or the application of fresh fuel. The second test resulted in a run of 8½ miles without replenishment of tank, six inches of water still remaining at the termination of the journey, the engine condensing her steam the whole way, no smoke or steam being visible. The quantity of fuel put on board at the commencement of the trial was 97 lb Queensland coke, supplied by the Company, the amount consumed being 57 lb for the 8½ miles run, or 6.7 lb per mile, or 3.3 lb per mile less than the contract limit for consumption ... maximum speed, was equally successfully accomplished, and the required speed of twenty miles an hour obtained. All present expressed themselves highly satisfied with the manner in which each of the tests was complied with, May 7, 1880. This car cost, f.o.b. London, £1,150."

GENERAL DESCRIPTION OF THE CAR USED IN THESE TRIALS.

Length	29' 6"
Breadth	7' 6"
Height	13' 9"
Passenger Capacity	62
Weight of Car and Engine, empty	about 8¼ tons

Although the Glenelg & South Coast ran other locomotives including their No.1, a Dübs product (w/no. 1196) of 1878, they ran out of money in April 1880 and the car was separated from its steam bogie (T5) and the two halves were sold, although the liquidators of the tramway company owned neither. Perhaps since this was Australia in the 1880s neither Kitson, Scandia (the body builder) or ourselves should be surprised, but the saloon fitted with an orthodox bogie passed to the Adelaide, Glenelg and Suburban Railway, who just happened to have acquired a Merryweather steam tram (works no.80 built 1878); they coupled the two together and ran a six minute service between Victoria Square to Forestville for at least twenty years. The motor unit was used as a locomotive by the Wallaroo & Moonta Mining & Smelting Company, shunting ore wagons (and men) for many years. Neither Kitson or Scandia saw any financial return.

When Kitsons moved over to independent tram engines one can well imagine the experimenting that went on in the works – it was not their intention to emulate Hughes or Fox Walker who seem to have built trams they thought would work and then tried to sort out problems later. Hon. R.C. Parsons, heading the experimental shop, would have none of it, although we do know that T6 (485) was a Rowan car sent out to the New South Wales Government Tramways as their class D No.46. This combined car did not leave Kitson's until 10 January 1882 by which time "T" numbers had reached T43. The original Kitson list shows: "Vertical Engine and Loco Type Boiler altered" T6 was also fitted with the American-type Eames vacuum brake which was standard on the New South Wales Government Tramways, having been fitted to their original Baldwin engines; it might well have done well in the UK being very quick acting on short tram-type engines. The bodywork was supplied by Brown Marshalls of Birmingham and Kitson's records show "altered here", whether for extra ventilation or modified bogies is unknown. The motive power unit (bogie) must surely have been regarded as an experimental – "Parson's Pet" perhaps – where he could experiment with different boilers, motions and cylinder sizes. One does wonder, too, how much was left of T6 – when first laid down in 1878/9 the New South Wales Government Tramways did not even exist.

The first "T" tram where we have definite proof of her number is T7 sent out on 13 August 1879 to Dunedin – the New Zealand boiler inspector noting this serial as "Kitson No. 7" when he first certified it to run in New Zealand in January 1880, so that number must have been visible in plate form on the engine or in the documents; famously boiler inspectors do not pull numbers out of the sky.

This well tank 0-4-0 engine, with locomotive type boiler was fitted with a now-traditional wooden and iron 'house' or cabin built by the Birmingham Railway Carriage & Wagon Company which concealed from view not only most of the boiler but the now-adopted-as-standard modified Walschearts valve gear which included sharply inclined 6½" x 12" (165 x 305mm) cylinders. The alterations to the valve gear were sufficiently different to justify a patent (4512 of 1879). In this the reciprocating movement of the valve is taken from the vertical rather than the horizontal component of the crank path, by attachment to the connecting or coupling rod. This was designed and helped to keep all the working parts raised (as far as they could be) above the sludge of horse manure, grit and general filth that comprised so many roads in the 1880s – far worse than anything seen today outside a neglected farm yard. Wheels were 27" (686mm) in diameter and the all-up weight comparatively light at 5¾ tons. An air condenser, almost identical to the pattern designed by Rowan, was mounted on the roof. This machine, which was to set the pattern for most later Kitson 'standard' steam trams was sent out to the Dunedin City and Suburban Tramways, 2½ years before 485/T6.

T7, regrettably, had a very short life as a tram engine, from 15 January to 23 December 1880, when virtually all the Dunedin stock was destroyed by arson, the fire was said to have been caused by cabmen, but unsurprisingly no-one was ever brought to book.

The remains of what Dunedin's engineer, James Craig, regarded as the best of a mixed fleet of Hughes, Baldwin and Kitson engines, was greatly altered to an 0-4-2 saddle-tank industrial engine, working in Southland's logging service until being condemned in 1940.

The next batch of engines T8-T12 were sent out virtually as completed to New Zealand, but to the Canterbury Tramway Company (Christchurch) between No.8 ex-works on 16 August 1879 and No.11 ex-works 23 December 1880. No.12 was seemingly dispatched out of sequence on 23 September 1879, but No.11 was held back for an incredible 14 months "as some trials are about to take place, the engineers propose to keep it for a week or two to show what can be done by it and to prove to the colonies as well as the people of England the advantages of steam power on tramways and the excellence of the engines manufactured" as the New Zealand Lyttleton Times put it. This class of engine was built to Board of Trade requirements and Kitson hoped that approval would be forthcoming from the B.o.T Inspector, General C.S. Hutchinson, when this engine (shown as Canterbury Tramway Co. "E") was trialled on the Dewsbury, Batley and Birstall Tramways from 8 November to 13 December 1879. It is also believed that this locomotive was used on the Leeds trials in 1880 and possibly elsewhere. When on the Dewsbury, Batley and Birstall she ran 1922 miles; not unsurprisingly Kitsons felt it necessary to make a peace offering, T11 being fitted with a set of brand new steel tyres and, furthermore, a full set of steel tyres for each of the other four engines was included in the crate carrying T11 on the good ship *'Gareloch'* when she left London on Christmas Eve 1880.

All must have been forgiven for another three engines (T27-T29) followed on 30 & 31 May and 11 June 1881, as an "urgent order", Christchurch being unable to run a Sunday service not for religious reasons but having no spare engines, maintenance, boiler washouts and general repairs could only be properly carried out then. Right from the outset these engines were to carry out some prodigious work – a famous photograph dated March 1897 shows 4 Kitson engines with 19 fully loaded tramcars for a St Mary's Church picnic en route to the beach at Sumner near Shag Rock.

In all the Christchurch services were to total 17 miles (27 km), the last regular steam service, Richmond to North Beach, being electrified in 1912, but, and it is a magnificent "but", No.7 (originally numbered or lettered! G) has not only survived but is kept at the Ferrymead Historic Park, Christchurch, and not only is she in road-worthy condition but from time to time is operated.

However, while all this was happening the Rowan car design had moved on and in T13 and T14 sent from the Kitson works in October 1879, the design reached its fruition. The bodies were built, as befitted the design, at the Scandia Works – all the more important as they were for use on the Gribskovens Dampsporvej or Gribskov Steam Tramway. A Wantage-type roadside light railway, the Gribskov was ideal territory for Rowan-type cars, although being single ended they needed either a reversing triangle or, as in the case of the Gribskov, a turntable. Some 12.43 miles (20km) long when opened in 1879, the two Rowan cars (I and II) and a small Winterthur tram engine w/no. 156 of 1879 maintained the service until 1892 when the two Kitson units were converted to orthodox mini-tank engines and the tramway became a true light railway. In all 27 Rowan cars operated in Scandinavia, although only the two Gribskov engines (T13/T14) and the shortlived T1 and T5 in Copenhagen came from Kitson, which was in many ways a shame as the re-design with enlarged cylinders (8" x 13"/203 x 330mm compared with 6" x 10" for T1) and boilers, reliable and easy to maintain Stephenson valve gear, and most of all lengthened bogies, ensured these engines were fast and efficient.

At the National Tramway Museum, Crich, and in the hands of the Librarian of the Stephenson Locomotive Society there exist two lists relating to Kitson "T" locomotives which give a considerable amount of information about the tram engines' gestation. My copy, incidentally, came from Ron Grant the New Zealand 'Kitson man'. In this list the fate of T48 and T50 is given bleakly enough. The original Kitson entry reads: "Altered to order 672, Independent [i.e. not Rowan-type] loco-type boiler, Sand box on boiler, slides to window, 8" cylinders and condensers and tanks added to" (then in a different hand) "Davey Jones Locker" "Sydney September 14, 1882."

Ron Grant in his updating of the list has added "Then these must be the two Parramatta River Steamers and Tramway Company engines lost at sea".

T52 entry reads (in part) "Altered to order 778, Independent Sandbox on boiler, 8" cylinders and condensers and Tanks." Cast iron roof brackets to a rather fancy design were to be fitted and a final note in a different hand reads "Tried on Headingley Ty with 2 Cars Aug.7/82". T52 was despatched to Sydney, 23 April 1883. Logically, then, this is the replacement engine for Parramatta which was built as part of the 'run' of locomotives including T48 and T50 and had been, as has always been rumoured, used as the works shunter and probably a demonstrator until an order marked no doubt 'exceedingly urgent' arrived at Hunslet.

The comment by Ron Grant on T96, known for the question marks hanging over its existence is apposite: "As 672 and 778, New Style of door, trailing tank, Australia, December 6, 1883." This is stated in the illustrated list to have been delivered to Parramatta and the coincidence of order numbers detail would suggest this. Was no.96 ordered as a second replacement for the lost at sea T48/50? When delivered it proved to be already superseded at Parramatta by Baldwin 4343/1878, ex Adelaide, Unley & Mitcham. Did it get sent elsewhere? 96 could not possibly have opened the Parramatta tramway in October 1883. It left Kitsons works in December. We have a mystery here." And a mystery it still remains. It was built. It left Kitsons for Australia, certainly never worked on the Parramatta Tramways or the New South Wales Government Tramways. Is there yet up-country (perhaps even in South America) the friendly ghost of Kitson T96 still waiting for work?

Kitsons always classified their tram engines as Standard No.1, No.2, etc. No.1 Standard was similar to those sent out to New Zealand normally with 7¼" or 7½" x 12" cylinders, a boiler with 116sq.ft (10.78sq.m) of heating surface, and an all-up weight of around 7 tons. Driving wheels varied slightly between 27"/686mm (T27 etc) to 28¼"/718mm (Vale of Clyde). The No.2 engine was brought into service as a riposte to the improved Wilkinson engines and was first supplied to work the heavily loaded trams on the switchback lines of the Birmingham & Aston. T75 was sent out in 1882, and brought into service on 29 January 1883 at a cost of £675. Two Wilkinson engines purchased at the same time (fleet nos. 7/8) cost £750 each but a second batch of Kitsons (T82-3, 85-86/fleet nos. 9-12) showed how their prices were rising, with T82-3 purchased 30 September 1883 at £685 each and 85-86 November/December 1883 at £700 per engine, an increase of £25 in a year.

The No.2 Standard had a larger boiler, cylinders generally 8" or 8½" x 12" stroke; typical users were all the Birmingham based companies plus Leeds, Dudley & Stourbridge etc., with the larger, 28¼", wheels being favoured. The gauge made little difference to the working dimensions and heating surfaces only had an 11% increase to 129sq.ft. (11.98sq.m) although an increase in water capacity from 80 to 170 gallons (364-774 litres) caused all-up weight to rise to 9 or 9½ tons.

60. Bradford Tramways & Omnibus Company's no.1, seen here in 1882 when still new was a standard Kitson product no.T63. The trailer was one of 12 similar four-wheelers built by Ashbury for horse or steam traction ... and that's hedging your bets if ever was!

No.3 Standard was, in the UK at least, a heavyweight job with T163-168 going out to the Birmingham & Midland Tramway in 1885. These monsters had 9" x 15" (229 x 381mm) cylinders, 34" wheels, a somewhat larger boiler, an increase in heating surfaces to around 150sq.ft.(13.93m) and were supposed to turn the scales at 11 tons; after some representations from the Birmingham Engineer (the Birmingham and Midland lines in Birmingham were only leased) the company claimed they were lightening this class as they went through the workshops; but it seems no more No.3 Standards were built, perhaps for as well as the weight-causing problems, their voracious appetite for coke outweighed their service advantages. Water capacity had again increased to 455 gallons (2070lt) held in two well tanks.

The genesis of the No.4 Standard came from an abortive attempt to rival the Baldwin much larger tram engines rather than the small well-tanked machines in use in Britain. Kitsons under pressure from Captain Rowan, built two 0-6-0 configuration trams (i.e. 3 pairs of driving wheels rather than the normal 2) numbered T59 and T60 with 11½" x 15" (292 x 381mm) cylinders and 30" (762mm) wheels having a weight of 12¾ tons. Numbered 42 and 43 in the Sydney fleet they were rapidly disliked for a tendency to derail and probably due to poor design of the steam passages no matter how bright the fire,

61. This is probably one of the most elegant photographs in the book as there is a certain 'rightness' both in the proportions of Kitson T46 (1881) and that beautiful Milnes trailer No.5, new to Leeds Tramways Company in 1889 at a cost of £237. Wellington Bridge Depot Yard c.1895. Incidentally, the locomotive was plum coloured, the trailer sunshine yellow and white.

they were slow compared with the Baldwins, which were normally expected to tow three laden bogie cars at speeds of 30-40mph (50-65kph) on the 'country' ends of the lines. Converted to 0-4-0 configuration T59 and T60 were used where sheer 'slogability' was a requirement rather than speed. Three similar engines (T71-73) sent out to a tramway in Brisbane which never materialised, were on 9 January 1883 taken over by Queensland Government Railways (fleet Nos. 1-3), they were again found to be too slow in passenger service, ending their days as shunting engines.

From these however came the only examples of the 'pure' No.4 Standard, which unsurprisingly were not even as designed then! Two engines (T106, fleet No.1, 'MOURNE', T107, No.2, 'DERG') were sent out to the Castlederg & Victoria Bridge in 1884, the line being opened 10 July. Three trains a day were run with 40 minutes being allowed for the 7.1 miles (11.36km) but how even these super-heavy so-called '6-panel' condensing trams could cope with hauling 'mixed' freight/parcels/passenger traffics up 1:30 inclines is quite surprising, especially as 33" (838mm) wheel diameter was chosen – perhaps for speed! Weight on the road was in excess of 13½ tons, which must have punished the 45lb/yard rail. Water capacity was also altered from the 'Standard' from 250 gallons to 318 (1137-1447lt) At least these two engines bore an exterior similarity to orthodox trams. Not so No.3 (Kitson w/no. T257) sent out in 1891. Although classified as a 'six panel No.4 heavy improved class' T257 had an orthodox cab with only the motion shrouded. No attempt was made, or desired to be made, at providing a condenser, Board of Trade regulations having been eased. Water capacity, held in three well tanks was 455 gallons, and the heating surface an excellent 269.3 square feet (25.02cu).

Curiously, the last steam tram engine built by Kitsons was for a No.2 type destined for the Portstewart Tramway (their No.3) sent out two years after the last two for Birmingham Central Tramway, fleet nos. 61 and 62, delivered to them in 1898 and themselves, apart from a variation in wheel sizes, (29½" BCT, 28¾" Portstewart), classic examples of type 2.

62. This set of relatively happy workmen rather belies the industrial relations situation between the Leeds Tramways Company (later Corporation) and their men. The engine is one of the T209-212, fleet nos. 13-16 series supplied in 1886. The depot would seem to be Wellington Bridge in the late 1890's when men worked a minimum 64 hours a week for £1 10s. (drivers) or £1 (guards); this was, however, better than in Company days (prior to 1894) when a week could be 91 hours for even less pay.

Excluding experimental engines and early Rowan cars, in the four years 1879-1883 no less than 73 No.1 Standard engines were built, after which 174 No.2 Standard engines took to the rails. No.3 Standard was far less successful, only nine (including three compounds) being ordered and only the three engines for Castlederg bearing any resemblance to No.4 Standard. Four 'unclothed' No.2 Standards were built for railway use within the T series, and the 5 Australian 0-6-0 engines, however non-standard were still classified as trams: totalled up this gives us 267 'pure' tram engines plus nine Rowan car power bogies out of the 302 listed in the "T" series. The blanks were in part due to cancelled orders, while others were anomalous – for example T287 was an 0-6-2 with 14" x 21" (356 x 533mm) cylinders for the Cape Copper Company and T299 at 2-6-2 tank engine with a tender(!) for the Canning Jarrah Timber Company. Co-incidentally jarrah, described as "a Eucalyptus tree native to western Australia" was one of the timbers strongly recommended for use under tramway rails mainly as it is almost impervious to damp; similarly a number of canal lock and dock gates were made from this wood; pleasing for an ex-canal man if it should have been hauled from the forest by a Kitson engine.

A diversion into compounding was tried by Kitson's, and typical was T213 purchased by the Birmingham & Aston on 27 March 1887 as fleet no.27 at the high price of £895 compared with T219 (fleet no.26) which cost the company (albeit as part of batch T214-219) £790 on 30 July 1886. The apparent delay in delivery may have meant there were problems with T213 but it arrived with 9" x 15" h.p. cylinders and 12" x 15" l.p. coupled to 32" (813mm) wheels. When, in due course, the Birmingham & Aston was to be sold prior to electrification and the engines were valued on 31 July 1902 this lonely compound was poorly regarded, "No.27, 1887 Compound engine with outside cylinders 14½" and 9½" general appearance and condition fair, but the engine is rarely in service, the ordinary engine preferred ... £200." J. Pogson, engineer of the Huddersfield Corporation Tramway, acting as the valuation arbiter, "I do not think it is a serviceable engine. It is not an engine that is worked by the Company, and according to my knowledge of these compound engines, they are a very unpopular engine. They are not in service if it can be possibly avoided. As a matter of fact this [T213] is not put in service except on very very rare occasions". By contrast the older tram No.9 (T82, 1883) was worth £270 although it had new tyres, "the motion and working parts of the engine very fair", as it had been rebuilt by the Birmingham & Midland Steam Tramway Company in November 1897 at a price of £214.15s.9d: "Condensor new, cab in fair condition, boiler original one, new firebox 1897, copper firebox and stays, brass tubes new August 1891." T83 had four patches on her firebox, T140 three, one on each side and one on the tube plate. By contrast the two, expensive, Wilkinson engines were shown as "discarded and quite useless for traction purposes ... "I [J. Pogson, again] averaged them at ten tons each, and give £2 a ton for them. There is no brass work about them. Practically it is all wrought iron scrap ... £20 each".

In Paper No.1990 "The Working of Tramways by Steam", re-printed in the I.C.E. Proceedings, Vol.79, 1884-5, the Hon. R.C.

Parsons, a director of Kitsons, refers to compounds: "...efforts have been made to economise the consumption of steam in tramway-engines by compounding the cylinders, and in this way not only to reduce the consumption of fuel, but also to avoid to some extent the difficulty of rendering the exhaust steam invisible. The results of experiments so far have not been very successful, and the Author is of opinion that little economy can be effected with an arrangement of this kind. There is also considerable difficulty in starting a compound tramway-engine quickly. To obviate this several ingenious contrivances have been invented; but on the whole a simple high-pressure engine ... meets the requirements most satisfactorily." Presumably, then, the demand for compounds came from the operators.

It must never be forgotten that no matter how important tram engines were for the growth of passenger traffic and population movement, for a firm like Kitson & Co they merely represented a little jam on the bread-and-butter of ordinary locomotive manufacture. If we take tram building to start in earnest with T16 of 1881, destined for Edinburgh Tramways and end with T301 of 1898, allowing for blank numbers etc., we have roughly 275 tram engines built in 17 years, plus of course the unrecorded tram engines which are impossible to quantify. The 1876 Rowan power unit for Russia, the second Dunedin No.1 Standard are among those known to have existed but how many were there? During the tram engine building period 1881-1898 'normal' works numbers rose from 2314, an 0-6-2T sent out to the Lancashire & Yorkshire Railway, 11 January 1881 to 3,800, an 0-4-2T sent out 14 November 1898 to the Jersey (C.I.) Eastern Railway, a total of 1486 locomotives in the same period. Even if we deduct 275 trams, and allow 5% for vacant numbers we still have 1,150 at least; a ratio of 4:1. Financially as many of these engines were heavy, assuming costings were correct, the profits were at the same ratio, engine to tram engine.

The Hon. R.C. Parsons had other ideas to keep Kitsons busy, first by manufacturing torpedoes at the Airedale Foundry, then an attempt at a unitory steam engine and generator. Later (although not at Kitsons) the turbine engined ship gave him everlasting fame. It is strange that it was the brain of a Frenchman, J.J. Meyer, who was born long ago in 1804 and who died in 1877, that was to bring Kitsons their greatest fame for successful mechanical ingenuity. The first Meyer articulated engine was built as an 0-4-4-0 having in his phrase "double steam bogies", each being driven by its own pair of cylinders, "the boiler does not serve in any way for the transmission of traction from one of the bogies to the other ... it is only carried by the trucks which are connected by a coupling bar".

This engine, 'L'Avenir' was built in 1868 by M. Cail, Compagnie de Fives Lille (themselves to build steam trams) and ran 34,250 miles (54,800km) on local rail services in France, Luxembourg and Switzerland. Relevant in light of Kitsons later involvement was the use of 'L'Avenir' over the steepest and most difficult section of the Luxembourg lines between Jemelle and Arlon where it successfully hauled 275 ton trains over gradients varying between 1:53 and 1:55 at 9¼mph (15kph) – prodigious for 1872. 'L'Avenir' was sold to the Chemin de fer des Charentes where she ran as no.0401 until

63. Because of the highly standardised design of Kitson engines, it is often only the details, livery, destinations, and company name/number that identifies them. Here the driver with his spanner and guard with fare-box working on Huddersfield Corporation engine no.14 (T237/1888) running between Berry Brow and Lockwood pose for the photographer.

the end of 1886. Initial Meyer engines had the two pairs of cylinders back-to-back with the great ability to run on one bogie when working light or in the event of any problems with the other set.

The prototype Kitson-Meyer works no. 3532 destined for the Anglo-Chilian Nitrate & Railway Company (fleet no.10) was first tried in steam on 13 July 1894, the entry reading "Kitson 'Meyer' class Qo 0-6-6-0 with 14" x 18" (356 x 457mm) cylinders running on 3' 6" (1067mm) gauge rails."

The conditions these engines had to work in were hard even by colonial standards and it says much for Robert Stirling, the Locomotive Superintendent, that he was able to modify the basic Meyer design and then to persuade Kitsons to build it! The railway started 52½ft. (16m) above sea level at the port of Tocopilla and ran to Barriles 3284ft (1,000m) above sea level, achieving this climb in 17½ miles (28km) running, with adverse gradients of more-or-less continuous 1:25 of which three-quarters involved sinuous and fearsome curves of model-railway standard trackwork at a minimum 181ft (55m) radius. From Barriles life became easier with only 1:34 gradients for 7¼ miles (11.6km) to Tigre.

In all 78 Kitson-Meyer engines were to be built in ever increasing sizes and power culminating in works nos.5471 and 5472 for the Ferrocarriles Nationales (Columbian National Railways) although by then Kitsons were only a shadow of their old selves having dismantled and sold for scrap the cranes etc. necessary for such work so that the assembly was undertaken by Robert Stephenson & Hawthorn of Darlington as their works nos. 4110/4111.

All the parts were produced at Kitson's works and these 2-8 + 8-2T engines were truly magnificent. Running on 3' 0" (914mm) gauge rails, they developed a tractive effort of 58,564lb and could haul 330 tons plus their own weight (130 tons) up a 1:22 incline at 10mph, and yet so as not to punish the track axle load was only 14.55 tons. Dimensions made a great contrast with our little trams at 66' 4¾" (20.23 m) long over buffers, 9' 0" (2.74m) wide (on 3' track remember!) and 12' 4½" (3.78 m) high, and yet they could still negotiate curves of 213' (65m) minimum radius. Writing in 1937 Edwin Kitson Clark (1888-1938) wrote that after World War I financial problems (falling sales down from 100 a year to less than 100 between 1925 and 1935 due mostly to more work being carried out 'in house' by the Big Four companies after the 1923 grouping and the dumping of thousands of ex WD locomotives on the market after WWI) affected Kitsons badly "and because of the unavoidable withdrawal of capital, and the unsuccessful venture into a new type of locomotive, the position changed for the worse."

The Kitson-Still diesel steam engine (works No.5374 of 1924) drained money for a decade, and while technically went on the way to success, had to be abandoned as there was little likelihood in the 1930s of any market. KS1 (as she was numbered) failed according to E. Kitson Clark through three faults he thought he should have foreseen. "As to the first: I ought to have recognised that however much the system was distinguished by a remarkable characteristic of flexibility the patentees had not given me actual proof of its principle to the extent required for locomotive service. As to the second: the type of locomotive which I proposed never seemed to fit the traffic available ... As to the third: with some diffidence I submit a very egoistical fault. I avoided too often, as the design developed, having the courage to act on my instincts. I knew how ignorant I was of the practice in internal combustion work, and recognised that I was being taught at the time by able and attentive authorities – but I now feel convinced that sometimes calculation should have been swept forward ... by imagination". When we consider that Kitson's at one time spurned compound tram engines as too complex the KS1 was really an amazing effort by a private firm. Cylinders (8 of them) were 13½" x 15½" (343 x 394mm) and it weighed 70 tons with 1,000 gallons (4546 lt) of water and 400 gallons (1818 lt) of oil. Roger Kidner described its workings thus: "One such engine, built in 1927, ran for some years on goods trains between York and Hull. This had eight horizontal combined cylinders with an internal combustion chamber at one end and steam at the other, the piston passing through both. When starting a load, the boiler (heating surface 562sq. ft) supplied steam in the normal way. When the train was moving steadily, the oil was introduced to the combustion cylinders, and when a good cruising speed was attained, the steam was cut off entirely, the Diesel engine taking over the entire load. The heat of combustion in the internal combustion cylinders was employed to raise steam in the boiler."

By 1934 it was obvious that Kitsons had little hope of riding out the slump in Britain and the debenture holders had a receiver appointed. "Up to that time", said the Yorkshire Post on 21 June 1937 "control of the business had remained in the hands of members and relatives of the Kitson family".

In 1938 following a decision to abandon locomotive manufacture some patterns, drawings and goodwill passed to Robert Stephenson & Hawthorn of Darlington and when they, in turn, closed in 1964, most drawings were united with those of Manning Wardle under the aegis of the Hunslet Engine Company, and are now (2003) in the hands of the Leeds Industrial Museum.

64. The power in this very late-built locomotive, Birmingham and Midland no.26 was said to be impressive, but although a Kitson product this engine and her sister (so-called 'ironclads') do not appear in the 'T' lists as they were all assembled by the operator from kits of parts, the sheet steel cabs and Conaty patented 'Cannon' condensers being home-made; the whole ensemble entering service in 1896 in a brown livery. This may well have been a posed photograph for shareholders, as the trailer no.26 was also home-built to a unique and logical design in 1899, in a green and white colour scheme.

Kitsons go to Kurrachee

The East India Tramways Company Ltd. was registered on 31 January 1884 and acquired a concession (in perpetuity) for the construction and working of a steam tramway in Karachi. The commonplace (in Britain at least) 21-year period of operation "from the opening of the line" was guaranteed although after that (and every seven years thereafter) the municipality of 'Kurrachee' could purchase the tramways at cost + 40% either in cash or with state bonds paying 7% interest. Rent of £50 per mile per annum was payable to the municipality in lieu of taxes or other charges.

The primary objectives of the tramway were to carry both goods and passengers (three classes, First, Second and 'Native') between the town, railway station and the jetty at Kiamari.

The Company got off to a bad start when the contractor failed to pay his men, and John Brunton, one-time apprentice at Harvey's of Hayle, assistant engineer under Robert Stephenson and Chief Engineer of the Scinde Railway (Karachi to Kotri), took over and completed the work. One curiosity was the use of "Brunton's Way" tram-track; a variant on Brunel's bridge rail albeit with a groove for tram wheels rolled from Bessemer steel it weighed 67 lb per yard (33.3kg/m) and rested on heavy cast iron chairs at the joints with wrought iron fishplates locking the rail lengths together. Well laid, as it was for the City of Oxford (horse) tramway it could last a long time, although cleaning the groove was awkward, but laid on bad ground as in Kurrachee, less so. Despite problems the main line opened with some aplomb as recorded in Engineering, 15 May 1885: "We are informed that the directors of the East India Tramways Company have received a cablegram announcing the completion of the main line of their system of tramways in Kurrachee, and its public opening by the Commissioner of Scinde on the 21st of April, the trial having proved perfectly successful. In view of possible military operations in Afghanistan, this new line of communication between the shipping port and the town may probably render important service in bringing up stores to the Government depots, and to the railway station, as the line has been constructed with a view to the goods traffic between those points, which is always a traffic of considerable magnitude, and of late years has greatly increased. The engineers of the line are Mr J. Brunton and Mr T. Claxton Fidler*. The gauge is 4ft. The engines are of the make of Messrs Kitson and Co., of Leeds, with certain modifications introduced by the engineers to meet the conditions of the traffic which they will have to work. The passenger stock consists of long bogie carriages upon eight wheels with a continuous central communication. The goods wagons, like the passenger cars, are provided with a simple form of continuous brake, made by Messrs Starbuck and Co., who are the builders of the carrying stock; all the wheels of the train being braked by a steam cylinder carried upon the footplate of the engine. Branches and sidings for the working of the goods traffic are also in course of construction at Keamari, at the native jetty, in the goods yard of the Kurrachee terminus of the Scinde, Punjaub, and Delhi Railway, and in the grain compounds of the principal exporting merchants; and it is expected that the whole will be practically completed in the course of a few weeks. The contractors for the work are Messrs Matthews and Crawford."

The locomotives were T144-149 inclusive (nos. 1-6) with 2' 4¼" (718 mm) driving wheels, 8" x 12" (203 x 305mm) cylinders, although the use of 4' 0" (1219mm) gauge trackwork was unusual.

At this point £75,210 worth of shares had been issued together with a further £12,000 in 6% debentures. A financial oddity was that the contractors guaranteed 6% on shares issued while building the tramway, but those shares issued to the contractor in lieu of cash carried a dividend of 7% payable by the company until 30 June 1888.

With hindsight it is apparent that the company had woefully over-estimated the traffic potential, as bullock carts continued to carry most of the freight to the jetty, and what traffic the tramway got was intermittent being

** T. Claxton Fidler was the Patentee in 1868/9 of various articulated locomotives and "Fidlers Patent Steam Omnibus" Manning Wardle built 50ft long push-and pull sets used in Buenos Ayres.*

KARACHI 2

KITSON TRAM ENGINES T144-T149
Lettered Karachi Tramways 1-6 0-4-OWT
4' 0" gauge
Tested in steam September 1885

Cylinders	8" x 12"
Driving Wheels	2' 4¼"
Boiler barrel	4' 5" x 2' 9"
Tubes:	73 x 1⅝" dia
WP	160psi
Firebox	length 2' 9" breadth 3' 0½"
Heating surface:	tubes 106 sq.in.
	firebox23sq.in.
Total	129sq.in.
Distance between axles	5' 0"
Water (cold)	105 gallons
Water (condensate)	40 gallons
Fuel capacity	9cu.ft

Primary difference from standard (mentioned in the Director's report) was that although the boiler and wheels etc. were cased in, the platforms were open.

In compiling this item I gladly acknowledge the assistance given by the SLS Librarian, Reg Carter.

dependent on ships arriving with bulk cargo. Even passing through the bazaar was objected to, sometimes violently, due to noise and fumes, and there was very little first and second class passenger traffic.

This was indeed no ordinary tramway and made the worst of our home-grown ones appear positively thriving. By 1890: "Negotiations are in progress with the Indian government for the compensation to be awarded to the company in view of the construction by the Government of a line of railway which competes and otherwise interferes with the company's line."

Quite simply new quays had been built at the port by the Port Trust, and, partly as a result of various main line rail mergers, a new main line was built parallel to, and crossing, the tramway. "Owing to the construction of this railway the company gave up the use of locomotives and wagons constructed, and horse traffic with light cars has been substituted."

Eventually (probably 1890) the company received the rather derisory sum of £5,450 in compensation: "this sum was applied to extinguishing certain debts". By 1891 they still owed £22,361.

And it got worse as by 1895 their issued funds stood at:

Ordinary shares	£75,070
5% debentures	£29,950
Other	£2,325

Debenture holders received half their interest in 1893 and nothing at all thereafter, debts (including some money to Kitsons) totalled by 1896 £29,746 although "Negotiations are now proceeding with the Indian government for further compensation in respect of a second crossing of the company's line ...". 1902 is the last entry I can find for the old company, bleakly: "Being wound up for the purpose of reconstruction". Whether the Kitsons went off as shunting engines or not is uncertain, but the new company had two engineers design a pair of petrol-engined trams in 1909, which had totally replaced horses by 1912 ... and still later diesel trams took over!

Steam-Tram Brakes – More-or-Less How They Work!

A technical note of interest regarding Kitson engines is to be found in Edwin Kitson Clark's story of *Kitsons of Leeds*, published by the Locomotive Publishing Company in 1938. As both a history and a book it deserved a wider audience, the outbreak of war stultified sales. This exposition on steam tram brakes of the 1880s comes from pp.86/87:

".....the brake and regulator were so joined that the one came into, as the other went out of, action. The brake deserves some notice. The blocks were pressed on to the tyres by a toggle-thrust downwards from a brake shaft arm. As there were two driver's positions, so there were two driver's quadrants in each of which was a lever coupled to the pin in the brake shaft arm, and the rods that make the coupling were united by a hinge. In the ordinary course the brake was applied by hand power, but it was compulsory in law that at 10 miles per hour the brake should come automatically into action. Therefore on the axle was a centrifugal governor that at the speed limit swung out so far as to cause a disc which

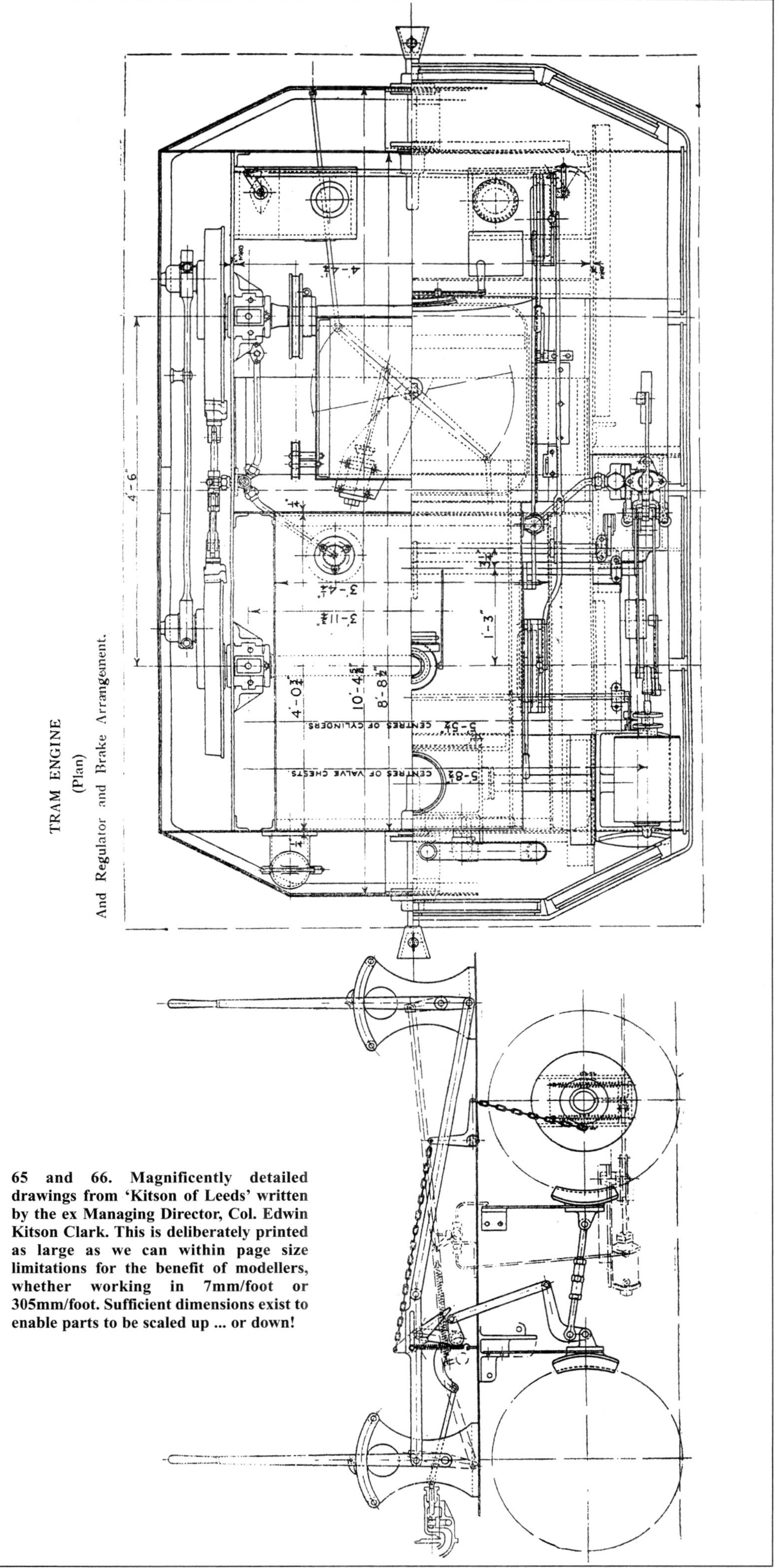

65 and 66. Magnificently detailed drawings from 'Kitson of Leeds' written by the ex Managing Director, Col. Edwin Kitson Clark. This is deliberately printed as large as we can within page size limitations for the benefit of modellers, whether working in 7mm/foot or 305mm/foot. Sufficient dimensions exist to enable parts to be scaled up ... or down!

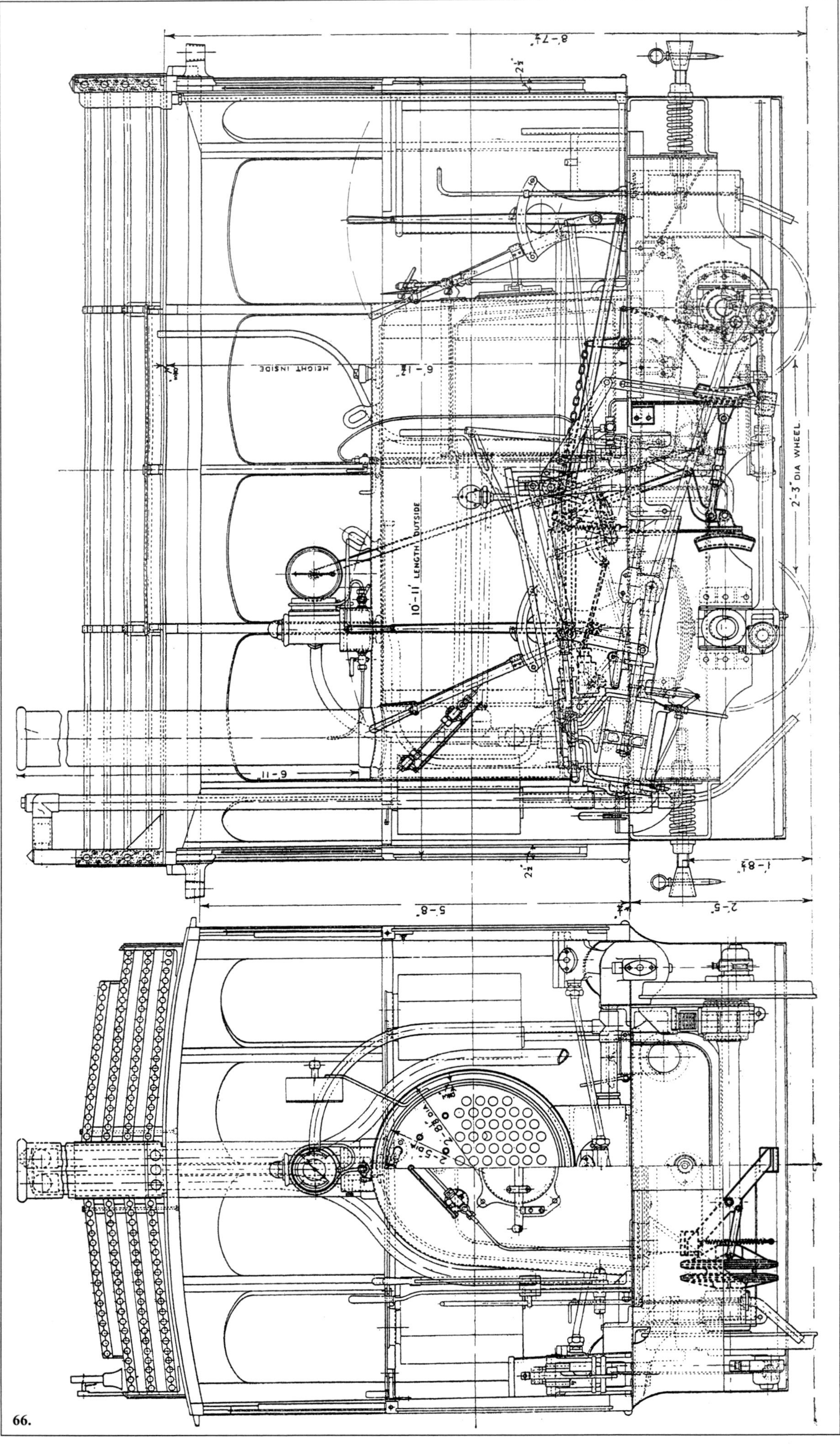

66.

was loose on the axle to engage with one which was fastened to it. The loose disc thus becoming one with the axle, revolved and wound on itself a chain that eventually brought the brake shaft into play by means of an interesting elaboration on the brake shaft arm attachments. There was pivoted on that shaft arm pin a floating member at the top of which the automatic brake chain was fastened. To this member the title of Trigger was given. In an elbow of this Trigger was fixed a pin which was free to move along a slot in one of the hand brake coupling rods. When at 10 miles per hour the chain exerted a pull at the top of the Trigger, the Trigger swivelled on its brake shaft pivot, the last mentioned pin then rose in its arc of movement and lifted the pair of handbrake coupling rods clear of the pin of the brake shaft arm, then the lower end of the Trigger at once came to rest on the body of the brake shaft, and thus acted as a fulcrum causing the Trigger to become virtually the functional arm of the brake shaft, so that the automatic device came into action. There was sufficient clearance at each point of contact in the system to allow free action, and after release an unhindered return to the original position under the recoil of counter springs."

Excellent no doubt when new and tight, but we know that most of the time such engineering nightmares were out of use; one could blame the fitters of course, but given E.K. Clark's own footnote ("In later examples a cataract pumping arrangement was tried, but was not found entirely reliable. It is perhaps permissible to suggest that the driver's interest was not always the same as that of the governor") maybe (and who was to blame them) the drivers helped incipient failures to fail quicker!

Extracts from Kitson fleet list. The 'T' numbers are for Tramway Locomotives, Rowan Cars and Light Tank Locomotives. Please note that the 'T' numbers are recorded in the Kitson records but there is no reference to the allocation of works numbers from the main list. The works numbers I have used for these are shown in various sources as being for tram locomotives. There is no other record for any other use of these works numbers. These works numbers are blanks in the Kitson Trial Book, the 'T' number being recorded in a separate ledger. I have included the 'T' numbers in this list to complete the record.

Kitson of Leeds

Possible works no	"T" numbers	Date of order/test	Type	Driving wheels	Cylinders	Customer + fleet no or name where known
2375	1	1896	Rowan	1'9"	6x10	Std demonstration car ordered by W.R.Rowan, Copenhaven, Denmark; test car order No.678
2376	2	1878	0-4-0 Tram		6x10	Std Hamburger Strassenbahn, Germany
2377	3	1878	0-4-0 Tram		6x10	Std Leeds October 1877-Jan 1878; Dewsbury, Batley & Birstall Mar-Apr 1878; Tramways de Rouen, France, 1879-1884
2378	4	1878	0-4-0 Tram		6x10	Std Gt Eastern Rly 230, used to work Millwall Dock Extension Ry to Stratford Works to power traverser
T2-4, order nos 918, 921 & 922, enclosed tram locos.						
2379	5	1879	Rowan	2'3"	6.5x12	5'3" Glenelg & South Coast Tramway, Kitson/ Scandia double deck steam car, engine unit to Moonta Mining Co Australia
2380	6	1879	Rowan	2'4.5"	7.5x12	Std Sydney Tramways 46 50, Kitson/Scandia double deck steam car
All the above have vertical boilers						
2381	7	1879	0-4-0 Tram	2'3"	6.25x12	3'6" Dunedin City & Suburban Tramway; destroyed in fire 23.12.1880, insurance write off
T7 was reboilered as 0-4-2ST in 1881, to Komata Reefs Gold Mining Co. Upper Thames, New Zealand; a second Kitson engine arrived in Dunedin in 1883 could be &53 or T55.						
2382	8	1879	0-4-0 Tram	2'3"	6.25x12	Std Canterbury Tramway 'A' Renumbered 1
2383	9	1879	0-4-0 Tram	2'3"	6.25x12	Std Canterbury Tramway 'B' Renumbered 2
2384	10	1879	0-4-0 Tram	2'3"	6.25x12	Std Canterbury Tramway 'C' Renumbered 3
2385	11	1879	0-4-0 Tram	2'3"	6.25x12	Std Canterbury Tramway 'E' Renumbered 5
2386	12	1879	0-4-0 Tram	2'3"	6.25x12	Std Canterbury Tramway 'D' Renumbered 4 Christchurch Tramway Board, New Zealand
2387	13	1879	Rowan	2'6"	8x13	Std Gribskov, A11, Denmark
2388	14	1879	Rowan	2'6"	8x13	Std Gribskov, A11, Denmark
T13 & 14 Kitson/Scandia double deck cars reboilered 0-4-OT 1892, 1 & 2, vertical boiler						
2389	15	1880	0-4-0 Tram	2'3"	7x12	Std Leeds Tramway 1
2390	16	1881	0-4-0 Tram	2'3.75"	7.25x12	Std Edinburgh Tramways 1
2391	17	1881	0-4-0 Tram	2'3.75"	7.25x12	Std Leeds Tramways 2
2392-2397	18-23	1881	0-4-0 Tram	2'4.25"	7.25x12	4'0" Blackburn & Over Darwin 1-6
2398	24	"	"	"	"	4'7.75" Vale of Clyde Tramway 1
2399	25	"	"	"	"	as above
2400	26	"	"	2'3.75"	"	Std Leeds Tramway 3
2401	27	"	"	2'3"	"	Std Canterbury Tramway 'F' Renumbered 6
2402	28	"	"	"	"	Std Canterbury Tramway 'G' Renumbered 7
2403	29	"	"	"	"	Std Canterbury Tramway 'H' Renumbered 8
2404	30	"	"	2'4.25"	"	4'7.75" Vale of Clyde Tramway 3
2405	31	"	"	"	"	4'7.75" Vale of Clyde Tramway 4
2406	32	"	"	"	"	Std Burnley & District Tramway 1
2407	33	"	"	"	"	Std Calcutta Tramway 1
2408	34	"	"	"	"	Std Calcutta 2
2409	35	1883	"	"	8x12	4'7.75" Vale of Clyde Tramway 9
2410	36	1881	"	"	7.25x12	5'2.5" Dublin & Southern District 1
2411	37	"	"	"	"	5'2.5" Dublin & Southern District 2
2412-2415	38-41	1881	0-4-0 Tram	2'4.24"	7.25x12	4'7.75" Vale of Clyde Tramway 5-8
2416-2419	42-45	1881	0-4-0 Tram	2'4.25"	7.25x12	Std Burnley & District Tramway 2-5
Tramway locomotives – see note by works no 2375						
2541	46	1881	0-4-0 Tram	2'3.75"	7.25x12	Std Leeds Tramways 4
2542	47	"	"	"	"	Std Edinburgh Tramways 2
2543	48	1882	"	2'4.25"	8x12	Std Parramatta Tramway (NSW) 1 lost at sea
2544	49	"	"	"	7.25x12	Std Cavehill & Whitewell (Ireland) 1
2545	50	"	"	"	8x12	Std Parramatta Tramway (NSW) 2 lost at sea
2546	51	1882	"	"	"	Std Wm Hurst/Cavehill & Whitewell 3
2547	52	"	"	"	"	Std Australia (Sydney), possibly Parramatta River Steamers & Tramway Co 1
2548	53	"	"	"	"	Std Parramatta Tramway (NSW) 3
2549	54	"	"	"	7.25x12	Std Cavehill & Whitewell (Ireland) 2
No record of T53 and T55 in Australia? if built?						
2550	55	1882	"	"	8x12	Std Parramatta Tramway (NSW) 4
2551	56	"	"	"	"	3'0" Portstewart Tramway (Ireland) 1
2552	57	"	"	"	"	3'0" Dublin & Lucan Tramway 1
2553	58	"	"	"	7.25x12	4'0" Blackburn & Over Darwin 7
2554	59	"	0-6-0 Tram	2'6"	11.5x15	Std Sydney Tramways (Australia) 42
2555	60	"	"	"	"	Std Sydney Tramways 43
2556	61	"	Rowan	3'0"	8x12	5'0" Poutiloff Tramway (Russia) 1

Possible works no	T nos	Date of order/test	Type	DW	Cylinders	Customer + fleet no or name where known
2557	62	"	"	"	"	5'0" Poutiloff Tramway 2
2558-2563	63-68	1882	0-4-0 Tram	2'4.25"	8x12	4'0" Bradford Tramways 1-6
2564	69	1883	Rowan	3'0"	9x13	5'3" Victorian Gov. Rys 1
2565	70	"	"	"	"	" 2
2566	71	"	0-6-0 Tram	2'6"	11.5x15	3'6" Brisbane Tram 1 QGR 1 105
2567	72	"	"	"	"	3'6" Brisbane Tram 2 QGR 2 106
2568	73	"	"	"	"	3'6" Brisbane Tram 3 QGR 3 107 QGR = Queensland Government Railway
2569	74	"	0-4-0 Tram	2'4.25"	8x12	3'0" Dublin & Lucan Tramway 2
2570	75	1882	0-4-0 Tram	2'4.25"	8x12	3'6" Birmingham & Aston Tramway 1
2571-2575	76-80	1883	0-4-0 Tram	2'4.25"	8x12	3'6" Birmingham & Aston Tramway 2-6
2572	77	"	"	"	"	" 3
2573	78	"	"	"	"	" 4
2574	79	"	"	"	"	" 5
2575	80	"	"	"	"	" 6
2576	81	"	"	"	"	3'0" Dublin & Lucan Tramway 3
2577	82	"	"	"	"	3'6" Birmingham & Aston Tramway 9
2578	83	"	"	"	"	" 10
2579	84	"	"	"	"	3'0" Portstewart Tramway 2
2580	85	"	"	"	"	3'6" Birmingham & Aston Tramway 11
2635	86	1883	"	"	"	3'6" Birmingham & Aston Tramway 12
2636-2640	87-91	1884	0-4-0 Tram	2'4.25"	8x12	3'6" Dudley & Stourbridge Tramway 1-5
2641-2644	92-95	1883	0-4-0 Tram	2'4.25"	7.25x12	Std Calcutta Tramway 5-8
2645	96	"	"	"	8x12	Std Parramatta Tramway ?1 No record of this loco in Australia
2646	97	1884	0-4-0T	3'0"	8x12	3'6" South Australian Harbours Board Port Germein Jetty
2647	98	1883	0-4-0 Tram	2'4.5"	7.25x12	Std Calcutta Tramway 9
2648	99	1884	"	"	8x12	3'6" Dudley & Stourbrdige Tramway 6
2649	100	"	"	"	"	" 7
2711	101	"	"	"	"	" 8
2712	102	"	"	"	"	Std Leeds Tramway 4
2713	103	"	"	"	"	Std Parramatta Tramway 2? No record of this loco in Australia
2714	104	"	"	"	"	4'0" Bradford Tramway 8
2715	105	"	"	"	"	3'0" Dublin & Lucan Tramway 4
2716	106	"	"	2'9"	12x15	3'0" Castlederg & Victoria Bridge 1 "Mourne"
2717	107	"	"	"	"	" 2 "Derg"
2718	108	"	"	2'4.25"	8x12	3'0" Dublin & Lucan Tramway 5
2719	109	"	0-4-0T	3'0"	8x12	Std West Lancashire Ry 10 "Hesketh Park"
2720	110	"	"	"	"	" 11 "Crossens"
2721	111	"	"	"	"	" 12 "Churchtown"
T109 to Price, Wills & Reeves, to Corringham Ry, renamed "Cordite"; T110 to Liverpool Overhead Ry, T111 to Rea Ltd; there is doubt about T109-111 as to which went where from the West Lancashire Ry						
2722-2727	112-117	1884	0-4-0 Tram	2'4.25"	8x12	Std Leeds Tramways 5-10
2728-2747	118-137	1884	0-4-0 Tram	2'4.25	8x12	3'6" Birmingham Central Tramway 1-20
2748-2751	138-141	1884	0-4-0 Tram	2'4.5"	8x12	3'6" Birmingham & Aston Tramway 13-16
2752-2753	142-143	1884	0-6-0T	2'9"	11.5x15	5'3" Strathalbyn Tramway, South Australian Rys 97-98
2754-2759	144-149	1885	0-4-0 Tram	2'4.25"	8x12	4'0" Karachi Tramway 1-6
2760-2766	150-156	1885	0-4-0 Tram	2'4.25"	8.5x12	4'0" Barrow in Furness Tramway 1-7
2767-2772	157-162	1885	0-4-0 Tram	2'4.25"	8.5x12	3'6" Birmingham & Midland Tramway 1-6
2773	163	1885	0-4-0 Tram	2'10"	9x15	3'6" Birmingham & Midland Tramway 7
2774-2778	164-168	1885	0-4-0 Tram	2'10"	9x15	3'6" Birmingham & Midland Tramway 8-12
2779-2792	169-182	1885	0-4-0 Tram	2'4.25"	8x12	Metre Singapore Tramways 1-14
2793-2799	183-189	1885	0-4-0 Tram	2'4.25"	8.5x12	3'6" Birmingham Central Tramway 21-27
2906	190	1885	0-4-0 Tram	2'4.25"	8.5x12	3'6" Birmingham Central Tramway 36
2907	191	"	"	"	"	3'6" Dudley & Stourbridge Tramway 9
2908	192	"	"	"	"	Std Leeds Tramways 11
2909-2913	193-197	"	"	2'6"	"	Std Dudley, Sedgley & Wolverhampton 1-5
2914	198	1886	0-4-0T	2'10"	9x15	2'6" Cape Copper Co 1 "John Taylor"
2915-2920	199-204	"	0-4-0 Tram	2'4.25"	8.5x12	3'6" Birmingham Midland Tramway 14-19
2921-2924	205-208	"	"	"	"	3'6" Birmingham & Aston Tramway 17-20
2925-2928	209-212	"	"	2'4.75"	"	Std Leeds Tramway 13-16
2929	213	"	"	2'8"	9/12x15	3'6" Birmingham & Aston Tramway 27 compound
2930-2935	214-219	"	0-4-0 Tram	2'4.75"	8.5x12	3'6" Birmingham & Aston Tramway 21-26
2936	220	1886	0-4-0T	2'10"	9x15	2'6" Cape Copper Co 2 "Juanita" (SA)
2937-2939	221-223	1887	0-4-0 Tram	2'6"	8.5x12	3'6" Costa Rica 1-3
2940	224	"	"	2'4.75"	10x12	3'0" Dublin & Lucan Tramway 6

Possible works no	T nos	Date of order/test	Type	DW	Cylinders	Customer + fleet no or name where known
2941-2942	225-226	"	"	2'4.25	8x12	Metre Singapore Tramways 15-16
2943-2944	227-228	"	"	2'4.75"	8.5x12	Std Leeds Tramways 17-18
2945	229	1888	0-4-0T	2'6"	8x12	Metre North West Argentine Ry 11, to FC Central Cordoba "S5" 1001, 21
2946	230	1887	0-4-0 Tram	2'4.75"	9.5x12	4'7.75" Huddersfield Tramway 10
2947	231	1888	0-6-OWT	2'11.5"	11.5x15	3'6" Western Australia Land Co; Gt. Southern Ry 1 "Princess"; Western Australian Gov. Ry "S" 1; Naval Base Henderson in 1915; Associated Blue Metal Quarries Ltd in 1927
2948-2949	232-233	"	0-4-0 Tram	2'4.75"	9.5x12	4'7.75" Huddersfield Tramway 11-12
2950	234	"	0-4-0T	2'10"	9x15	2'6" Cape Copper Co 3 "Jackal" (SA)
3189	235	"	0-4-02T	3'6"	11x15	3'0" Cork & Muskerry Lt Ry 4 "Blarney"
3190-3193	236-239	"	0-4-0 Tram	2'4.75"	9.5x12	4'7.75" Huddersfield Tramways 13-16
3365	240	1889	0-4-0T	2'4.25"	7x12	1050mm Fry Miers & Co "Etelvina"
3366-3368	241-243	"	0-6-0T	3'0"	13x18	1000mm Shaw Bros1-3 FCCN 'D5' 202-204 FCCN FC Central Northern (Argentina) T241 & T242 to General Belgrano in 1948
3369	244	"	0-4-0 Tram	2'4.75"	9.5x12	4'75" Huddersfield Tramways 17
3464	245	1889	"	"	"	4'7.75" Huddersfield Tramways 18
3465	246	1890	0-6-2	3'0"	14x21	2'6" Cape Copper Co 4 "Clara" (SA)
3466-3467	247-248	1891	0-4-0 Tram	2'4.75"	10/13.	4'7.75 Huddersfield Tramway 21-22 5x12
3468	249	1891	"	"	8.5x12	3'6" Dudley & Stourbridge Tramway 10
3469	250	1892	"	2'4.25"	9.5x12	4'0"Barrow in Furness Tramways 8
3470-3474	251-255	1893	"	2'4.75"	9x12	3'6" Wigan & District Tramway 10-14
3475	256	1895	"	2'6"	"	Std Dudley & Wolverhampton Tramway 7
3476	257	1891	0-4-0T	2'9"	12x15	3'0" Castlederg & Victoria Bridge 3
3477	258	1891	0-6-2	3'0"	14x21	2'6" Cape copper Co 5 "Marie"
3478	259	1891	0-6-0T	2'11.5"	11.5x15	Metre Mysore Gold Mining Co
3479	260	1892	0-6-0WT	"	"	3'6" West Australia Land 2 "Duchess"
West Australian Govt Ry S 163 in 1896 to Henderson Naval Base in 1915 ACT Constructions in 1923, Sydney Met. Water Board in 1926, Prospect Quarry						
3480	261	"	0-6-2	3'0"	14x12	2'6" Cape Copper Co 6 "James Kitson"
3481-3490	262-271	1893	0-4-0 Tram	2'4.75"	8.5x12	3'6" Birmingham Central Tramway 71-80
3491-3492	272-273	1894	"	"	"	" 81-82
3493-3494	274-275	"	"	"	10x12	4'7.75" Huddersfield Tramways 31-32
3495	276	1895	"	"	8.5x12	3'6" Dudley & Stourbridge Tramway 11
3496-3497	277-278	1895	"	"	9x12	3'6" Wigan & District Tramway 15-16
3498-3499	279-280	1896	"	"	"	" 17-18
3500	281	1895	"	"	8.5x12	3'6" Dudley & Stourbridge Tramways 12
3620	282	1896	0-4-0T	2'10"	9x15	Champion Gold Reef Mining, India
3621-3622	283-284	1897	0-4-0 Tram	2'4.75"	9.5x12	4'7.75" Huddersfield Tramways 8-9
3623	285	1897	"	2'5.25"	"	4'0" Blackburn & Over Darwin 15
3624	286	1897	"	"	"	4'0" Blackburn & Over Darwin 2
3625	287	1898	0-6-2	3'0"	14x21	2'6" Cape Copper Co 7 "Albion"
3626-3633	288-295	1898	0-4-0 Tram	2'5.5"	8.5x12	3'6" Birmingham Central Tramway 83-90
3634	296	"	"	"	"	" 57
3635	297	"	"	"	"	" 60
3636	298	"	0-4-OT	2'10"	10x15	2'6" Champion Gold Reef Mining Co
3637	299	1899	2-6-2T+T	3'0"	13x18	3'6" Canning Jarrah Timber Co "J.H.Smith" (Western Australia)
3638-3639	300-301	1898	0-4-0 Tram	2'5.5"	8.5x12	3'6"Birmingham Central Tramway 61-62
3640	302	1900	"	2'4.75"	9.5x12	3'0" Portstewart Tramway 3

67. Extracted from Parsons/Kitson catalogue.

CALCUTTA TRAMWAYS.

Awarded a Gold Medal, the Highest Prize,

AT THE

CALCUTTA EXHIBITION OF 1883.

68, 69, 70. Extracted from Parsons/Kitson catalogue.

71/72. Left: The Barrow-in-Furness Tramways Company operated 5½ miles (8.85km) of line between Roose and Furness Abbey via Barrow. Opened in 1885, this intermediate-guage (4' 0"/1219 mm) tramway remained, theoretically at least, in existence until 1904, although two years earlier the Board of Trade would only give them a month-by-month permit. Looking at the incredibly dishevelled condition of both locomotive and trailer by 1901 it is hard to realise both photographs show No.1 engine (Kitson T150, 8½" x 12"/216 x 305mm) cylinders, and its Falcon 1885-built trailer. At least the advertisement is the same, but look how bowed the trailer has become; clearly the truss rods are beyond tightening.

73. I am not absolutely sure this is Portstewart No.3 (Kitson T302), but it shows a typical 'mixed' working.

Manning, Wardle & Co.

The story of Manning, Wardle & Co. is really the story of Britain's locomotive building industry. In the field of steam trams they were really a very small player, and particularly so in Britain, for at most they only produced 23 tram engines, of which just 13 ran in England, but as a firm they traced their history right back to the roots of locomotive engineering when Fenton, Murray & Wood built Blenkinsop's patent rack-rail steam locomotive way back in 1811.

After some success, with around 9-10 locomotives built, Matthew Murray, once the most forward thinking partner, reverted to the steady trade in mill engines and other machinery in regular demand.

When he died in 1826, his son-in-law Robert Jackson turned the firm, by now Fenton, Murray & Jackson back to building locomotives at The Round Foundry, Holbeck, Leeds, but for reasons that are unclear they went out of business in 1843. Eventually the works passed to Todd, Kitson & Laird, but shortly afterwards the partners had a 'falling-out' and Messrs Kitson and Laird set up their Airedale Foundry which in 1863 became the sole property of Kitson & Co. After some vicissitudes the Railway Foundry on the other side of Jack Lane was being run by E.B. Wilson, who, apart from designing and building locomotives far in advance of most other firms' offerings developed a trademark pattern of fluted domes and safety valve covers – a Russian colleague of ours looking at the photographs of these in John Simpson's 'Locomotives of Quality' asked where the tap was. It seemed he mentally likened them to the samovars of his native country! In 1856 Wilson left the Railway Foundry which on closure in 1858 was divided into lots; but with no sales all the buildings were pulled down.

C.W. Wardle was the son of a vicar in a nearby village, while Alexander Campbell who had been Works Manager of Scotts of Greenock and was said to be an "upright man" had managed the Railway Foundry in its last seven years, and it was due to his canniness that in the last year of E.B. Wilson & Co, a profit of £12,000 was made – in difficult trading conditions railway companies would be worried about spare parts in the future. Others involved in the new company were Wilson's ex-cashier and the ex-head of the Stationary Engine department, but a shortage of funds led to some of the original partners leaving to be replaced by John Manning, who brought in £3,000, leading to a partnership that lasted from 1860 to 1872.

The firm had already acquired 5½ acres of land, which had belonged to the Rt.Hon. G.F.H. Russell, Viscount Boyne, and logically they named their new factory "Boyne Engine Works".

In passing it should be mentioned, as shown on the map, by 1864 four locomotive manufacturers occupied a relatively small area of Hunslet; but the workmen were housed in terraced cottages, said to be some of the worst in Leeds, built between and up to the walls of the factories. The dirt, smells, fumes and sheer volume of noise from all four loco builders must have been quite rough – but they and their men made 'brass' enough.

The four were:

Airedale Foundry, Kitson & Co. 1863

Boyne Engine Works, Manning, Wardle & Co. 1858

[New] Railway Foundry Hudswell, Clarke & Co. 1860

Hunslet Engine Works Hunslet Engine Co. 1864

By one of the strange twists of fate out of 2004 locomotives built by Manning, Wardle, they produced a number for what were ostensibly at least "tramways", for example Jersey Railways & Tramways St. Heliers (w/no. 916) and St. Aubin (w/no. (17), Kettering Ironstone Tramway (nos. 6-8. w/nos. 1123, 1370, 1675), Hundred of Manhood & Selsey Tramway (all secondhand but w/nos. 21, 178, 890) and the Oxford & Aylesbury Tramroad (616, 1249, 1415) although none of these engines were in any sense tramway engines. At least one railway that was lucky to escape using shrouded engines, the Weston, Clevedon & Portishead had a number of Manning, Wardle products, again secondhand (731, 1135, 1970) but as the Weston, Clevedon & Portishead ran through the middle of towns it really was surprising that Manning, Wardle or another maker was not required to provide real tram engines – instead classically "a man with a red flag" had to walk beside (or, theoretically in front of) the engine in urban areas.

Two Manning, Wardle engines were to work on a true tramway, albeit after the Board of Trade had stopped worrying about their own rules, but as at one time or another the Wantage owned seven real ex-horse tramcars (1, 2 Starbuck 1875; 3 Milnes 1890; 4,5 ex Reading nos. 11,9 bought 1903; 4(ii), 5(ii) Hurst Nelson built 1900, 1904 bought 1912) a passenger could enjoy the sensation of riding in a true tram, alongside and across roads, being hauled by a perfectly good Manning, Wardle tank engine No.7 bought 1893, and built 1888 (w/no. 1057) a member of the standard 'F' class with 10" x 14" (254 x 356mm) cylinders, 2' 9" (838mm)) diameter wheels, a 4' 9" (1448mm) wheelbase and with a pressure of 125psi she weighed 14¾ tons. Sadly an 'H' class engine No. 581 of 1876 with 12" x 18" (305 x 457mm) cylinders was a poor buy in 1919, lasting only a year.

74. Manning Wardle engine 1057 was always said to be the most useful engine ever to run on the Wantage Tramway. As their no.7 this machine was purchased in 1893 for £300, the enclosed cab being built later by the company. The sad part is that after 53 years service with the tramway, and another ten in a steel mill she nearly made it into preservation, but was broken up in 1957.

The story of the Ryde Pier Tramway will be given later in this series, but here it is worth noting that the first trial engine 'Vectis' was built by Manning, Wardle in 1864 – long long before even the first 'real' tram engines appeared – with w/no. 111, this little 0-4-0 saddle tank engine had 6" x 12" (152 x 305mm) cylinders, but after delivery on 14 March 1864 vibration was found to be weakening the piers structure and the engine was returned to the works being sold without difficulty to the Northfleet Coal & Ballast Company.

Of similar size were two engines of 4' 0" (1219mm) gauge (w/nos. 208/9) sent out to the Pernambuco Tramway Company in 1866, with coupled 2' 5" (762mm) driving wheels giving an 0-4-0 configuration on a 4' 7" (1397mm) wheelbase. 6" x 12" (152 x 305mm) cylinders were fitted and in effect these machines were standard Model 'B' saddle tank engines with outside cylinders but they were covered with a wooden 'house' or enclosure, although unlike later urban tramway locomotives they were only driven from the open firebox end and the mechanism was entirely unshielded. No.1 in the fleet was sent out on 27 August 1866, No.2 26 September 1866, and following these, which must have given satisfaction, came w/no.232 on the 6th August 1868, albeit this had cylinders enlarged

76. The outer shells of these engines were, I suppose, a gesture to hide the boiler and such components from animals and people alike. The massive brake blocks and their mechanism show the date of building

to 7" x 12". The next batch (5) based on Model "D" tank engines were delivered between 1868 and 1870 with a further increase in cylinder size to 8" x 14" and an increase in wheel diameter from the 2' 6" of w/no. 208 to 2' 8" (813mm) of w/no. 314, sent out 28 June 1870. Later engines supplied to the Brazilian Street Tramways Company as successors to the Pernambuco Tramways Company forewent the houses and were orthodox 2-4-0 tank engines; although the last ever to the tramway, bearing No.8 reverted to the original 0-4-0 saddle-tank design with 9" x 14" (229 x 356mm) cylinders and 2' 9¾" (857mm) wheels. W/no. 1831 was sent out on 27 September 1913, the last of 21 locomotives supplied between 1866 and 1913. Three less than usual tram-type locomotives were to be ordered from Manning Wardle in 1869. Works nos. 295, 296 and 297 were, in effect, powered bogies with vertical 3' 8" (1118mm) boilers which supplied steam to cylinders believed to be 6" x 7" (152 x 178mm), these driving 3' 0" (914mm) coupled wheels, on a 4' 0" wheelbase. To enable fumes to be carried clear of the coachwork the height of the chimney was 11' 9" (3.58m) the whole power unit being surmounted by rather jolly frilly canopies. Named La Plata, Paraquay and Uruquay, they were to run on the Ferrocarril de la Provincia de Buenos Ayres (Provincial Railways of Argentina) 5' 6" gauge lines. These bogies were then articulated to passenger units, one at each end, giving an overall wheelbase of 41' 6" (12.65mm), a total length of 55' 6" (16.92m) and a height of 10' 6" (3.2m). Sent out from Manning Wardle on 8 July 1870 as skeletons it is to be assumed that bodywork was built locally. We know they were used for a shuttle service between Parque, Once and Central stations in Buenos Aires, and were extant, if derelict, as late as 1890. They were built, one might add, under Fidler's Patent (details in a later volume) but one does wonder what sort of communication the driver/stoker had with the whoever sat up front; especially as the only braking provision seems to have been on the power unit!

When we turn to 'proper' tram engines it is unfortunate that their first batch (w/nos. 764/5 delivered 6 December 1880) were quite unsuccessful. It could be that time did not allow for a re-design of their orthodox engines, although as we have seen the firm were more than capable of building almost anything required. One can understand Henry Vignoles, the engineer (ex-Isle of Man Railway) requiring a relatively powerful and heavy engine to tackle the gradients of the North Staffordshire Tramway Company's lines within Longton, Stoke-upon-Trent, Newcastle-under-Lyme and Tunstall.

These first two engines were still regarded as unsatisfactory by the Board of Trade inspector in April 1881 (five months after delivery) and for one reason or another (mainly due to trackwork clearance problems) it was not until June or July 1882 steam power was authorised for use from Longton to Burslem via Stoke and Hanley. At this juncture the original two tram engines (nos. 1/2 w/no. 764/5) had been augmented by the arrival of w/no.805-8 (fleet 6-9), 827-828 (7,8), 829-30 (14,15), during the end of 1881 and May 1883. All were similar with 9" x 14" cylinders running on 4' 0" gauge (1219mm) outside Vignoles patent trackwork which was designed to give a rigid, unyielding line; partly because of heavy wagon traffic that already existed in the Potteries and partly, one must guess, to allow for the weight and vibration of the steam trams, but by 1884 even this was being re-laid. During early running the directors at an AGM of the company stated the Manning Wardle engines were able to haul two loaded trailers with ease. "On April 23rd we ran cars from Stoke to Longton worked by steam. The service has been continued regularly though under great disadvantages, the severe gradients on the line rendering it difficult to obtain engines which could comply with the stringent requirements of the Board of Trade,

77. The manufacturer's plate proudly proclaims "Manning Wardle & Co., Leeds 1881, 808." This latter is the works number and the photograph was taken in 'dummy' livery for record (and sales) purposes. On the extreme bottom left hand side of the original is the notation "N (orth) S (taffs) T (ramways) Co. No.9"; the lack of lifeguards is obvious but this loco does not look as clumsy as those delivered to the MBRO.

and, at the same time, efficiently and economically carry the traffic. To this question of motive power the directors have had to devote much time and labour. So many persons having recommended different types of engines, they determined that no exertion on their part should be spared in endeavouring to secure the most perfect. I feel sure the result will be a considerable saving to the shareholders, and, notwithstanding the travelling expenses, as shown in the accounts, may appear large, it must be borne in mind they extend over a period of nearly two years, and the amount necessarily devoted to this purpose of inspection will, it is believed, prove of permanent advantage to the company. The directors believe the engines built by Messrs Manning and Wardle, of Leeds, are the best adapted for the traffic of this line, being powerful and well constructed, they draw with perfect ease two loaded cars after each engine, a very important element in the working of steam tramways, the additional hauling power enabling the company to obtain better returns for their outlay and thus reducing the proportion of working expenses ... We have six engines, built by Messrs Manning and Wardle, and so satisfied are we that they are the best, we have ordered four more ... As I reminded the last meeting, tramway engines are in their infancy, and it is a very difficult thing to work a tramway engine on a road where the dirt is constantly working up into the machinery. It also increases the difficulty when we have to condense all our steam. If you were to watch the working of these engines and see the dirt that accumulates among the machinery you would not be surprised at the difficulty we have on the selection of engines. We have, I believe, in the case of the Manning and Wardle engine overcome the difficulties that we have experienced from the first. I may say that Messrs Manning and Wardle took precisely the same view as one of the shareholders – 'Tell us the weight and the gradients and we will provide an engine; we may not succeed at first, but we will do it' and they have done so. The local authorities are very much pleased with the result, and so, I believe, are the Board of Trade."

In 1883 the same men were reporting to shareholders that the line was to be re-equipped entirely with Wilkinson Patent engines (to be supplied by Beyer Peacock) which in some ways is curious as due to worm-wheel drive of the Wilkinson design no springing could be given to one axle, making for even more vibration!

The end for the Manning Wardle engines is uncertain as by April 1885 eight were being offered for sale but it seems the other two were held back until the early 1890s for working heavy fair and football day traffics. There seems no doubt that for these traffics Vignoles' design was vindicated, but it was at the expense of the trackwork and a very high running cost of 1s.2d. per mile, compared with costs elsewhere as low as 6d. per mile and eventually about 8d. for the Wilkinson type engines used later on these lines. That Manning Wardle built solidly is undeniable, but the use of a water condensation tank which entailed an extra 2-3 tons deadweight, contributing to an overall 13-15 tons weight, must be regarded as a design failure. Another difficulty with the use of such a tank, into which all the waste steam had to go, was that quite quickly it boiled and then there were difficulties in disposing of the water which of course was contaminated by tallow and other lubricants in the engine and which could not be emptied anywhere near horses for fear of scalding. The enginemen, too, apparently loathed the design as there was insufficient space to provide proper footplates especially at the firebox end and the driver had to work sideways. Incidentally at this time the North Staffordshire company were one of a tiny handful who used two-men crews (driver + stoker) but stokers were disposed of very quickly!

The overall dimensions of the Manning Wardle locomotives were 13' 10" (4.21m) long, 6' 6" (1.98m) wide and overall height 13' 6" (4.11m), the wheelbase being quite long at 4' 9" (1.45m). The North Staffordshire engines were, perhaps, the ultimate example of the old engineering dictum "if it looks right, it is; if it ain't, it ain't". They really w'ain't!

The final three tram engines manufactured by Manning Wardle for the UK market were sent out to the Manchester, Bury, Rochdale & Oldham Steam Tramways Company in 1885 (w/nos. 850-2, fleet 52-54) with 8½" x 14" (216 x 357mm) cylinders but otherwise similar to those supplied to the North Staffordshire except for being standard gauge. The delay in their supply led to their route Royton-Oldham-Hathershaw not being fully operational until 1 August 1885, although the Board of Trade had passed the line for use the previous February. It is not clear exactly why the MBRO company only received three Manning Wardle engines, but as they and the North Staffordshire were promoted (and fleeced!) by the City of London Contract Corporation some deal had no doubt been struck; but whatever it was the this company was lumbered with not only two gauges, narrow and standard but a truly

78/79. Two views of the same engine, albeit with radically different trailers. Both ran on the Royton-Hathershaw service of the MBRO; the Manning Wardle plate is visible as well as that of the owners.

80. The same class of engine but with a three-man crew presumably at Royton. All three seem to be enginemen and happy enough with their lot. But isn't 54 a clumsy looking beast...

heterogenous mixture of engines from not only Manning Wardle but Falcon, Wilkinson, Beyer Peacock and Thomas Green and within those makes a number of different sizes and shapes. And the company were in such a parlous state their later locomotives from Beyer Peacock were bought on – effectively – hire purchase as the builders plates gave not only the number but Beyer Peacock as the builders and owners; when payments were completed the "owners" was ground away.

The Manning Wardle engines remained at Royton Depot (Dogford Road) only leaving when heavy repairs had to be carried out, but were finally scrapped in 1899, long outlasting their North Staffordshire sisters.

Manning Wardle always paid their men weekly wages without any element of piece-work, although from time to time bonuses were paid. Unfortunately in an ever increasingly mechanised age they found it necessary to enter into voluntary liquidation during 1926, the good-will, patterns and drawings passing to Kitson & Co who built another 23 engines to Manning Wardle design. When in turn, Kitsons could no longer survive (1938) this material passed to Robert Stephenson and Hawthorns who built five more Manning Wardle styled locomotives. Apposite, I suppose, for Manning Wardle's pred-ecessors, Fenton, Murray & Jackson started in 1826 carrying out sub-contract work for Robert Stephenson.

Dream Unfulfilled – Messrs Manning Wardle & Co.
The Times – 26 November 1881:

"Messrs Manning, Wardle, and Co., locomotive engineers, Leeds, have recently delivered a number of tramway engines, specially designed and adapted for the traffic of the North Staffordshire Tramway Company. They have overcome some serious difficulties peculiar to that tramway system, which runs from Stoke to Longton, will be extended to Hanley shortly, and then pushed forward to Burslem. The difficulties arose from exceptionally severe gradients, some of which are on curves. It appears that this is the most difficult tramway as regards motive power with respect to which any mechanical engineers have yet been consulted. The gradient is some-times as steep as 1 in 14, but there are others ranging from 1 in 16 to 1 in 20 over long lengths. Messrs Manning, Wardle and Co.'s engines work on a new system of silent condensation by water, which has answered the purpose admirably, the discharge of any steam at all being completely avoided and impossible. Between Stoke and Longton at busy times one engine regularly draws two fully-loaded passenger cars over gradients of 1 in 18 for considerable distances; and the brake power can stop a car within its own length and a half while going down hill at the rate of seven miles an hour. By the use of this engine the requirements of the Board of Trade are strictly fulfilled."

Merryweather & Sons Ltd.

Messrs Merryweather & Sons' tram engines received a number of mentions in *The Times*; this was the earliest I have traced dated 7 October 1876.

"STEAM WORKED TRAMWAYS. Although considerable progress has been made on the Continent in the introduction of steam for working tramways, we in England have hitherto remained somewhat behind our neighbours in this respect. Continental progress, however, has been largely due to our own countrymen, as Paris, Vienna and other foreign cities citing evidence, for there – especially in Paris – the tramway engines of Messrs Merryweather and Sons are extensively adopted. At length we at home appear to be making a move in this direc-tion, as both on the Ryde pier and on the Vale of Clyde tramways are the engines of this firm now working. It is, however, but right to point out that the difficulty which has hitherto stood in the way of their adoption has been the noise caused by the exhaust steam from the cylinders, and which was supposed to frighten horses. This difficulty having been overcome by the manufacturers has led to the adoption of their engines on several street tramway systems. The Vale of Clyde Tramway Company have only recently succeeded in obtaining Parliamentary powers for working their lines by steam and the first engine has just been started there. The Merryweather tram-engine is a small locomotive encased in a square wood and glass house, in appearance not unlike a diminutive cabman's shelter. There is no indication of its having any machinery whatever, the working parts being boxed up inside. There is scarcely any appearance of chimney, and what there is emits neither steam nor smoke. The fire-place is closed in, so that there is no glaring light thrown upon the roadway at night. The working sound of the engine is completely muffled, and by a simple arrangement the exhaust steam, instead of causing the puffing noise usual in locomotives, is practically unheard, the rumbling of the wheels on the rails being the predominant sound. The engine is sufficiently powerful to draw several cars, but at present it is considered sufficient in crowded thorough-fares to draw one car only until the public and the horses have become familiar with its working. The engine on the Glasgow line has only been at work for a short time; it is, however, reported to be running very successfully. Its trials have been attended by tramway engineers from Edinburgh, Leeds, Batley, and other towns, and while running at a speed of 15 miles an hour it was stopped in two seconds. The engine is fitted with all the arrangements prescribed by the Board of Trade regulations, some of which requires that it shall have a self-acting, shut-off brake, which controls the speed within a certain fixed limit. By this means it is out of the driver's power to propel it at a higher speed than is permitted by the authorities. The engine is also fitted with a speed indicator and an adjustment by which it catches up any one who may perchance fall across its track. The engine on Ryde pier is in all respects similar to the one just described. In Paris there are 15 of these engines working, and Messrs Merryweather have a large number building for the same lines, for which purpose they have had to start a large factory at Greenwich. The annual saving in Paris in working each car by steam, as against horse-worked cars, is stated to be £300 per annum. The advantage of the steam-worked car over those drawn by horses are increased speed of travel-ling (if desired), quicker starting and stopping than with horses, quicker connecting and discon-necting from the car, a shorter length of space occupied on the roadway, and capability of being used in all weathers, especially when frost and snow render it impossible for horses to draw the tram cars. It is stated to have been fully proved during the past 12 months of working that when-ever these engines have been running the horses have never been affected by them; they pass them unnoticed. As the supposed fright to horses has hitherto been the chief stumbling-block in the way of the use of steam on tramways, it is to be hoped that this prejudice is in a fair way of being overcome. Our ponderous steam road rollers, with their puffing and crushing noises, should be excellent tutors to horseflesh to say nothing of the locomotives constantly shrieking and thundering over the iron railway bridges in the very heart of the Metropolis."

Merryweather, as a firm, could trace their

STEAM TRAMWAYS – On the occasion of their visit to the Wimbledon Camp on Tuesday last, the Prince and Princess of Wales, quitting their barouche near the umbrella tent, entered one of the cars on the camp tramway drawn by Messrs Merryweather and Sons' noiseless tramway locomotive, and proceeded to the further end of the grounds, accompanied by several members of the Council, all expressing themselves very pleased with the arrangement.
Engineering, 21 July 1882.

ancestry right back to 1690 when Nathaniel Hadley set up his works in Cross Street, Greenwich, London. In 1836 Moses Merryweather absorbed the business which by now was located in Bow Street. In due course, probably from the mid-1860s the company – or partnership – was known as Merryweather and Field; the Field side specialised in boilers with the ability to produce steam at great speed – it was of little use in the event of a fire to expect the householder to wait three or four hours for steam to be raised in the pump's boiler.

But the company's first foray into the world of tram building was relatively unsuccessful, the two vertical boilers provided for John Grantham's combined car in 1872 and which contained hanging water-tubes with internal circulating tubes – the classic Field flash boiler, were really too small (18"/457mm diameter, 52"/1321mm high and tiny firegrates of 15"/381mm diameter) with their low boiler pressure (90psi) to maintain steam to feed the 4" x 10" (107 x 254mm) cylinders of the horizontal engine. To make matters worse, 30" wheels had been specified, presumably to improve ground clearance for the underslung power unit and it was not until the car was tried out on the Wantage system that solutions were found, a single Shand, Mason water-tube boiler offset to one side being substituted for the pair of Merryweathers, while the wheel diameter was reduced to 24" (610mm). In fairness to the manufacturer it has to be said that the vehicle was quite hefty (27' 3" long 6' 6" wide, 11' 1" high/8.31m x 1.98m x 3.38m) having an unladen weight of 6½ tons; another, larger, variant was completed later either by Merryweather or Shand, Mason, or a collaboration of both, for use in Vienna in 1876.

This had learned lessons from its predecessor, and had 6" x 9" (152 x 229mm) cylinders and driving wheels 24" from the outset. Other dimensions were similar although it seems its Achilles Heel lay in its low water capacity even on relatively short tramway journeys. The Wiener Tramwaygesellschaft had three routes totalling 8.06 miles (12.9km) and seemed to have been somewhat unsuccessful in their choice of steam motive power units, especially as their tracks were only designed for horse tram usage, the first being a tiny Merryweather engine of 1874, w/no.2, probably that used on the Ryde Pier experiments, (see Vol 4) the "Grantham" car of 1876 and a tiny Henschel engine, w/no.974, of 1878 named "Cassel". The tramway company ceased their experiments that year and waited for electricity! The other Viennese companies were more successful but did not enter the steam world until it was proven successful in the 1880s.

In 1876 in order to cope with the demand for steam tramway engines while still being able to manufacture their fire appliances and ancillary equipments, Merryweather moved from their old works at Lambeth (which duly closed in 1879) to the new Light Locomotive Works in Greenwich High Road, where they remained until the second world war.

Particularly in Scandinavia there was something of a vogue for "Rowan" cars which, in essence, were Mk.II Granthams. Kitson built a few, but most came from the German firm of Borsig. However, and it is only right to add there is some dispute over how much of the machine actually came from Merryweather, there is no doubt they provided the power unit for one machine in the Rowan 'family' which was delivered to Copenhagen in 1875. This had a six horse-power engine with cylinders 5" x 9" (127mm x 229mm) attached to which, and articulated from, was a single deck 30-seat saloon car built by the Scandia Company. This ran on Copenhagen tramways until 1879 when the body was converted to a horse-tram trailer. In 1902 it found itself being towed behind electric cars, not being scrapped until 1933. Presumably the power unit was broken up.

The Viennese car had been forwarded to the concessionnaire, G.P. Harding, and he then (1875) approached Merryweather for a supply of tramcars for his other set of tramlines, the southern Paris route operated by the Compagnie des Tramways de Paris – Reseau Sud, the two steam operated lines being Place de la Bastille to Gare de Montparnesse (3.31m/5.3km) and Gare d'Orleans to Ville Juif (5.44m/8.7km), although others were tried experimentally to St. Germain and Place Valhubert.

In all 46 Merryweather engines were to be built for this service, although there was some delay as the Greenwich works got into full production – this, at maximum, being one engine per week. As well as the Merryweather engines there were a dozen of 2-4-0 configuration from Fox Walker of Bristol 1877/8 and another dozen from Falcon (w/nos. 19-30) in 1879.

Before covering the technical aspects of the Paris engines – and they were extremely interesting for the period, we can give their obituary as written in *The Engineer*, 9 June 1882:

"MECHANICAL POWER ON PARIS TRAMWAYS.

Those who have had most experience in the use of steam on the Paris tramways are perhaps least surprised that after about five years' trial the system has been abandoned, and a return to horse-power has been decided upon. It is not too much to say that the design of a tramway locomotive for working in the streets of a city presents more difficult points than the design of any other class of engine, and hence the really satisfactory tramway engine has yet to be made. The objections that are now made to the engines about to be entirely superseded by horses are numerous, and some are equally to be applied to tramcars hauled in any way, but the real objection to these engines has been the cost of maintenance and working, and the comparative frequency of stoppage by reason of breakdowns, of small or great importance. The Paris company has tried twenty-one different engines, and the results are that horse traction is on the whole more satisfactory to the company. This will probably be felt as a blow to mechanical propulsion, and no doubt it will have a retarding effect, but the various causes of failure and the experience gained will form the basis upon which engineers must start anew to make an engine that will stand the abnormal wear due to bad permanent way, dust, mud, frequent stoppages, and very short curves, and that can be run without danger by one man. We have several times given some ideas on the construction of tramway locomotives, and until engines are made with parts and fittings that will be indifferent to dirt and mud, very bad permanent way and short curves, no success will be achieved."

The first engine sent out to Paris was unashamedly an experimental job, w/no.3, fleet no.1 of 1875. One of only two with vertical boilers it was a rather sweet little thing and must have amused Pernod drinkers at the Gare very greatly. It weighed no more than two tons, was 5' 3" long over extremities, 6' 6" wide and 11' 0" high (1.6m x 2.01m x 3.35m) and had the ubiquitous 5" x 9" cylinders. The boiler was similar to that used in Merryweather fire engines since 1861 and could raise steam to 90psi in 35 minutes from cold. Anyone passing by must have had an irresistible urge to pat the thing especially as 'Field' type boilers can give an occasional pant. The second sent to Paris was a rather better machine although still puny by later designs. The cylinders were larger at 6" in diameter and by 9" stroke and the motor was placed underfloor centrally between the axles, both of which in deference to the light horse tram rails were fitted with coil springs. Water was carried at one end, coke at the other, while waste steam was superheated by passing through the ashpan and firebox and hence to the chimney. Slightly longer and lower nonetheless the all-up weight doubled at 4 tons. This was nonetheless the last vertical boilered steam tram built by Merryweather, although as late as 1907 a steam inspection locomotive for Buenos Aires retained this manner of working. The problem the company (and presumably Mr Harding) found with these vertical boilers was that they were too sensitive in ordinary use on rough horse-tram tracks, but this may not have been helped by the arrangement for eliminating safety-valve steam whereby a pipe led down to the uptake, so that as the excess steam tried to escape, the surface of the fire was deadened and the production of steam arrested. So there we are, a tiny little engine with little steam in reserve, with two horse trams and 70 passengers in tow ready to climb away and the valves blow off, the fire dies and pressure falls away. One can imagine the 'pshaw' and 'drat' of the Parisien engine driver!

According to Nicholas Watts writing in 1878 another problem followed this method of superheating steam – "in foggy or damp weather the engine is described as showing a continuous volume of steam out of the funnel while the discharge of 'blacks' produced by discharging steam into the fire is stated as objectionable". One guesses passers-by would add 'zut' and 'alors' to the drivers' mutterings. The final evolution of the Paris trams seem to have been, logically, the largest, Merryweather's type 4 (w/nos.51-60 of 1877, fleet nos.37-46) and it is as well at this juncture to show the basic six types that the company offered:

Type No.	Cylinders Bore x Stroke Inches	Millimetres	Weight empty Approx (tons)
1	6 x 9	152 x 229	4
2	6½ x10	165 x 254	5
3	7 x11	178 x 279	6½
4	7½ x12	191 x 305	7½
5	8½ x14	216 x 356	8½
6	10 x14	254 x 356	9½

Merryweather's entries into the export market seem to have met with mixed fortunes – for example w/nos. 33-37 in 1877 and 81 of 1878 were supplied to Cassel where services under the aegis of a British company commenced on 9 July 1877 running between Cassel (Königsplatz) and the Wilhelmshöhe Park, some 3½ miles (5.6km). Passenger vehicles were also British with single deckers from Starbuck of Liverpool. The Stock Exchange Year Book of 1881 reads, bleakly "1880. Cassel Tramways Company Limited – In Liquidation". A German company, Casseler Strassenbahn Gesellschaft took over seamlessly in 1881, steam remaining in use until 1899 when the line was electrified. Further engines, though, came from Henschel and SLM.

Prior to this a number of the Parisien engines had been transferred to Rouen together with a batch of Fox Walker's best and Kitsons w/no.T3 (2377). Operation involved another concession to Palmer Harding and two separate companies, the Compagnie des Tramways de Rouen the bulk of whose capital of 3,742,500 francs in 500 franc shares (plus 4½% 'obligations' of 836,000 francs) was held by the Tramways Company of France Limited who, in turn, had a capital of £142,480 in £10 shares and 6% debentures totalling £15,000. The Rouen company paid 1.6% in 1882 (its best year) but the London company managed 1⅛% that year. Each company seems to have paid ½% in 1888 and then nothing. By 1884 Rouen had reverted to horse traction on their 10¼ miles (16.4km) of routes, electrification arriving in 1896 probably to the relief of the directors running, and losing money on this unfortunate concern.

One quite remarkably successful foray by Merryweather was to Holland, and more particularly, the Nederlandsche Rhijnspoorweg Maatschappij (Dutch Rhenish Railway) who not only bought early Type 3 standard gauge Merryweather engines but came back for more in 1892, giving them a total of 19 for their line from 's Gravenhage to Scheveningen which remained steam hauled until 1924.

An engine which did not gain any partners from Merryweather and whose usage remained unique was w/no.32, a Type 1 supplied to the National Rifle Range in 1877 as their No.1 for use on Wimbledon Common. The N.R.A was set up to provide a summer camp for the Yeomanry, the arrangement from its inception in 1864 being that the trackwork, passenger vehicles initially horse-powered operated were laid to the rear of the firing ranges, but in 1878 it was extended to the NRA office giving an overall length of about one mile, although by 1886 this had been varied and was no more than 1,000 yards long overall. The rails used weighed 14lb/yard (6.926kg/m) and there were at least half a dozen passenger vehicles which were initially fitted with back-to-back (dos-à-dos) seating, later some were modified and enclosed or renewed – our illustration shows transverse, toastrack, seating. Up to six vehicles were towed by the engine as required.

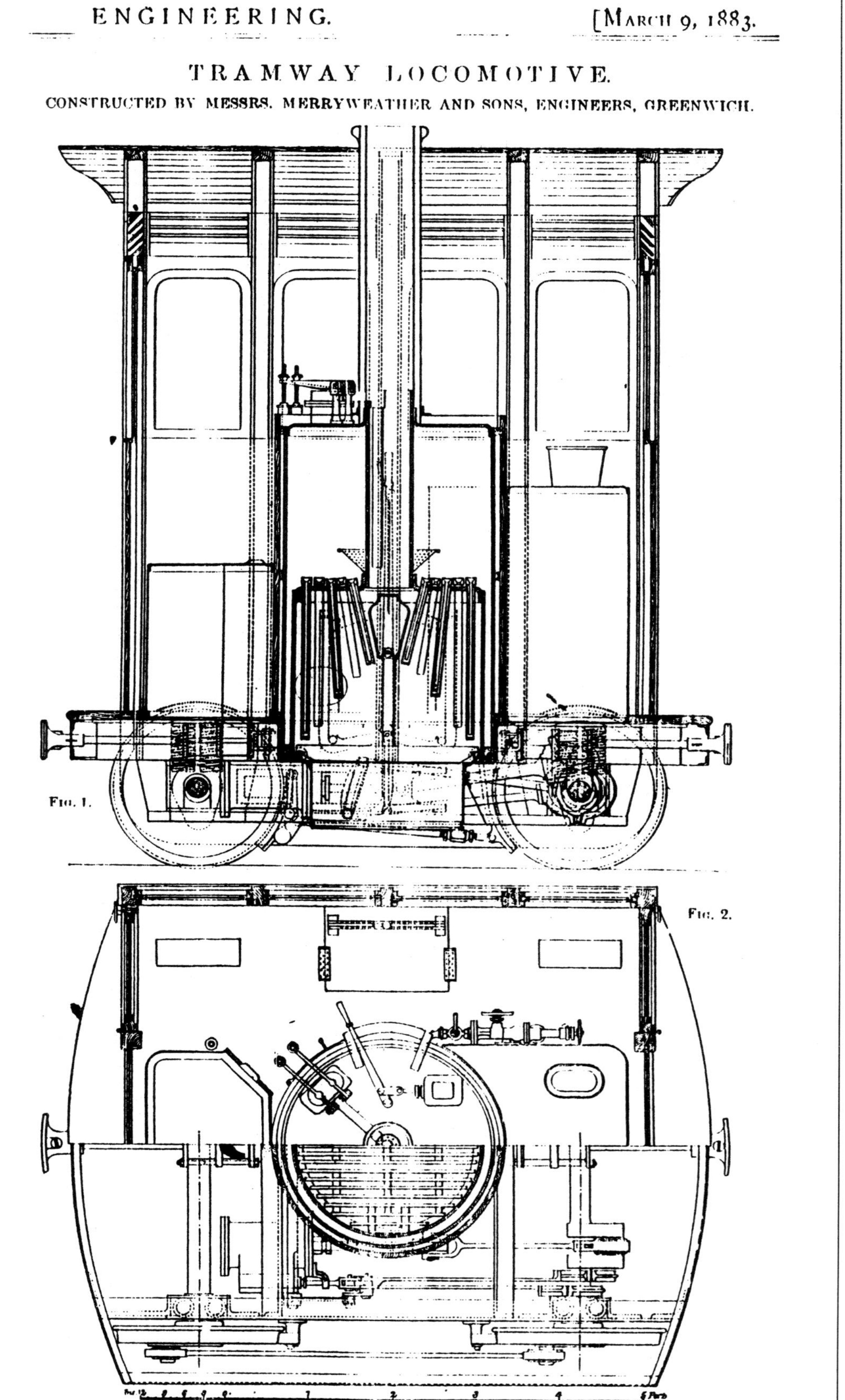

81. Merryweather works no.4 showing the vertical 'Field' boiler. Twin 6" x 9" (152 x 229 mm) cylinders placed horizontally (unlike Wilkinson's vertical fittings) drove one axle, the other being powered by orthodox connecting rods. Unlike Wilkinson's gear drive, Merryweather were at least able to fit springs to this sub-4 ton rather toy-like engine.

Initially loaned, the engine was purchased in 1878 and it was said by Major Edmond St. John Mildmay, the Secretary of the N.R.A. "the experiment made with the little traction engine was most successful and the Executive Committee have much pleasure in testifying to the zeal with which the persons in charge worked, and to their courtesy towards the numerous visitors who were all day crowding around the engine". In this context one should add the service was open to all members of the public for a small fare, and believed to be 2d return. Despite an attempt at electrification the engine may well have run at Bisley after the

N.R.A. moved there in 1890 and could have been extant as late as 1914. Its longevity was easily explained for at Wimbledon every year at the end of the annual meeting everything, track, carriages, and the engine were carefully packed up and after greasing etc., were stored until the following year. Named "The Wharncliffe" after the then chairman of the N.R.A. Council, perhaps somewhere in an army camp an elderly, well preserved, Merryweather tram engine may be waiting discovery!

Moving back to more serious matters. In Britain the Dewsbury, Batley and Birstall Tramways Company bought five tram engines in 1879-80, following this with a further four in 1887. A rather odd reading of Board of Trade regulations led to some difficulties, details of which will be given in Vol.2, Chapter 6, but basically it was to the advantage of Merryweather. The first engine, a Type 2, was supplied in 1879 but it was not until 10 April 1880, when following ratification of the Board of Trade Byelaws governing the use of steam on public highways that a mixed steam and horse drawn service began between Dewsbury and Birstall via Batley, some 3.325 miles (5.32km) which represented the first regular use of a steam tram on England's roads. In 1880 four further engines were supplied (fleet nos. 2-5) and the following year w/nos. 117-120 (fleet nos. 6-9) arrived thus eliminating horse haulage. The twist in this particular saga lay in the machinations of the Batley Borough Council's engineer who insisted on his right to examine all new engines to ensure they were identical to the one he (and B.O.T. Inspector) had agreed to. Presumably he had gone by the time the last two (probably second-hand) engines arrived in 1898 as they were two of Merryweather's larger type 4 with 7½" x 12" cylinders and 2' 4" (711mm) wheels rather than the original 6½" x 10" cylinders and 2' 2" (660mm) wheels. They all remained until electrification and were probably not scrapped until 1905/6.

Perhaps rather surprisingly, given that the

82. National Rifle Association's Wimbledon Common Tramway. 'Wharncliffe' Merryweather engine no.32 of 1877 was the motive power used on the occasion of the Royal visit. It is seen on a London and South Western Railway 'low-flat' probably en route from maintenance work.

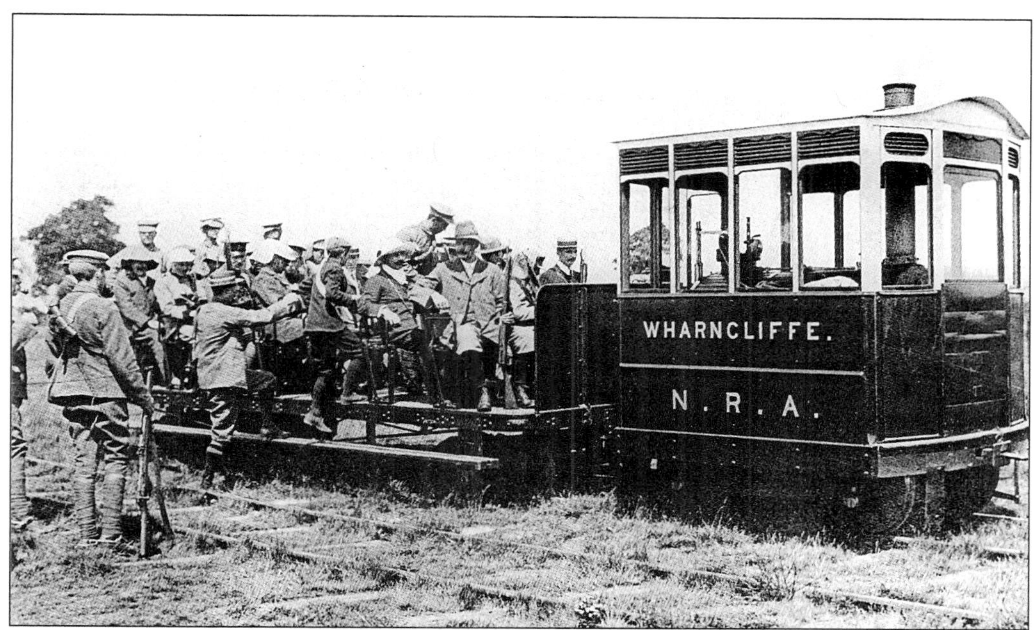

83. National Rifle Association. The one locomotive, Merryweather works no.32, is seen at Bisley c.1912.

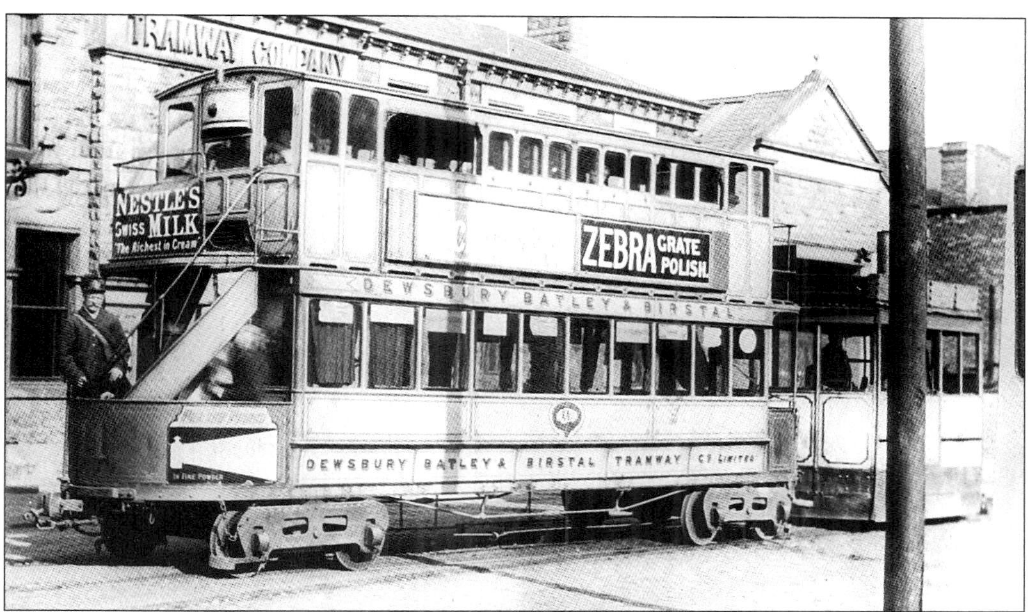

84. Although not a clear photograph of the Merryweather engine, it is an excellent illustration of a standard gauge top-covered 1886 Ashbury trailer. The location is Carlinghow Depot at Batley along their line from Dewsbury to Gomersal.

85. Two engines of type 3 were supplied to Guernsey in 1879 where they operated on an awkward tightly radiused and hilly route between St. Peter Port and St. Sampson. A heterogeneous mixture of rolling stock was owned with some degree of freight work. The story of this long-lost tramway will be told later in this series.

hills around Dewsbury could make anyone's eyes water, two cars supplied to the North Staffs Company, w/no.113 (Type 4) and 114 (Type 5) in 1881 were quite unsuccessful on the Potteries hills as our ingenious, if dishonest, chairman put it in December 1881:

"A SHAREHOLDER: You did not explain whether Merryweather's engines are condemned. THE CHAIRMAN: No, they are not condemned. In the case of the Stoke and Longton road there are some very severe gradients, and those engines are not sufficiently powerful for that line; the first two engines we had were not sufficiently powerful to work the traffic along that road. They did so for some time, and I dare say they are good engines for a certain purpose, but we have the opportunity of using them in another part of Stoke for a separate traffic. We have a branch, the London-road Branch, now being worked by horses, and we purpose to put these smaller engines on that road, so that they will be fully utilised and not put aside."

But he also placed his finger on what must have been Merryweather's sore spot, their inability despite a new factory to make enough machines. It has to be said that there were a couple of strikes over, I believe, piece-work at the time, but nonetheless failure to meet promised delivery times did not encourage further orders. J. Beattie, the Chairman of the North Staffordshire Tramways again: "We have also on hand two engines built by Messrs Merryweather, and two more are shortly expected; there has, however, been considerable delay in delivery of these engines, which has caused the company much inconvenience, and the directors will feel it their duty to enforce the penalties to which the builders are liable under their contract."

Later on he procrastinated when asked a question by another shareholder: "Then there was the question of the engines. He did not understand why the engineer should have any difficulty, as it was simply a mechanical question to find out the power required to haul certain weights up any particular gradients. It appeared that the engines would not haul the traffic. Was that not so? THE CHAIRMAN: It was partially so in the case of the two Merryweather engines."

Works nos. 132/3 both as Type 6 the largest 'standards' arrived in 1882 but were still less than successful.

One tramway where steam tram traction proved to be technically workable but ran into unbelievable opposition from the 'carriage classes' was on the North London line, and it is probably more accurate to reproduce a quotation from Engineering dated 30 January 1885 than to rely on local and hostile reports. "THE FIRST STEAM TRAM IN LONDON – Some little time since Messrs Merryweather and Sons had instructions to make seventeen of their steam tramway motors for the North London Tramways, and on Wednesday evening one of these engines was run over their lines from Edmonton to Stamford Hill and back. The engine is classed as one of their 'Economical'

86. Undoubtedly a North Staffs Tramways service as this location was used for other photographs, but is the engine from Merryweather? In outline it is correct, and the trailer appears to be a Starbuck 4-wheel creation. Clearly something exciting is happening!

87. The Stockton and District Tramways Co. operated two disconnected lines totalling 6¼ miles between 1881 and 1898. All their eight engines were from Merryweather (works nos. 121-126, 1881 and 138/9, 1883) and the trailers of which this is a typical example were all, with one exception, 4-wheel open-topped double-deck cars from Starbuck, being easily converted to horse haulage. No.6 (works no.126) on the Norton run is seen with the Manager regarding the photographers quite benignly.

88/89. Two excellent photographs of North London Tramways locomotives and trailers in numerical order of the former. The darker painted engine no.6 was works no. 147, and shining new, with no advertisements on the power car is no.10, works no.151, the 'Gold Medal' engine. The trailers, 10 and 17, were products of Milnes, Birkenhead, works. Opened in 1885 and technically successful, this was the only steam tramway to operate in London, and fell foul of the 'traps and barouches' people, closing in 1891.

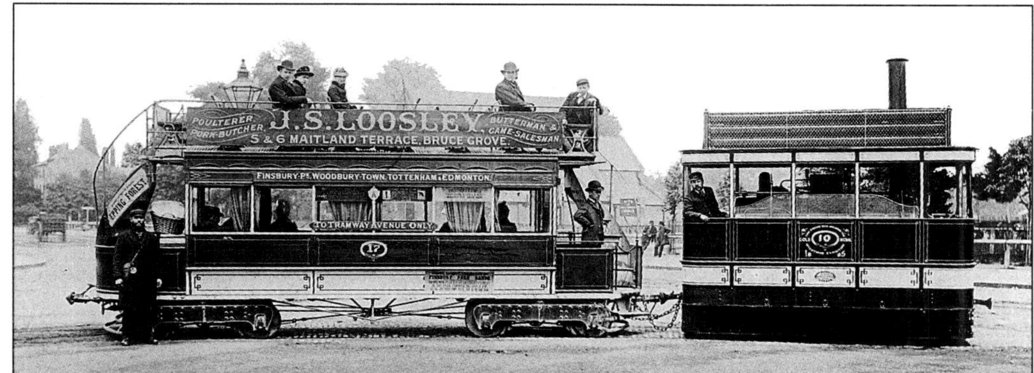

steam tram engines, having 7½" cylinders with 12" stroke. The road is very similar to those at Dewsbury and Stockton where steam traction is accomplished at something under 3d per mile, or, as has been conclusively shown during the past three years, at about half the cost of horse traction. The road is fairly level, but in parts there are gradients of 1 in 37 and 1 in 26. The engine is fitted with the Board of Trade requirements, and these work satisfactorily, neither vapour from the chimney nor steam from the engine showing in the least degree. The condenser with which the engine is fitted reduces the whole of the exhaust steam sufficiently so that it is returned to the boiler after passing through the feed cistern. The distance traversed was 9¼ miles in 80min., including stoppages, the temperature in feed tank at starting, being 80deg. Fahr. and at the end of the journey 140deg. The line will, within three weeks, it is expected, be running with these engines." In June 1891 the service ceased and reverted to horse traction.

It has to be admitted that steam trams were eventually only a small part of Merryweather's output despite their new factory, as steam pumping engines gradually gained ascendancy. Old type wooden manual fire engines were relatively easy for any competent workshop to build and prior to 1829 when Braithwaite and Ericsson invented the first steam pump a plethora of companies fought over the market. Merryweather introduced their first steamer in 1861, gaining the first prize at the Hyde Park Exhibition in 1863, thereafter virtually all steam pumpers coming from either Shand Mason or Merryweather, who by 1878 – the start of the tramway age – had built over 500. Somehow steam fire engines going at full gallop (they remained horse-drawn until 1899) with smoke

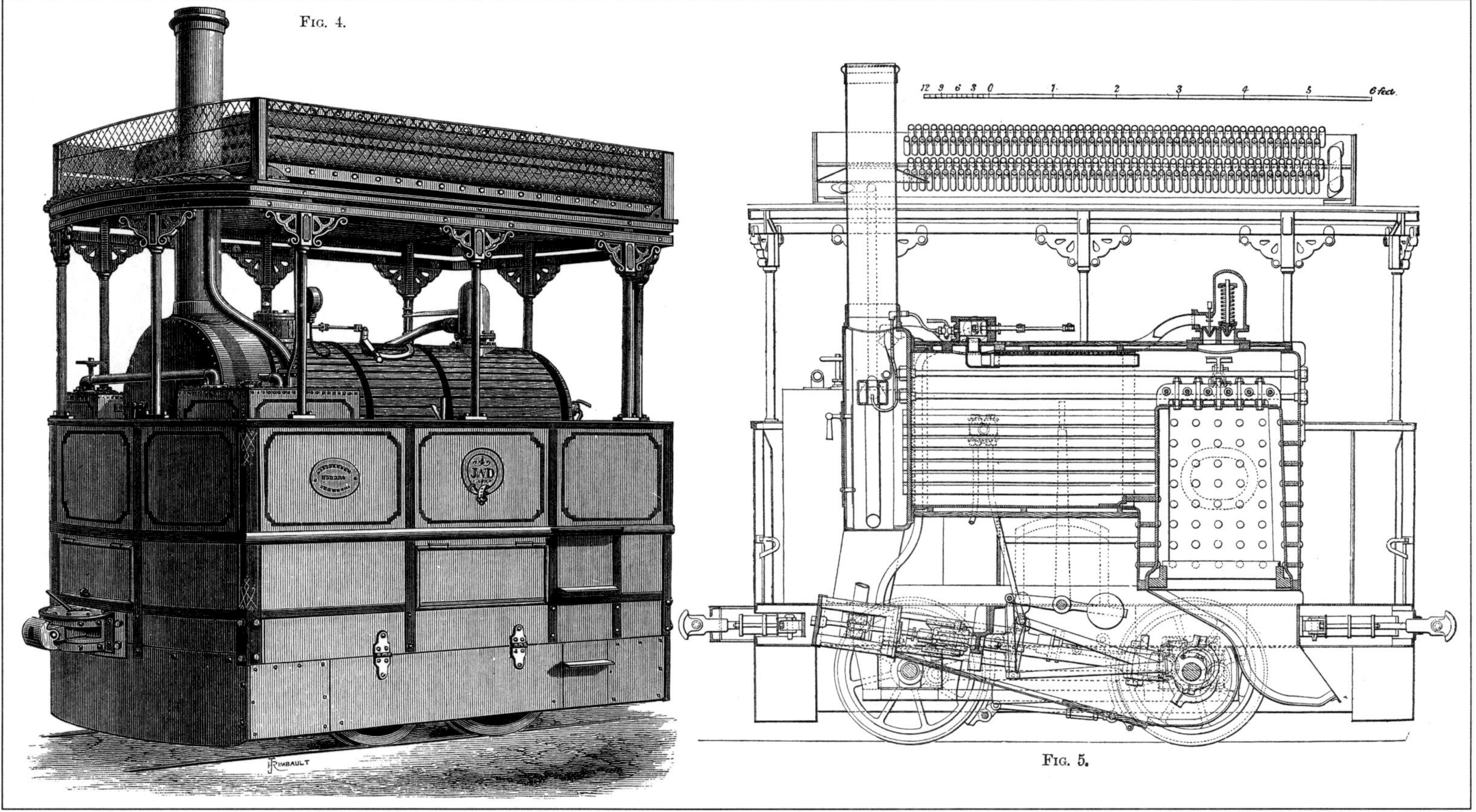

90. One of Merryweather's more successful exports was to Rangoon where they had works nos. 103-108, and 120 of 1882, plus 156-163 in 1885. The open sided but exquisitely finished cab typifies the conditions that were expected to be met. This drawing is from Engineering 16 March 1883, when the second batch "which have just been shipped to a new tramway in Rangoon. The necessary ironwork and machinery for the sheds and repairing shops have also been ordered of the same firm."

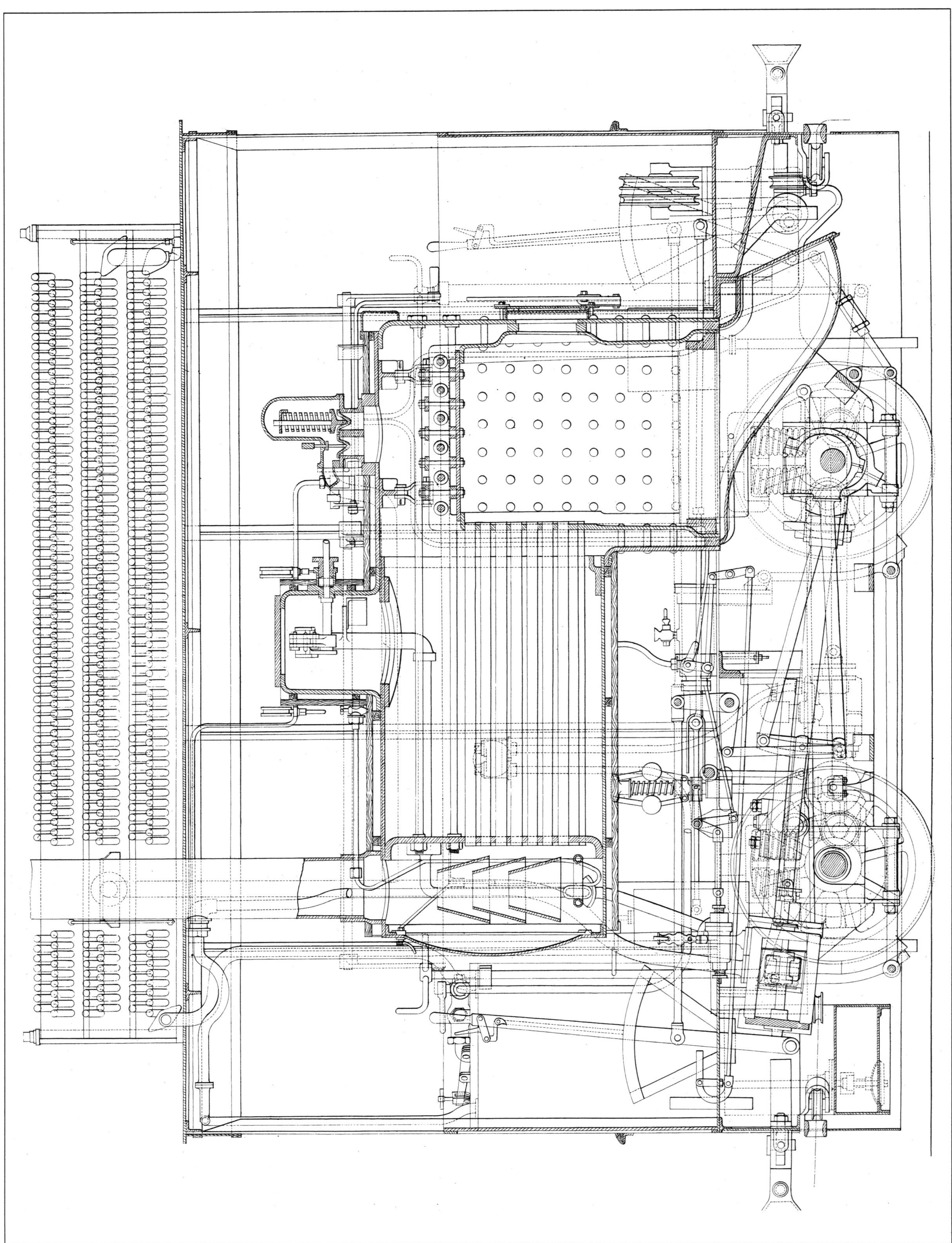

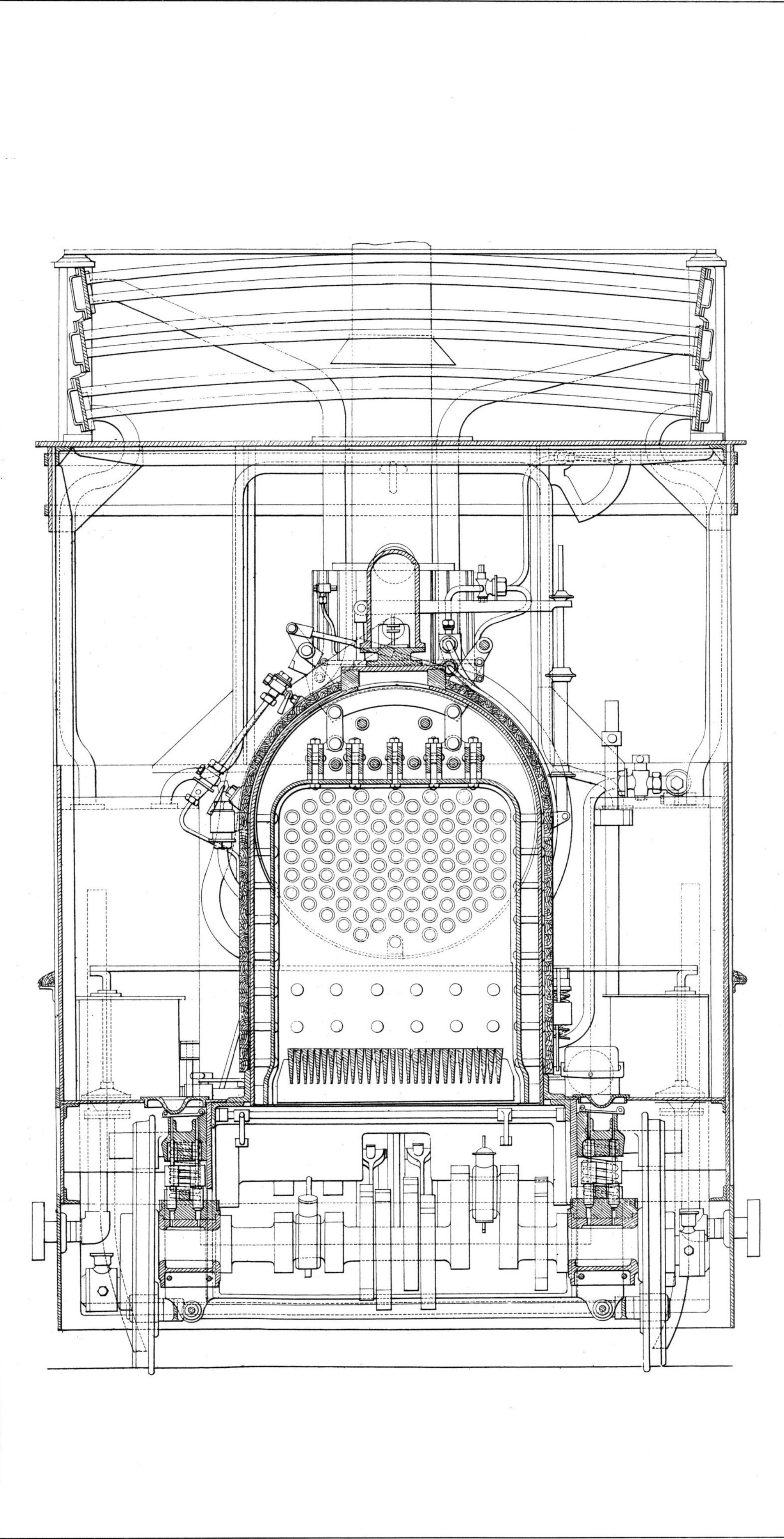

91. We have reproduced these two drawings (left and above) as large as possible mainly to show how intricate and ingenious tram engines were. British workmanship at its very best!

pouring from the funnel and the gleam of the crew's brass helmets reflected in the polished brass of the engine always caught the public's imagination more than the humdrum, if technically advanced, steam tramcar going about its business.

In 1892 with, probably, 174 engines built, Merryweather's ceased the manufacture of tram engines, those supplied to the Dewsbury, Batley & Burstal Steam Tram Company in 1898 being almost certainly two of the redundant North London machines. Perhaps this cessation was not unconnected with the formation of a new limited company (Merryweather and Sons, Ltd) on 22 March 1892 "which acquired the business of engineers of the firm of the same name". Shareholdings were interesting, out of an authorised capital of £110,200, £60,000 was in 6% preference (A) shares of £10, £200 in management (B) shares of £1 and £50,000 in ordinary (C) shares of £10. To show to what extent this was a paper manoeuvre £40,750 of the A, all the B and £45,350 worth of C were issued as "fully paid". Only one Merryweather, J.C., was on the Board of Directors, he bearing the old title of Governor. However, despite this and the last new trams being delivered early in 1892 (w/nos. 173/4) to the Dutch Rhenish Railway, nonetheless one notable survivor is w/no.110, No.2 in the Rijnlandsche Stoomtram Maatschappij, a Type 3 of 1881. Continuing in work until 1932, No.2 was laid aside due to the electrification of the Haarlem-Leiden line, but thriftilly the Dutch stored a number of engines at Roosendaal, where among other stock, it was damaged in 1944, some say by Allied bombing, others by retreating Germans, but somehow it survived to be happily and fully restored, even down to the polished mahogany strips lagging the boiler.

The engines for the ill-fated Lisbon Steam Tramways Company Limited, designed to run on the Larmanjat guide rail principle, were built by Sharp Stewart & Company Limited, Manchester, under w/nos. 2254-2255, 2270-2275 and 2286-2293. It is said not all were assembled and may not even have left Britain before the Company failed, although this does not agree with the engineer, Mr F.H.Trevithick's reports. Whatever the truth of it sixteen were built for around £1,500 each, but on a bankruptcy sale fetched, according to the magazine Iron 4 April 1884, only £150 per machine. The magazine continued, "The purchaser, having a market for contractors locomotives, handed them over to Merryweather's Steam Tramway Works at Greenwich, where the engines were remodelled at a cost of from £300 to £400 each, and they may now be found in full work at the Tilbury Docks and on the works of the H. & B. Railway". Unusual work for a versatile company but tram engine sales were already in decline and they may have had spare capacity. It does not appear that they routinely built other industrial locomotives.

Merryweather & Sons Ltd.

Works No.	Date	Type	Customer + No.
1	1872	-	Wantage Tramway 3
2	1874	-	Vienna via Mr G.P.Harding
3	1875	-	Paris Southern Tramway 1
4-8, 10-31	1876	-	Paris Southern Tramway 2-28
9	1876	-	Wantage Tramway
32	1877	1	N.R.A. Rifle Range ('Wharncliffe') 1
33-37	1877	4	Kassel Tramways 1-5
38-45	1877	-	Paris Southern Tramway 29-36
46-50	1877	3	Barcelona à San Andrés 1-5
51-60	1877	-	Paris Southern Tramways 37-46
61-68	1878	3	Wellington Tramways N.Z. 1-8
69-73	1878	3	Barcelona à San Andrés 6-10
		1 (x9)	Rouen Tramways
		3 (x1)	
74-79			-
80	1878	2	Adelaide Tramway
81	1878	4	Kassel Tramway
82	1878	3	Dutch Rhenish Rly 1
83	1878		Dunedin Tramways N.Z
84-85	1879	3	Guernsey Steam Tramway Co 1&2
86-87	1879	3	Wellington Tramways N.Z 9&10
88-93	1879	3	Dutch Rhenish Rly 2-4,6,7,5
94	1880	2	Dewsbury, Batley & Birstal Trys 1
95	1880		Oporto Tramways
96-100	1881		Dutch Rhenish Rly 8-12
	1881	2	Dewsbury, Batley & Birstal 2-5
101	1881	1	Calcutta Tramways 1
102	1881	3	Calcutta Tramways 2
103-108	1881	2	Rangoon Tramways 1-6
109-112	1881		Dublin & Lucan Tramway 1-4
113	1881	4	North Staffordshire Tramways Co 3
114	1881	5	North Staffordshire Tramways Co 4
115-119	1881		Dutch Rhenish Rly 13-17
120	1881	2	Rangoon Tramways 7
121-126	1881		Stockton & Darlington Steam Trys 1-6
127-130	1881		Dewsbury, Batley & Birstal Trys Co 6-9
131	1882		Rhineland Tramway Co. Holland 5
132-133	1882	6	North Staffordshire Tramways Co 3-4
134-137	1882	3	Barcelona à San Andrés 11-14
	1882	3	Barcelona à San Andrés 15
138-139	1883	3	Stockton & Darlington Steam Trys 7-8
140	1883	4	Alford & Sutton Tramway 2
141	1883		Sydney Tramways 55
142-155	1885		North London Tramways 1-14
156	1885	2	Rangoon Tramways 8-13,14,15
164-17	1885		North London Tramways 15-21
171-172	1885		North London Tramways
173-174	1892		Dutch Rhenish Rly 18-19

Type No.	Cylinders	Wheel Dia.	Approx. Weight Empty T	C	Tubes No.	Dia.	L	H/S	F'box H/S	Total H/S	Grate Area	Wheel base
1	6"x9"		4	0								
2	6½"x10"	2' 2"	5	0				146.56	26.85	173.41	3.66	4' 6"
3	7"x11"	2' 0"	6	10	78	1¾"	4'	139.0	20.75	159.75	4.25	4' 6"
4	7½"x12"	2' 4"	7	10	85	1¾"	4'					4' 6"
5	8½"x14"		8	10								
6	10"x14"		9	10								

Wm. Wilkinson & Co. Ltd. Holme House Foundry, Swinley, Wigan.

Over the years there have been a number of misconceptions regarding the location of the foundry. The site of the factory on the current Ordnance Survey maps is at SD 581 070 and if a hundred or so years ago we had stood in field no.317 adjacent to Swinley Lane at approximately nine o'clock there were the Gidlow and Swinley Collieries, at ten o'clock Holme house, with behind it Holme House Farm, and at eleven o'clock adjacent to fields 309 and 371 was Holme House Foundry, occupying about ½ acre. Continuing the clock picture between one and two o'clock was the Royal Albert Edward Infirmary in rather a curious juxtaposition! Three o'clock was occupied by a gravel pit and from there round to seven was a swathe of housing, plus a hotel and a monument!

The first entry in any existing directories appears in 1869 "Wilkinson, William, Ironfounder, Holme house foundry, house 27 Scarisbrick street", but by 1876 he was moving his family upmarket to Monument Terrace, 125 Wigan Lane, where he lived until at least 1888, then (1890) moving to Swinley Road, this address being still given at his last entry in 1898 by which time the trade entry was showing under ENGINEER – MECHANICAL – "Wilkinson Wm. & Co. Limited (T.Margeson, sec.) Holme House foundry, Swinley Lane, Wigan; T.N. [telephone number] 28, TA [Telegraphic address] Wilkinson, Engineer, Wigan."

It is perhaps rather unfortunate that a number of authors have sought to show Wilkinson as a man in a small way of business prior to his rather suddenly building steam trams, whereas recent researches (helped by more documents becoming accessible) show him to have been running a busy foundry employing, in 1871, ten men and ten boys, making primarily mining equipment including steam winding engines: a major factor in the provision of this type of gear was that it had to be reliable, a trait encouraged in him during his apprenticeship at the Haigh Foundry, an old established foundry and boilermaker which functioned between 1790 and 1884. On 4 February 1879 he converted his private company into a Limited Liability Company having an initial capital of £6,000 in £10 shares, the agreement being that Wilkinson would be appointed Managing Director at £250 per annum for not less than seven years, and that, inter alia, he was not to set up another similar business within 100 miles of the Foundry. He was also to be allotted £250 in shares deemed to be fully paid up.

Shareholders were more or less as one would expect in a town like Wigan including, as well as Wilkinson himself who had a total of 30 shares (25 + 5) – Albert Crossley, a clothier (60 shares); T. Taylor, a cashier (60 shares); Thomas Margeson, a cashier, who was to be the Company Secretary (38 shares); George Pollard, a tool dealer (20 shares) and a pair of boilermakers, said to be brothers but possibly father and son, Richard and Ralph Hough (60 and 1 respectively), who were to provide many of the boilers used by Wilkinson, not only for his trams, but also winding engines and marine motors.

Initially there can be little doubt Wilkinson was undercapitalised and on 9 February 1883 at the peak of his steam tram production the nominal capital of the firm was increased to £30,000, although no more than 1,500 of the £10 shares were issued, these only having £9 per share called up; however the new issue did more than double the company's capital to £13,500 – the problem being of course that the share dividends now required a larger sum of money per annum. Succinctly 5% on £6,000 = £300, whereas £13,500 required £675 which presumes either greater profit on normal work, difficult in a fiercely competitive market, or a far greater throughput, not easy if the premises cannot be expanded.

If we compare the shareholdings at three periods of the company's life, we can get some idea of how loyal the shareholders were and how initially they were prepared to sink money into a thriving tram-building concern, (all are of £10 nominal value). See table below.

Perhaps the most ominous line in the share register for 1898 reads "Wilkinson & Co. Ltd. 75 shares".

Eventually although the firm was still solvent, the shareholders forced the company into voluntary liquidation on 17 February 1899; winding up being completed on 14 November 1902.

However in 1880 this was far in the future. The following table [Based on a table in the late E.K.Stretch's *Tramways of Wigan* MTMS 1978] shows the rapid growth in the number of Wilkinson-type engines built and the equally rapid decline in orders. Some reservations exist over who exactly built what; for example both Wilkinson and Green are credited with three of the MBRO engines, it seems almost certain that MBRO fleet numbers 1-3, built by Wilkinson were re-built to such an extent by Thomas Green they were classified as new engines, and similarly No.4 in the Giant's Causeway fleet was probably not built at the Wilkinson works, but sub-contracted.

Conversely there is a mystery photograph showing a Dübs of Glasgow-built steam tram car with Wilkinson Patent plates as well as the manufacturer's plate, but this machine does not appear in Dübs works lists. There are other anomalies but, allowing for these possible corrections, the general pattern of orders still applies.

Of William Wilkinson patents four are relevant here, the first, No.4268 left with the Commissioner of Patents on 1 October 1881, is rather a portmanteau job and is also the most important. Made out to William Wilkinson, of Wigan, in the County of Lancaster, Mechanical Engineer (but not to his company) it is entitled "Improvements in Traction Engines for Tram Cars and Other Purposes" part of the preamble shows his thinking:

"My Invention relates to a combination of mechanical contrivances whereby the engine is rendered most effective, and in particular free from noise by blast, emission of visible steam from chimney or safety valves or cylinders, and clatter of machinery, and whereby the working parts of the engines shall be free from road dirt or other debris which may cause undue wear and tear, the engine as a whole machine being made to comply with the regulations of the Board of Trade. The locomotive consists of a vertical boiler fitted with what are known as 'Field's patent tubes' and other appliances hereinafter mentioned. The engine consists of two inverted direct vertical cylinders driving two cranks at right angles to each other, the crank shaft being rigidly attached to the framing of the engine and fitted with a wrought iron spur wheel gearing into a second spur wheel keyed on the driving axles, on which are also keyed the driving wheels to run on the tram rails, and which wheels are both in turn coupled to the trailing or leading wheels, or to both if required. By this method of connection of engines to driving wheels I obviate the 'galloping' or jumping action of the engine on the road that would otherwise take place if the engines were attached direct to the driving wheel axle without the intervention of spur wheel gearing ... A governor is employed, preferably of the class known as 'Allen's paddle governor' to reverse the valve gear, and to apply the breaks when a speed is attained higher than what is allowed by the authorities; this is effected by means of an eccentric cam and lever motion which opens a valve against the pressure of the boiler, thereby allowing the water of steam from the boiler to pass to the under-side of a piston or hydraulic ram which is in direct connection with the reversing shaft and also with the break shaft, reversing the engines and applying the brake at one and the same time. By this means the governor acts as an automatic brake in accordance with the Board of Trade regulations." [The variation in the spelling of break/brake is as written in the original, similarly each cylinder is counted as an 'engine', thus twin-cylinder = 'engines'.]

NUMBER OF WILKINSON PATTERN LOCOMOTIVES BUILT

	Wilkinson	Black Hawthorn	Beyer Peacock	Green	Total
1881	1				1
1882	9			2	11
1883	38	10	20	22	90
1884	5	6	25	14	50
1885	3	13	1		17
1886	6	1	25		32
1888		2			2
1896	1				1
TOTALS	**63**	**32**	**71**	**38**	**204**

92. This locomotive is at least built under Wilkinson patents and to his designs. South Staffs no.12 is seen with another, Kitson, engine and their trailers at a reversing 'wye'. I am not certain where this is, but I suspect near Burnt Tree Island (Dudley) would not be too far out. Photograph dated 1898.

NAME	OCCUPATION	SHARES HELD 1879	1888	1898
S. Melling	Forge Master	60	347	330
T. Taylor	Cashier	60	150	
later S. Taylor	Confectioner			143
A.H. Crossley	Clothier	60	300	
Richard Hough	Boiler Maker	60	93	88
Ralph Hough	Boiler Maker	1	1	1
W. Maynard	Cashier	10		
William Wilkinson	Engineer	30	245	233
George Pollard	Tool Dealer	20	114	108
E.H. Crippin	Colliery Proprietor	50		
T. Margeson	Cashier & Company Secretary	38	38	36
J. Marsden	Clothier		212	201
J.D. Murray	Merchant			285

Unless one day someone unearths his diary we shall never know how much time was spent working on Wilkinson's first tram; there must have been failures along the way, but the engine No.1 seems to have been complete around late Spring or early Summer 1881.

A rather tiny 5½ ton machine (although far heavier and more robust than, say, Merryweather's little 2-tonner), cylinder dimensions were quite puny at 6" x 7" (152 x 178mm) driving wheels 2" 3" (686 mm) – a dimension Wilkinson was to adhere to for most of his tram engines, narrow 3' 6" (1067 mm) gauge, it was supposed to be kept deliberately light to allow for its running on the horse-tram rails in Wigan. He was certainly quick off the mark as it was not until May 1881 that the Wigan Tramways Company Ltd., approached the local authorities to allow the use of steam (the local gradients were quite literally killing the tram horses) and

93. A very typical Wilkinson engine, probably in the fleet nos.4-8 range of those owned by the Manchester, Bury, Rochdale and Oldham Steam Tramways Co., dwarfed by its Starbuck trailer, itself a conversion from an odd 6-wheel design. Modellers may like to note the odd wheelsets; there is a precedent for everything somewhere!

only in July that they were authorised to use for one month, although not for passenger carrying, a steam engine built by Wilkinson (but no other). The final delivery date is uncertain but this little single ended unit was certainly demonstrated on 5 November 1881 to those Very Important People, the local councillors, from Adam's Bridge to Lamberhead Green on the Pemberton line.

On 7 February 1882 Major-General Hutchinson approved the use of No.1 for the completed lines of the Wigan network but the company had to lay in reversing triangles at Market Place, Wigan and Chapel Street, Pemberton, as the driver always had to be at the leading end of the cavalcade.

Three more engines (2-4 in the fleet) arrived in June and July; we do not know whether Wilkinson was too busy with other work to concentrate on the trams or whether operation of No.1 had thrown up a number of faults needing correction, but the delay was certainly there. These three, incidentally, were still single ended but had slightly larger cylinders at 6½" x 7".

94. A spectacularly clear photograph well over 100 years old, illustrating a pure-bred Wilkinson tram engine, albeit one coupled to a trailer showing decades of wear; even the sign-written advertisements have faded. Engine no.5, works no.52, had led quite an adventurous life, being supplied to the Brighton District Tramways Co in 1884 as their no.1; it and no.2 which were probably on (unpaid) hire-purchase, were returned to Wilkinson around 1888. After their rebuilding he was fortunate that the Wigan tramways had been taken over by the Corporation who needed new, or newish, engines.

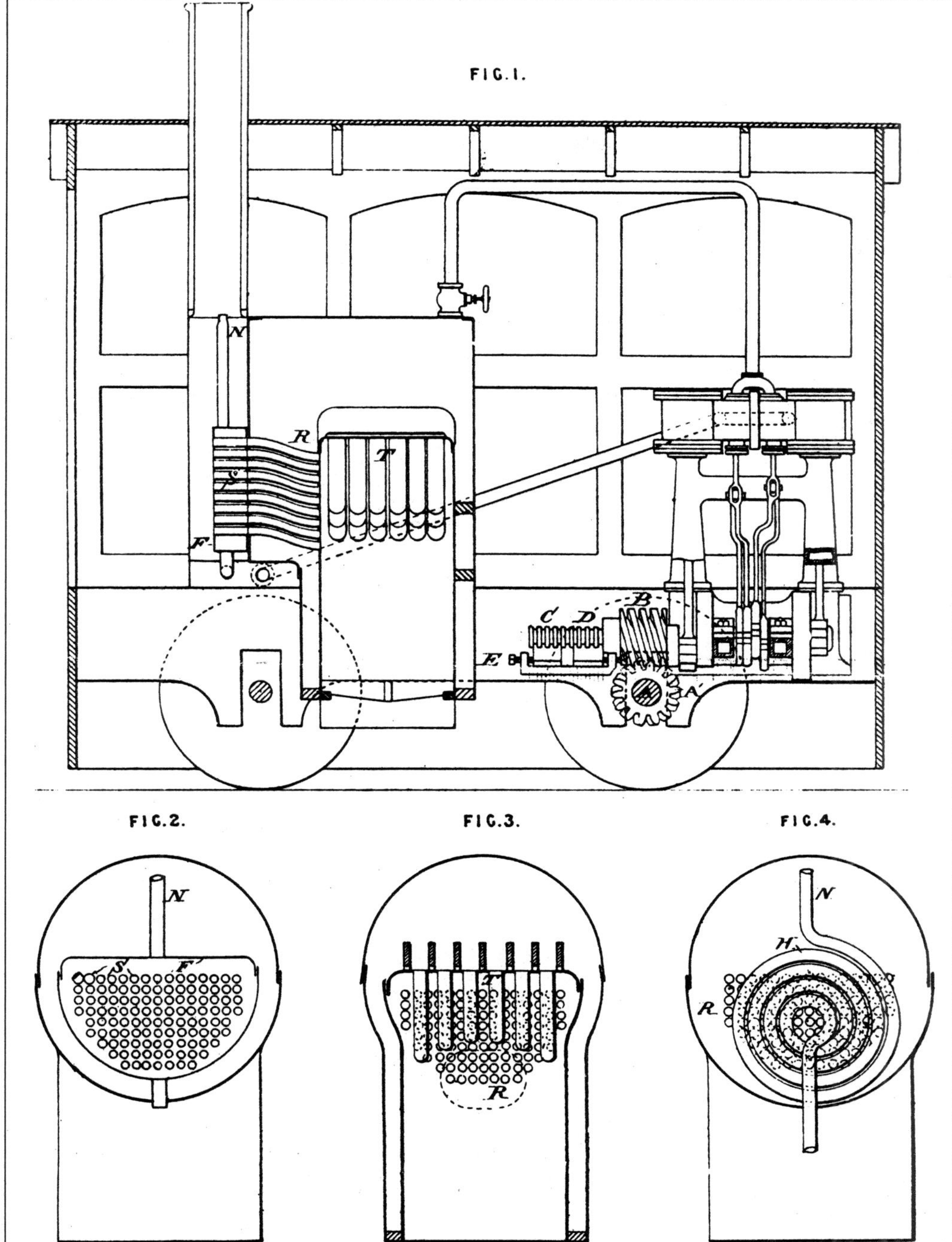

95. ***"...in his next Patent, No. 5560, 28 November 1883, William tried to overcome this by changing his final drive..."***

After Nos. 1-4 cylinder dimensions of 7" x 9" (178 x 229mm) with a commensurate increase in weight were to be adopted for the next 32 engines which went to operators as diverse as Huddersfield (2), Nottingham (their one and only steam tram), the MBRO (8, plus another 8 with 6½" x 9" cylinders), Birmingham & Aston (2, laid aside very quickly), South Staffs (2), and Giant's Causeway (2), plus probably Plymouth, Devonport & District (2), plus another 4 for Wigan.

Early days on the lines of the Manchester, Bury, Rochdale & Oldham Steam Tram Company (MBRO) were fraught with difficulties for the Wilkinson engines. One can imagine the excitement when the first trams began to run on 10 March 1883 from Bury some six miles to Kersal Bar. Unfortunately all the cars were fully loaded on that and subsequent days, the all-up weight of four tons totally winding the engines (possibly not helped by ill-trained enginemen) to the point where delays of two hours (on a six mile journey) were being reported – the trams having to try to rush the short steep gradient over Blackford Bridge. Even tactics like waiting for the next engine to arrive, its driver unhooking his car and acting as a banker by pushing from behind were tried, almost certainly doomed to failure as the passengers all tried to climb on the leading car, make it even more overloaded! The opening of the Rochdale lines in May 1883 made matters worse as the climb of 5% (1:20) up Drake Street led to ignominious sight of a loaded trailer pulling a vaguely protesting engine backwards. Small wonder fires clinkered from coke residue, steam wreathed the cars and the pyrotechnics from the chimney were noted in the newspapers!

The first three engines as supplied were totally enclosed with three glass windows on each side, but when they returned from Green's after rebuilding the cab sides and windows had gone to be replaced by an almost open cab, only sheet steel panels hiding the new, larger boiler. The sad part of this expensive interlude (and I wonder were Wilkinsons ever paid for their engines and if so who paid Green?) is that the geared drive gave excellent acceleration and hill climbing ability when properly matched to the anticipated trailers' weight. Later arrivals on to the MBRO were fleet nos. 35-38, still supplied in 1883 they were to be the first 'heavy' Wilkinson engines with larger boilers and 7½" x 11" (191 x 179mm) cylinders and a weight of 9½ tons and were to prove very satisfactory.

One problem with the 'pure' Wilkinson engine regardless of the manufacture was that using gears which must be kept in mesh there was no way of springing the axles so in his next Patent, No. 5560, 28 November 1883, William tried to overcome this by changing his final drive to that of a worm and 'screw' having "a number of threads proportionate to the required power and speed, ... and the depth of the teeth and worm threads is proportionate to the amount of play required by the bearing springs of the

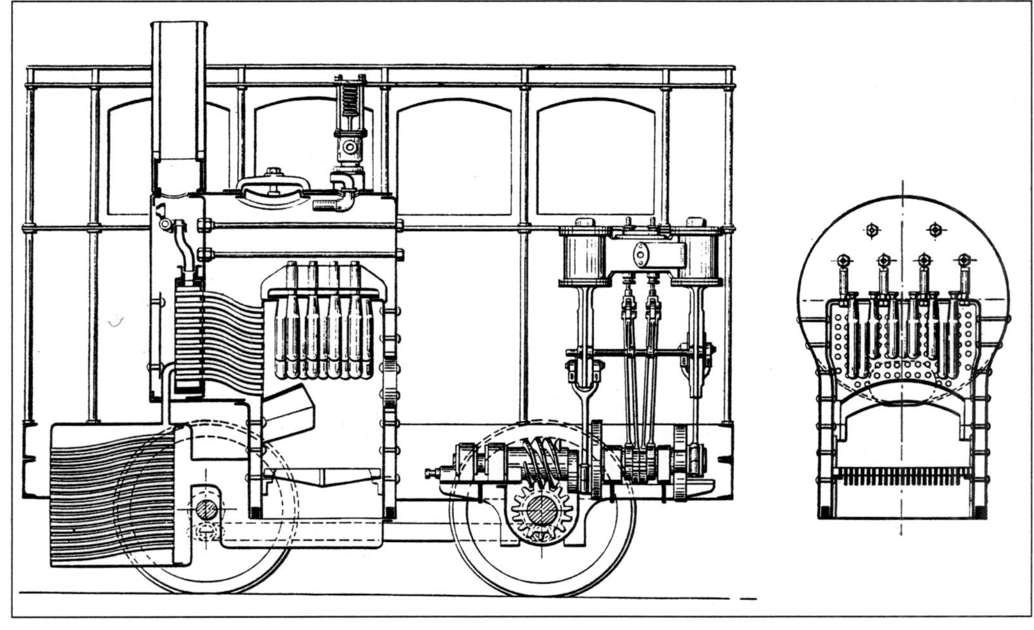

96. In their issue of 17 June 1955 The Engineer published and illustrated a retrospective look at various tram engines, including Wilkinson's worm-drive machine. This, apart from the patent drawing, is the only outline I have seen of Wigan Tramways No.9 works no.49. No steam drier/superheater was fitted, but an air-cooled condenser on the footplate kept the driver's feet warm. Delivered in 1884 it did little work, and was gone by 1886, when the 'proper' no.9 arrived.

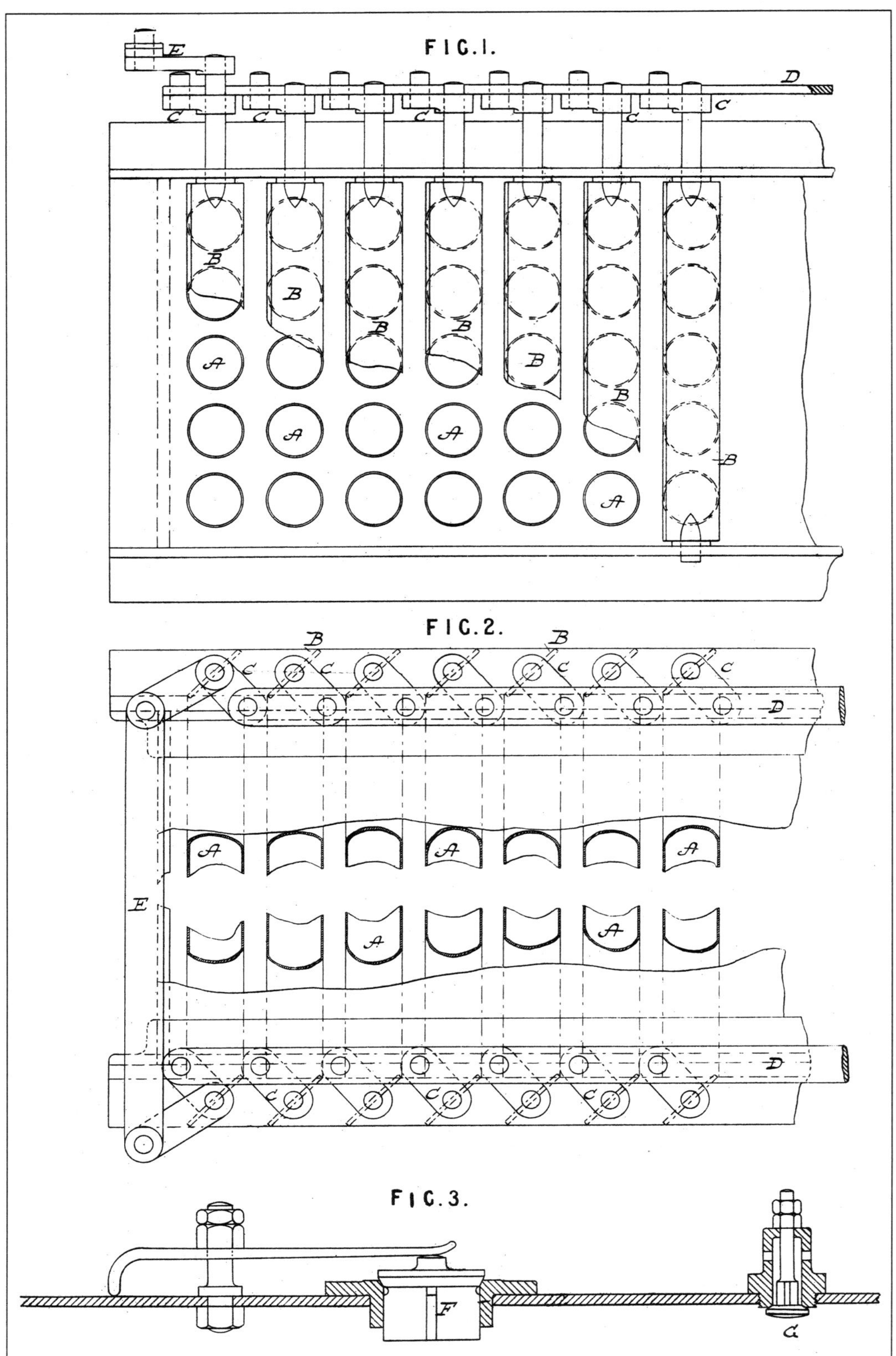

97. *"...as a tram engineer he had one last patent application to make which emerged as no.9955 dated 21 August 1885..."*

engine..." Adjustable blocks ensured that slap and backlash were eliminated. His boiler changed to the so-called 'pistol' type incorporating both vertical and horizontal tubes thus he proposed using a "locomotive type [boiler] with the ordinary firebox, but between each two stay girders on the fire box crown or roof I suspend a number of 'Field' tubes of suitable length vertically over the fire-bars ... I make the boiler tubes in the form of a reverse curve, to compensate for the extreme expansion or contraction, thereby obviating risk of leakage at the tube plates – so great in short tubed multitubular boilers." A further 'Improvement' involved a modified superheater.

Just one tram engine was built to this new specification which in 1884 became Wigan No.9. Strangely very tiny cylinders were fitted at 6¾" x 7" (171 x 178mm) – since no doubt any experimental has to be done on the cheap was he using a spare pair of cylinders from the first tramcars? Whether to compensate for the worm-drive gearing or not, the driving wheels were (relatively) gigantic at 3' 2" (965mm). How long it operated on the tramways of Wigan is not clear, but a new No. 9 appeared in April 1886 on the side of a standard 'heavy' Wilkinson machine.

In the meantime William Wilkinson's inventive mind was still clearly bubbling away and his next patent, 1773, 19 January 1884, might have offered one answer to the steam condensation problem. Something of the design was tried on Wigan No.9 and must have worked to some extent for him to go the bother and expense of patenting the plan. Conversely, the quotation below clearly shows the proposed location of his air condenser – and with experience of crowded footplates I can say that the engineman would have cursed the (wretched or xxxx) thing!

"My invention relates to certain improvements in apparatus for the condensing of steam and heating of the furnace supply draught to steam engine boilers, and is designed to secure a thorough current of cold air through the tubes of a surface condenser without abstracting any of the engine power for driving a fan or other mechanical draught-creating appliance, and at the same time to utilise the heat abstracted from the steam to raise the temperature of the air, which constitutes the furnace supply draught. My invention consists essentially in the combination of a surface condenser with the furnace supply draught and its operation thereby, and I effect this by placing a condensing chamber, traversed by numerous tubes (preferably of very thin section of metal) in front of the closed ash pan of the furnace, and, in the case of a locomotive engine with the mouths of the tubes preferably facing the direction of travel of the engine, which will to some extent aid the draught. These air tubes are in communication with the ash pan of the furnace by a suitable pipe or trunk. Consequently all the air drawn through the furnace bars, either by the natural draught or by a forced blast, is made to pass through the tubes of the condenser, and, abstracting the heat from the steam in the chamber, condenses same, and is itself raised in temperature by the heat so acquired in its passage before entering the furnace. By suitable pipes I lead into the condensing chamber the exhaust from the cylinders and discharge from the safety valve or other waste, and what steam remains uncondensed I lead to the chimney in the usual manner."

Although orders for tram engines to be built at his works dried up, as a tram engineer he had one last patent application to make which emerged as no.9955 dated 21 August 1885 and in it, I suppose, he admitted defeat for all his efforts at superheating, for this was an air cooled tubed roof condenser. On the roof he placed "a tank or casing with thin metal tubes running transversely through it from side to side, or longitudinally from end to end horizontally, the steam to be condensed being led into said casing surrounding the tubes, and the air for cooling flowing through the tubes in the same manner as the water in marine surface condensers. My invention applied more particularly to the following device, viz: To induce a current of air to flow through the tubes by the action of the wind, or in case there is no wind, by the motion of the condenser through the still air, I fix opposite each vertical row of tubes a metal screen, hereafter called a 'venetian' pivoted on centres and so placed as to be capable of being turned to any suitable angle relative to the axis of the tubes, and to be reversible at will."

The patent application then clarified the operation of his interlocked venetian blinds; although what is not stated is precisely who was to operate his "coupling rods and levers" – not, I think, the already overworked driver. And maintenance of any tishy bits of linkages, rods, levers, baffle plates and the rest was another no-no. Although four of the engines supplied to Wigan (fleet nos.9-12) were fitted with this device, it seems probable they were later converted to the Kitson type of condenser which was more successful and reliable; although this would not have been before 1890 at the earliest as prior to this, their sale being on hire purchase they bore rectangular plates reading "W.Wilkinson & Co. Limited, Wigan, Makers and Owners".

A contemporary report (Wigan Observer 14 August 1886) gave the new machines for Wigan something of an eulogy and included a relevant note on the grandiloquently named "Wilkinson Patent Tubular Air Surface Condensers".

"We last week called attention to a new type of tramway locomotive, which has been built and put to work on the Wigan and Pemberton tramways by Messrs Wilkinson and Co., engineers, of this town, and for the information of the mechanical portion of our readers we now, by the courtesy of the above firm, have pleasure in pointing out some of the many great improvements made by them since the introduction of the first engines on this tramway in February, 1882. The engine in question has some 65 to 70 per cent more hauling power, and burns 30 per cent less fuel than the original ones in use on this line, and uses only one-third of the quantity of water for boiler feeding purposes. It is fitted with one of Wilkinson's Patent Tubular Air Surface Condensers, which effectually condenses all surplus steam from the engines and safety valves, preventing emission of the same from the funnel in bad weather, in accordance with the Board of Trade regulations. This condenser is of an entirely different construction to any hitherto in use for the same purposes, and rather adds to, than detracts from the general appearance of the engine. It has the great advantage over all other so-called condensers of possessing over 100 per cent more cooling surface in one half of the cubical space then any now in the market for tramway locomotives."

In 1881 William Wilkinson was 43 and shown as the 'Managing Director, Engine Works', while Harriet, his second wife, was 38. Living at home was an 18 year-old daughter Louisa, plus a maid and, probably, a sister-in-law as Ellen Mills, a 37 year old 'unattached' lady, hailed from Harriet's home town, Lytham. In a day when father/son relationships were important it would be normal to incorporate "and Son(s)" in the firm's title, given that William Henry Wilkinson lived nearby at Holmes Houses, although it may be there were problems for by the time William Henry, an 'engine fitter', was 20 he was married to Ellen (18) and had a six-month old son, also William. We must note however that 'our' William Wilkinson's first wife Elizabeth (a year older than William) had died between 1871 and 1881. Was it this that caused William Wilkinson to take his eye 'off the ball' insofar as improvements to his tramway engines were concerned? Certainly the pressure of other work may also have been responsible.

In 1879/80 experiments were undertaken to see if steam barges and tugs would be operated on the Leeds & Liverpool Canal, and in 1880 a tug using a 'diagonal compound double tandem' engine built by Wilkinson was ordered and supplied, which foresaw modern tramway operation to some extent by having a shaft, propeller and rudder at both ends to save winding. The majority of engines supplied by Wilkinson to the Leeds & Liverpool Canal were of similar pattern with high and low pressure cylinders in each leg of a V-formation. This provided a simple, robust and easily maintained engine suitable for the "semi-civilised men [used] for drivers i.e. ordinary barge men." The steam for these engines was provided by 'Field' type boilers, not unsurprisingly supplied by Hough and Son. After the first four 'fly' i.e. express steam barges built in 1880 which reduced journey times by 40% or more compared with horses, the fleet, owned by the Leeds & Liverpool Company, rose to 46 steam barges and ten tugs. Incidentally Foulridge tunnel, rather inexplicably was built without a towpath, the barges having to be legged through and the introduction of tugs reduced the time taken from two hours to 25 minutes – it also kept the men out of the alehouse – deaths by drowning for drunk leggers was commonplace wherever they worked.

Within the Leeds & Liverpool Canal Company minutes dated November 1891 we find them ordering a number of new boats including "Two steel boats (Wigan Fly) at £500 each from Messrs Smith and Company, Lytham. Engines for same at £336 each from Wilkinson and Company Limited, Wigan." The amount does not, of course, compare with between £870 and £1,000 each for tram engines but far less labour, materials, time (and aggravation) was required.

The genesis of this book lay in a number of studies carried out relating to steam tram boiler explosion, the results of which, together with a complete listing will appear in a later volume. Some of William Wilkinson's trams, and especially 'Field' type tube boilers, were among those involved, but one wonders why, with this long experience of these boilers, he carried out a poor repair on a steam boat boiler on the Leeds & Liverpool Canal. In passing though it should be mentioned that on the boats a cure for the sediment which became trapped in the bottom of the tubes was found to be filters in the form of natural sponges in a long sectional rectangular box; were experiments of this nature carried out on steam trams? I can find no record.

The boat concerned in the explosion that must have had an adverse effect on Wilkinson's activities was the *'Sun'*, fleet no.26, and the date 4 July 1892. The mate, Richard Youds, died from "extensive scalds on the face, neck and body." The boiler was of the orthodox vertical pattern with one vital variation, 69" (1753mm) tall and 36" (914mm) diameter and working at 150psi, it was made of steel, other than the 78 tubes which were of drawn copper, 2" (51mm) in diameter and 1/8" (3.175mm) thick with brass cups brazed on to the end of the tubes. The boiler was almost new, as it "was made in the month of May 1892 **by Mr William Wilkinson, trading under the name of Messrs Hough Brothers, New Town.**"

The nature and indeed cause of the explosion was easy to ascertain as one of the copper tubes which had been leaking from its lower end was plugged up from the tube-plate end by means of a hardwood plug which became saturated and

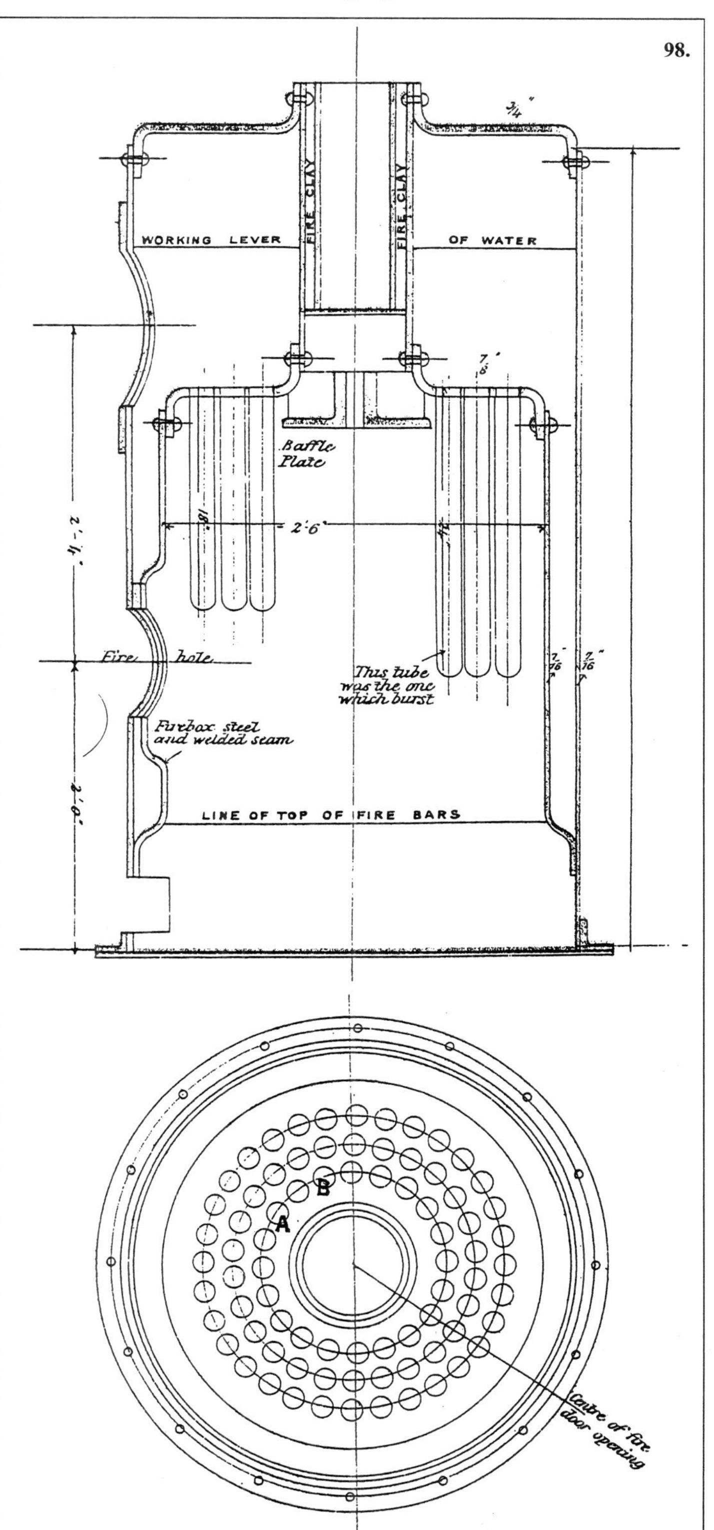

weakened and was forced down the tube by steam pressure through its lower end which had previously been weakened by the action of the fire; bursting through it blasted steam and water through the firebox door. The unfortunate mate, who took one and a half days to die, was bending down to stoke the fire at the time. Many years later a plugged tube on a locomotive boiler blew out its plug; we heard the racket 100 yards away in our cabin – but no-one was more than frightened.

"At the close of 1891 Mr William Wilkinson, manufacturing engineer and iron founder ... was instructed to construct engines and boilers for two new vessels ... a consultation took place between Mr Wilkinson and the engineers of the Company, when it was determined to fit the boilers for these vessels with copper tubes instead of iron tubes ... as it was thought thereby the heating surface would be increased, which no doubt would be the case, as copper conducts heat better than iron" ... The hanging tubes were obtained from Messrs Roger Bolton, of Wigan, and were composed of the best copper. The lower ends were formed by means of a brass cup brazed into the ends of the tube. These tubes were bored out 1/32in. deep to receive the cup, and afterwards the ends were drawn over the brass cup and brazed. The tubes were tested by steam to 50lb or 60lb and by hydraulic pressure to 450lb per square inch, and we have been told by the person who applied these tests that every tube in each boiler was subjected to them. Before the boiler was delivered to the *'Sun'* several of the tubes were sent back to Messrs Bolton and Son, on account of defective brazing, and were by them rebrazed and afterwards tested as before. Two trial trips were made of the *'Sun'*, one a short one and the other from Liverpool to Wigan, when the vessel was fully laden. On both these occasions Mr Wilkinson was on board, no leak was detected, and the boiler appeared to work very well.

On 4 July 1892 Mr John Ross, the Leeds & Liverpool's engineering superintendent received information that the *'Sun'*, lying at Burscough had a leaking tube and the technique used by the fitter to make a temporary repair was relevant to many steam trams as, from reports, there were few boilers that did not have plugged tubes; here it was treated by the Board of Trade inspector as a matter of course. "He thereupon instructed George Denning, a fitter, to construct an iron stopper, to proceed to the vessel, take the tube out, and plug up the aperture with the stopper. Denning accordingly proceeded to Burscough and did what was required." But what followed was perhaps not so usual, although Wilkinson offered an ingenious defence: "In the meantime Mr Wilkinson having heard of the defective tube proceeded to the *'Sun'* and found that the iron plug had been put in the aperture marked B on the plan which had been put in and was satisfied that the work had been properly done. When the water was admitted into the boiler he looked into the furnace, and, by means of a lamp, examined the bottom of nearly all the tubes, especially those in the inner or smaller circle, and found that one tube marked A on the plan was leaking. There being no iron stopper available he recommended Denning, the fitter, to procure a piece of hard wood about 7in. long and to shape it so as to form its diameter of 1½in. at the point and 1⅞in. at the head and with it to stop the hole in the tube-plate so as to prevent the water from going into the tube. this operation having been performed by Denning to the satisfaction of Mr Wilkinson, the latter sent a telegram to Mr Ross requesting an interview on his arrival at Wigan, whence he proceeded by train."

The explosion took place at 7pm about 200 yards below Bankhall Bridge: [said the Commissioners] "In our judgement the explosion was caused by the action of Mr Wilkinson in recommending that a wooden plug should be inserted in the tube ... Mr Wilkinson has admitted that this proceedings was wrong, but has said that at the time it did not occur to him to be so, for he had then in his mind the fact that he had used two or three wooden plugs to stop up tubes of a boiler used on a steam launch of his own, and that with the tubes in that condition he had worked the launch from Beaumaris to Liverpool and on to Wigan in safety. It has however to be remembered that Mr Wilkinson is a manufacturing engineer and in our opinion it should have occurred to him that he was recommending a proceeding that at all events was a very risky one. It has been said that he was only acting as a volunteer, but even if this were so we should hold him to blame for having voluntarily given wrong advice. In fact, however, as he had constructed the boiler, he was interested in its working, and the master of the vessel and Denning, the fitter, would naturally act under his directions and follow his advice. Besides, it is clear to us that Mr Wilkinson considered the tubes to be unsafe, for he telegraphed to the company at Wigan, asking their representative to meet him, and there informed Mr Ross that he considered the tubes a failure, or, in other words, that they were unsafe. As we consider the conduct of Mr Wilkinson reckless, and as the explosion was caused by it, we find him to blame for it. We desire, however, to say that Mr Wilkinson has given his evidence very fairly, and certainly with no desire to shirk responsibility and we are convinced that he now feels that his conduct was not that of a careful engineer. We directed that Mr William Wilkinson should pay to the solicitor to the Board of Trade the sum of 20£ towards the costs and expenses of this investigation. Dated the 4th day of August 1892. HOWARD SMITH, Commissioner. G. FULLERTON BELL, Commissioner."

A severe indictment for a man who had spent all his adult life in and around boilers.

In 1893 Wilkinson & Co became involved, albeit peripherally, in a cable tramway as shown by this quotation from the Southport Observer; "The Southport Pier Tramway. After an interval of rather less than two months, the tramway on the Southport pier has now resumed its proper function. As we indicated last week, the time has been spent in an almost complete refit in the working stock. New girders, new rails, new sleepers, and new engines have been laid down, and now the tramway is furnished in a manner which must be thoroughly satisfactory to everybody concerned. On Thursday Major-General Hutchinson, the Board of Trade inspector, went over the work, and expressed complete satisfaction with every essential detail. Indeed, we understand he went so far as to compliment the Pier Company on the thoroughness and efficiency with which the alterations have been carried out. The vertical diagonal engines, which have been built by Messrs W. Wilkinson and Company, of Wigan, are about four times the power of the old ones. Consequently by their means the trams could now, if it were thought advisable, be run at a very much higher rate of speed than could be achieved by the old ones. But the directors and managers have decided, after having considered the matter and tested the machinery and plant to run the tram at a maximum speed of not more than fifteen miles an hour. This is very little in excess of the rate formerly achieved; but it is perhaps quite as well that this decision has been arrived at. The more nervous section of the public would not care to be careering on the pier at the rate of 20 miles an hour. The risk of accident is also lessened by the renewal and strengthening of the brake power on the cars. These latter, too, have been thoroughly overhauled, and now present a very spick and span appearance in new coats of paint. The brake power now existent gives double control over the cars that the old brakes had; and taking the whole of the alterations into notice, the safety and effectiveness of the tramway has been increased twenty-fold."

In their issue dated 11 August 1894 the Wigan Observer noted that "Messrs Wm. Wilkinson and Co. of this town, who have fitted and made the machinery for some thirty steamers on the Leeds and Liverpool Canal, have received an order from the promoters of the Grand Canal at Dublin for the engines, boilers, &c. for eight steam barges, to ply between the Liffey and the Shannon."

The same year it is apparent that mining machinery was still being provided for at Wood Colliery (SJ 572967) three shafts were in operation during 1896, No.2 downcast, had a twin horizontal winding engine by "Wilkinson of Wigan" dated 1894, with 24" (610mm) cylinders, 54" (1372mm) stroke, slide valves, powering a 12-foot drum. However No. 3 upcast had an engine dated 1896, built by Robert Daglish & Company, St. Helens, and for No. 4 downcast the engine came in 1900 from Stevenson & Company, Preston. It would be logical that had Wilkinson still been functioning in 1896 or 1900 that their quotation with little transport involved would have been lower. Perhaps he could take consolation that of the fifteen tram engines built by his works for the Wigan & District Tramway Company and their predecessors nine survived to be municipalised in 1902 and were operated for a further two years by Wigan Corporation Tramways.

Postscript:

The Wilkinson patent engine: an 1883 layman's guide to how the gubbins *really* worked:

"On Friday the completed portion of the Manchester, Rochdale, Bury and Oldham Steam Tramways was officially inspected by Major-General Hutchinson, Government Inspector. This tramway is one of the most important in the North of England, the works being extensive and laid out in the most complete manner. Of special interest to Wigan is the facts that the directors have decided to work the line with the Wilkinson steam tram engines, and a depot is being erected in which there will be accommodation for 21 engines and carriages. At the inspection two engines, with a car attached to each containing the Government inspector, the engineers and members of the Corporation, went over the line, the inspection being thoroughly satisfactory. Major-General Hutchinson stating that he was much pleased with the entire system and its connections. Afterwards the leading gentlemen in the Town Council and the officials of the district local boards on the line of route were invited to luncheon by the directors of the company at the Reed Hotel. The chair was occupied by Mr J. Bishop, vice-chairman of the company. Major General Hutchinson, in responding to the toast of his health, said the route of the new line seemed to him to be a very suitable one for the introduction of mechanical power, as the roads in the districts were of fair average width, and he thought there were very few places where objection could be taken to the use of steam on the newly laid line. Mr Clifford Winley, one of the contractors, said he was convinced that the Wilkinson engine was the best tramway engine in the world. The Chairman next gave the health of the contractors for the engines, Messrs Peacock and Co., and Mr Wilkinson of Wigan. It was a very difficult thing indeed to get an engine that would meet all the requirements which were necessary in the case of a tramway; but he thought that the engines which were working on this line could be surpassed by none. (Cheers).

Mr Wilkinson in acknowledging the toast paid a compliment to Messrs Peacock and Co., for the manner in which they had turned out their engines; and with regard to his own patent he could only say that after it had been worked a little it would be much more satisfactory than it was at present. The gradient on this part of the lines are very difficult in some places, and he was scarcely prepared for them with his engine only working one hour or two before it was to be used. By and by, when it was a little more used he would guarantee that it would take the ascent of Drake-street with 70 men or more behind it without a 'budge' or stopping to go ahead again. (Cheers). If anything would try a new engine it was the dust which blew so all day – particularly at the depot – and he thought the trial on the whole had been very satisfactory. They might be aware that one of the requirements was that there should be an automatic governor on the engine which should stop it when it got to a certain speed without any interference from the engineer. His engine had been tried in this way, and so well did the governor act that the Government inspector was almost thrown down, and he expressed himself as entirely satisfied. (Laughter and cheers). With regard to the engines some were made by Messrs Green, of Leeds, and these too were very good pieces of work indeed.

The *Rochdale Observer* of Saturday last says: A very animated discussion is at present going on in reference to the merits of steam as a motive power on tramways; and in view of this a description of Messrs Wilkinson's patent engine may not be uninteresting. The appearance of the engine will very soon be one of the most common objects of the streets, and as at present it occupies the position of being one of the best criticised pieces of workmanship among professional men generally, it is worthy of particular notice, internally as well as externally. In the Wilkinson tramway locomotive the boiler and machinery are housed in the usual way. The engine may be said to be a combination of old devices, with several new and peculiar applications, which render it on the whole the best tramway engine at present in existence. Some people think this is not saying a great deal, as all tramway engines are imperfect, and have many faults from an engineering point of view. But when we begin to disassociate the invention of Messrs Wilkinson from the arena of professional discussion and look at it as a piece of machinery, compared with its rivals in manufacture, there cannot be a doubt that none of its competitors can show the same results in point of safety and efficiency. We have said that the engine is a combination of old devices. Thus vertical boilers have been used in road locomotives by Chaplin, Thompson, and others. The mode of getting rid of exhaust steam by superheating it, as is done in this engine, has the effect of causing an almost complete absence of smoke, which is the most noteworthy feature of this engine, and one which renders it specially adapted for use in crowded thoroughfares. The working parts are much the same as in other engines, but the steam from the cylinders is exhausted through two pipes into jackets fixed on each side of the boiler, so as to be heated to the same temperature as the boiler. These chambers serve to superheat the steam after it is exhausted from the cylinders, thereby intercepting and partially evaporating any water that may pass with the exhaust steam into the jackets. From these jackets are led two pipes passing down and into the inside of the uptake to the chimney of the furnace into a vessel made of cast iron or other material, and suspended inside of the furnace – this chamber also acting as a distributor of the heated gases amongst the tubes. From this vessel a blast pipe opens into the lower part of the chimney, thereby directing the exhaust steam which has passed into the chambers up the chimney in, it is said, a perfectly dry superheated and invisible condition. The vessel inside the furnace is exposed to the greatest heat, and it effectually superheats and dries the steam so that no water can be emitted from the chimney to the annoyance of passengers. The action of the engine is comparatively silent; and this result is attained by the steam being expanded in separate vessels after leaving the cylinders of the engine, the pressure of the exhausted steam being thereby reduced as to minimise the noise of exhaust on reaching the chimney. The safety valves are enclosed in a box, from which pipes are led into each of the before mentioned jackets, which has the effect of reducing the noise made when steam is blowing off from over pressure in the boiler. In this engine the boiler is the ordinary Field boiler (vertical), and provision is made for preventing the fouling of the circulating tubes by fitting a removable dish to catch and intercept any "scale" that may have been formed on and drop from the uptake, and thus prevent its falling into the tubes. The uptake or lower part of the chimney passing through the steam space of the boiler being subjected to a very high temperature wastes away much more rapidly at this point than at any other portion of the boiler. To prevent this it is fitted with a casing of wrought or cast iron, between which casing and the uptake an annular space is formed which is filled with fire clay. The engine has two inverted direct acting vertical cylinders, the piston rods of which drive two cranks on the shaft. The crank shaft is keyed to the driving wheel, which again are coupled to the trailing wheels; and the object of this is to prevent the galloping or jumping action of the engine on the road which would take place if the engines were attached direct to the driving wheel axle without the intervention of such gearing. It is, of course, impossible to give an exact technical description without the aid of diagrams, but the foregoing remarks will enable any one with a slight knowledge of mechanics to understand pretty clearly the construction of the engine. It may be mentioned that the engine is neat in appearance, and much smarter than some of the movable boxes which were used a few years ago, and which are still in use on some of the tramways systems in this country. The principal merits claimed for this engine above others are first the getting rid of exhaust steam by superheating; second the employment of quieting chambers to keep down the noise of exhaust steam; and third, the use of gearing in the construction of the working parts. None of these inventions are new – they have all been more or less in use. The invention is simply a combination of old devices – and the novelty consists in the combination. In this respect the Wilkinson engine has much to recommend it, and we believe will be found very suitable indeed on this line, looking to the gradients and the nature of the work expected from it."

Patent tram locomotives manufacture 1881 – (nominally) 1896

Sixty-three locomotives were credited to William Wilkinson's works. The list overleaf (upper) is based on that prepared by the late Dr H.A. Whitcombe in his History of the Steam Tram, (reprinted by this publisher in 2000) with additional information provided by the late E.K. Stretch. Additional notes are reproduced by permission of Nick Kelly, but notwithstanding all this information some customer details must, in the absence of manufacturers' own works or progressive lists, remain hypothetical.

Technical supplement:

Although in Britain the design of tram engines polarised into the Wilkinson vertical boilered patterns which in our period did not progress much in power or versatility, and the locomotive-styled engines. Although a number of experimentals – the Burrell or Aveling & Porter for example – advanced the design, by and large any improvements were governed by the relatively weak trackwork generally in use, 'heavy' engines caused too many problems. Not so on the Continent where tram locomotives ended up looking like, and being as solidly built as, orthodox tank engines, albeit with skirts on.

In The Locomotive magazine of 15 May 1947 there appeared a comparative table showing just this growth from which I have selected three quite typical designs overleaf (lower). Engine numbers are those allocated within the Staats Spoorwegen series, although the Merryweather engines originated with the Nederlandsche Rhijn Spoorweg Maatschappij (NRS), the Backer & Rueb and Hanomag with the Nederlandsche Centraal Spoorweg Maatschappij; the first two sets of engines were standard gauge (4' 8½"/1435mm) the Hanomag engines, rather improbably give their power, ran on 3' 6"/1067mm tracks. Merryweather = Merryweather & Sons, London; Backer & Rueb = Backer & Rueb, Breda (later Machinefabrik 'Breda'; Hanomag – Hannoversche Maschinenfabrik A.G. Hannover – Linden.

Wm. Wilkinson & Co. Ltd.

Works No.	Year	Driving Wheels ft in.	Cylinders in. dia. x stroke	Gauge ft in.	Customer	Fleet No.	Notes
1	1881	2 3	6 x 7	3 6	Wigan	1	
2-4	1882	2 3	6½ x 7	3 6	Wigan	2-4	
5-6	1882	2 3	7 x 9	4 7¾	Huddersfield	1-2	
7	1882	2 3	7 x 9	Std	Nottingham	1	Only Nottingham engine
8-10	1882	2 3	7 x 9	Std	Manchester, Bury Rochdale & Oldham	1-3	Sent to Thos.Green Leeds for rebuilding
11-15	1882	2 3	7 x 9	Std	MBRO	4-8	
16-17	1883	2 3	7 x 9	3 6	Birmingham & Aston	7-8	
18-25	1883	2 6	6½ x 9	Std	MBRO	13-20	More likely 7 x 9 cylinders
26-27	1883	2 3	7 x 9	3 6	South Staffordshire	1-2	
28-29	1883	2 3	7 x 9	3 0	Giant's Causeway	1-2	No.2 possibly named "W.A.Traill"
30-31	1883	2 3	7 x 9	Uncertain Possibly Dublin Southern 5' 3" gauge; probably tried on Dublin & Lucan 3' 0" gauge			
32-35	1883	2 3	7 x 9	3 6	Wigan	5-8	
36-39	1883	2 6	7½ x 11	Std	MBRO	35-38	
40-43	1883	2 3	7½ x 11	3 6	South Staffordshire	17-20	
44-47	1883	2 3	7½ x 11	4 7¾	Huddersfield	3-6	
48	1883	2 3	7½ x 11	3 6	South Staffordshire	21	
49	1884	2 3	6¾ x 7	3 6	Wigan	9	Experimental boiler and worm gear drive made from spare cylinders etc.
50-51	1884	2 3	7 x 9	3 6	Plymouth Devon-port & District	1-2?	If PD&D had 4 engines, w/nos 30-31 may have been nos.1 & 2, w/nos 50-51, 3 & 4
52-53	1884	2 3	7 x 11	3 6	Brighton District	1-2	Cylinders probably 7½ x 11
54	1885	2 3	7½ x 11	3 0	Giant's Causeway	3	Named "Dunluce Castle"
55-56	1885	2 6	7½ x 11	3 6	MBRO	61-62	
57-60	1886	2 6	7½ x 11	3 6	Wigan	9-12	59 & 60 are 'mystery' engines said to be "a couple Wilkinsons happened to have in stock". Were they built for stock or re-furbished or made from spare parts?
61-62	1886	2 6	7½ x 11	3 6	MBRO	89-90	
63	1896	2 3	7½ x 11	3 0	Giant's Causeway	4	Named "Brian Boroimhe". Wilkinsons Works closed by 1896. Was this locomotive built up from parts? It carried Wilkinson plates but may have been assembled elsewhere.

Engine Nos	1-19	26-30	41-47
Date of building	1879-81, 1892	1907/8	1913/14
Builder	Merryweather	Backer & Rueb	Hanomag
Diameter of cylinders, mm	178	225	310
Stroke	280	350	400
Diameter of driving wheels, mm	740	840	900
Boiler pressure kg/cm²	10.3	14.5	12.4
Tractive force 0.7kg	860	2130	3710
Heating surface of firebox, m²	2.0	2.5	3.0
Heating surface of tubes, m²	9.8	18	21
Heating surface of total, m²	11.8	20.5	24
Heating surface of super heater, m²			11
Grate area, m²	0.4	0.58	0.65
Small tubes number	66	81	15
Small tubes diameter out, mm²	45	45	50
Large tubes number			44
Large tubes diameter out, mm²			60
Length between tube plates	1187	1800	2150
Capacity of water tanks, m³	1.8	1.4	1.5
Capacity of coal bunker, t	0.4	0.5	0.5
Weight in working order, t	9	16.4	18.8
Radius of smallest curve, m	25	30	30
Maximum speed, km/h	35	35	35

Chapter 7

DIGRESSIONS

(BEING SOME OF THE ODD-BODS THAT CROSSED A TRAMWAY'S PATH)

Airborne

The inclusion of compressed air engines in this chapter may seem slightly misleading insofar as the trams themselves did not need steam directly but their chances of success were ruined by the excessive cost of maintaining the boilers in the power houses – boilers that not only powered the compressors to fill the engines' tanks but in one maker's patent also the hot water that was so vital for their efficient use.

The types of cars used varied as did the means of locomotion, all of which were improved over a number of years. Probably the most successful in Britain was that of Colonel Beaumont, a Royal Engineer, whose engine began running on the Stratford and Epping Forest Branch of the (London) North Metropolitan Tramways, in 1881. The compressing engine was a compound with a high pressure cylinder 12" in diameter using steam at 95psi, exhausting into a low pressure 20" diameter cylinder. The resulting compressed air then 'worked' through a set of reducing cylinders; each being smaller in diameter, the compression became greater until it reached 1000psi, this air being conveyed via 250 feet of 1½" iron pipe to The Broadway, Stratford, where a flexible hose fed the engines' cylinders; each charge sufficing for the 4½ mile round trip from Stratford to Leytonstone. Outward was a steady ascent with a total rise of 82 feet taking 22 minutes (little different to horses) and the return on a falling gradient 16-17 minutes. The problem was that with only one car ('dummy') 23 lb of fuel (coal) was used each mile as the pumping station sat idle for three-quarters of the day, whereas with four engines at work (replacing all horse-cars) the cost would drop to 10 lb/mile. The on-board engine, built by Greenwood & Batley was itself a four-cylinder compound with volume ratios of 1, 3, 9, and 27, enabling four impulses to be gained from each fresh cylinder full of air. In October 1880 Colonel Beaumont struck his deal with NorthMet to work the branch at 6d per mile in lieu of the 8½d horsing cost; but it was not until 28 October 1881 the month's trials could start. Although successful the contract price was now quoted as 7d. per mile.

After much haggling in July 1883 NorthMet declined to proceed, being by now much more interested in electric systems.

The only other compressed air design to be seriously tried in Britain followed the Mékarski system, which, unlike Colonel Beaumont's "dummy", was built into the passenger car and comprised four primary units, the air reservoirs at 450psi, the heater, the regulator and the propelling gear. Although the type of car illustrated did not enter service in Britain (being used in Paris) the cut-away drawing clearly shows the layout.

The interconnected reservoirs varied in diameter between 12 and 16 inches and had a total

99. The Beaumont compressed air engine for tramways.

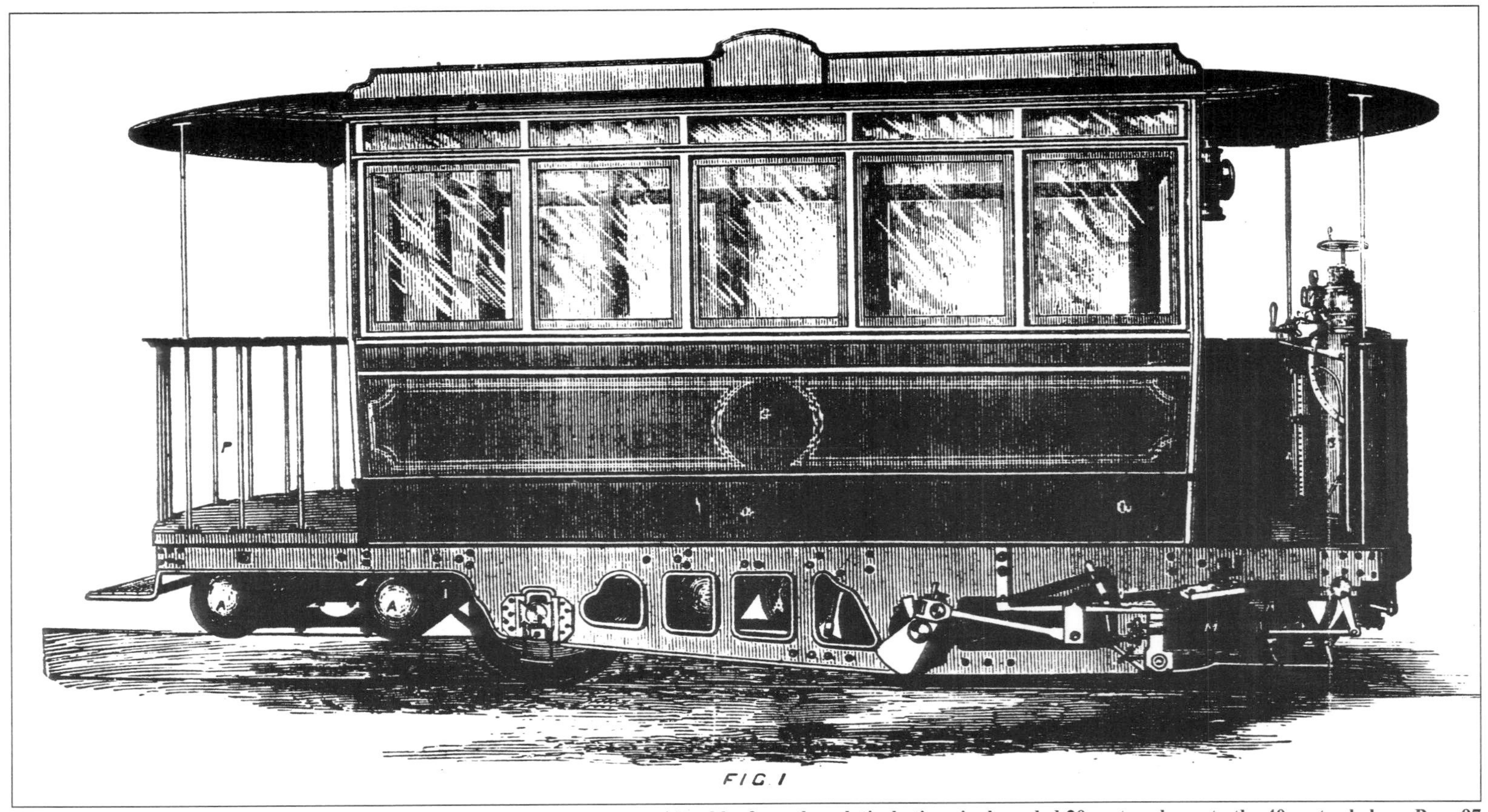

100 & 101. The variety of designs incorporating Mékarski motors was considerable, from the relatively tiny single-ended 20 seater above, to the 40 seater below. Page 97 shows another view of this machine.

Fig. 2.

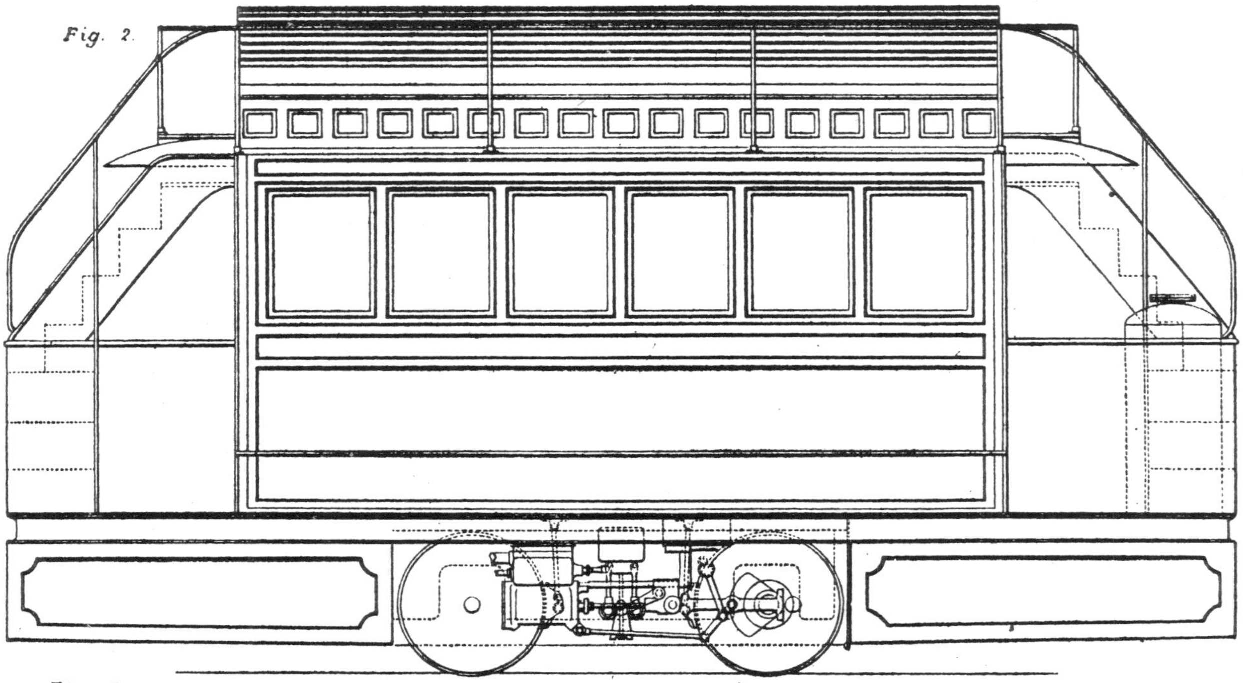

Fig. 3.

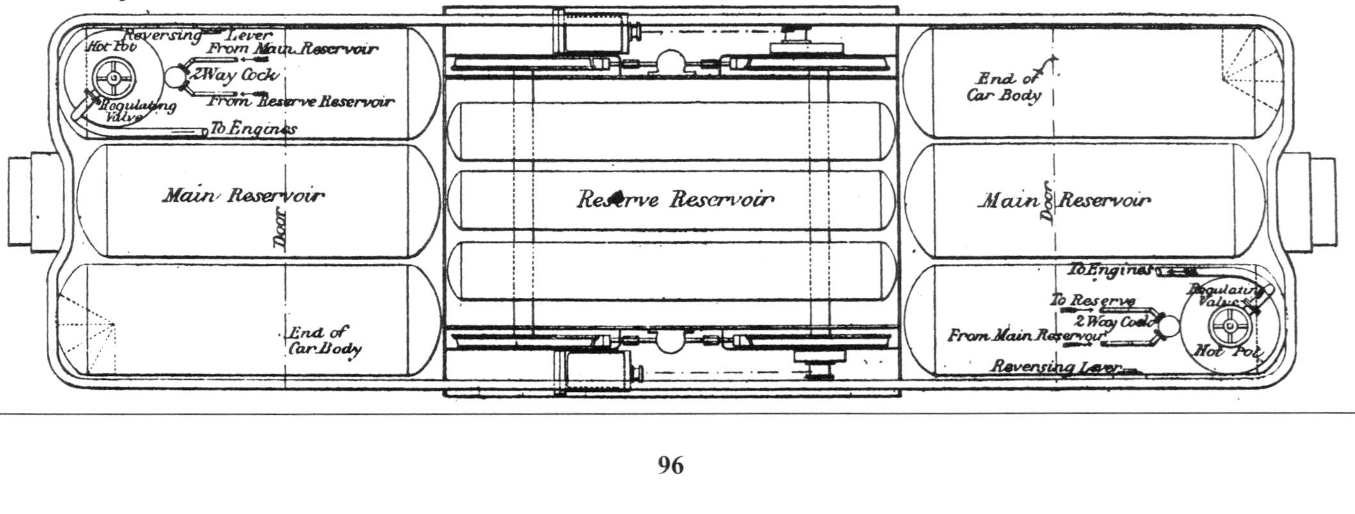

Reversing Lever
Hot Pot
From Main Reservoir
2 Way Cock
Regulating Valve
From Reserve Reservoir
To Engines
Main Reservoir
Door
Reserve Reservoir
Main Reservoir
Door
End of Car Body
End of Car Body
To Engines
Regulating Valve
To Reserve
2 Way Cock
From Main Reservoir
Hot Pot
Reversing Lever

FIG.2. PLAN OF FRAMING WITH CARRIAGE REMOVED
SCALE.0m.05 TO 1 METRE

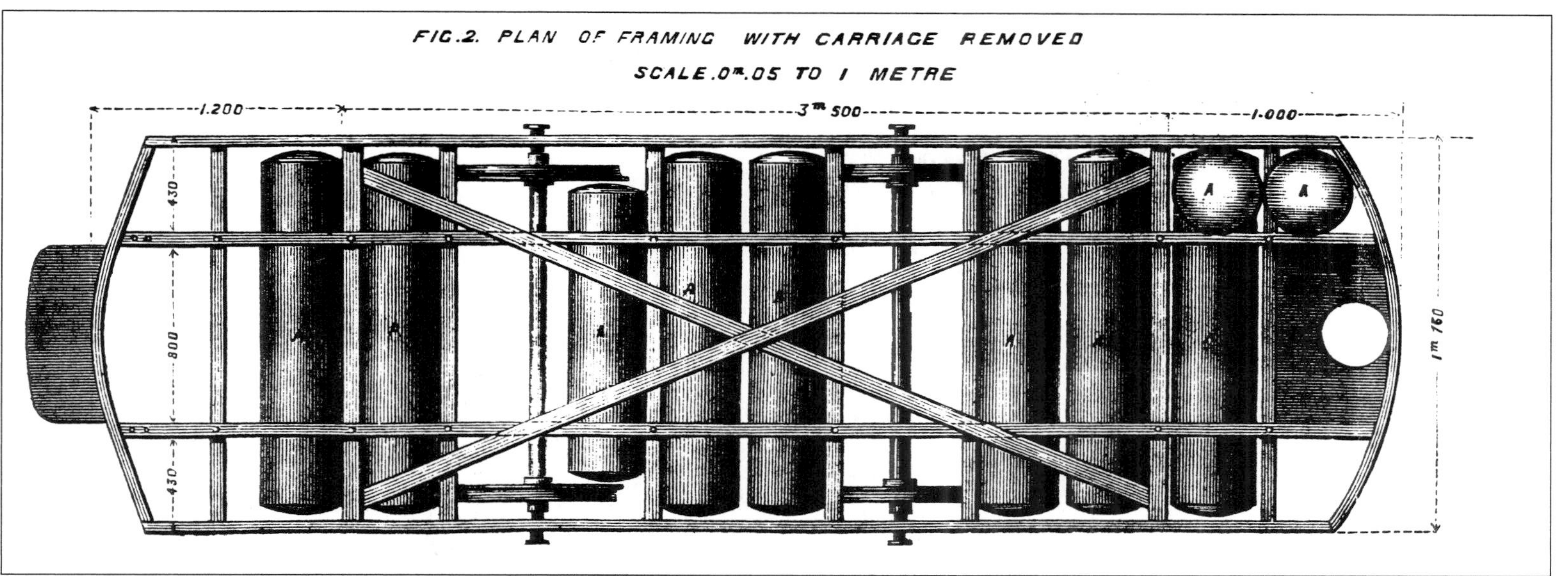

102 & 103. No set of drawings seems to have survived for Beaumont's arrangement, but the drawings of the Mékarski car show the relative complexity of compressed air propulsion compared with steam, especially as there was a requirement for a pumping station as well.

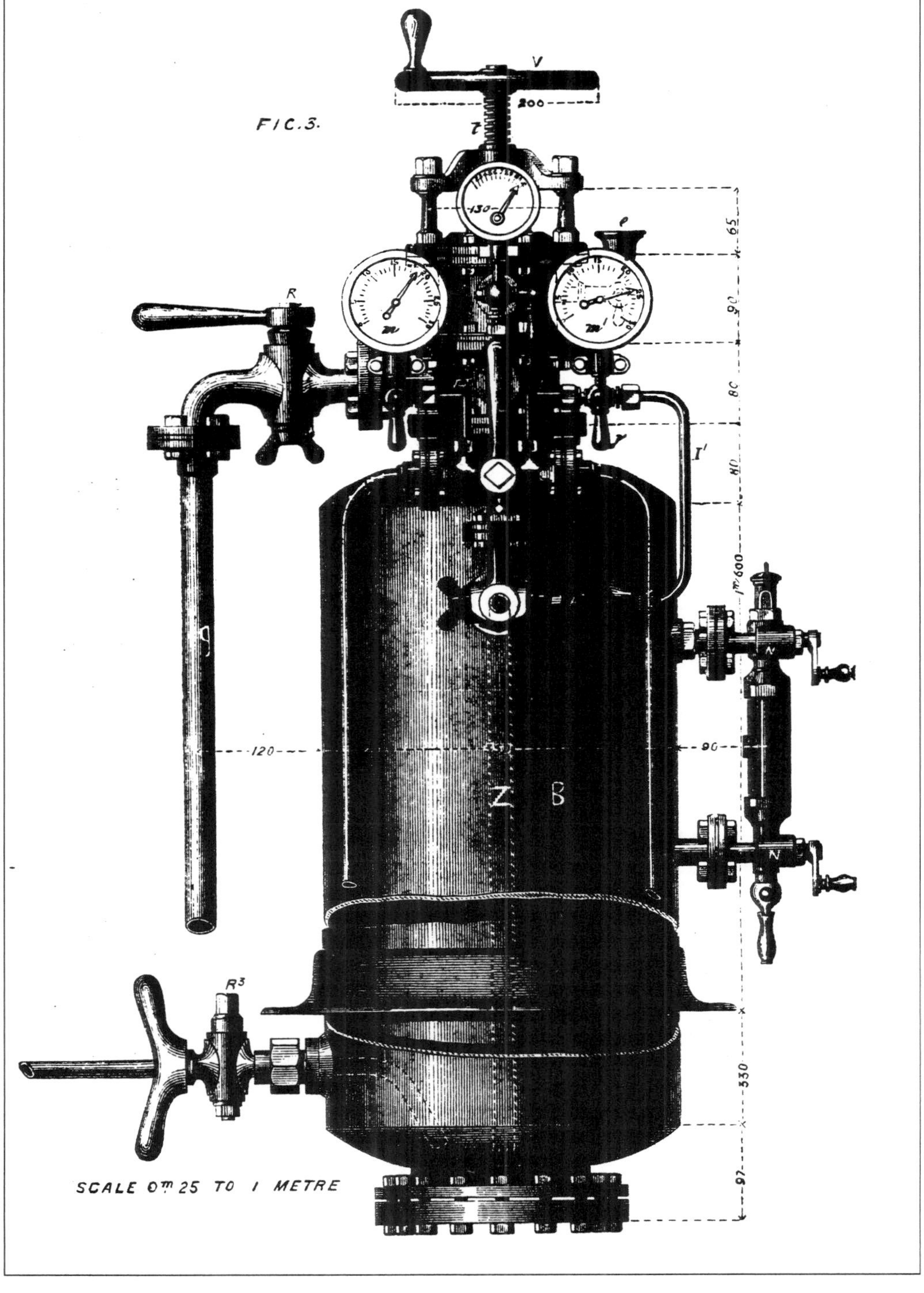

capacity of between 50 and 80 cubic feet for working and a further 15 for emergency use. On leaving the reservoirs the air entered and passed through a tank of hot (170°-180°C/212°-248°F) water "by means of which it becomes saturated with steam at a high temperature." For 50 cubic feet of air around 18-20 gallons of water sufficed; this was then passed through a patent regulator to equalise the pressure, this in turn being altered by the driver through a small hand-wheel and valve, thus controlling the speed "the pressure of air and steam is ... regulated automatically, irregardless of any variation in the available [tank] pressure ... the gaseous mixture then enters the cylinders, where it connects upon pistons connected with gear more or less like a locomotive."

Two Mékarski's engines were used on the Wantage Tramway from 5 August 1880 for three months but not entirely successfully. It was expected each engine, towing one or (on special occasions) two cars, would carry out two return trips (10 miles) on one charge but sometimes they ran out of air and could not make it up the 1 in 47 gradient at the end of the run, although the description of the time as "a very beautiful power, clean and noiseless" must have heartened the British agents. The problem was that the power station (which cost £2,000 when the attendant received £1.30 per week in wages) required 24cwt of coal per day's work compared with 6cwt for an orthodox steam tram engine. And yet Mékarski engines worked on the Continent right up to 1910! A second trial was essayed on various lines of the London Street Tramways Company in 1882 and again between King's Cross and Holloway Road for three months in 1888.

In Paris, Louis Mékarski obtained the concession for a line from Vincennes to Ville-Everard, where 19 motor-trams were operated by his company the Chemins de Fer Nogontais, from August 1887. Seating 44, these machines proved both viable and efficient running until 1900. Among others, the line Cours de Vincennes to Saint-Augustin used compressed air on the

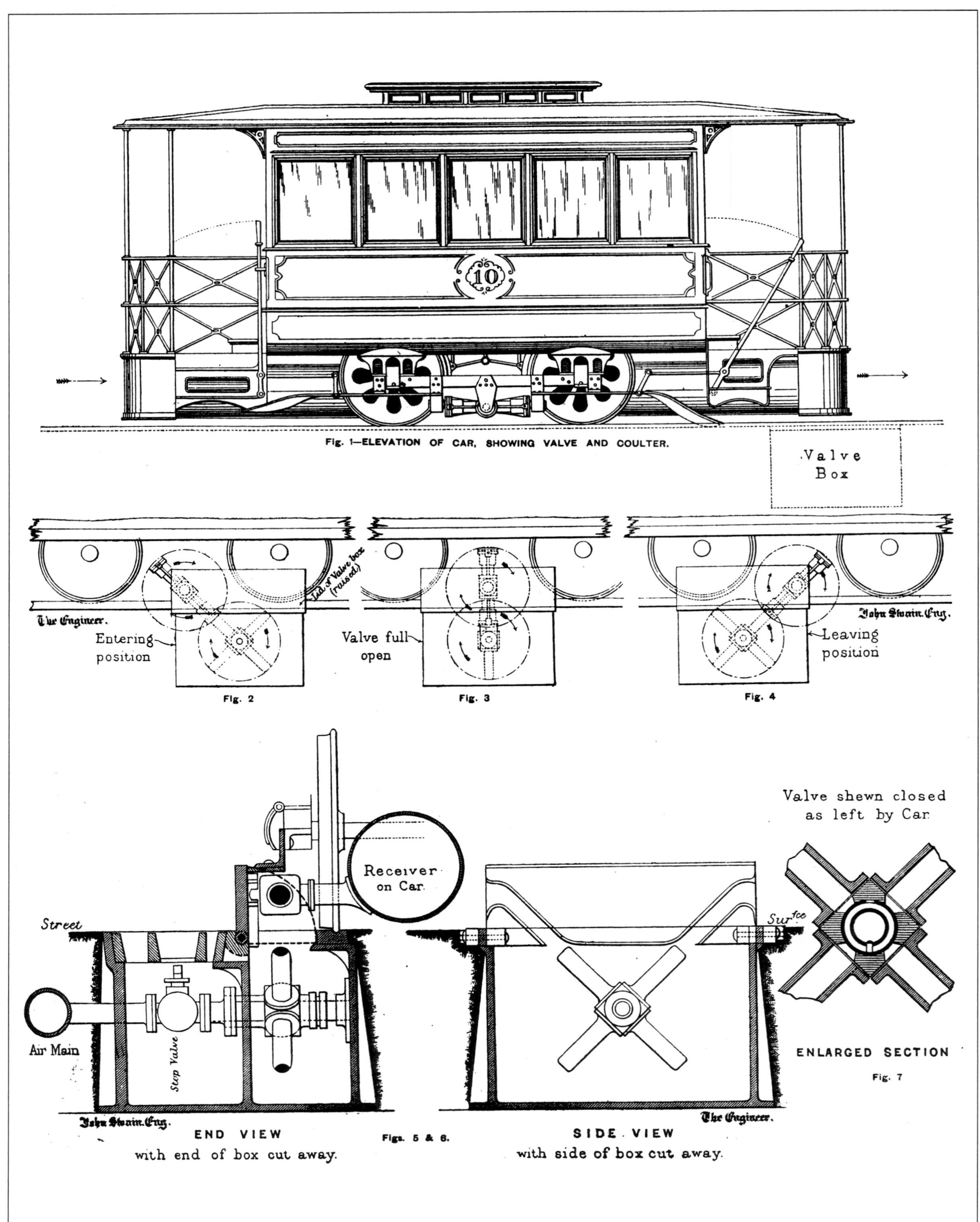

104. These drawings from The Engineer 21 March 1890 show the workings of the Hughes & Lancaster system; I suspect that, like later electrical surface contact designs, there were just too many working parts. I also wonder what the horses would make of a blast of cold compressed air between their legs! In any event it was too late, electricity was in the air.

A.D. 1888.—N° 8886. 3

Hughes & Lancaster's Improvements in Tram Cars Propelled by Compressed Air.

COMPLETE SPECIFICATION.

Improvements in or Connected with Tram Cars Propelled by Compressed Air.

We, JOHN HUGHES and CHARLES LANCASTER both of City Road, Chester, in the County of Chester, Engineers, do hereby declare the nature of our said Invention to be as follows :—

Our Invention relates mainly to that class of Tram Cars which are propelled by the expansive force of compressed air acting by means of an engine contained and carried by the Tram Car, the air being supplied to receivers carried on the car from a "main" (pipe) laid along the track on which the car runs, or from stations along the route.

According to our Invention, we form the reservoir for the compressed air, by constructing the main framework of the car of tubes or chambers, so jointed and connected together as to form one continuously connected receiver, thus the main longitudinal beams, and cross beams, and the main uprights with their cross ties, constituting the skeleton framework of the car, under our Invention, consist of tubes or chambers screwed into or otherwise connected to one another, all of as large diameter as can be conveniently employed, and upon which the woodwork constituting the floor, sides, roof, and seats of the car, or some of them, can be laid. We also place underneath the car tubular vessels surrounding the axles of the running or driving wheels, such vessels being built with internal tubes sufficiently large to allow the axles to pass through them, and to have clearance for the rise and fall of the car upon its springs; the vessels form annular reservoirs round the axles, and are connected together by tubes at right angles to them, and have tubes from each end extending under the end platforms of the car, and are also connected to the tubes forming the frame of the car. In some cases these air vessels are placed longitudinally under the car side by side, extending the whole length of the car, the axle clearance tubes passing through them at right angles. By the above described arrangement of tubes and vessels a large reservoir is provided for the storage of compressed air upon the car.

In order to avoid any interference with or diminution of the space required for the air reservoirs, we use, to drive the car, a revolving engine, such as "Riggs" or "Wilsons" revolving engine, or their equivalents, and we place the engine or engines underneath, or at the side of the car, preferably about midway between the two axles. The engine works a shaft carried across the car and geared to the two axles at one or both ends by suitable wheel, chain or other gearing, the starting, reversing, and regulating levers being fixed on the platforms at each end, and connected by rods or tubes to the engine, so that it can be controlled from either end of the car. This arrangement allows for the rise and fall of the car on the springs without materially affecting the gearing between the wheels and the engine, whether such gearing be wheels or chains. In working, the air reservoirs can be

4 A.D. 1888.—N° 8886.

Hughes & Lancaster's Improvements in Tram Cars Propelled by Compressed Air.

charged with compressed air as required from depôts or stations at suitable distances along the route, or by means of valves placed at intervals in a compressed air main, laid along the track, suitable hose or other connections being used to connect the reservoirs with the main.

Any of the methods of supplying the air and charging the air reservoirs with air at points along the route which have from time to time been designed for such purpose may be employed.

Having thus specified generally the nature, object, and purposes of our Invention, its description will now be proceeded with in reference to the annexed drawings, which make a part of this specification and explain more fully the nature of our Invention, like letters and figures being used to denote like parts throughout the several figures.

DESCRIPTION OF THE DRAWINGS.

Figure 1 is a side elevation of a Tram Car with the improvements according to our Invention applied thereto.

Figure 2 is a sectional plan of the Tram Car taken at X. X. Figure 1.

Figure 3 is a sectional end elevation of the Tram Car taken at X, X Figure 2.

Figure 4 is a side elevation of the back of the engine showing the expansion and reversing gear.

Figure 5 is a perspective view showing the framework of the Tram Car.

With reference to the drawings, it will be seen that the main frame work of the car is constructed of tubes, so jointed and connected together, as to form one continuously connected receiver. Thus the main longitudinal beams a, cross beams a^1, and the uprights a^2 constituting the skeleton framework of the car, consist of tubes screwed or otherwise connected to one another. Upon this tubular framework the woodwork constituting the floor, sides, roof, and seats of the car are laid. b are tubular vessels placed underneath the car, and surrounding the axles c of the wheels d, the axles c passing through internal tubes b^1 and having clearance for the rise and fall of the car on its springs. These vessels b form annular reservoirs round the axles, and are connected together by tubes b^2 at right angles to them and are also connected with tubes b^3 extending under the end platforms of the car. These tubes b, b^2, b^3 are connected to the tubes a, a^1, a^2 forming the frame of the car. By this arrangement a large reservoir is provided for the storage of compressed air upon the car.

e is the engine for driving the car. It is of the revolving type such as "Riggs" or "Wilsons" revolving engine, and it is preferably placed about midway between the wheel axles c as shown. The engine e works a shaft f, carried across the car and geared to the two axles c by chain gearing g. h are the reversing and regulating levers which are connected by rods h^1 to levers fixed on the platforms of the car at both ends, so that the engine can be controlled from either end of the car.

For working, the air reservoir,—consisting of the tubes such as above described,—can be charged with compressed air from suitable stations along the route, or by means of valves placed at intervals in a compressed air main laid along the track any of the known methods being employed to connect the air reservoir with the main.

Having now particularly described and ascertained the nature of our said Invention and in what manner the same is to be performed we declare that what we claim is :—

1. A tram car in which the frame or framework is constructed of tubes, interconnected, and adapted to serve as a compressed air reservoir ; for the purposes set forth.

2. The improvement in pneumatically propelled tram cars substantially as herein described, which consist in forming the reservoir for the storage of compressed air by constructing the main framework of the car of tubes, so connected together as to

A.D. 1888.—N° 8886. 5

Hughes & Lancaster's Improvements in Tram Cars Propelled by Compressed Air.

form a continuously connected receiver, and connected to tubular vessels underneath the car.

3. In a pneumatically propelled tram car, tubular vessels adapted to surround the axles of the running or driving wheels, and to serve as compresed air reservoirs ; for the purposes set forth.

4. In a pneumatically propelled tram car in which the axles are surrounded by tubular vessels for the purposes described, constructing such vessels with internal tubes in which the axles are placed and free to move ; as set forth.

5. The combination and arrangement of vessels, b, b^2, b^3, adapted to serve as compressed air reservoirs, substantially as set forth with reference to Figures 1, 2 and 3 of the Drawings.

6. A pneumatically propelled tram car comprising a system of air reservoirs and a revolving engine, of the type such as specified, said engine being adapted to operate the wheels of the tram car, and arranged in such a manner as not to interfere substantially with or diminish the space available for air reservoirs ; substantially as described.

7. In a pneumatically propelled tram car, the combination of a system of air reservoirs disposed below the body of the car, and a revolving engine, such as of the type described, also disposed in the lower part of the body of the car ; substantially as set forth with reference to Figures 1. 2. 3. and 4.

Dated this 16th day of March 1889.

JOHN HUGHES.
CHARLES LANCASTER.

By Cheesbrough & Royston,
15, Water Street, Liverpool,
Patent Agents.

LONDON : Printed for Her Majesty's Stationery Office,
By DARLING AND SON, LTD.
1889.

Mékarski system, but the two cylinders drove the rear axle through Walschaerts valve gear, with rod drive to the forward pair (all these trams were single ended) giving an estimated (nominal) 35 horse-power. But to add a twist to the story, when a new fleet of 148 trams were built, 60 had a coke-fired boiler to provide the steam which, as we have seen, was vital to the Mékarski system. The other 88 in the tranche refilled their boilers at each terminus but were eventually converted to the mobile boiler, which neatly brings them into the steam tram story – boiler + coke + chimney! In all 208 Mékarski cars ran in Paris, the last on 2 August 1914.

A third, rather more ephemeral design by Hughes and Lancaster, worked around Chester for a while in 1890, which ingeniously carried a plough that, at will, knocked open a valve in the road where it could quickly recharge its very small reservoirs and go on its way; having further sucks taking 40 seconds or so from valves laid at half mile intervals as and when required. Despite the fact that "in comparison with other systems of propulsion, this one offers the great advantage that every car is perfectly independent" this machine faded and went away.

The Beaumont Compressed-Air Locomotive Company was in voluntary liquidation in 1885; the last return being dated 1887 while the British Mékarski Improved Air Engine Company followed them in 1891, the final meeting being held on 12 April 1892. So, for Britain at least, died the plans of two clever men.

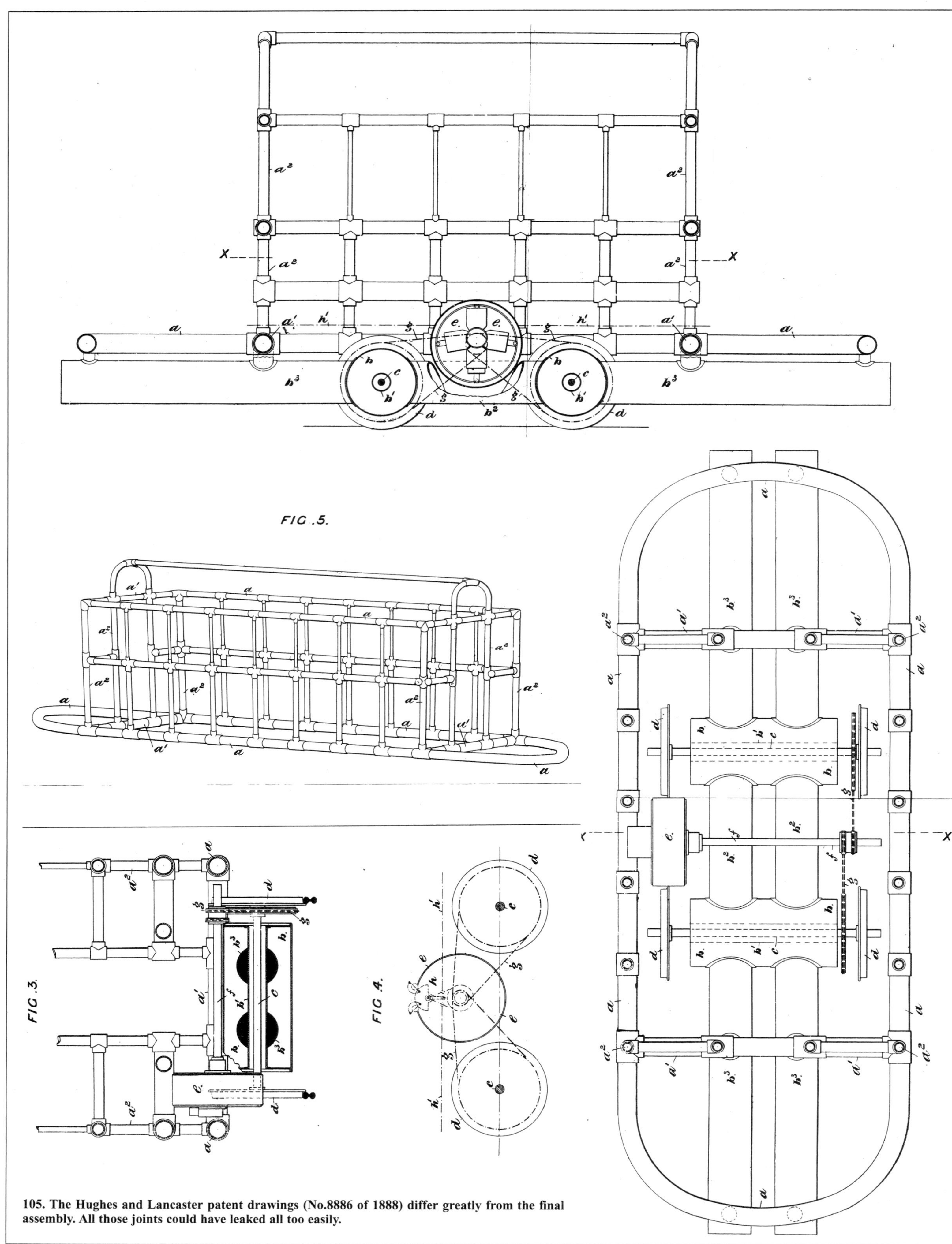

105. The Hughes and Lancaster patent drawings (No.8886 of 1888) differ greatly from the final assembly. All those joints could have leaked all too easily.

Brunner Car

A rarity which represented a cross-over into one of the more esoteric railway locomotive systems was a car designed by Mr A. Brunner of Berne. In outline it was obviously meant to be gorgeous to allay the fears of both people and horses. The mechanical components were to Fairlie's System, giving in this instance two swivelling bogies said "to provide for the free movement of the trucks, and thus notwithstanding its length the vehicle can pass readily round curves of very short radius."

Two 5.9" (15cm) cylinders with 11.8" (30cm) stroke were fitted to one bogie driving the front pair of 1.11½" (50cm) diameter wheels. The overall wheelbase of each bogie was 3' 11.2" (120cm) but the car itself measured an

106. BRUNNER'S STEAM TRAMCAR; LAUSANNE AND ECHALLENS RAILWAY.

CONSTRUCTED AT THE SWISS LOCOMOTIVE WORKS, WINTERTHUR.

Fig. 1.

Fig. 2.

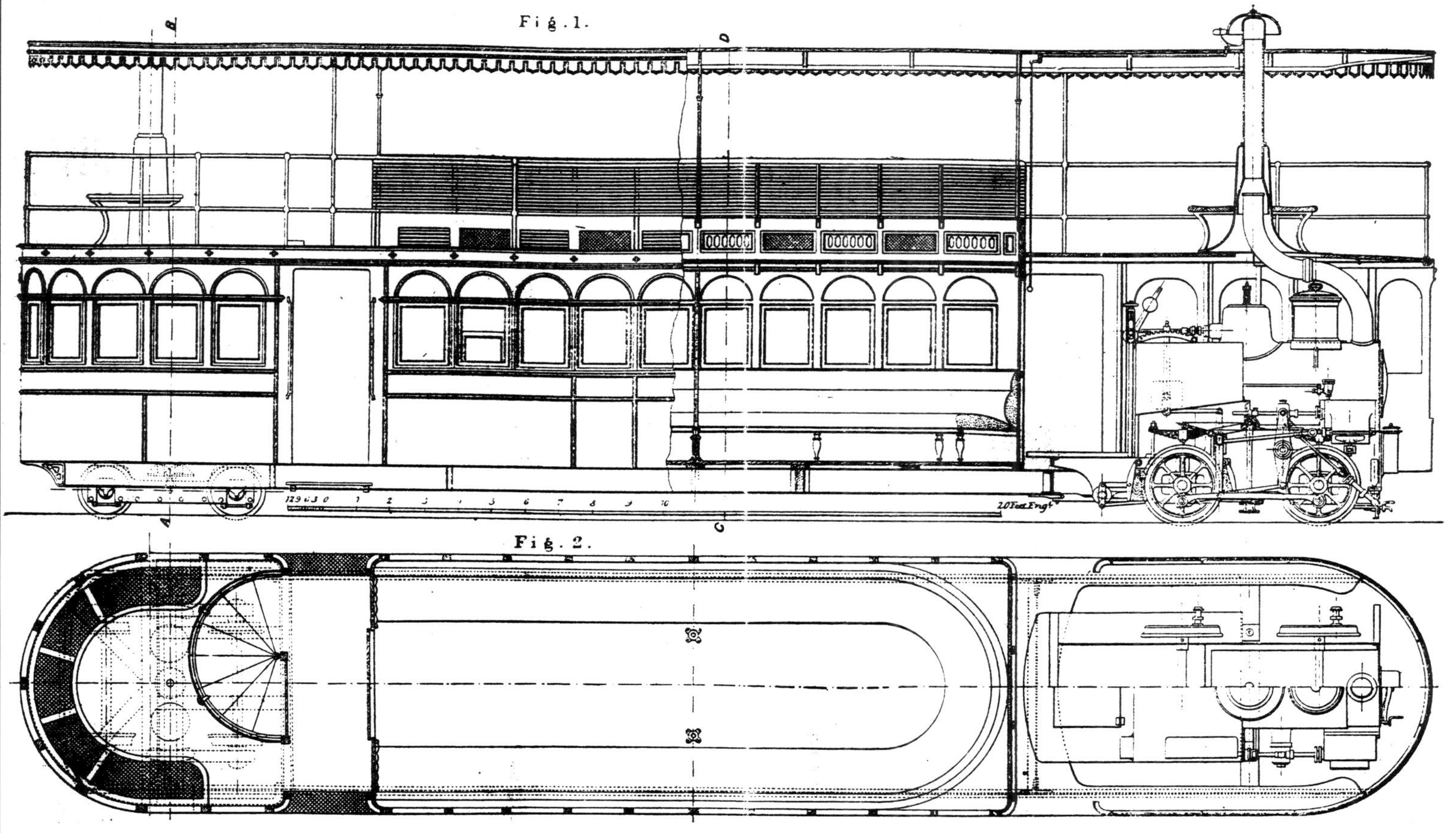

107. BRUNNER'S STEAM TRAMCAR; LAUSANNE AND ECHALLENS RAILROAD.

CONSTRUCTED AT THE SWISS LOCOMOTIVE WORKS, WINTERTHUR.

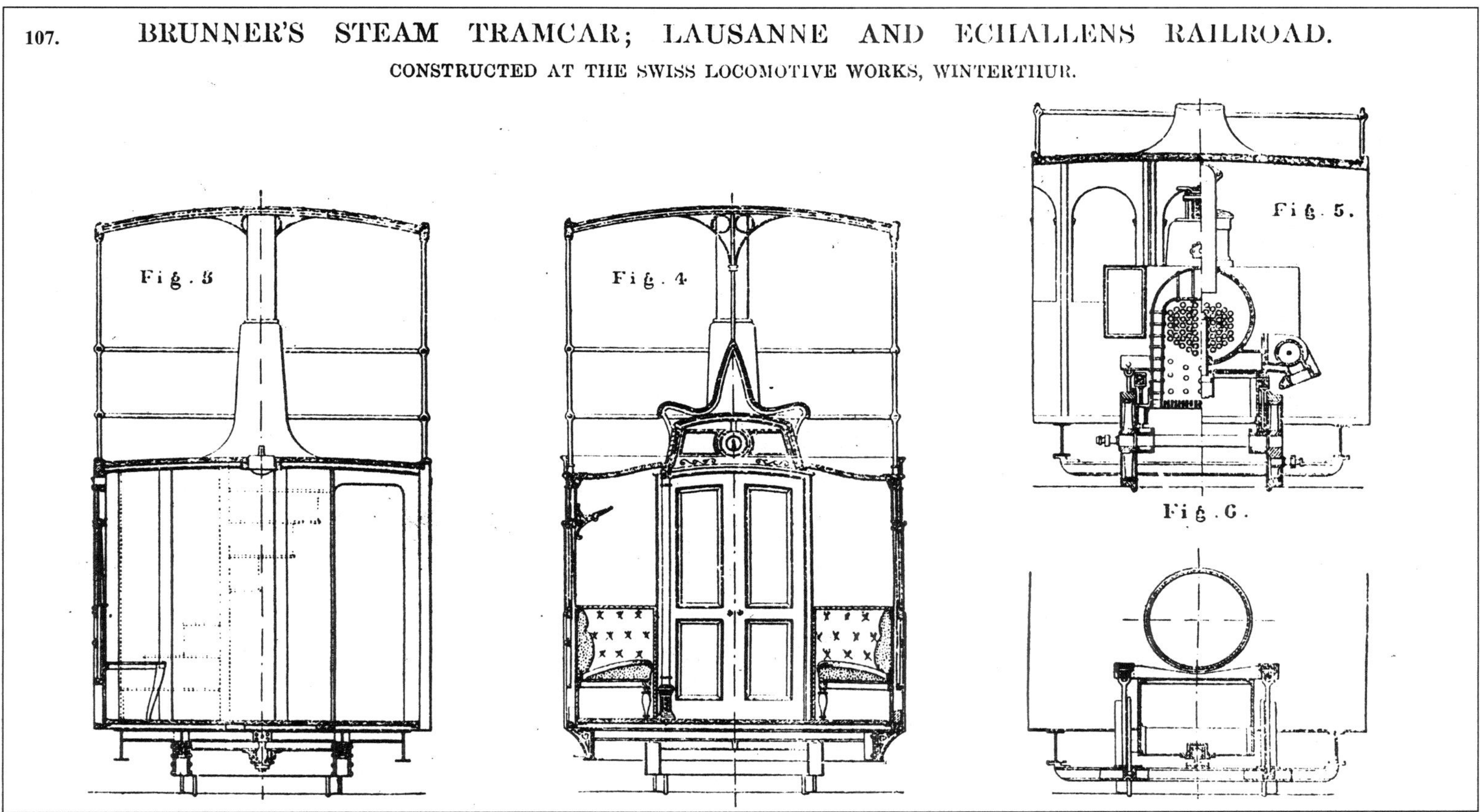

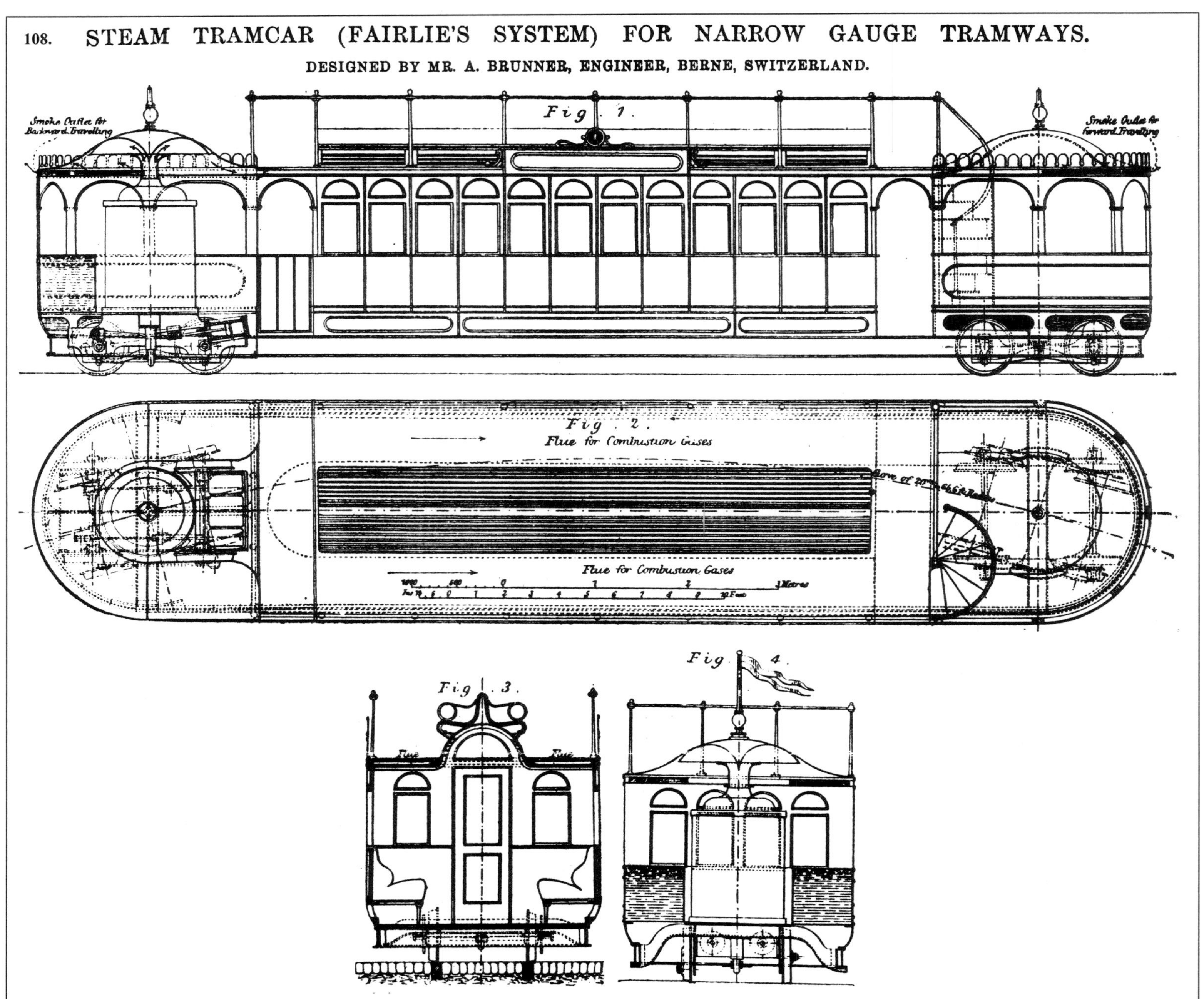

improbable 40' (12.19m) x 8' 2.4" (2.5m), weighing empty 8½ tons, laden 12. The designed speed, though, was a mere 6¼mph (10kph). It was intended to carry steam (at 147psi) from the rather tishy boiler to the second bogie which was also to be fitted with cylinders. An additional twist was added by the use of a swivelling chimney so designed that when running loco-end foremost the fumes were carried the length of the carriage between the decks, exhausting through the tail. "In winter these flues are turned to account for warming the vehicle, but in summer they are protected by a non-conducting coating, so as to prevent the radiation of heat".

Twenty-four passengers were seated in the saloon, seven in the "pavilion" over the trailing bogie and twenty-four upstairs. A slightly later variant with larger cylinders and boiler and capable of 10mph (16kph) built at Winterthur incorporated Brown's Patent drive and, within limits, this machine was quite successful on the Lausanne and Echallens Railway where it ran between proper trains (some of which were acquired from the Mont Cenis Fell Railway) as "an excursion omnibus ... on fete-days the car was fully outrigged with flags and banners and it was indeed a sight to see the gallant 'Mouette d'Echallens' taking her gentle course like a steamer when the sea is smooth". Nice epitaph.

Continental Selection 1876

1876 is again a vital date insofar as these quotations show how lines were advancing in Europe:

"(May 1876) On Saturday week last the new steam tram engine, built at the Tubize Works, made a trial trip on the line of the Bois de la Cambre [Belgium]. The journey from the Bois to the gate of Namur was made four times running. This trial on a common road confirms the experiments made at Tubize on the Quencast quarry line. The journey was made without noise, smoke or alarm to horses". ...

"(June 1876) Tramways (in Paris) are taking up a good deal of attention. The idea has been started to throw open a competition for the best type of tramway locomotive. That of Larmanjat was tried at the end of last month on the 'Tramway Nord' with results qualified by one or two defects. It is not considered strong enough for independent use, but is recommended as an auxiliary to horse power. This would make it a steam engine helped out with horseflesh. The 'Tramways Sud' are about to try a fresh experiment with Harding's locomotive, which has been improved since the date of the former experiments". (G.P. Harding was a representative of Merryweather & Sons). ...

"(July 1876) The steam tram engine, built by the Société Metallurgique Belge, is at work daily on the line from the Bois de la Cambre to Schaerbeck [in Belgium]. ...

"(August 1876) A new section of the 'Tramways Sud' from Gare Mont Parnasse to the Gare d' Orleans, was opened on the 9th. It is remarkable as being the first tram-line served by steam in the open streets of a crowded city. The total journey takes twenty minutes". ...

Two years later the steam tramway as an entity had been accepted by the French, although details of gauge, coaches, locomotives, or even motive power was still subject to experiments. For example on Sunday, 14 April, 1878, "was inaugurated the steam tramway, or road railway, between Rueil and Marly-le-Roi. Three types of engine were experimented with: (1) Leon Francq's adaption of Lamm's fireless engine

continued on page 105

CONTINENTAL PHOTOGRAPHIC SELECTION

Although this book is basically the story of British tramways and tram people, nonetheless it is as well to take a sideways look at the products of our continental competitors. The bulk of these illustrations are from a catalogue issued by Hohenzollern and copied by Derek Rayner, a road transport historian. The most important factor is the sheer size of these tram engines compared with the Board of Trade restricted machines used in the UK, and secondly, that many were built and run long after the bulk of ours were scrapped, reflecting the relatively long journeys undertaken. Curiously there was little cross-over between British and continental designs after the first flurry of Hughes, Merryweather and Fox Walker engines staggering their ways in France and Germany, and the importation of Krauss trams for the Wolverton & Stony Stratford and, of course, Hohenzollern's "Feuerlose Strassenbahnlokomotive" for Croydon.

Two Parisian photographs. The first (109) shows a totally alien engine (at least to UK eyes) towing two variants of trailers. The owning company is, I presume, from the route (Louvre-Versailles)the Compagnie Générale des Omnibus (Tramways Department) and the tram a Purrey built machine on its last year of operation, electrification taking place in 1914. A steam lorry lurks in the background. The second illustration (110) shows how well steam trams fitted in the wide boulevards of Paris. The route is to Gare de L'Est; both sets are probably Serpollet-built. Would that St. Michele were as quiet today!

111. Locomotive no. 15 of the Compãnia General de Tramvias, Barcelona, was like its predecessors a product of Winterthur, in this case works no. 268 of 1882. In all this company operated 15 km (9.4 m) of tramway. Not only were all their engines 6-wheeled (rather than four in the UK) but they were chain driven.

112-114 are all engines found in use on Dutch tramways. 112. No.21 of the Central Limburgsche Spoorweg Mij. is a Hanomag (German-built) 0-4-0 engine, albeit barely a tram engine, built as works no 9857 in 1922 and now preserved.

114. No. 21 was a 17.8 tonne locomotive built by Hohenzollern (works no. 4084) in 1921 for the Westlandsche Stoomtramweg Maatschappij for their Hague-centred 47 km (29 miles) network. It was named after the engineer, M. S. Verspijck.

113. No.22, facing us (works no. 9858 of 1922) was not so lucky, but here shows the relatively simple life-guards in use. The re-railing jack by the smokebox was no doubt very useful.

115. One of a batch of five 'pure' tram engines from Hohenzollern (works nos. 1885-89 of 1905), no. 3 of the Stoomtram Walcheren N.V. only carried the name 'Vlissingen' for photographic purposes. Very confusing for the historian!

116. By coincidence this photograph, showing No. B1508 in the nationalized PNKA fleet, was sent to me by the transport historian, R.W.Kidner, and shows No.8, the sister of the catalogued No. 10 in service at Pare, Indonesia, where it formed one of class B15, most trams of the old company (pre-nationalisation) being supplied in turn by Henschel & Hohenzollern. 3' 6" gauge.

117. Unlike the UK roadside tramways became a vital part of continental infrastructure, and the tram engines grew up to match the journey length and loads carried. This is no. 801 of class 11, built by St. Léonard (works no. 730) in 1886 as a 28 tonne standard gauge 0-6-0 fully fitted with railway-type side buffers, screw coupling and air brakes. Nos. 800-802 were used on the SNCV (Société Nationale des Chemins de Fer Vicinaux) Poulseur – Sprimont – Trooz, some 22.2 km (13.8 m) long hauling heavy stone traffic.

118. Rotterdam engine No. 3 (Werkspoor works no. 139, 1905) is seen leaving Rotterdam with a mixed train in June 1935. Apart from the smoke, steam and exhaust noise which the locals ignored (and would have given the youngest B.O.T. inspector severe palpitations) the condition of the locomotive is exemplary. "Werkspoor" was the trading name of the Nederlandsche Fabriek van Werktuigen en Spoorwegmaterial who built in all 22 locomotives for Dutch tramways, including 14 for the Rotterdamsche Tramweg Maatschappij, but who went out of business in 1912.

(Weighing 6 tons and drawing three carriages); (2) the Tilkin – Menton engine (weighing 5½ tons, built at Liege, vertical engine, drawing a goods van and a passenger car); (3) a locomotive of 8½ tons, built by Corpet and Bourdon expressly for narrow-gauge lines. The rails of the line are steel vignoles rails, made at Creusot. They weigh about 36lb to the yard, and are laid on a track by the side of the footpath. The cars were made by the Belgian Ironworks Company at Nivelles. The adoption of this supplemental railway, of a nature unknown to this country, is at present favoured by the public powers of France".

Dick, Kerr

The story of Dick, Kerr is the story of two Scotsmen. William Bruce Dick was an oil merchant who eventually went into business with his brothers building railway rolling stock in Glasgow as W.B. Dick & Co., with John Kerr as manager.

W.B. Dick as an individual owned the Alford & Sutton Tramway, although by now the firm had metamorphosed into Dick, Kerr & Co of Kilmarnock having taken over the works of Barr, Morrison & Co in May 1884, following Barr, Morrison's bankruptcy, but shortly after this (probably following the debacle of the Alford & Sutton) W.B. Dick left the Company.

John Kerr, who was twenty years younger than William Dick, was initially connected with the railway and tramcar builders Hurst Nelson but within two years of joining W.B. Dick (1881) had accepted a partnership.

The firm were to build an incredible range of machinery including cable tramways, stationary (winding and pumping) steam engines and all manner of mining materials. It was, therefore, no real problem for them to build steam locomotives, including trams. But the latter may not have totalled more than eighteen or so, of which the first traced went to the Alford & Sutton, the second to Penang Tramways in Malaya where Kerr, Stuart,(another company in which John Kerr had an interest) were contractors. Like the Alford & Sutton, this tramway seems to have been a failure.

Three more trams of far greater power (cylinders 9½" x 16" rather than the 7" x 12" of the earlier engines) were supplied in 1886 to the West Carberry Tramways & Light Railways Company (later Schull & Skibbereen Tramway & Light Railway Company) which was built to "open up and improve communications" within the south west of the county of Cork. The three trams, as supplied, were a disaster, although building the West Carberry to the specification of an urban tramway was incredible. The problems with the engines were manifold, the firebox design and materials used were quite unsuitable, while leakage from the firebox end of the tubes became endemic due to unequal expansion. Even as new, despite weighing 15 tons they were unable to pull as little as twice their weight up any gradient. The condenser, probably designed to avoid paying patentee's fees, was odd as it was nothing more than a nest of tubes built into the roof of the firebox through which exhaust steam passed forming, in effect, a superheater although these tubes, which would be lethal if they exploded, were protected by a flat fire brick arch, a design ill thought-out as vibration immediately caused their collapse. The engines having

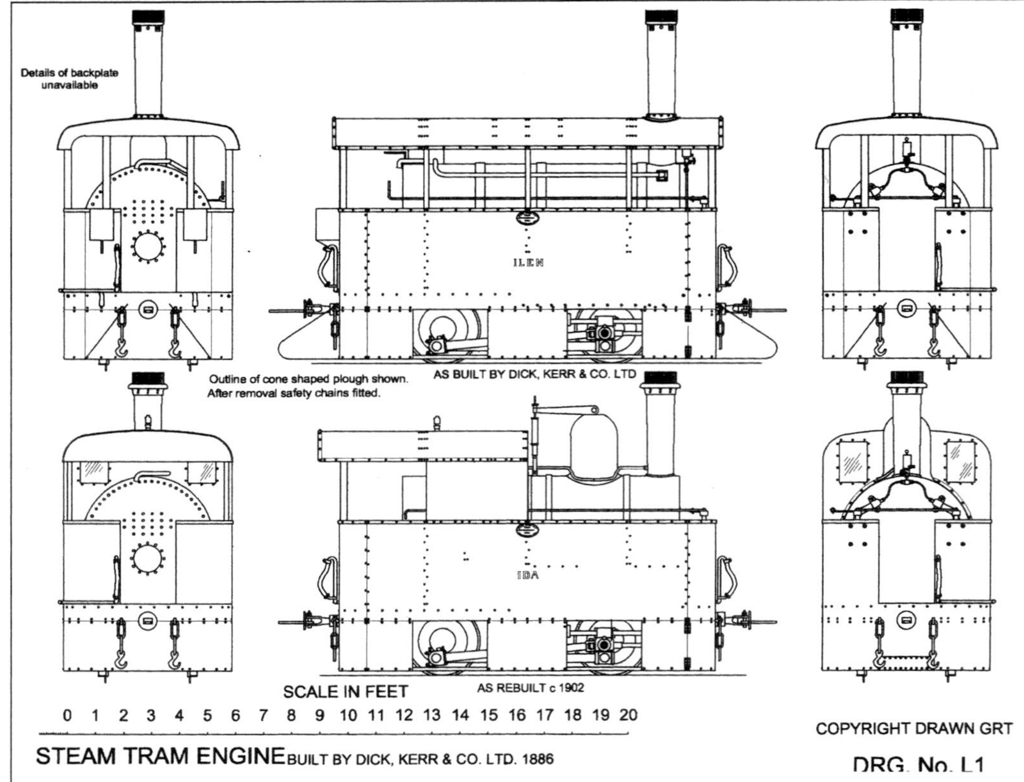

119. This drawing, reproduced by permission of James I.C.Boyd, shows one of Dick Kerr's failures which had to be rebuilt.

no dome the live steam suffered from condensation, to the degree that to get any work out of the machines first the condensation gear in the firebox was removed or blanked off and then (riskily) the vacuum brake was disconnected. I am reminded of a dreadfully neglected and leaking engine we had where keeping up steam pressure was impossible, the elderly driver gloomily peered around the cab and told me we could have steam heat, keep moving or do without "wackum"; we shut off the first, gradually lost speed and as we ran into a siding for a 'blow-up' wackum went and brakes came on. When we had regained some puff (150psi instead of 225 he wack-ummed the wackum valve in fury!

The good thing about these three engines was that they were named, Marion, Ida and Ilen; a rare attribute to tram engines. Marion was dismantled by 1906, Ilen probably disused but still extant then, and a totally rebuilt Ida survived until at least 1924.

The next batch of engines were ten standard gauge (4' 8½") machines supplied to North London Tramways during 1886/7. Cylinders were 8" x 14" and driving wheel diameter 2' 6". The first fifteen locomotives supplied to this line came from Merryweather & Sons and a contemporary report (December 1885), after writing about the "complete absence of steam, vapor, or noise, from the engine" continued with the information that the line had been opened for twelve months and that there had not been a single accident in that time on the road, "although a large number of carts drawn by two or four horses are continually passing along to and from Covent Garden Market and Enfield [then fertile land], the drivers frequently being asleep". In fact, the horses got so used to the steamers the driver only had to ring the bell for them to move off the line.

We do not know why the North London officials deserted a local (Greenwich) firm in favour of a Scottish one, perhaps the price or the hire-purchase agreement was more favourable.

The trailers, built by Milnes, were unusual in being open-topped, despite complicated condensing and "smoke absorbing" fittings no doubt the coke fumes made eyes water.

The problems with all of these engines is the short wheelbase which made engines 'shimmy' along, despite inside cylinders being used to

120. Smart enough here, no. 25 looks suspiciously new, together with the matching-numbered Milnes built trailer. Locomotive and trailer predominantly dark (Brunswick) green with white relief and lining out.

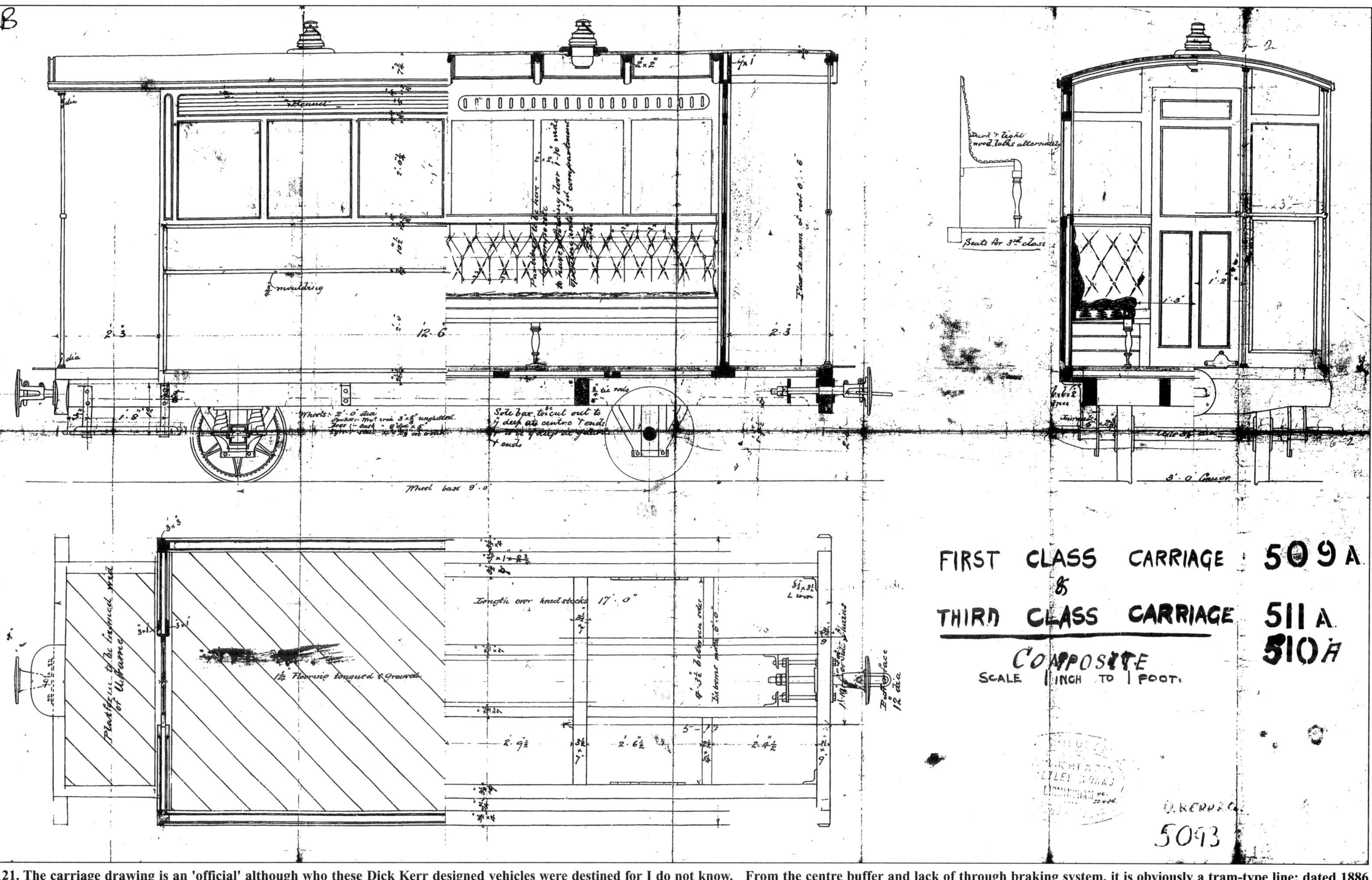

121. The carriage drawing is an 'official' although who these Dick Kerr designed vehicles were destined for I do not know. From the centre buffer and lack of through braking system, it is obviously a tram-type line; dated 1886 and of 3' 0" gauge.

122. FIRELESS TRAMWAY LOCOMOTIVE FOR JAVA.

CONSTRUCTED AT THE HOHENZOLLERN LOCOMOTIVE WORKS, DÜSSELDORF.

reduce the pendulum effect. The North London line, to make matters worse, used Henry Vignoles system of trackwork which involved a rail with separate head and foot, bolted together and bolted to wooden sleepers buried in concrete. Although laid in 1881, within ten years it was falling apart and the North London Suburban Tramway Company, always financially shaky was only too glad to sell out to the North Metropolitan Tramways Company in 1891 following an injunction on the use of steam from the Board of Trade as the residents had petitioned that body, claiming the steam trams were a nuisance; NorthMet withdrawing almost all of the steam stock.

The final steam tram engines supposed to have been built by Dick, Kerr may have been sent to Calcutta in 1890, although it has been suggested these were three of the North London machines refurbished.

Dick, Kerr were to eventually find their forte in the field of electric tramways, although they carried on building light industrial-type locomotives, mainly to encourage skills in their apprentices.

123. "Cleve" was a narrow gauge (750mm/30") twin cab tram engine, designed, I suspect, for works use. It weighed 6.8 tons empty, 8.3 in normal, trim.

Fireless

In 1882, Dr. G. Lentz wrote in a number of articles in the technical press, extolling the virtues

124.

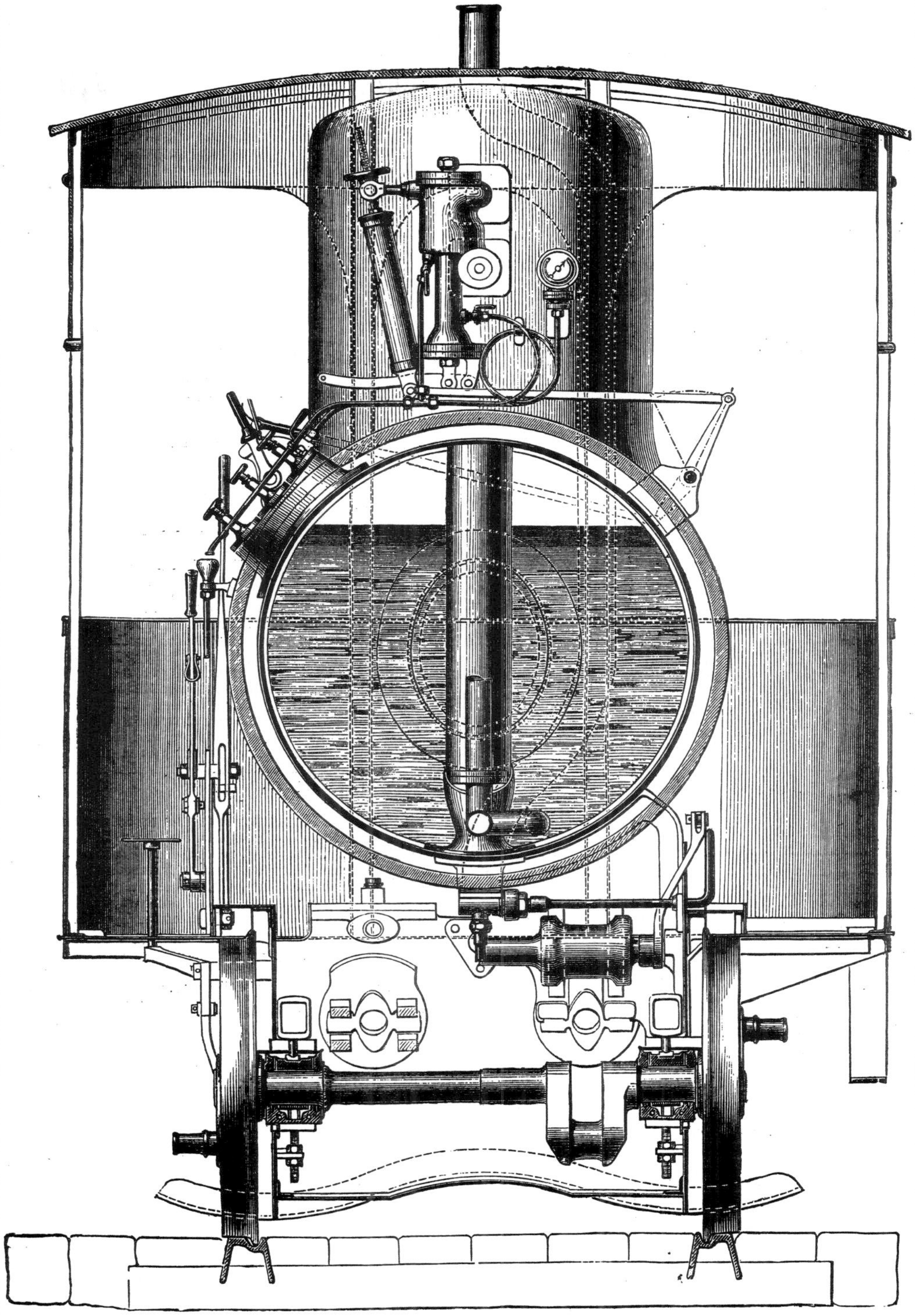

of 'Fireless' tramway locomotives. He was, admittedly, biased, being the engineering director of the Hohenzollern Locomotive Works, Düsseldorf, who made rather a speciality of these engines, but even 120 years later his enthusiasm still bubbles through. He inveighs against orthodox tram locomotives stating that while, especially in agricultural areas, land, buildings, etc., and even highroads are "in a very liberal spirit, placed at the disposal of the tramway companies" the cost of running steam trams is inordinately high, citing the use of expensive coke to avoid smoke, which in turn means small and inefficient grates, cost of repairs are heavy and "a large number of hands are necessarily employed in working, cleaning, and repairing a large number of small locomotives, the wages for which figure as heavy items on the balance sheet." He also adds that flying sparks could easily cause conflagrations. The interesting point in this is that not only were the same arguments put forward by protagonists of cable tramways, but that he was, of course, right – it is illogical for each tram engine to hump about the necessary paraphenalia used by steam engines; it is all weight and mechanical complexity. The fireless was (and is) merely a heavily insulated hot water reservoir, three-quarters filled with water and then topped up by steam at 240psi. The engines, on a 'horses for courses' arrangement could weigh as little as 2½ tons for a towed weight of 6 tons, thus using lightly laid track, whereas to pull 20 tons over twelve miles, the locomotives would weigh 15 tons, carrying 1,000 gallons of water. Because of the nature of a fireless gradients are only limited by the adhesion of the engine wheels.

Operational mathematics are intriguing as although the stationary boiler fires would be damped at night and some pressure lost, engines charged the evening before lost no more than 25% of their pressure and were instantly available for work in the morning. A normal steam tram took 30-40 minutes before it could even move itself.

Statistically the good doctor quotes the following: According to the size of the boiler each engine requires 20-30 minutes to recharge; if trains run at 5 minute intervals then 4-6 engines will always be re-charging. Presuming the journey time is 45 minutes and the charging time takes an average of 25 minutes this gives a total of 70 minutes. On the required 5 minute headway 14 locomotives will form the 'stud', allow three being serviced (although it is not clear why this could not overlap the charging) and three spare, then 20 engines would be desirable.

125. FIRELESS TRAMWAY LOCOMOTIVE.
CONSTRUCTED AT THE HOHENZOLLERN LOCOMOTIVE WORKS, DÜSSELDORF.

They appear to have been successful in Java (Dutch East Indies) but a total failure on the line from West Norwood to Croydon, probably because the number ordered (six, works numbers 319-324 of 1884) were insufficient to run either a regular service or to make the cost of running the boiler house even remotely viable. In Java, with 30 engines, boilers were being recharged at the rate of one every 1½ minutes during three peak hours a day, and one every ten minutes for the other nine hours.

Fox Walker

Unfortunately it seems most if not all Fox Walker records are lost so that except when the machines have been physically inspected and noted at some time, output must necessarily be conjectural. Dr H.A. Whitcombe in his History of the Steam Tram, written in 1937 (but in the mid 1890s he used to ride on the footplate, hidden behind the coke-bunker) states that Fox Walker built three classes of steam tramway engines, all with horizontal boilers, one of which appears to correspond with entries in the Industrial Railway Society's works list as No.361-367 of 1878, sent out to Rouen, but there said to be of 0-6-2 configuration (three driven axles and a pony truck). It is difficult to see why at such an early date tram engines with three driven axles would be required; and again of the twenty-four engines recorded as running in Rouen during 1881, seven were from Fox Walker, two from Merryweather and six built by

FIRELESS TRAMWAY LOCOMOTIVE FOR JAVA.

CONSTRUCTED AT THE HOHENZOLLERN LOCOMOTIVE WORKS, DÜSSELDORF.

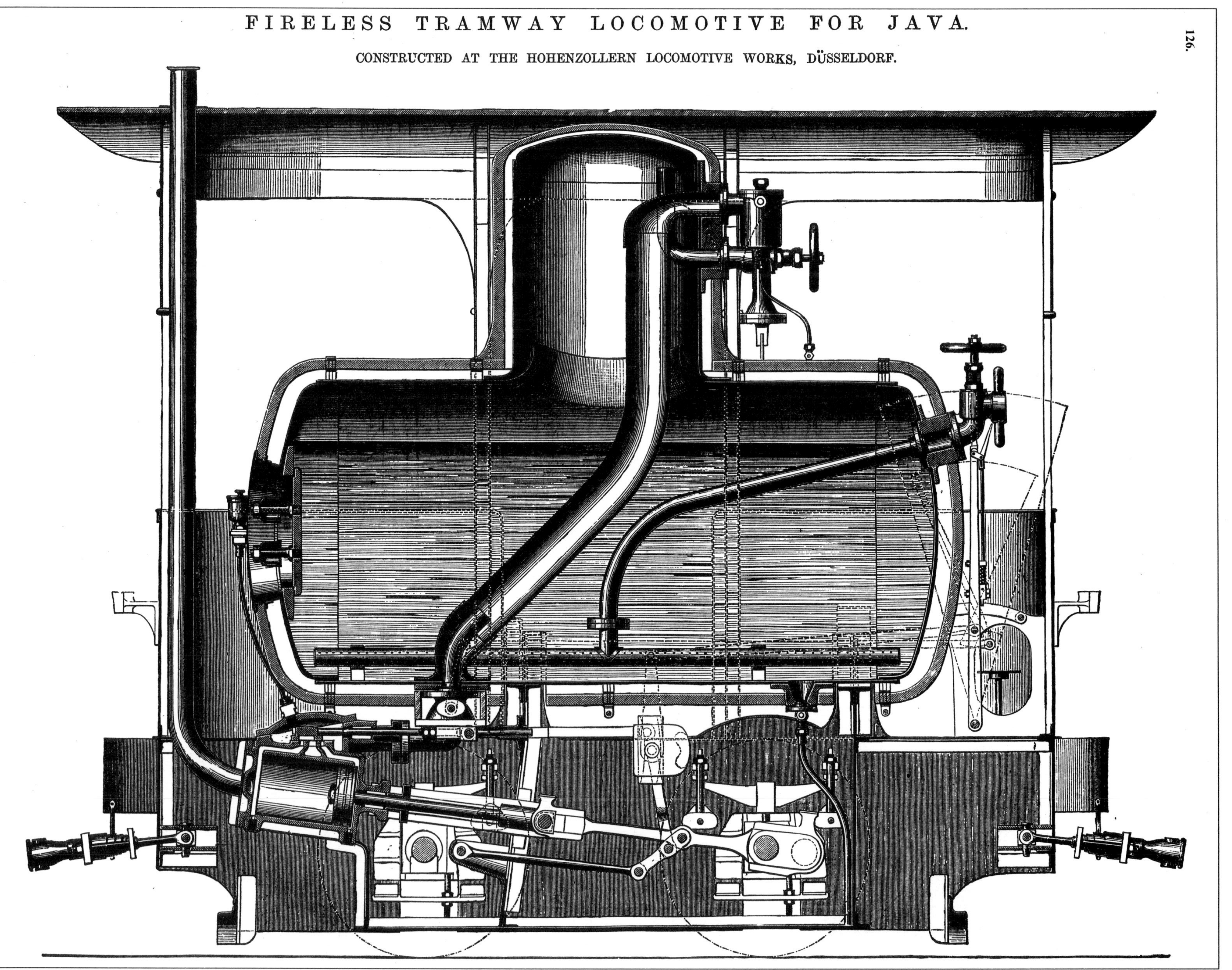

127. This is believed to be a Fox Walker-designed engine at the time when Peckett & Sons, Atlas Engine Works at Bristol had taken over the assets of Fox Walker. The late Jim Peden, photographer to two specialist railway societies gave it the number FW 387. The details are of great interest as it is of 0-4-2 configuration with oddly spindly wheels.

128. This little Fox Walker engine no.386 of 1878 was used on part of the Royal Arsenal Railway at Woolwich. Incredibly this engine ran on rails just 18" (457mm) apart. By 1880 there were eleven locomotives from various makers running on about 25 miles (40 km) of track. FW 386 was disposed of, probably for scrap, before 1923, when the bulk of the system fell out of use. It, too, carries a Peckett plate, has 5¾" x 6" cylinders, and was made "to Mr. Webb"s drawings as furnished by him." This was F.W.Webb of LNWR and Crewe fame.

Fives-Lille, and a lonely one from Kitson, but with the exception of the Fox Walkers (0-4-2) all the others were recorded as 0-4-0. By 1884 Rouen returned to horse traction. Using other evidence as corroboration, it seems more probable that Fox Walker built no more than 19 tram engines, six of which were two axled (0-4-0) and the balance had three axles including a pony truck, thus 0-4-2.

One of the earliest batch ran trials in Bristol, including ascending the incline to St. Georges. Weighing around five tons it was a bantamweight in steam trams, with only 8" x 9" cylinders and a 4' 6" wheelbase. Curiously it burned coal which was made up into brown paper packets to reduce dust and dirt – something of this kind used to be available here for domestic use, but the thought of a tram driver carefully laying neatly wrapped packets of coal in a firebox makes one boggle. No visible condenser appears to have been fitted, although we know cylinder condensate was exhausted through the ash-pan. Pecketts, who took over the Atlas Works, Fishponds, Bristol, of Fox Walker on their bankruptcy in December 1878, do not seem to have built any further tram engines to these designs.

129. This was one of the tram engines built by Fox Walker and tried in Bristol. The engine plate shows a date of 1877. It is believed that this is one of two built then (works nos. 380-381) with 8" x 9" cylinders, type SWTE for the Pont de Pierre to Maromme line in Rouen, being, as it were, test run on the Horsfield line of Bristol Tramways & Carriage Co. Ltd. However, alas, the photograph does not agree with an undated drawing showing a tram of this type!

Conundrum, – Fox Walker

The following advertisement, of which the second item is the most relevant to steam trams, appeared in issues of the magazine *Iron* dated 22 February 1879, 1st and 8th March 1879. These would no doubt be similar to those in Fox Walker's prospectus and presumably were some of the engines hired out for use on the Continent but subsequently returned to Bristol, although another school of thought has it they were used for experimental workings on Bristol Tramways in 1877. Would so many have been used for an experiment at that early date?

"LOCOMOTIVE AND TRAMWAY ENGINES FOR SALE BY PRIVATE TENDER.

For the benefit of whom it may concern. Two six-wheeled Locomotive ENGINES, 4ft 8½in. gauge, each four wheels coupled with four-wheeled Tenders, second-hand, cylinders (inside), 15in. diam. and 18in. stroke, coupled wheels 4ft 11in. diam, fitted with 2 injectors, copper firebox, brass tubes, best Yorkshire boiler plates, best Yorkshire tires. Tender tanks 1300 gallons each. Weight of each Engine empty, about 24 tons; and of each tender about 19 tons; recently thoroughly repaired, most of the brasses new, and boilers tested to 200lb per square inch, working pressure 120lb.

Eleven Six-wheeled TRAMWAY ENGINES, 4ft 8½in. gauge, four wheels coupled with hind pair of wheels on radiating axle, cylinders (inside) 8in. diam; and 9in. stroke, coupled wheels 30in. diam., water tank 150 gallons, one injector, one pump, copper firebox, brass tubes,

'Farnley' boiler plates, crucible steel wheels, weight of engine empty about 7 tons, of complete modern design. This Engine is stated to be capable of drawing two loaded cars up a short incline of 1 in 26.

N.B. – Some ordinary six wheels coupled LOCOMOTIVE TANK ENGINES also for sale.

For further information and Tender, application to be made to

JOHN C. WILSON, M.Inst M.E., 84 Redland Road, Bristol."

130. This specification of a tramway engine would be rare enough from any manufacturer, let alone Fox Walker, and is reproduced in its entirety for this reason.

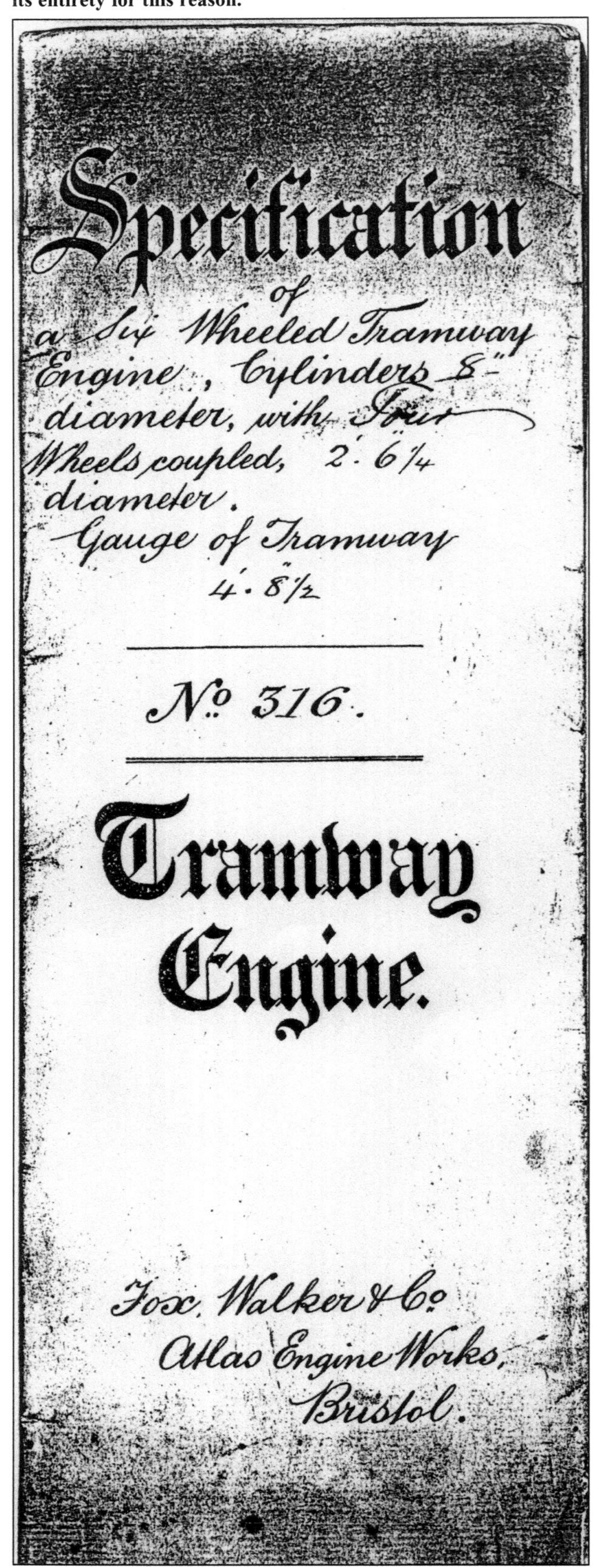

Specification of a Six Wheeled Tramway Engine, Cylinders 8" diameter, with Four Wheels coupled, 2' 6¼ diameter. Gauge of Tramway 4' 8½

No 316.

Tramway Engine.

Fox, Walker & Co. Atlas Engine Works, Bristol.

Specification of a Six wheel Locomotive Tank Engine for Tramways, Cylinders 8" diameter 4 Wheels coupled 2' 6¼ diameter.

Description. The Engine to be of the Inside Cylinder class the general design of which is shewn in the accompanying Woodcut having 4 wheels 2' 6¼ diameter, coupled, and for a gauge of Tramway 4' 8½. The rigid wheel-base is 3' 6 and the total wheel base 6' 3; and to facilitate the passage of the Engine round sharp curves the Engine is carried on a Two wheeled Bogie at the leading end.

Boiler. The Boiler is made of the Best Yorkshire Iron, the longitudinal seams are double rivetted. Rivets are pitched 1¾ from centre to centre.

External Fire Box. The External Fire Box to be made of plates 3/8" thick

Internal Fire Box. The Internal Fire Box to be of the best selected copper, the plates to be 3/8" thick, except where the Tubes pass through where it is to be 7/16 thick.

Staying. The Shell to be stayed by Longitudinal Stays, the top of Fire Box by Bridge Stays, and the flat surfaces of the inner and outer Fire Box by stays 7/8" diameter, arranged as near 4½ pitch as possible. The Boiler to be suitable for an ordinary working pressure of 140 lbs: per sq: inch, and tested by hydraulic pressure to 200 lbs: per sq: inch.

Tubes. The Tubes to be 85 in number, of the best solid drawn Brass 1⅜" in diameter, No 12 – B W G.

Safety Valves. A pair of 2" Safety Valves to be fitted on the Boiler, and held down by Levers and Spring Balances.

Frames. The Frames to be made from one solid plate of wrought Iron, strongly secured to one another by cross stays.

Buffers. Buffers to be made to suit cars.

Wheels. The Wheels to be 2' 6¼ diameter, of C Steel, with solid Tyres 2½" wide.

Axles. The Axles to be of the best Steel

Axle Boxes. The Axle Boxes to be of Cast Iron, with gun metal bearings and arranged for lubrication by oil from underneath.

Springs. The Springs to be of best Spring Steel, and the Trailing and Driving connected by compensating Beams

Cylinders. The Cylinders to be of the best hard Cylinder Metal, 8" diameter. Waste Water Cocks to be fitted to each Cylinder and worked from the footplate.

Pistons. The Pistons to be of metal 2" in width, and fitted with C I. packing rings.

Piston Rods. The Piston Rods to be 1⅛" diameter, secured by nuts to the Pistons and by cotters to the Crossheads.

Connecting Rods. The Connecting Rods to be of the best Wrought Iron, having gun-metal brasses secured by suitable cotters.

Coupling Rods. The Coupling Rods to be of Wrought iron, having strong gun-metal brasses and fitted with extra large oil cups.

Valve Motion. The whole of the Valve Motion to be accurately fitted, and afterwards case hardened.

Brake. A powerful — Brake to be fitted so as to lock all the coupled wheels the Brake being on the right hand side of the Engine.

Feed Apparatus. The Boiler to be fed by one pump worked from the Cross Head, and by 1 – No. 4 Giffards Patent Injector, all the handles being conveniently worked from the footplate.

Pipes. All the steam & feed pipes to be of copper.

Tank.	The Tank to be fixed behind the Boiler, and to contain 150 Gallons of water.
Fuel.	The Fuel space to have a capacity of 3. cwt.
Case.	A neat Case to be fitted on Engine as shewn in the accompanying ~~Photograph~~. Woodcut.
General Fittings.	The Engine to be fitted with Water Gauge, Gauge Cocks, Jet Cock, Steam Gauge, Blow off Cock, mud plugs, and Safety Plug.
Painting.	The Engine to be painted with two coats of lead-colour, two coats of green and finally lined out and varnished.
Materials and Workmanship.	The materials and workmanship throughout to be of the best description.
Tools.	The following Tools to be supplied with the Engine, viz:- A lock up Tool Box containing a set of spanners, one moveable spanner, one Copper hammer, one lead hammer, one hand hammer, three files, three chisels, spare gauge-glass, oil cans, and one crow-bar; also a complete set of firing irons and shovel.

Atlas Engine Works,
Bristol.

131.

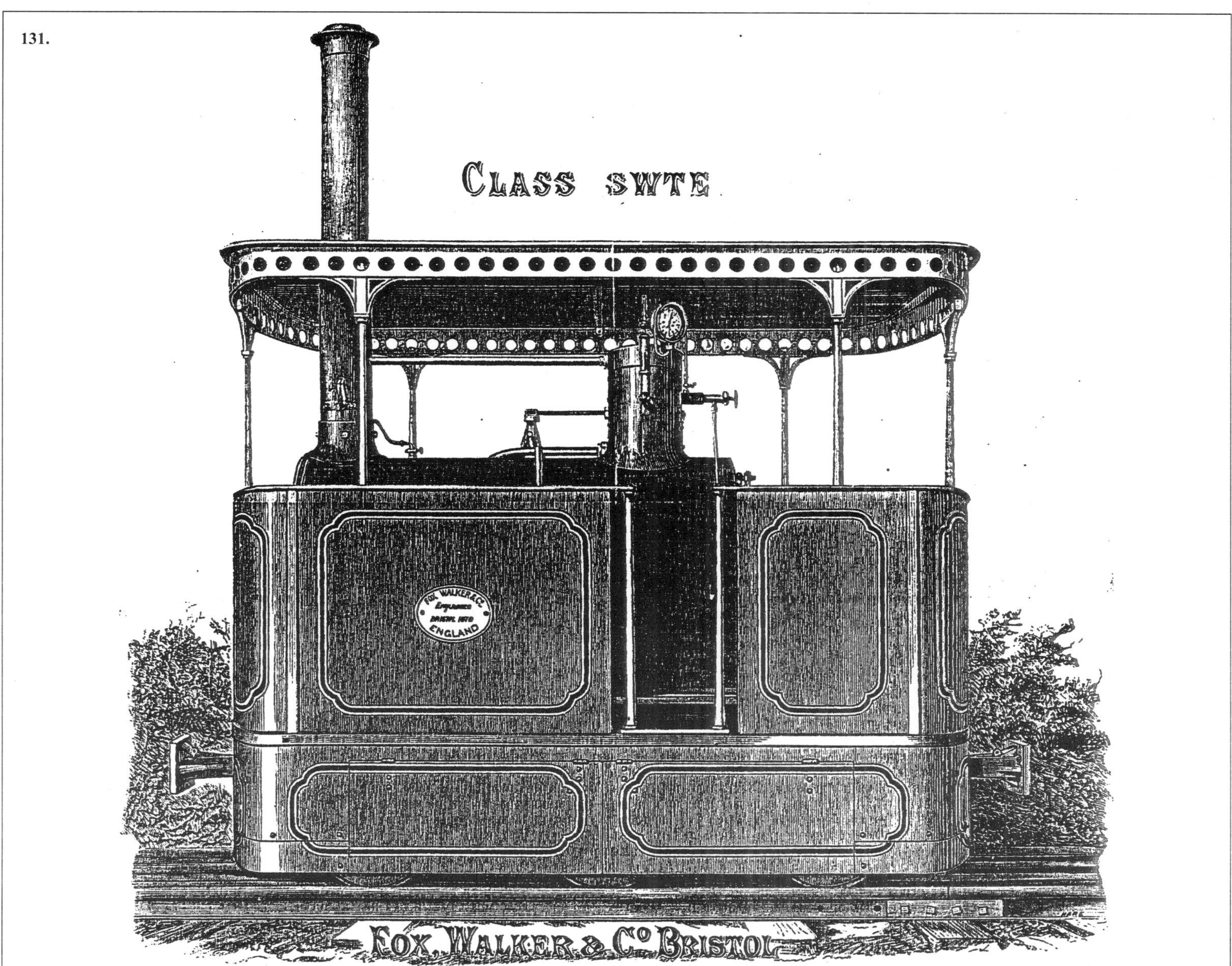

ROWAN'S STEAM CARRIAGE AT THE ANTWERP EXHIBITION TRIALS.

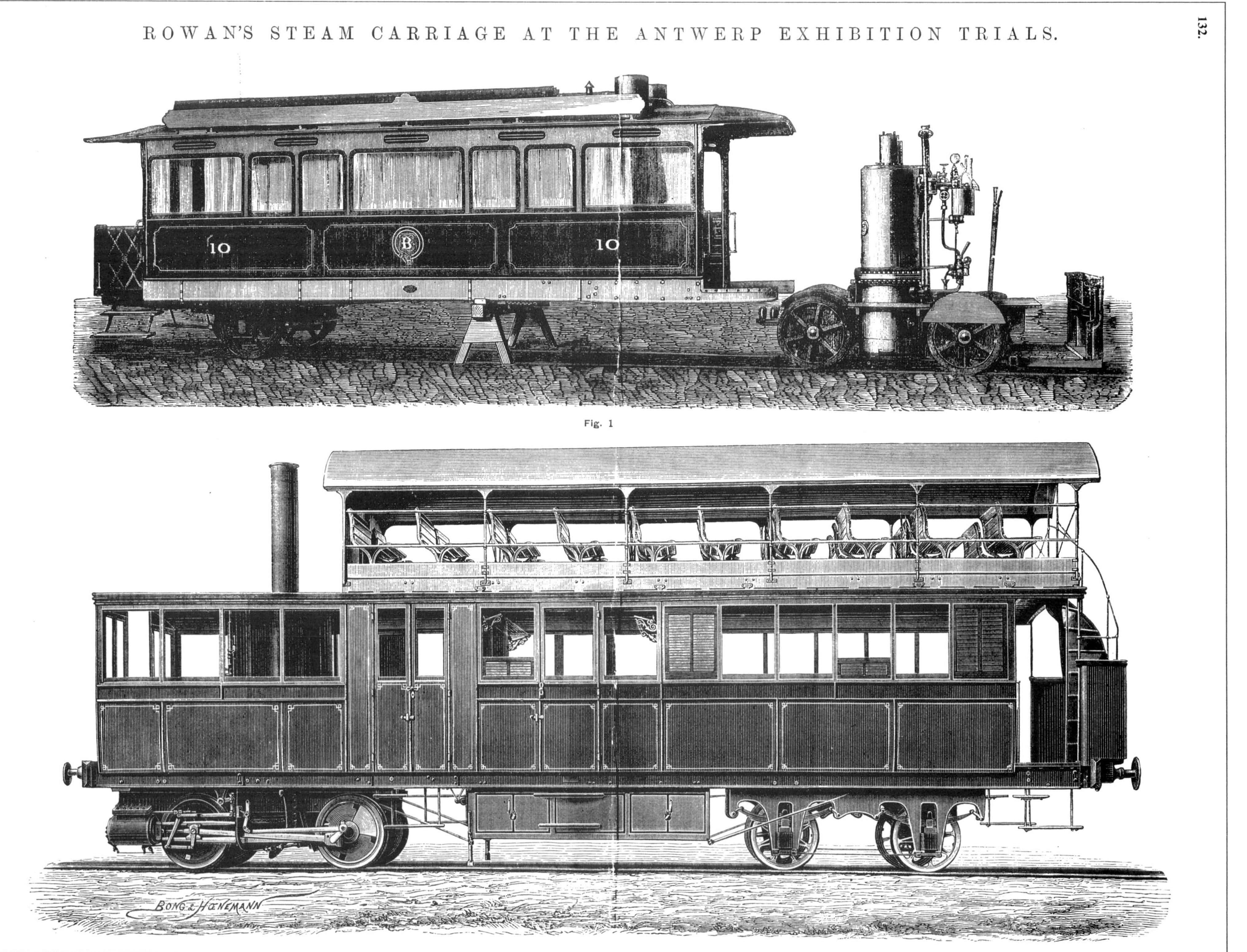

Fig. 1

Fig. 2

ROWAN'S STEAM CARRIAGE.

As stated in our article on the Antwerp* tramway trials, the Rowan steam carriage was awarded the gold medal in the first competition of Group I.—locomotives or automotive vehicles for towns and cities. In seeking a method of working tramways and light railways economically, Mr. Rowan adopted the principle of reducing the dead weight by the use of an engine whose power considerably exceeds its adhesion, while utilising the weight of the passengers for the balance of adhesion; and this he accomplishes by supporting the vehicle on two bogies, one of which is the motor. Fig. 1 of the accompanying illustrations shows the manner in which this principle is carried out. The body of the carriage may be raised by a pair of screw jacks, and the front bogie carrying the engine and boiler run out, thus rendering it perfectly accessible for cleaning, inspection, and repairs. This operation, which is common to all three types of these carriages, viz., for town tramways, light or secondary lines, and railways, is accomplished most easily and rapidly, eleven minutes being sufficient to run the engine out and in again.

Fig. 2 shows the steam carriage which took part in the Antwerp competition, and Fig. 3 a plan thereof one-fiftieth actual size.

Fig. 4

Although the middle is shown open for summer traffic, it may be completely closed for the winter, and also warmed by the exhaust steam without extra expense. The total length is 9½ metres, or 31ft., and that of the body 8·15 metres, or 26ft. 9in., while the width of latter is 2·2 metres, or 7ft. 2in. The wheel base is 22ft. 6in.; and the car, of normal gauge, is capable of running round curves of 15 metres, or 16½ yards' radius. The total weight in running order is 7¼ tons; and the maximum weight of the wheels on the rails with full load 1·7 ton, the weight available for adhesion in this state being 6·2 tons. The steam carriage as shown will carry 50 passengers, and 110 when drawing a supplementary car after it. One man is sufficient to stoke, drive, and brake, so that, with the conductor for tickets, only two men are required for working. The tractive power is 500 kilogrammes, or 25-horse power, sufficient to mount gradients of 1 in 20; and on the level a speed of 20 kilometres, or about 12½ miles an hour, is attainable. When running at half that speed, with dry rails, the carriage may be pulled up in 10 metres. The car was made by Herbrandt, of Ehrenfeldt, near Cologne; and the engine by Borsig, of Berlin.

The engine shown run out in Fig. 1 is of an early type, with inverted cylinders; Fig. 4 illustrates the engine of a larger form of steam carriage for light railways; and Figs. 5, 6, and 7 give details with metrical dimensions. But, as shown at Fig. 3, the boiler for the town steam carriage is made double, in accordance with the sketch above, with two internal fireboxes and two chimneys with natural draught, the horizontal member considerably strengthening the vertical shells of 0·54 m. = 21¼in. diameter, containing cross water tubes. This arrangement provides a large steam space, and affords plenty of dry steam, which can be raised in thirty-five minutes, 400 kilogrammes, or 881 lb., of water being evaporated per hour under a pressure of thirteen atmospheres, or 195 lb. per square inch. The boiler is so constructed that, by unbolting a flange and lifting off a plate, the tubes with turned flanges are freely exposed, so that the inside may readily be cleaned; but, thanks to the active circulation, no scale has yet been formed. There is no coke bunker, but the fuel is contained in sheet iron boxes, containing about 4½ lb., and hooked on to the hand-rail, so that

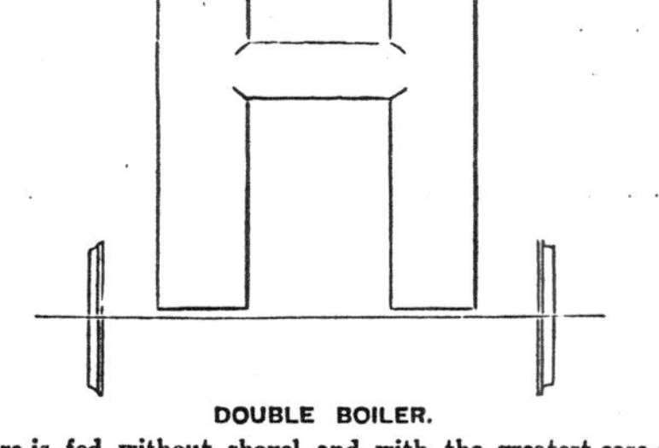

DOUBLE BOILER.

the fire is fed without shovel and with the greatest ease and cleanliness. At Antwerp 100 kilogrammes, or 2 cwt., of gas coke were burnt every day for the run of 80 kilometres, or nearly 50 miles, which amounts to 1¼ kilogramme per kilometre, or about 4½ lb. per mile. The consumption of oil is only 1 litre, or less than a quart, a day.

The cylinders, 0·13 metre, or 5·1in., in diameter, and of 0·25 metre, or 9·8in., stroke, are bolted to the feet of the boiler, this arrangement bringing the whole weight between the two axles, and distributing it uniformly over the four wheels. The weight of the front portion of the body carried by the engine bogy also bears evenly between the two axles, which circumstance, in addition to the horizontal position of the cylinders, causes a remarkably regular and noiseless motion of the engine. This is a point of the greatest importance, because, combined with the slight weight and low centre of gravity, it has great influence in preserving the way. The axles are not coupled because, with the slight gradients usually encountered in towns, the adhesion of two driving wheels generally permits of drawing a supplementary car. The other pair of wheels can, however, be coupled with a chain, or with side rods in the ordinary manner. The

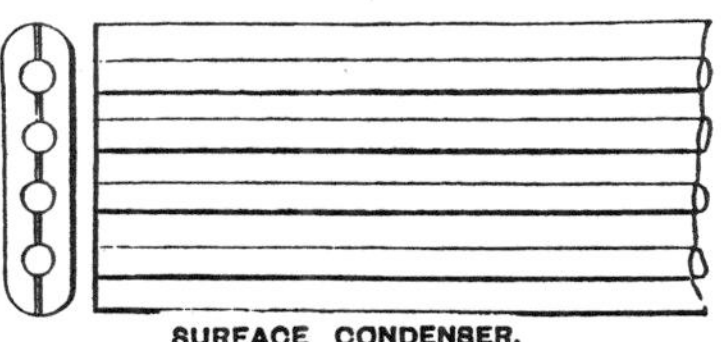

SURFACE CONDENSER.

connecting rod brasses are cast with a cap over the end of the crank-pin, for keeping out dust and mud.

Under the seats are placed two feed tanks, composed of copper tubes, one containing cold water, and the other the hot water from the surface condenser which is placed on the roof. The latter consists of a series of copper tubes, of the form shown in the sketch above, presenting about 80 square metres, or 860 square feet, of condensing surface. The parts are hung freely so as to allow for expansion and contraction, and the surface exposed to the air is sufficiently large to dispense with the necessity of water for cooling. The feed pump is constantly at work circulating the water, which is thus used over and over again, so that a steam carriage can run for forty or fifty kilometres without renewing its water supply. The passengers feel no heat from the condenser or hot-water tank; and the motion of the engine is completely deadened by springs introduced between the engine and the carriage. The thrust of the bearing-springs is

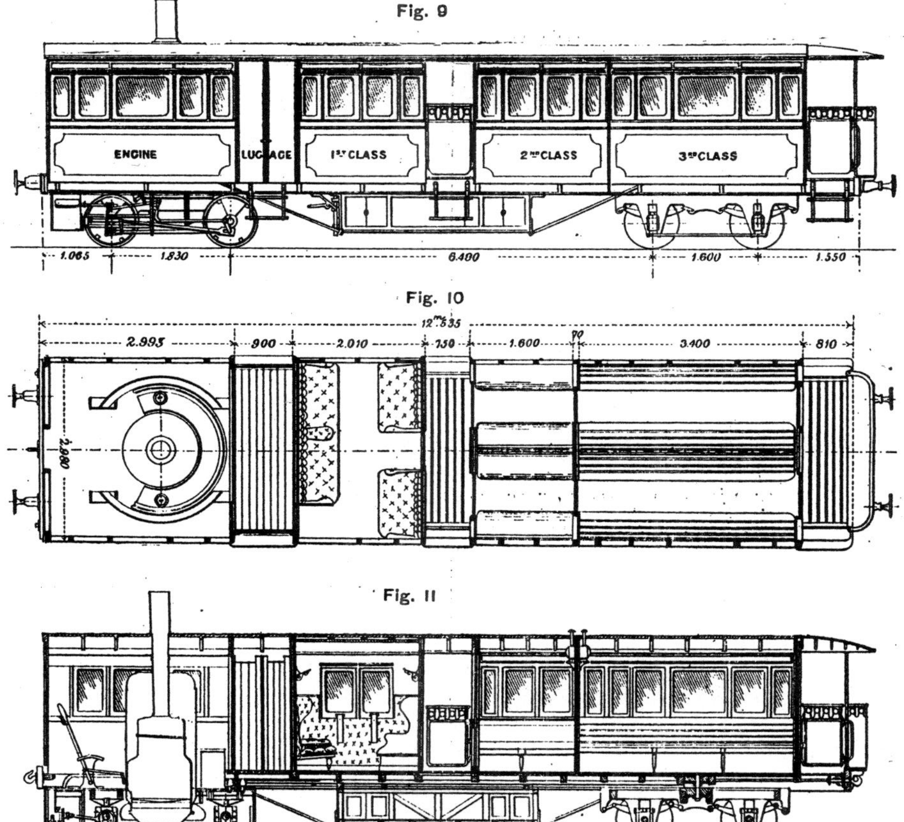

* The Engineer, 29th January, 1886.

134. received by shoes which slide in segmental guides, shown by the annexed sketch, thus producing the effect of a radial axle-box. There are two sets of brake blocks, four, worked by pedal, on one pair of wheels for ordinary use, and four, worked by screw, on the other pair for pulling up sharp in case of an emergency. In place of the ordinary clearing iron a bunch of canes is bolted

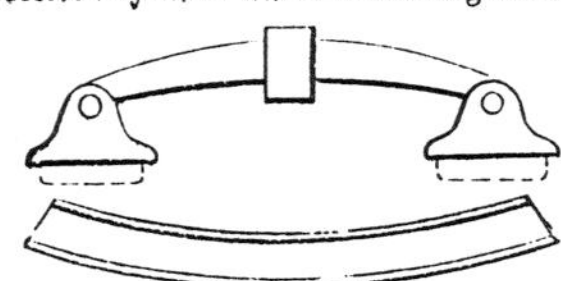

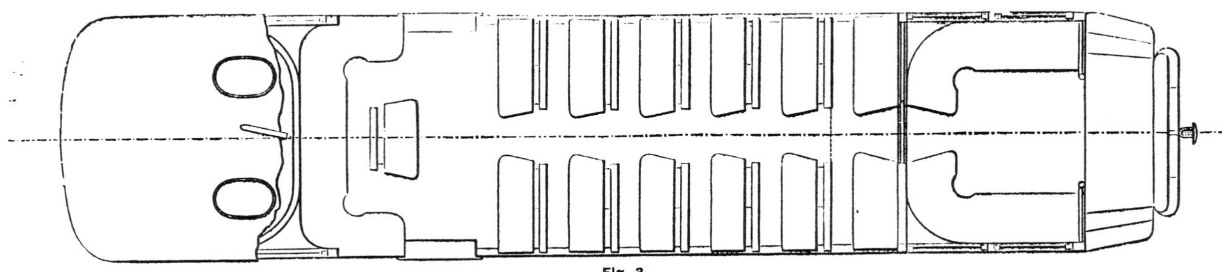

Fig. 3.

on to the tank. The body of the supplementary car—Cleminson's patent—is carried by three bogies, that in the middle sliding, and those at the ends swivelling, so as to run round curves of 20 metres, or 65½ feet. The following are the leading dimensions, including for convenience some given above, and also the relations determined by the jury during the trials:—

Length occupied by motor	3 m.	= 9ft. 10in.
Length occupied by passengers	6 5 m.	= 21ft. 4in.
Weight of fifty passengers, at 70 kilog., or 1cwt. 1 qr. 14 lb.	3500 kilog.	= 3½ tons.
Weight of vehicle	2500 kilog.	= 2½ tons.
Weight of condenser and reservoirs ..	600 kilog.	= 11¾ cwt.
Weight of vehicle, condenser, and reservoirs, empty p	3100 kilog.	= 3 tons.
Relation p weight empty to n weight of passengers	0·886	
Load on motor in running order without passengers	1400 kilog.	= 27½ cwt.
Load on motor fully loaded	2900 kilog	= 2¾ tons.
t Boiler pressure	13 atmosp.	= 195 lb. pr. sq in.
d Diameter of cylinders	0·13 m.	= 5·1in.
l Piston stroke	0·25 m.	= 9·8in.
D Diameter of wheels	0·75 m.	= 2ft. 5½in.
E Tractive effort = $\frac{0{\cdot}5\ td^2l}{D}$	366 kilog.	= 7 cwt.
S Heating surface	5·96 sq. m.	= 64 sq. ft.
G Grate surface	0·29 sq. m.	= 3 sq. ft.
C Condenser surface	80 sq. m.	= 860 sq. ft.
P′ Weight in running order (motor only)	4100 kilog.	= 4 tons.
P″ Weight, fully loaded	7000 kilog.	= 6 8 tons.
Content of water tanks	120 litres	= 26½ gals
Content of coke boxes	100 litres	= 3½ cub. ft.
Wheel base of motor	1·54 m.	= 5ft.

$\frac{P'}{E} = 11{\cdot}2$; $\frac{P''}{E} = 19{\cdot}12$; $\frac{P'}{S} = 688$; $\frac{P'}{G} = 14{,}138$; $\frac{C}{S} = 13{\cdot}42$; $\frac{E}{C} = 4{\cdot}57$.

By adopting this system of steam carriage, the fundamental principle of the tramway, in opposition to the railway, is maintained by running small trains at frequent intervals. As regards brake power, the combined engine and carriage is far more under control than a locomotive drawing a separate carriage, besides occupying less space in the street. An objection has been made that the steam carriage requires turning at each end of the line; but, with a triangle like that laid down at Antwerp, this operation takes up less time than detaching a locomotive, running it by a siding from one end of the train to the other, and again hooking it on. Besides, with the steam carriage there is no door in front, giving rise to draughts, which are much complained of in tramcars.

Fig. 8 shows a larger steam carriage, intended for light railways in the country, and therefore non-condensing, which ran regularly at Antwerp, but was disqualified from competing because no suitable car was found for it to draw in addition to that which forms an inherent part of itself. The seats and awning on the roof were, however, removed, on account of their being too high to go into the shed. This carriage was made at the Rhaismes works in France of the Société Anonyme Franco-Belge pour la Construction de Matériel de Chemin de Fer, and has been bought by the Société Générale des Chemins de Fer Economiques to run between Turin, Settimo, and Rivarolo. Similar steam carriages are also running successfully in Denmark, Sweden, and North Germany.

The total length is 12·3 metres, or 40½ft., and of the body 10·2 metres, or 31½ft., while the greatest outside width is 2·75 metres, or 9ft., and the height from rails to top of chimney 4·76 metres, or 15½ft. There are altogether eighty places, besides the luggage compartments. The total weight in running order is 15½ tons, and, when fully loaded, the weight available for adhesion is 15 tons, the tractive force of the engine being 1·7 ton. This steam carriage will mount a gradient of 1 in 25, run round a curve of 30 metres, or 33 yards, radius, and attain a speed of 30 kilometres, or 20 miles, an hour on the level, with a consumption of 2½ kilogrammes of coke per kilometre, or about 9 lb. a mile. All four wheels are coupled; and the brake acts upon two axles only, or all four in case of emergency. With dry rails, and going at a speed of 20 kilometres, or 12½ miles, an hour, the carriage may be pulled up in a distance of 20 metres, or 22 yards. Steam can be got up in the tubular boiler in half an hour. The cylinder is 0·23 metre in diameter, and the stroke 0·33 metre, or 9in. by 13in.

Figs. 9, 10, 11, and 12 show a similar carriage, made at the La Croyère works of the Franco-Belgian Construction Company above mentioned, which runs regularly on the Brussels Ceinture line of the Belgian State Railway, between the Luxemburg Station and Schaerbeck Junction. This, too, has no impériale, or seats on the roof, but compartments for all three classes, besides one for luggage. The total length outside buffers is 13·45 metres, or 44ft., affording space for the engine, a luggage compartment, a first-class compartment of eight places, a passage for entrance, a second-class compartment of twelve places, a third-class ditto of twenty-eight places, and a platform giving access and also standing room for twelve passengers—sixty altogether—while below is a large space where parcels may be stowed. The steam carriage, which weighs empty about 16 tons, including the 7-ton engine, makes 30 kilometres, or 20 miles, an hour, but can attain a speed of 40 kilometres, the coke and water space being sufficient for 20 kilometres, or 12½ miles, while curves of 120 metres, or 131 yards, radius are easily turned. The following are the principal dimensions:—

Grate surface	0·258 sq. metres	=	3 sq. ft.
Total heating surface	17· ,,	=	183 ,,
Number of tubes			190
Diameter of cylinders	0·205 metre	=	8in.
Stroke	0·33 ,,	=	13in.
Diameter of four-coupled wheels ..	0·82 ,,	=	2ft. 8¼in.
Between axles of engine truck ..	1·83 ,,	=	6ft.

The motion is very easy, even on a badly-laid line; and but little time is lost in stopping, while the engine soon gets into speed after starting.

As Captain Douglas Galton observed in his paper before the Society of Arts, "If tramways are to fulfil their object satisfactorily, it must be by mechanical traction;" and, when once the "interference from a centralised burocracy" is removed, Rowan's steam carriage may be expected to afford a practical solution of this question in England, as it has already done in Denmark, Sweden, Germany, Italy, and Belgium.

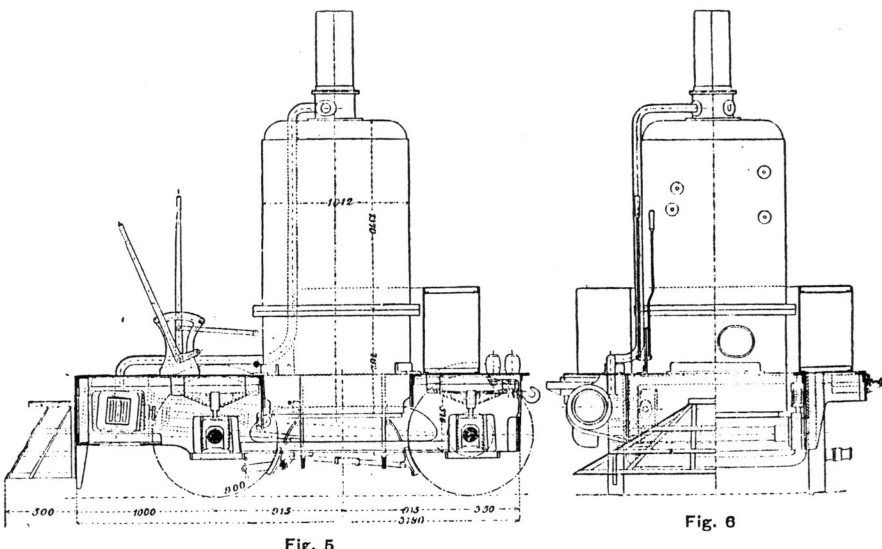

Fig. 5

Fig. 6

Fig. 7

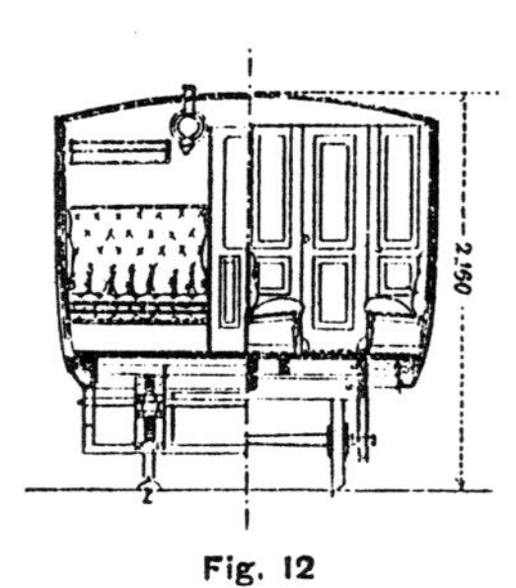

Fig. 12

Franco Belge

Built by the Société Anonyme Franco-Belge pour la Construction de Matérial des Chemins de Fer in 1885, two of these massive double-deck trams, classified as 'Rowan Cars' were supplied to the operator (Fratelli Ghigo Fu Pietro) of the (6.69mile/10.7km) service from Turin to Settimo. Overall dimensions were 40' 6" x 9' 0" x 15' 6" high with a weight of 15½ tons, but again there is this adherence to the Rowan principle, 15 tons is available for adhesion although the engine unit in isolation only provides 1.7 tons.

It was designed for three classes: 1st in the small compartment, 2nd also on the lower deck and 3rd upstairs in the unenclosed Imperiale, totalling between 56 and 62.

Grantham

The story of the famous Grantham car was one that had a happy ending insofar as it entered service, but a sad one as the designer never saw its successful working.

Built in 1872 to compete for the Society of Arts Howard Medal (awarded for a steam tram design that would replace horses) in November 1873 this self contained 'combination' tramcar essayed an unsuccessful run on the lines in London between Victoria Station and Vauxhall Bridge. It failed primarily because the twin Merryweather boilers could not provide enough steam to drag it along ill-kept and filthy grooved track although a contemporary report does add that the crowds on the car prevented the fireman from performing his duties. Whatever its failings in its original state, the then-new Wantage tramway directors had in mind the use of a steam car for the 2½ mile (4km) line from Wantage Road Station (GWR) to Wantage Market Place, and had already taken a look at Grantham's car in 1874 shortly after the death of John Grantham in July. The tram must have been a good design as his widow was the recipient of the Howard medal awarded posthumously in April 1875.

Interestingly, the three sets of illustrations show variants on the basic car – the wheel steering should not be laughed at – this was 1876 and everyone, including the greatest Victorian engineers, were feeling their way to the future. A contemporary note tells us that on the Wantage: "The car has from its commencement continued to run daily with satisfaction, and without in any way obstructing the traffic on the road, and from its freedom from noise, steam and smoke – the two latter being scarcely observable – horses travelling on the road appear to take no more notice of it than of an ordinary horse car. It may be stated also that on the occasion of the Berks volunteer review, which was held on the 7th of August last, on ground adjoining the Great Western Railway station, when it was computed that not less than 5000 persons travelled on the road in vehicles of all descriptions during the day, and the car was running backwards and forwards the whole time, no inconvenience or difficulty with the horses was experienced ... it appears highly popular with the public, and the

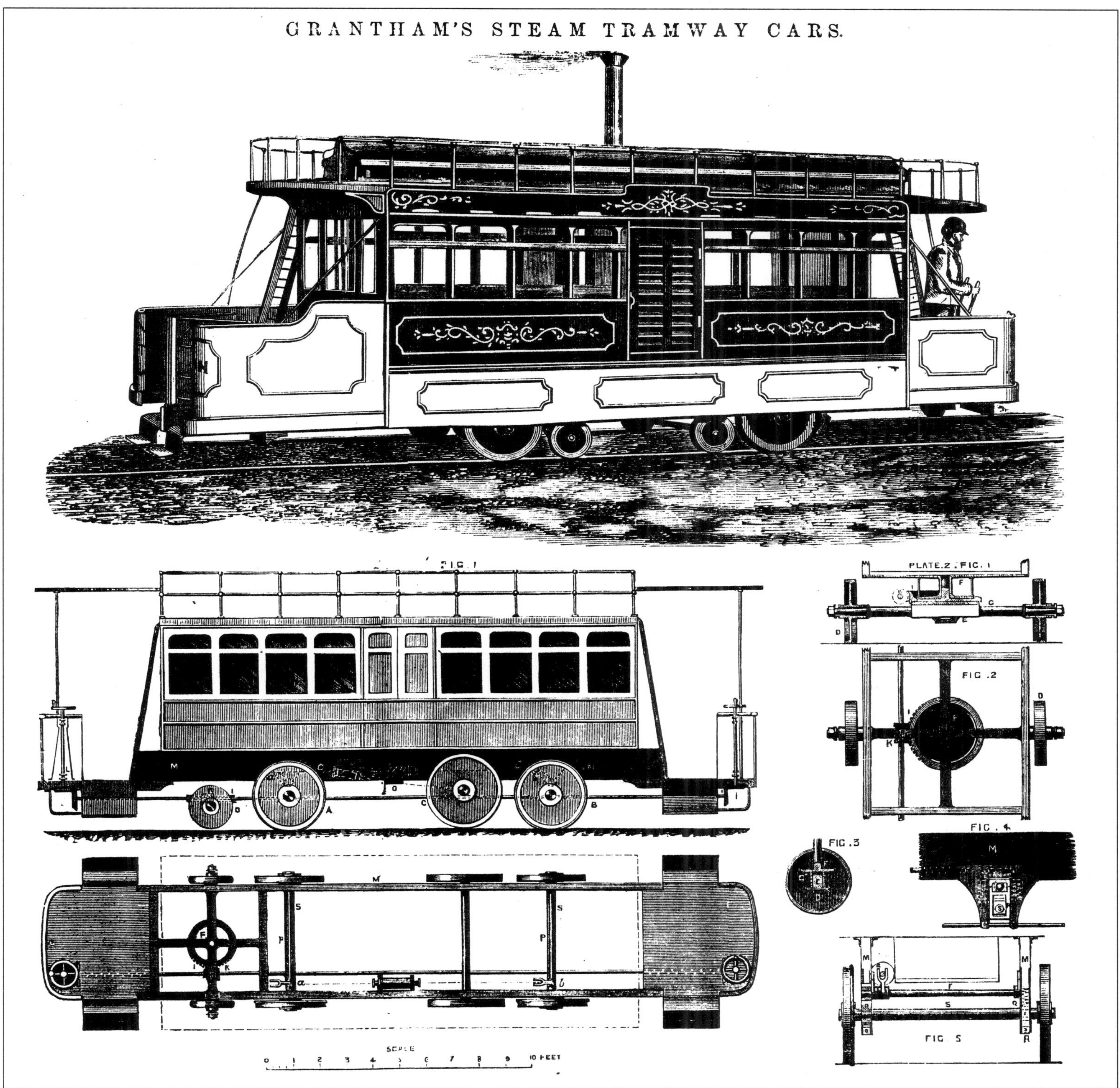

135. Fig.1 is an elevation of the car, A B are flanged wheels for the rails, C D are without flanges, and intended for use on asphalte roads, so that the car can be used either on road or rail. A and B can be raised to allow C D to take the weight. Figs. 2, 3, 4 and 5 show the fore carriage with steering screw at K and worm wheel I. The levers *a b* shown by dotted lines behind the wheels in Fig. 1 serve to raise or lower the wheels A B by the aid of the steam cylinder O. A propelling cylinder is seen at C behind the frame M. The eccentrics actuated by the levers *a b* and pressing on the tope of the axle boxes are shown in Fig. 4.
Steam is supplied by two boilers, Field's patent, one at each side of the car, and each being shut up in a kind of cupboard no heat or smell is transmitted to the interior of the car.
The view at the top of the page shows the car tried on Wednesday morning. The other views illustrate the principle of construction patented by Mr Grantham.

136. A NEW STEAM CARRIAGE FOR TRAMWAYS, BY MR. GRANTHAM, C.E.

travelling is much preferred to that of the horse cars, and judging from the silence with which it glides along on the rails, the absence of clatter and noise, as well as the ease with which the machine can be worked, it is considered by those competent to form an opinion of its action, that the time is not far distant when the expensive system of working our street traffic on tramways by means of horse power will be succeeded by the use of steam under proper restrictions."

The Wantage line opened on 1st October 1875 and experiments were carried out with the car, presumably when service trams were not running, on the private reservation between Grove Road and Mill Street, as the company had not received BoT permission to use steam. At some point it was realised that the two Merryweather boilers were not man enough for the job and a single Shand, Mason 'coffee-pot' boiler was substituted, the wheel diameter reduced and the bodywork altered. In this period only these two fine engine manufacturers seem to have had much knowledge of 'flash' boilers for road or rail use. Purchased in September 1876 as the railway's No.3 (1 and 2 were horse drawn trailers) for the sum of £250 plus £37 for the new boiler, it is known it ran from the previous month (August) although in November it had to be sent away again to the Avonside Engine Company, Bristol, having failed the BoT requirements. The Grantham car having had a hard life and although popular, seems to have been taken out of service in 1890 and sold for scrap the following year fetching less than £4.

Hydroleum

Built by Arnold Jung of Germany the Hydroleum locomotives offered one possible way forward for tram engines. The basic theory was a mixture of the old and the new. A Serpollet type boiler was used in which water was added in 'metered' quantities by a small (steam powered) donkey pump as evaporation and consumption of steam took place. Transmission was ultra modern as behind the boiler was a four cylinder 'simple' engine which then drove a transverse crank shaft. Final drive was unusual for the time (the early 1900s) being by a duplex chain. The greatest advantage of the type of steam engine was that heavy oil, rather than coal was the chosen fuel with an automatic feed being controlled through valves by the boiler pressure, lifting from the tanks to the oil spray nozzles and burners was by a neat horizontal steam pump. The Hydroleum Company had perfected or at least carried out extensive development of this method in their steam launch engines. Obviously reliability was essential as repairs could not be easily carried out when bobbing about on the water.

It is uncertain how many of these engines reached Britain – it may have been no more than a handful as King Coal still reigned and steam trams were on their last wheels.

Krauss

Lokomotivfabrik Krauss & Comp. was founded by George Krauss on the 17th of July 1866 in Munich, but eventually had three separate factories each meeting local demands.

Munich, for example, supplied the Wurttemburg State Railway with locomotives in 1867, while the 1880 works at Linz an der Donau (Austria) kept the Böhmische Northern Railway going in 1887. A further works in Sendling supplied, among others, both Moscow and São Paulo in the same year.

Another characteristic of Krauss was their willingness not only to manufacture locomotives in any gauge required but quickly. A look at 36 engines provided between 1868 and 1870 shows no less than ten separate gauge widths were required (671, 686, 687, 725, 760, 780, 785, 800, 900 and 1435 mm) with further oddities appearing later – 660 and 715 mm in 1886, 628, 740, 1000, 1445 and 1524 mm in 1887, and so on. It may have been this willingness plus low cost that appealed to the directors of the Wolverton and Stony Stratford District Light Railways Company Ltd who ordered four trams (Works Nos. 1861-4) of which we know two were delivered in 1886 from Sendling, and at least one of the second batch the following year. The use of 3' 6" (1067mm) gauge may have made for economies in construction but did little for either the engines' capacity or the interchange of the hoped-for freight. To make matters worse the little Krauss engines (built to pull 'ordinary' trams) were faced with dragging enormous, 44 feet long, 100 seater cars (carrying 120 passengers in "crush hour" mode) at a time when the normal horse-tram, at best, only carried 36.

TRAMWAY LOCOMOTIVE; WOLVERTON AND DISTRICT LIGHT RAILWAYS COMPANY.

137. CONSTRUCTED BY MESSRS. KRAUSS AND CO., ENGINEERS, MÜNICH.

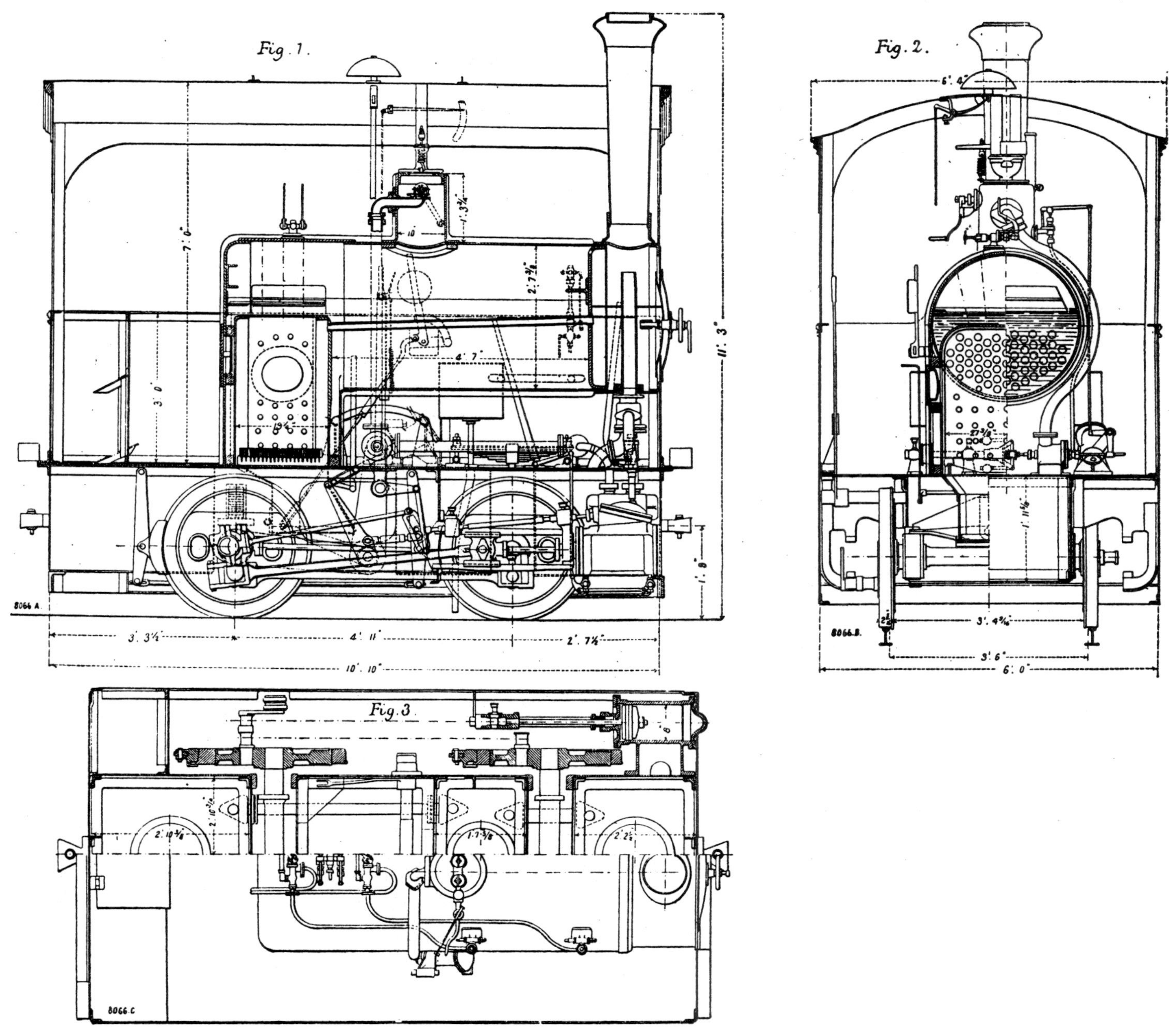

138. Photographs of the Krauss engines in use on the Wolverton & Stony Stratford lines are rare enough, but this, to add to its unique quality was taken on the Deanshanger extension. Locomotive No.3 (works no. 1863, 1877).

Whatever the causes, the first two engines were superseded by two from Thomas Green of Leeds, which had slightly larger cylinders and atmospheric condensers; as the Krauss engines were non-condensing the lack of water capacity may have been their Achilles heel. These two may have passed to Greens in part exchange.

The third Krauss engine (1863) was initially kept for the two-mile long Deanshanger extension, but when that closed it seems to have been kept in reserve.

A curiosity of the Krauss engines was that they did not comply, in some aspects, with the Board of Trade regulations, but this line as a 'country' route was perhaps regarded more benevolently. In 1887 similar engines were used in the Antwerp Trials and achieved "first place with respect to absence of smoke and noise, elegance of aspect, and boxing in of moving parts" in the light railway class.

It is salutary to think that one of the Krauss family (Conrad) was already thinking of alterna-

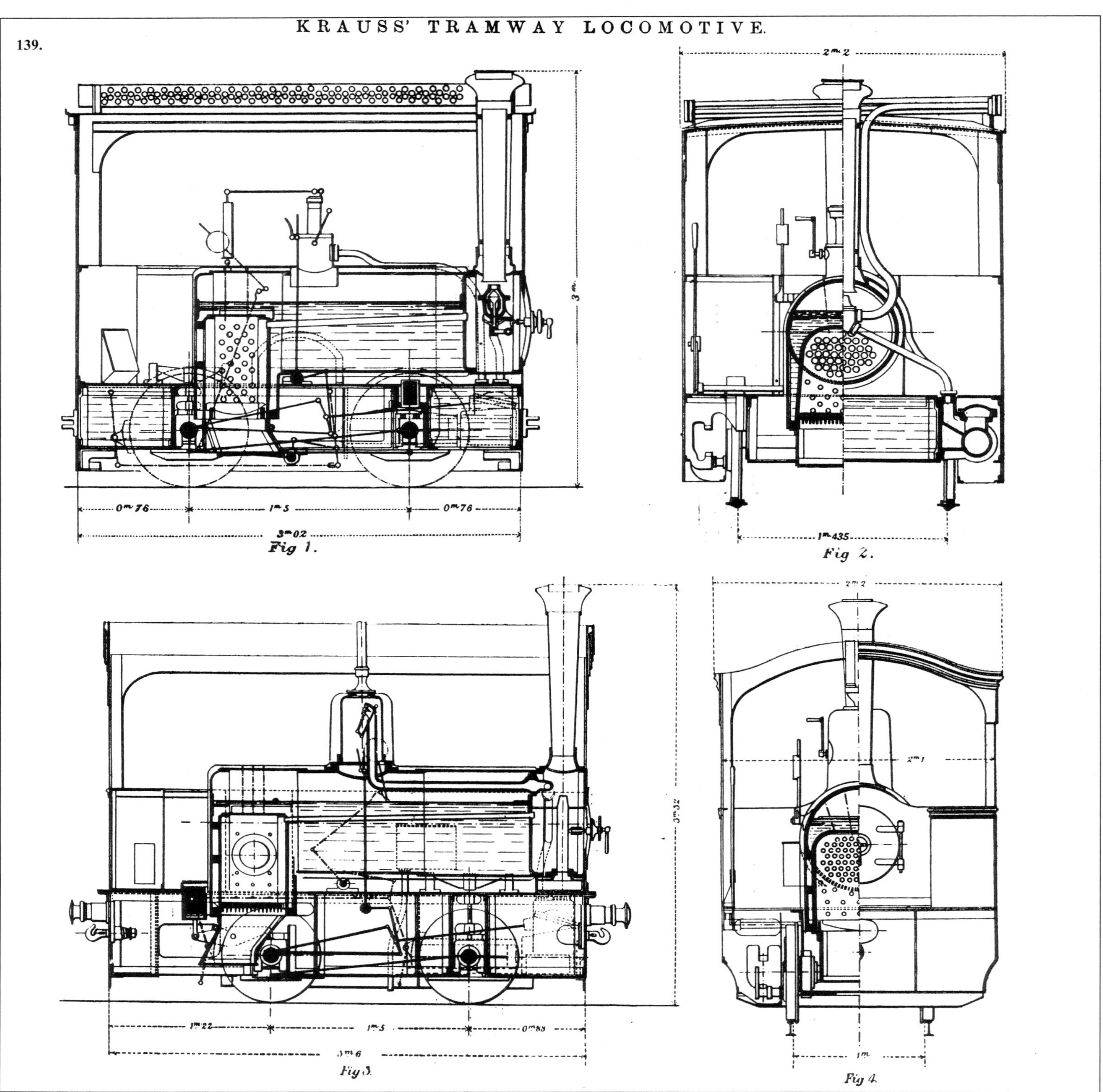

tive forms of power for "Tramways and Railways of Secondary Order" as long ago as 1879 when he obtained his patent No. 309 for a gas-power locomotive in the UK. Clearly the arrangement was for an urban environment as "The gas is either obtained from the supply-pipe of a gas-works or which may be specially produced for the purpose is compressed to the desired degree, say 10 atmospheres, by suitable pumps and delivered into reservoirs or accumulators, where it is kept ready for supply to the reservoirs of the engine. The filling of the latter therefore requires but very little time after the connections between them and the station-reservoirs have been made; consequently there is no material detention of the engines on this account." No smoke, little noise and very little fume output; only a dream alas...

Matthews

One tram engine, built to a patent design had a long and reasonably successful life. The patent number was 1429, the patentee James Matthews and the date 1879. And it is at this point that our certainties seem to get uncertain, as Dr Whitcombe, in his History of the Steam Tram (reprinted Adam Gordon, 2000) is of the opinion that it was built by Fox, Walker of Bristol in 1880. We know that it was tried out in Bristol and later, Liverpool, as in 1881 the Liverpool United Tramways & Omnibus Company arranged for a number of steam trams to be exhibited and run as though they were in service on the lines between Walton and Aintree i.e., outside the then Liverpool city boundaries. These included a Winterthur product shown by R. and W. Hawthorn, one from Duncan, Wilson & Co., and a third from the Manchester firm of Ormerod, Grierson & Co. The fourth engine was Matthews but unfortunately it was late in arriving and could not be made ready for steaming, although contemporary reports state the officials present and Major General C.S. Hutchinson of the Board of Trade were enthusiastic because all moving parts were neatly tucked away. In fact from photographic evidence it does seem to have been one of the few elegant tram engines to be built.

Reports of the time seemed to indicate that Matthews' engine was in fact built at the Kingsbury Ironworks, Ball Road, London over the three years (1879-81) since his patent application. However (and here is the most likely of the contenders for being the builder) Reg Wilkinson in his *The Wantage Tramway*

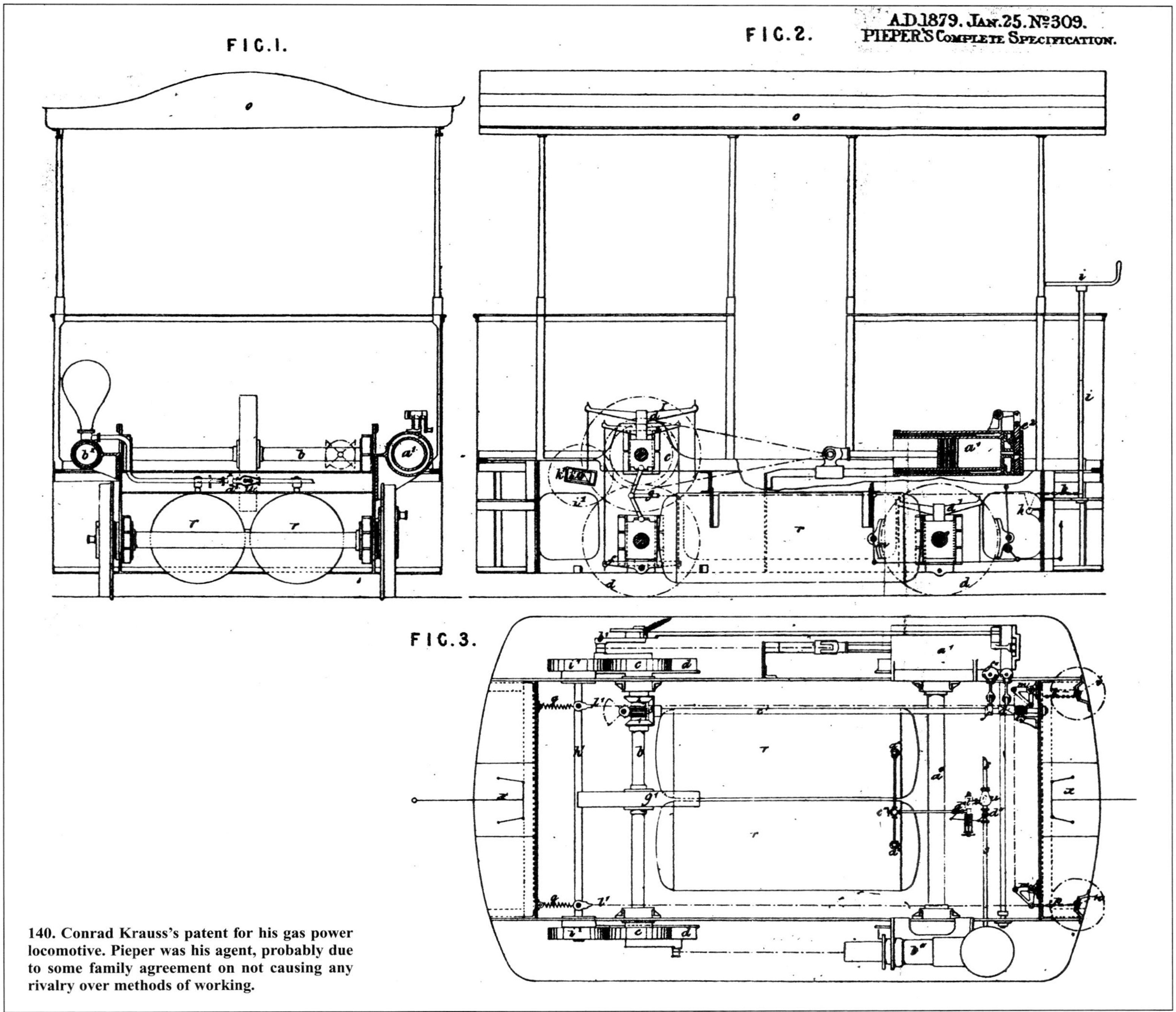
A.D.1879. Jan. 25. No 309.
PIEPER'S Complete Specification.
FIG. 1.
FIG. 2.
FIG. 3.

140. Conrad Krauss's patent for his gas power locomotive. Pieper was his agent, probably due to some family agreement on not causing any rivalry over methods of working.

Bahn-Omnibus-Berlin-Grünau.
300
300
GRUENAU

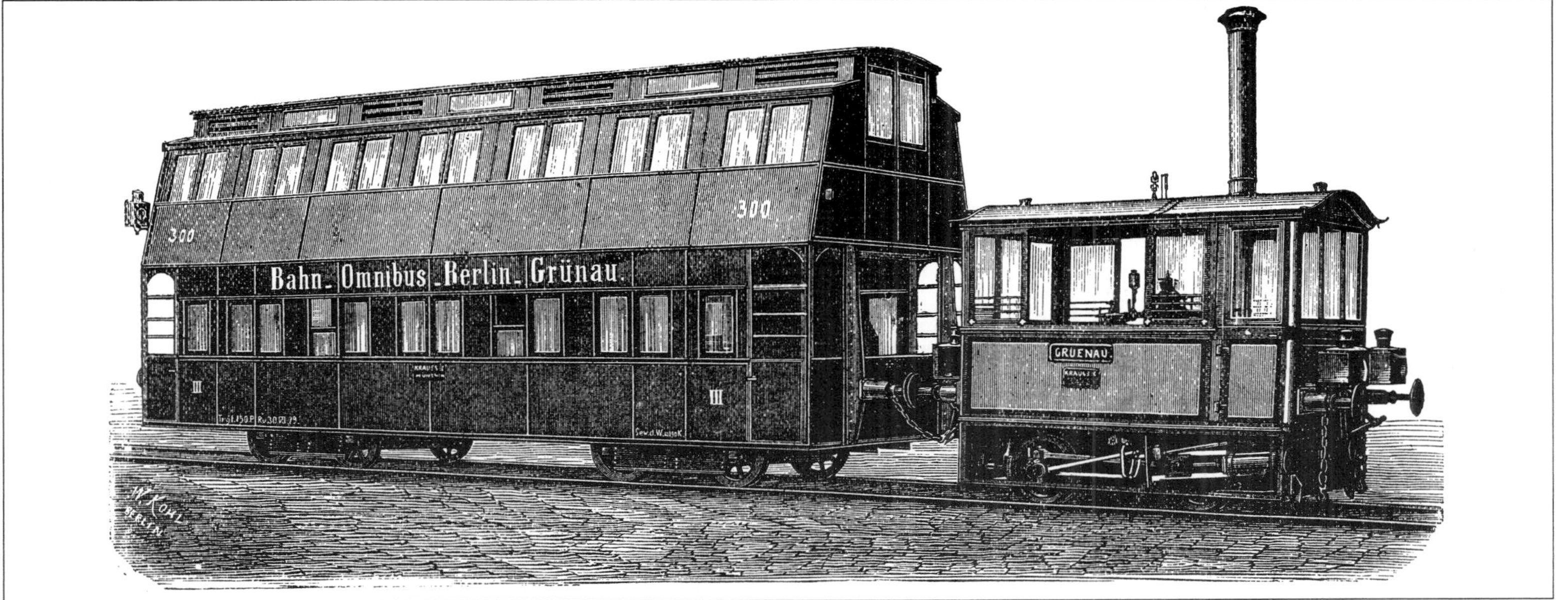

141. Locomotive No.2 Gruenau was a Krauss product (works no. 572 of 1877), and towed a tranche of 80 seat double deck trailers the 13.6 km (8.45 miles) from Berlin to Grünau. In all four Krauss tram engines were supplied to the Berlin-Görlitzer Eisenbahn between 1877 and 1881.

(Oakwood Press 1995) states, with evidence, that the engine was built by F.W. Jackson (a railway contractor) at Dalston, London.

After the Liverpool trials Matthews approached the Directors of the Wantage Tramway and asked if it could be trialled there, since they were one of a few tramways authorised to use steam and who were likely to take a friendly attitude being always short of motive power. In January 1882 they acceded to this provided Mathews supplied his own driver, presumably to reduce the risk of breakdown and to keep down the cost. The advantage to Matthews was not only could 'field trials' be carried out but visitors who were would-be purchasers had relatively easy access to the tramway and could see the engine in service.

But, sadly, in November 1883 this engine which had cost Matthews £900 to have built "of the very best materials" including a copper firebox, was offered for sale at £250, being suited to contractors as standard gauge, with a 140psi locomotive type boiler rather than a vertical 'coffee pot' and 6" x 10" stroke cylinders, although even at this time when many tramway companies were anxiously awaiting the belated supply of their ordered engines no-one made an offer even near this price. Perhaps the auctioneers (who were based at Cardiff) were disinterested or perhaps, although described as fulfilling "all the requirements of the Board of Trade for street tramway engines" insofar as she could be driven from each end and having "a special feature ... that its working parts are enclosed from dust and dirt, thus saving at least 40 per cent in wear and tear ..." during her two years at Wantage she had been grossly neglected?

Eventually, and I rather think the Wantage directors had bided their time until this particular ripe plum fell off the tramway tree, she was sold in 1888 where she stood at Wantage to the tramway company for just £60. Seemingly she normally ran with only one pair of driven wheels (2-2-0 arrangement) which precluded her from running the freight trains but, having been reboilered by the GWR in 1909, and having a new steel firebox in 1923, she remained in service, trundling up and down with one or two vehicles, until the end of the passenger services in 1925, although this engine was not broken up until 1931 at the marvellous age of 50. What a pity no-one thought to preserve Wantage No.6.

142.

Matthews Patent 1879

A (cylinders), B (connecting rods), C (crank plates), D (axles), also the slide rods, eccentrics and link motion are all arranged outside the frame-plates E. The casing F is provided with suitable doors for oiling and examination.

The vital part of this patent relates to condensation of exhaust steam. This is passed into a closed box, situated inside the locomotive's water tank; this box is partly filled with water supplied through "an equilibrium valve". From the base of the box a pipe extends upwards taper-

143.

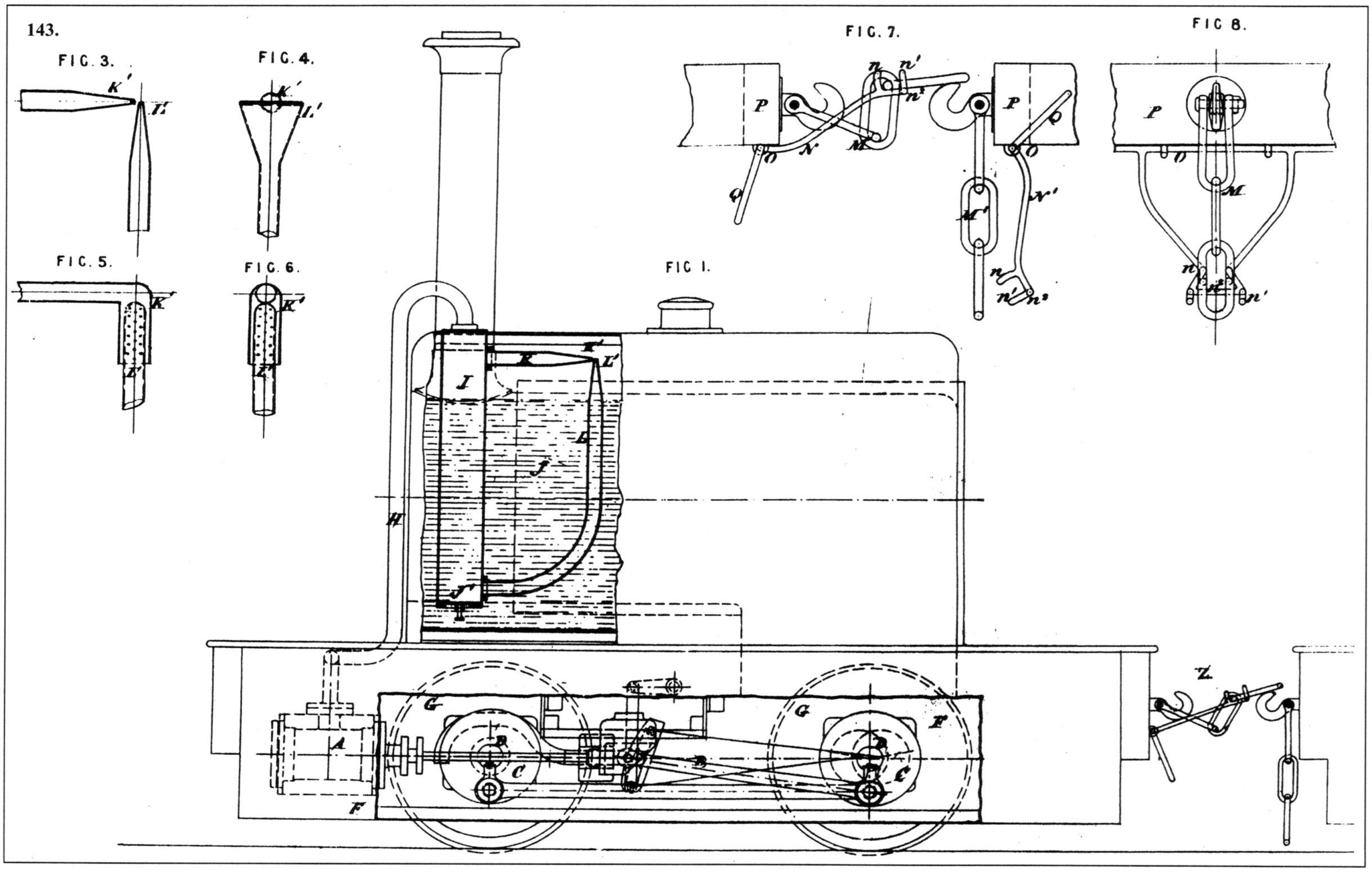

SPECIFICATION in pursuance of the conditions of the Letters Patent filed by the said James Matthews in the Great Seal Patent Office on the 10th October 1879.

JAMES MATTHEWS, of No. 109, White Ladies' Road, Clifton, in the County of Gloucester. "IMPROVEMENTS IN TRAMWAY AND OTHER LOCOMOTIVE ENGINES."

According to one part of my present Invention I construct tramway and other locomotive engines with four or more coupled wheels situated inside the frame-plates, and I arrange the whole of the driving mechanism, that is to say, the steam cylinders, with their slides, slide rods, eccentrics, link motion, slide bars, coupling and connecting rods outside the frame-plates, the axles having outside cranks or crank-plates for this purpose. The whole of these moving parts are covered by a close casing to exclude the dust and dirt, which casing is provided with suitable doors for oiling and gaining access to the parts. The above described arrangements may be applied to locomotive engines, as also to a combined engine and carriage, worked either by steam or compressed air. In engines with inside cylinders I arrange the wheels inside the framing, with the driving mechanism inside the framing as usual, and I enclose the whole of such mechanism by a close casing provided with doors for gaining access to the parts.

According to another improvement I effect the condensation of the exhaust steam of such engines by causing it to pass into a closed box or receptacle, situated by preference inside the water tank, which box is partly filled with water supplied from the tank through an equilibrium or balanced valve. From the lower part of this box a pipe extends upwards, terminating in a nozzle at right angles, or nearly so, to another nozzle situated close to it, and communicating with the upper part of the box, which is filled with steam. Thus, on the exhaust steam entering the box, it will issue through the last named nozzle, while by the pressure of the steam a jet of water is forced through the first named nozzle, so as to impinge on the jet of steam in the form of spray, whereby the steam is condensed.

For coupling the said locomotive engines to carriages or trucks I employ the following arrangement:—I provide the locomotive engine or other rolling stock with ordinary coupling chains, and below the buffer beam, in line with the coupling chains, I hinge with a suitable joint a forked curved lever or carrier, having near its free end a T or cross piece, beyond which it has an eye connected to a light chain passing through the free end link of the coupling chain to either side of the carriage, where it may be attached some height above the buffer beam, such chain being sufficiently long to allow the lever to hang down loosely.

When it is desired to couple the coupling chain onto the draw hook of the opposite carriage, the light chain is pulled up so as to draw the eye of the lever through the free end link of the coupling chain, and to raise the lever, whereby the end link of the coupling chain resting upon the T head of the lever will be raised up, so as to pass over the opposite draw hook. In order to cause the link to project forward as it is being raised, it may either be provided with a crossbar near its rear end, against which the eye of the raising lever bears, or the latter may be provided with a forked shoulder at the back of its T head, which is made to bear against the rear end of the link.

Instead of raising the lever by light chains as described, it may be connected to a transverse shaft extending to each side of the engine or carriage, where it is provided with hand levers by which the shaft can be turned, so as to move the raising lever upwards.

For uncoupling the chain the lever is raised, so as to lift the end link off the draw hook.

DESCRIPTION OF THE DRAWINGS.

Fig. 1 shews a side elevation partly in section; (and Fig. 2, a plan) of a locomotive engine having my before described improvements applied thereto. In this arrangement the steam cylinders A, with their connecting rods B, crank plates C of the axles D, as also the slides and slide rods, eccentrics, and link motion are all arranged outside the frame-plates E, and are enclosed by a casing F, provided with suitable doors for oiling and examination. The wheels G are inside the frames. When the cylinders are situated inside the framing, I arrange the wheels also inside the framing, but with outside cranks or discs for coupling the wheels on the outside of the frames, and I enclose the cylinders and driving gear inside the frame, as also the coupling rods and cranks outside the frames, with close casings such as I have described above, provided with doors.

The exhaust steam passes from the cylinders A through pipes H into closed boxes I, situated inside the water tanks J, the water of which enters the boxes at bottom through a valve J^1, so as to partly fill the same. From the upper and lower part of the boxes I lead respectively pipes K and L, terminating in flat broad nozzles K^1, L^1, situated close to and at an angle to each other. Thus the exhaust steam issuing through the nozzle K^1 will be met by a jet of water propelled through the nozzle L^1 by the pressure of steam in the box, and the steam will thus be condensed. The nozzles may either be constructed as shewn, detached in a side front view at Figs. 3 and 4, being arranged as just described, or they may be constructed as shewn at Figs. 5 and 6, where the perforated water nozzle L^1 enters the steam nozzle K^1, so that the water issues in a number of small jets into the narrow annular space of the nozzle K^1 through which the steam is escaping.

For coupling the engine to a carriage I employ the arrangement shewn at *z*, Figs. 1 and 2, and to an enlarged scale in side and front elevation at Figs. 7 and 8. M, M^1, are the ordinary coupling chains and hooks; N, N, are levers or arms fixed to transverse shafts O carried below the beams P, and capable of being both partly rotated and slid somewhat longitudinally by means of side hand levers Q. The arms are formed at their ends with four horns n, n, n^1, n^1, and a crossbar n^2, so that when they are turned up they will grasp and raise the end link of the chain M, as shewn on the right hand side of Fig. 7, the shaft with the arm and link being first slid somewhat to one side, so as to pass the hook of M^1, and then slid back again, so as to bring the link over the hook, so that on then allowing the arm to drop the chain will be coupled on to the hook. The shaft O may have eccentric bearings, so that the reach of its arm may be more or less extended. My above described improvements, except the arrangement for condensing exhaust, are applicable to locomotive engines or steam carriages worked by steam, compressed air, or other elastic fluid, the cylinders being arranged either in the ordinary manner or radially round the axles, in which case the coupling rods might be dispensed with, and each driving axle provided with its own cylinders.

Having thus described the nature of the said Invention, and in what manner the same is to be performed, I claim,—

First. Constructing locomotive engines or steam carriages with the whole of the driving gear arranged outside the framing and wheels, and covered by a close casing, having doors for oiling and inspection, substantially as described.

Second. Constructing locomotive engines or steam carriages, having inside cylinders with close casings covering both the driving gear within the engine frame, and the coupling cranks and rods outside the frames, substantially as herein described.

Third. The use for locomotives or steam carriages of condensing apparatus, consisting of a close receptacle partly filled with water, into which the exhaust steam passes, and from which it issues through a nozzle, in close proximity to which is a second nozzle placed at an angle thereto, and through which water is forced by the steam pressure inside the said receptacle, substantially as described with reference to Figs. 1 to 6 of the Drawings.

Fourth. The use in combination with the ordinary coupling chains and hooks of a locomotive or steam carriage, of an arm or lever on a transverse shaft, having horns or projections so arranged as to embrace the last link of the coupling chain and raise it for coupling on to the hook, substantially as herein described with reference to Figs. 7 and 8 of the Drawings.

In witness whereof, I, the said James Matthews, have hereunto set my hand and seal, this Second day of October, in the year of our Lord One thousand eight hundred and seventy nine.

JAMES MATTHEWS. (L.S.)

1879.

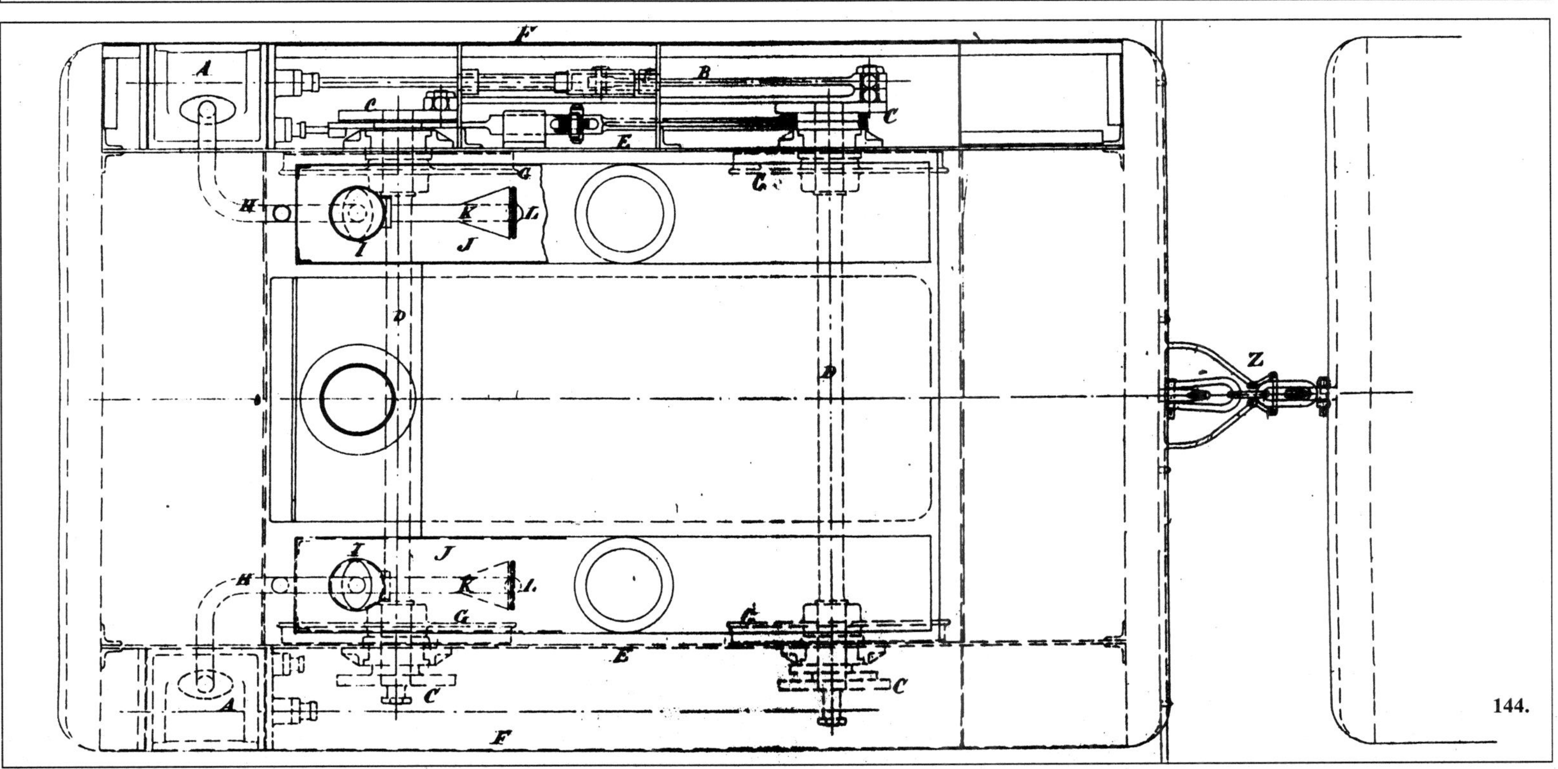

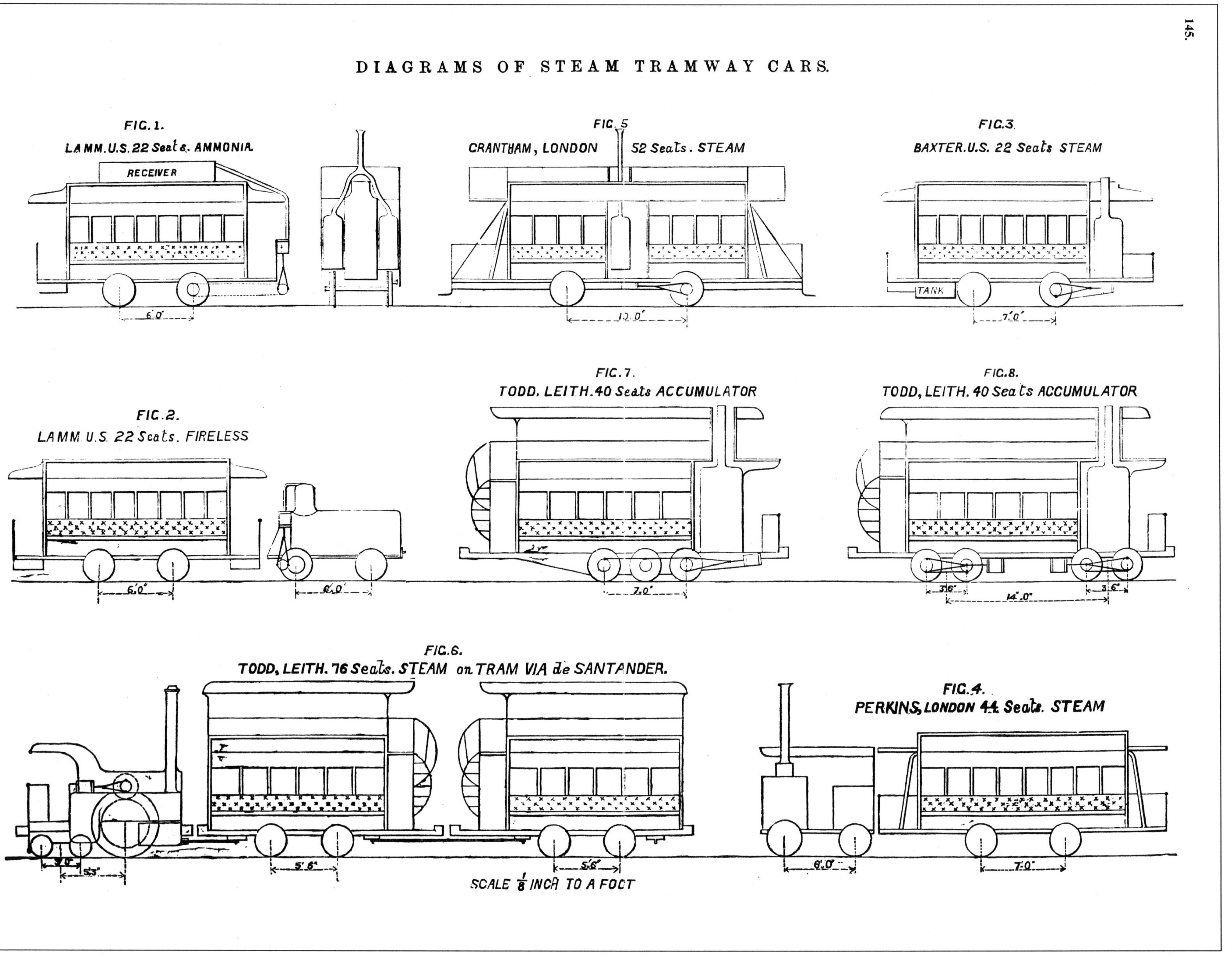
DIAGRAMS OF STEAM TRAMWAY CARS.
FIG. 1.
LAMM. U.S. 22 Seats. AMMONIA.
RECEIVER
6'0"
FIG. 5
CRANTHAM, LONDON
52 Seats. STEAM
10'0"
FIG. 3.
BAXTER. U.S. 22 Seats STEAM
TANK
7'0"
FIG. 2.
LAMM U.S. 22 Seats. FIRELESS
6'0"
6'0"
FIG. 7.
TODD. LEITH. 40 Seats ACCUMULATOR
7'0"
FIG. 8.
TODD, LEITH. 40 Seats ACCUMULATOR
3'6"
14'0"
3'6"
FIG. 6.
TODD, LEITH. 76 Seats. STEAM on TRAM VIA de SANTANDER.
5'6"
5'6"
SCALE 1/8 INCH TO A FOOT
FIG. 4.
PERKINS, LONDON 44 Seats. STEAM
6'0"
7'0"

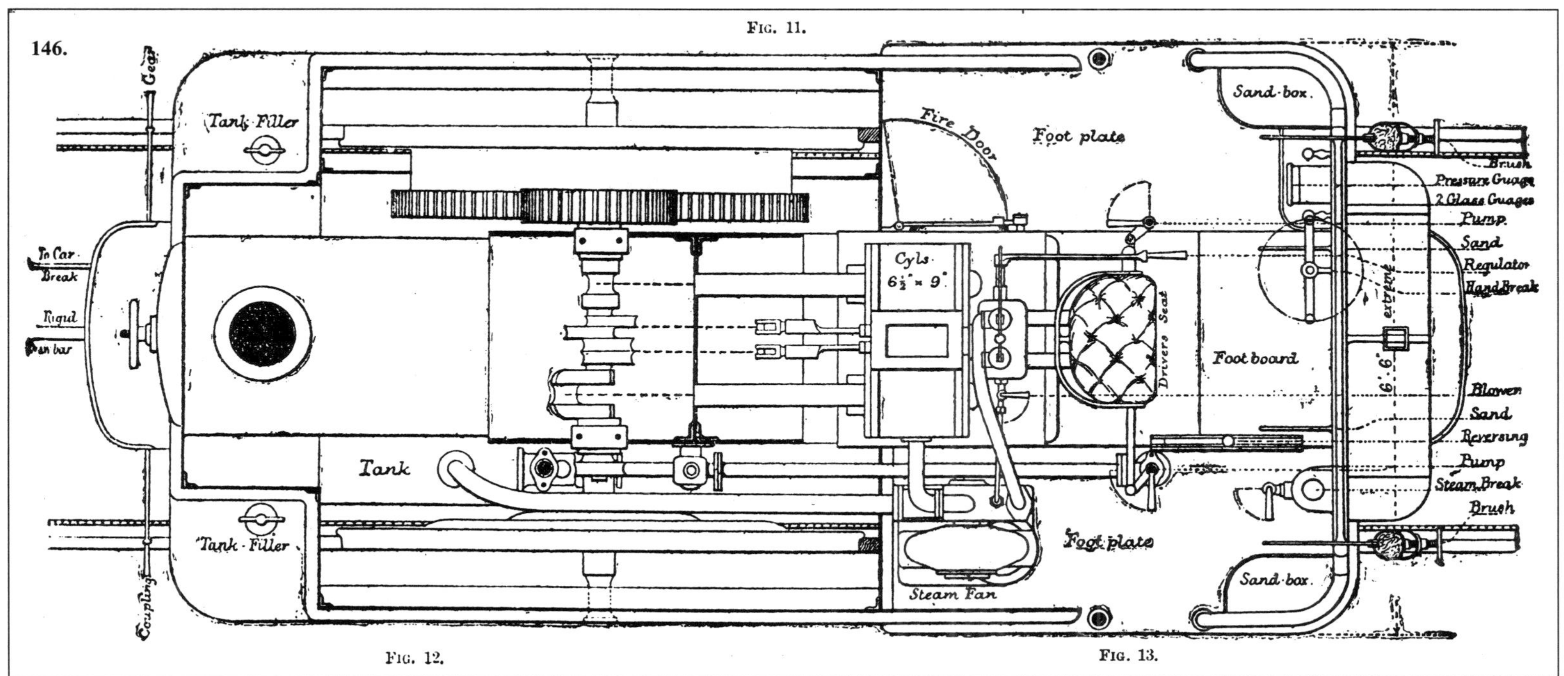

146.

Fig. 11.

Fig. 12.

Fig. 13.

ing into a nozzle which meets another nozzle or jet leading from the upper part of the box. Exhaust steam, under pressure, enters the box at the top from the cylinders and pressurizes the water in the box. As it seeks the shortest way out the steam squirts out of the nozzle and meets a spray of cold water forced up from the base of the box into the other jet. In effect given ideal conditions a form of perpetual motion could be attained; water from the main tank is converted to steam in the boiler, passed down to the cylinders, drives the engine, exhausts as steam, back into James Matthews box, and is condensed and returned to water ready for re-use.

Prima Donna

1874 saw the publication in *The Engineer* of, effectively, the most efficient tramway prime movers (one hesitates to call them all trams!) available in the known world. This was, of course, the era of experiment and dreams. Were they not marvellous though?

The tram shown here for the Tram-Via de Santander was built and certainly ran in the early 1870s. Shown elsewhere as a 0-2-4 in practice it does seem that the locomotive ran cab first – the trailer car braking system only being fitted at the (left hand of the drawing) smoke box end. Unfortunately the track was lightly laid and the locomotive may have been laid aside quite quickly.

Following his earlier experiments with steam

147.

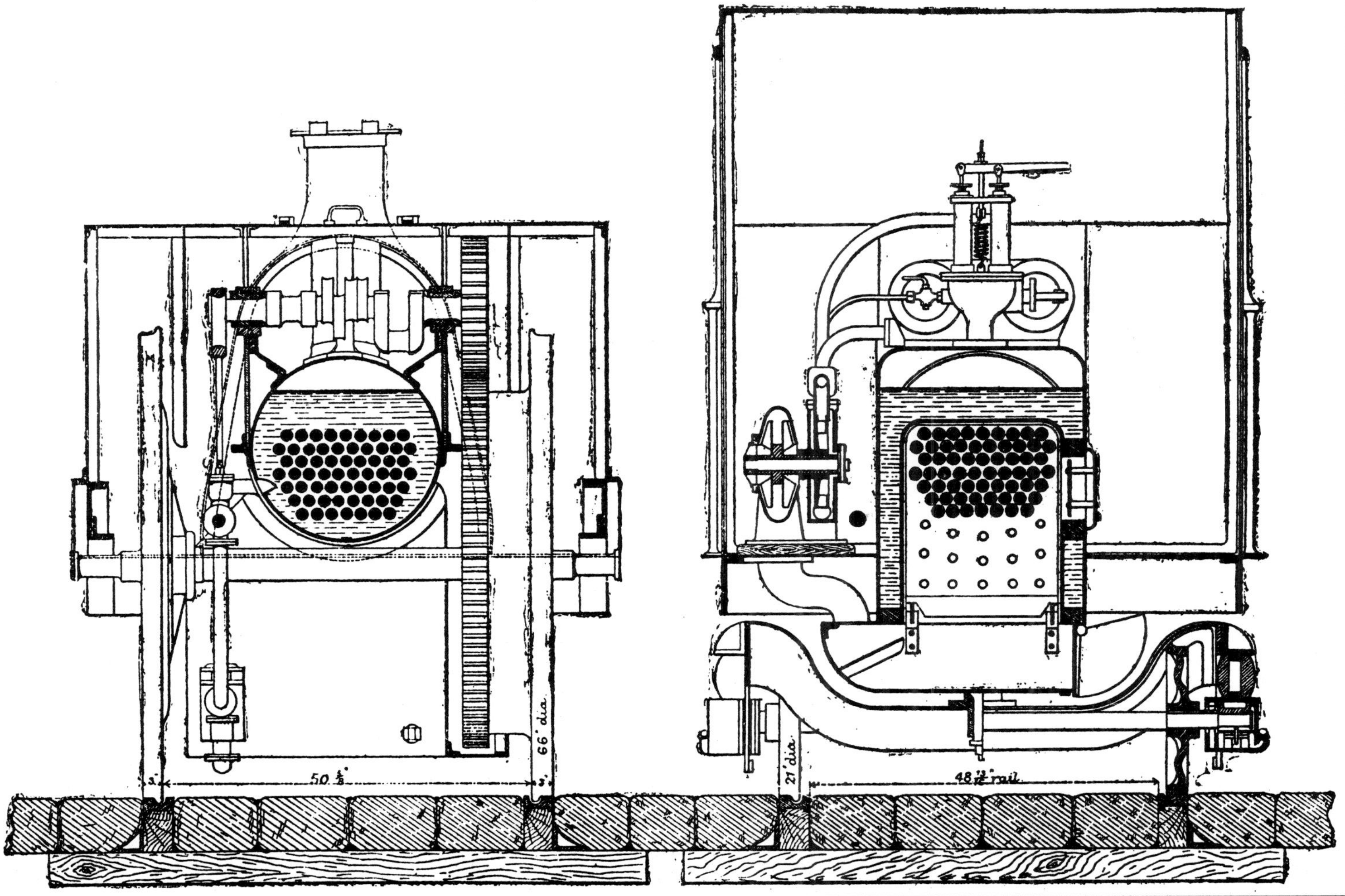

148.

ENGINE FOR WORKING STEAM TRAMWAYS.

MR. J. LEONARD TODD, LEITH, ENGINEER.

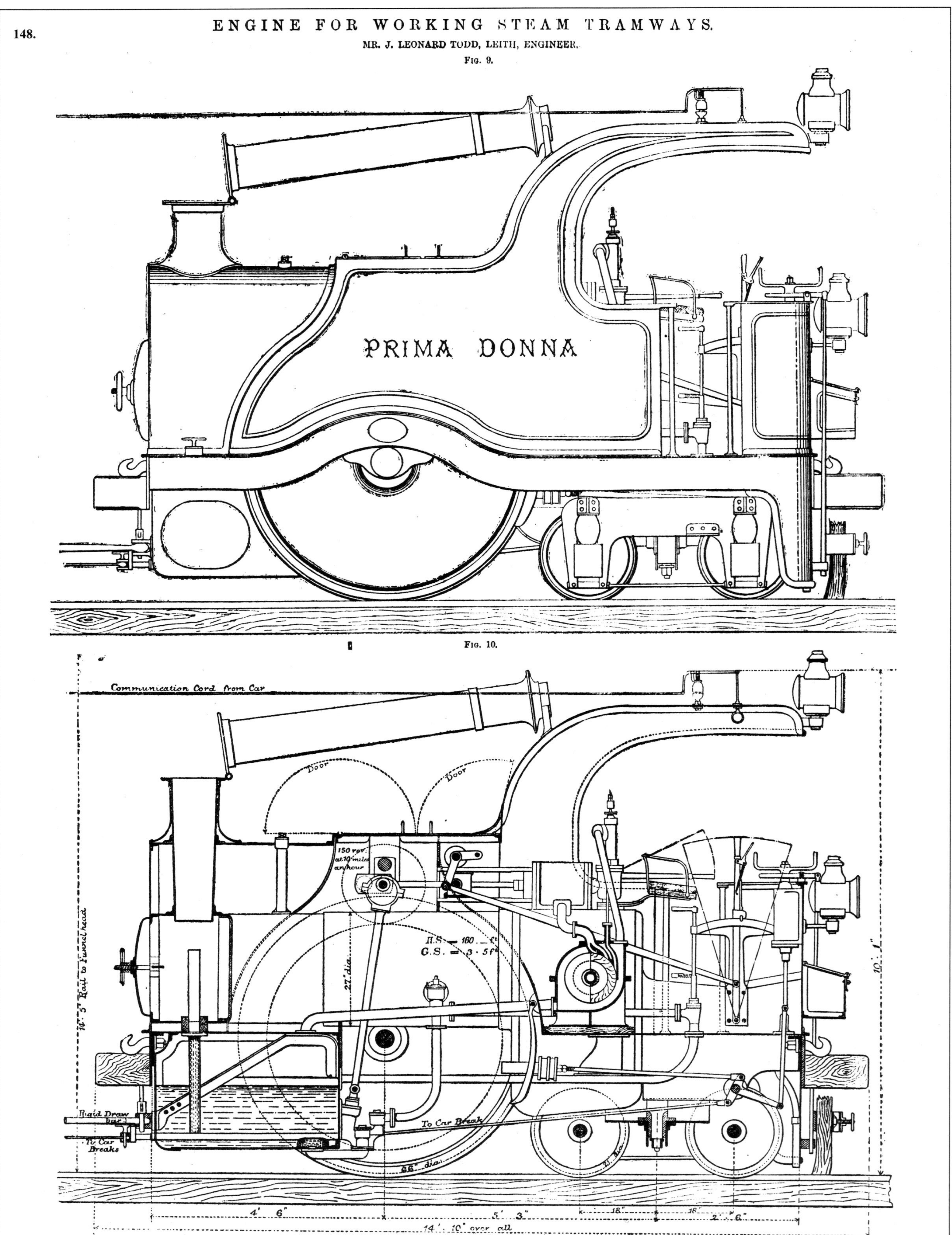

road vehicles Leonard Todd came to the conclusion the most efficient form of boiler was to use one of great capacity allied to a small firebox; 'Prima Donna' had two cylinders 6½" diameter, with a 9" stroke and at 10mph a crankshaft revolving at 150rpm. The driving wheels 5' 6" in diameter were, ingeniously, made of a disc of wood giving, theoretically, some degree of flex although the twisting stresses upon a single pair of driving wheels must have been horrendous. Drive as can be seen was by gears, redolent therefore of the later Aveling & Porter engines. Although Prima (was there a Secundus? – Todd elsewhere refers to a special locomotive named 'Santander') Donna was quite tiny at 14 feet 10 inches long by 6 feet 6 inches wide, her chimney in order to clear the trailers' roof was 14 feet 5 inches high. Unfortunately it has not been possible to obtain a photograph but she must have been beautiful!

The late Geoff Baddeley told me that Prima Donna only ran for a year or so on the Horse tram lines of the Tram-via de Santander towards Peña Castillo. But I bet it was fun while it lasted!

Serpollet

Trafford Park tramways had a fascinating history but only really impinges on us insofar as a Serpollet combination car made an appearance. In Paris the Serpollet car was quite successful with eighty-odd in service until the first world war, while Lille had four, St. Romain de Colbosc and Cherbourg three each and other towns one or two but in Britain only this one ran. The tramway itself was built when Trafford Park was still a park and was operated by gas tramcars although for various reasons opening was delayed until 8 April 1898, whereas the Serpollet car was brought to Trafford Park in September 1897 and was running for a short while in Manchester during February 1898. It was said that although the vibration was greater than that of a horse car the tram did not appear to particularly worry the horses. It was claimed that using coke 3.65d per mile would transport 50 passengers, including driver's wages, repairs and cleaning (but not depreciation) but if run on tar oil this would drop to 3.51d per mile. Eventually it passed into the hands of the British Serpollet Syndicate, with G. Palmer Harding as Manager, who was first involved in tramways back in the 1870s. Modified by Beyer Peacock to his requirements, Serpollet then re-entered service in Trafford Park for at least some months during 1899.

Sadly, though, it was then tucked away in its shed until 10 November 1905 when quite unceremoniously it was sold for scrap fetching £19.17s.9d after being advertised for sale as a "Serpollette Steam Tramcar, with double-cylinder engine, link reversing gear and tubular boiler". Perhaps, really, it was too late (and too foreign!) to be a success. The Darracq Serpollet Omnibus Co Ltd (registered 1906) was equally unsuccessful, voluntary liquidation occurring on 14 August 1912, although the company remained in being, if moribund, until 1923.

S.N.C.F. Vicinaux

A number of engines used on Continental tramways appear in these pages, normally as they were either British built or the lines were built with British capital. This particular tram fulfils neither of these requirements but is included to show just how far motive power on European light railways had diverged from British designs and also to assist miniature railway engineers.

One of a batch of tramway locomotives was built by Emile & Jules Halot & Co. of Brussels for use on the state-owned lines of the Société Nationale des Chemins de Fer Vicinaux (literally, Brussels national local or secondary steam trains) in 1889. This is illustrated on pages 128 and 129 (top). Running on metre-gauge (3' 3") the massive build of this 18 ton engine makes our native British engines look quite 'tishy', but of course using largely roadside running the Belgians saw little point in our BoT Regulations.

One of their prime advantages was that they did not start to build their lines until an Act of 1884 thus enabling the Belgians to draw from other countries' experience.

Although all the S.N.C.V. engines were shrouded (this is not entirely clear from the drawing), provision was made that in cities the steam was not turned directly up the chimney but instead condensed to some degree in a tank carried forward of the leading axle. Outside cylinder, outside frame design, three, rather than two, axles were used, thus spreading the load and giving a far better ride. Cylinders were 11" in diameter with 14.7 inch stroke, wheels 2' 8½" in diameter, and the overall wheelbase was 5' 11" (equidistantly spaced over the axles). Working pressure in the relatively massive boiler was only 140psi, water carried totalled 440 gallons and the fuel capacity (presumably briquettes) was 23 cubic feet – somewhat different to the lonely bag of coke carried on Wilkinson engines! Length overall was 29' 5½" and width 8' 2" (all dimensions, incidentally, are approximations from the

149. One of the Serpollet steam cars of the Compagnie Générale des Omnibus poses in a depot yard in Paris.

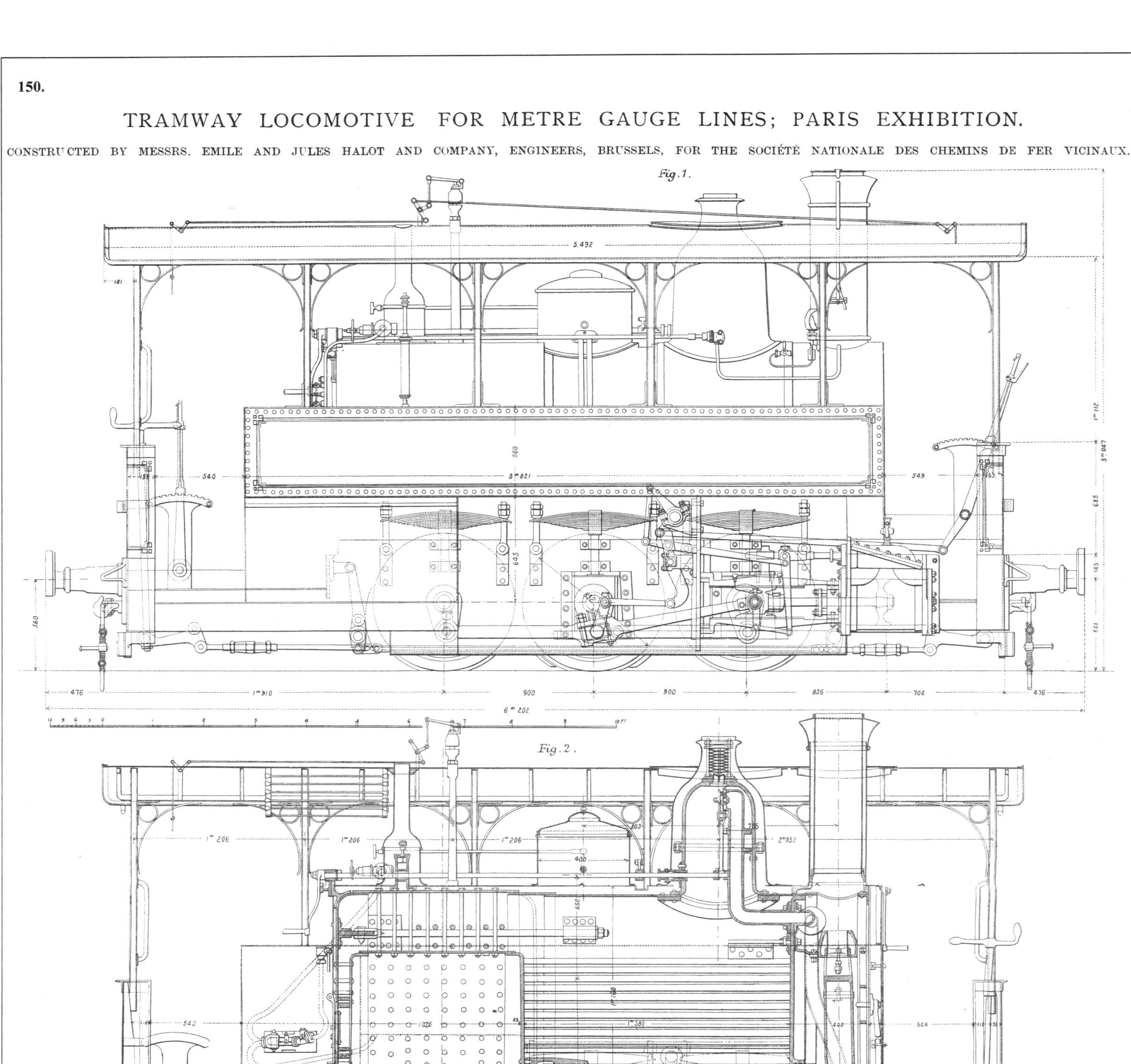

metric originals shown on the drawings). Operational speed was intended to be 30kph (18.64mph) and it was designed to run over trackwork with a minimum radius of 25 metres (82' 2").

Derived from a design of tram engine supplied by the Tubize works of the Ateliers Metallurgiques, Hulot were to build 22 in all for the S.N.C.V., although Tubize sold about 300, largely exported, and other companies some 300 or so. Still later variants, supplied by the Ste. Leonard works weighed as much as 30 tons, which says much for the quality of Belgium trackwork.

Telford Town Tramway

Probably one of the most unusual steam trams to run, this was the brainchild of the Telford Development Corporation who having consumed the old Shropshire villages of Coalmore, Dawley, Hadley, Hollinswood, Horsehay, Oakengates, Stirchley and Wellington found they wanted a link between the shopping centre and the complex of museums at Coalbrookdale. Alan Keefe Limited from Oxford (one of the foremost protagonists of steam) was chosen as consultant for the scheme, and as builders of the tram locomotive and its trailer.

The gauge selected was 24 inches (610mm) and a vertical boiler working at 150psi was manufactured by Pontis Steam Plant of Peterborough, powering a single (5" x 10" stroke) cylinder engine. This then drove a layshaft with a 1:1 chain drive to both axles, but

151.

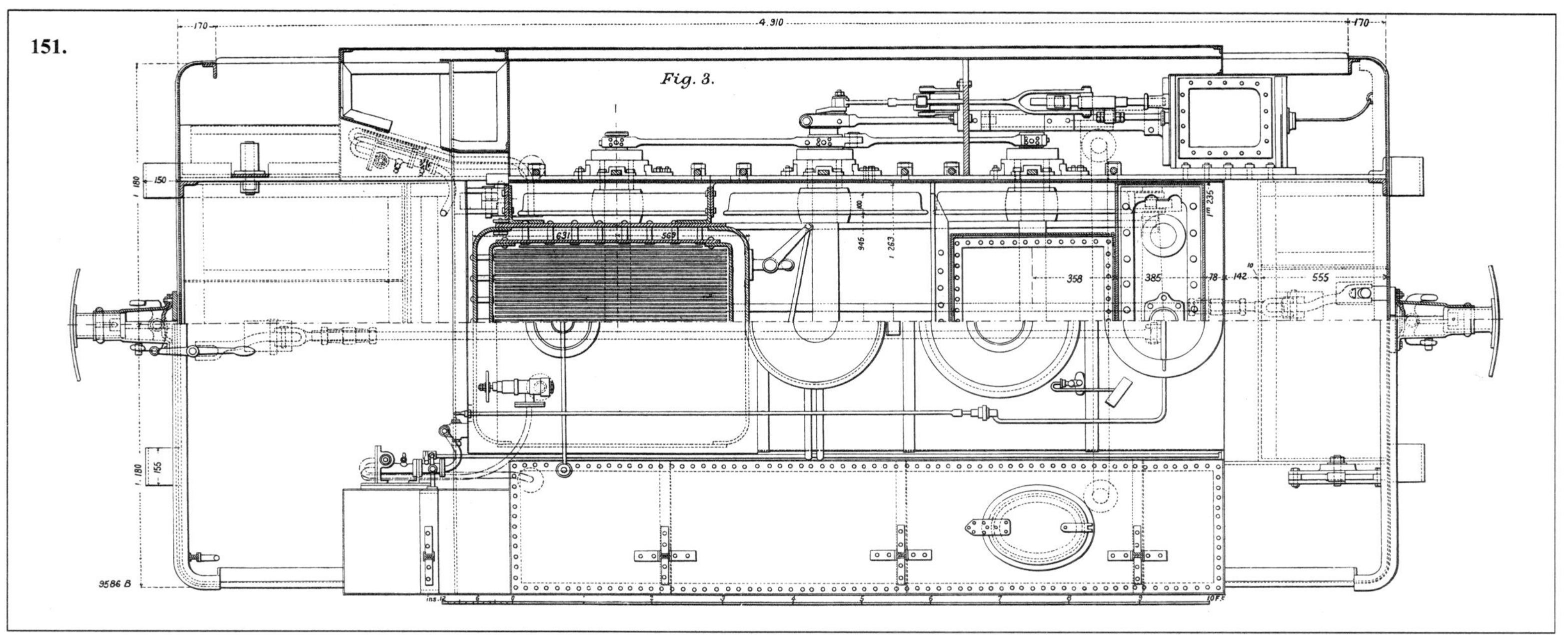

to add to the variety and to meet modern safety requirements the boiler also feeds a further tiny engine (one cylinder 2" x 2") to supply airbrakes on all axles.

The saloon is open-sided, seating sixteen and has an unusual feature: all four wheels are not keyed to the axle but can rotate independently, this reducing wear on circuitous track.

Finished in 1979 about 400 yards (365m) of track was laid in the Town Park, but for all their plans and dreams the tramway only ran for five days (8 September 1979, 9-12 April 1980) before it was realised that the Development Corporation were directly prohibited from carrying on "any undertaking for the supply of water, electricity or gas, or any railway, light railway, tramway or trolley vehicle undertaking".

Despite Telford being a Labour dream, this clause was, of course, a deliberate check on the Telford authorities trying to set up a Russian-type empire where they would control all aspects of their citizens' lives. Eventually the tram engine, trailer and track were moved to the Telford (Horsehay) Steam Trust site and by 1984 a 100 yard line was completed and the tram was once again running. The Trust is a registered charity run by unpaid volunteer enthusiasts with a short standard gauge steam line based on the old locomotive shed at Horsehay.

To provide yet another quirk in the life of this tram line, the engine was from 2001 wood fired, running on Sundays from Easter to the end of September. Perhaps it tells us something that the engine and its trailer have lasted much longer (since 1979) than most 'real' steam trams ever did!

151.

TELFORD STEAM RAILWAY

152. This class of locomotive with a pistol-type boiler was described in the catalogue as a "Brown'schen Tramway – locomotive" and after extolling its virtues the company then gave a table showing its haulage capacity, presumably in ideal conditions ("Rollender Widerstand" – Rolling Resistance – 7 kilos per tonne).

Winterthur

The Swiss Locomotive & Engine Works, Winterthur, had an Englishman (born in Uxbridge), Charles Brown, as their engineer and he perceived that one weakness in 'ordinary' tram engines lay in the necessarily low slung motion (used to convey the drive from the cylinders to the wheels) – with wheels normally only 2' 4" or so in diameter it will be readily understood just how much muck and dirt the moving parts would have to cope with. Under his system the cylinders and primary drive were all mounted very high, using a rocking lever to propel the wheels.

R. & W. Hawthorn of Newcastle assembled a batch of these

Legende:

	Nr. 1	Nr. 2
Cylinder-Diameter . .	180 (ev. 200) m/m	150 m/m
Kolbenhub	300 m/m	300 m/m
Rad-Diameter . . .	700 (ev. 600) m/m	700 (ev. 600) m/m
Radstand	1500 m/m	1500 m/m
Heizfläche	$13,_8$ m^2	$10,_9$ m^2
Dampfdruck	15 Atm.	15 Atm.
Wasser im Reservoir .	820 Liter	820 Liter
Coaks	200 Kilos	200 Kilos
Gewicht der Maschine im Dienst	9500 Kilos	8500 Kilos

Leistung der Maschine:
(Rollender Widerstand 7 Kilos per Tonne.)

	Nr. 1 Raddiameter 700	Nr. 1 Raddiameter 600	Nr. 2 Raddiameter 700	Nr. 2 Raddiameter 600
	Tonnen		Tonnen	
Auf der Ebene mit 15 - 20 Kilometer	65	65	50	50
„ 10 ‰ „ 12 -- 15 „	33	33	24	24
„ 20 ‰ „ 10 – 12 „	23	23	16	16
„ 30 ‰ „ 8 -- 10 „	18	22	$11,_5$	$14,_5$
„ 40 ‰ „ 8 „	12	16	8	$11,_0$

153. "Raddiameter" – wheel diameter, "Ebene" – gradient. The water capacity of both engines was 820 litres, "coaks" – 200kg, and the weight of No. 1 type 9500kg and No. 2 8500kg, i.e. 9½ and 8½ tonnes respectively. Cylinders were 180 or 200mm for No. 1, 150 mm for No. 2 with a 300mm stroke, (i.e. 7" x 12" or 6" x 12").

Liste der bis Juli bestellten Tramway-Lokomotiven

Patent Brown

		Im Betrieb			Bestellt
1.	Genf	1	seit	1877	-
2.	Mailand, Milano-Savonno	8	"	1878	-
3.	Mailand, Milano-Vaprio	6	"	1878/1880	-
4.	Regoa (Portugal)	2	"	1878	-
5.	Madrid	2	"	1878/1879	-
6.	Turin	5	"	1878/1882	-
7.	Strassburg	14	"	1878/1880	-
8.	Rom	8	"	1879	-
9.	Paris	17	"	1878	-
10.	Hamburg	5	"	1878/1879	9
11.	Rappoltsweiler	3	"	1879	-
12.	Cuneo-Dronero	5	"	1879/1880	-
13.	Cuneo-Saluzzo	3	"	1880	-
14.	Florenz	4	"	1879/1880	-
15.	Alessandria-Sale-Voghera	14	"	1879/1881	-
16.	New Castle on Tyne	6	"	1880/1882	-
17.	Bésier	2	"	1880	-
18.	Piaccenza	3	"	1880	-
19.	Liestal-Waldenburg	2	"	1880	-
20.	Barcelona	5	"	1880/1881	10
21.	Breda	6	"	1880/1881	-
22.	Novara-Galiate und Fortsetzung	3	"	1880	3
23.	Rotterdam-Delfshaven-Schiedam	7	"	1881/1882	-
24.	St. Petersburg	1	"	1881	3
25.	Tilburg	5	"	1881/1882	-
26.	Luxemburg	8	"	1882	-
27.	Tessin	2	"	1882	-
28.	St. Etienne	22	"	1881/1882	-
29.	Mülhausen	4	"	1882	8
30.	Ancona	2	"	1881	-
31.	Ariège	1	"	1881	-
32.	Gouda-Bodegraven	2	"	1882	-
	Transport	178			33

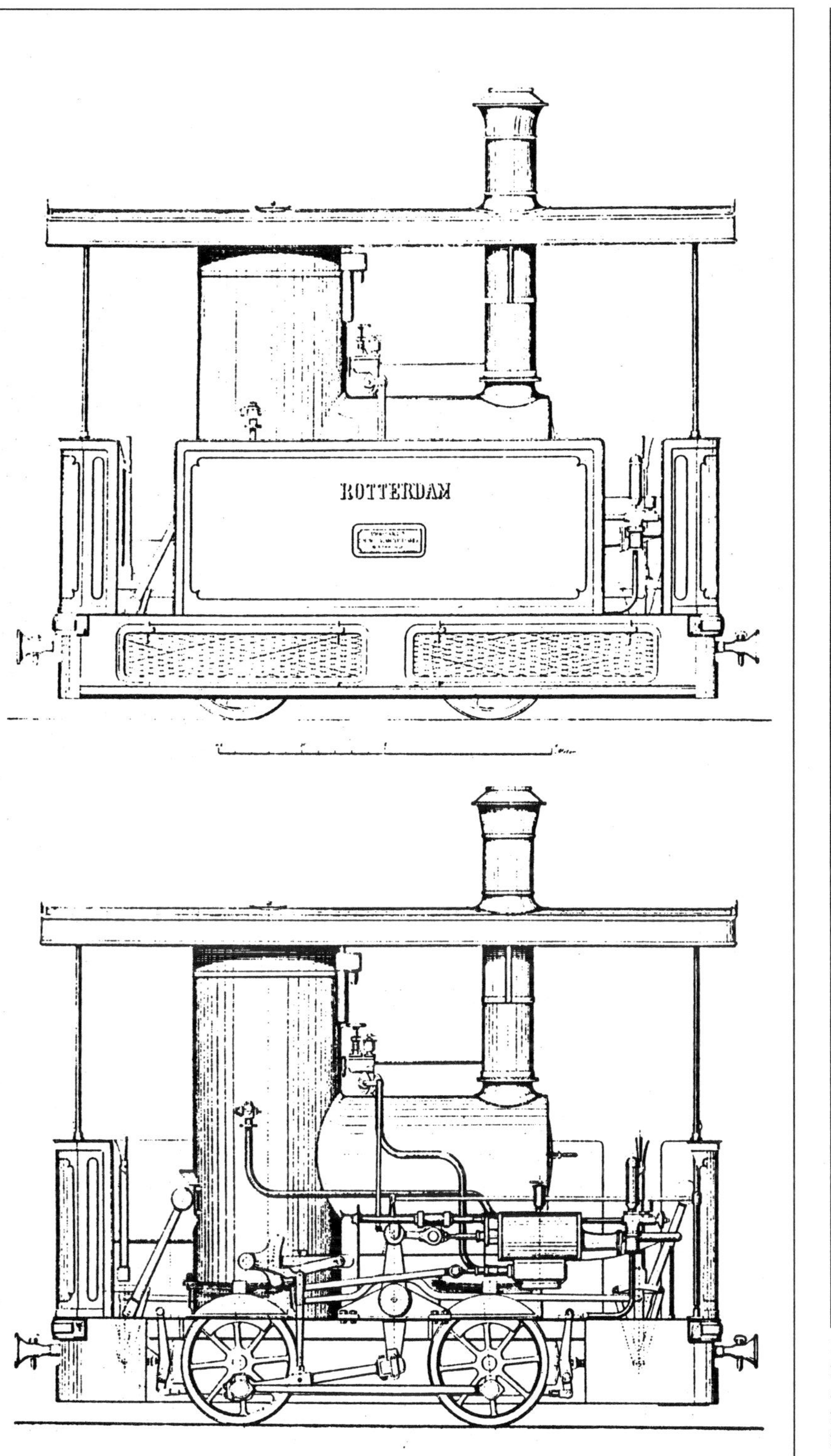

154. Works No.909 of 1881 ran on the Rottertdamsche Tramweg Maatschappij, but almost certainly did not carry a name.

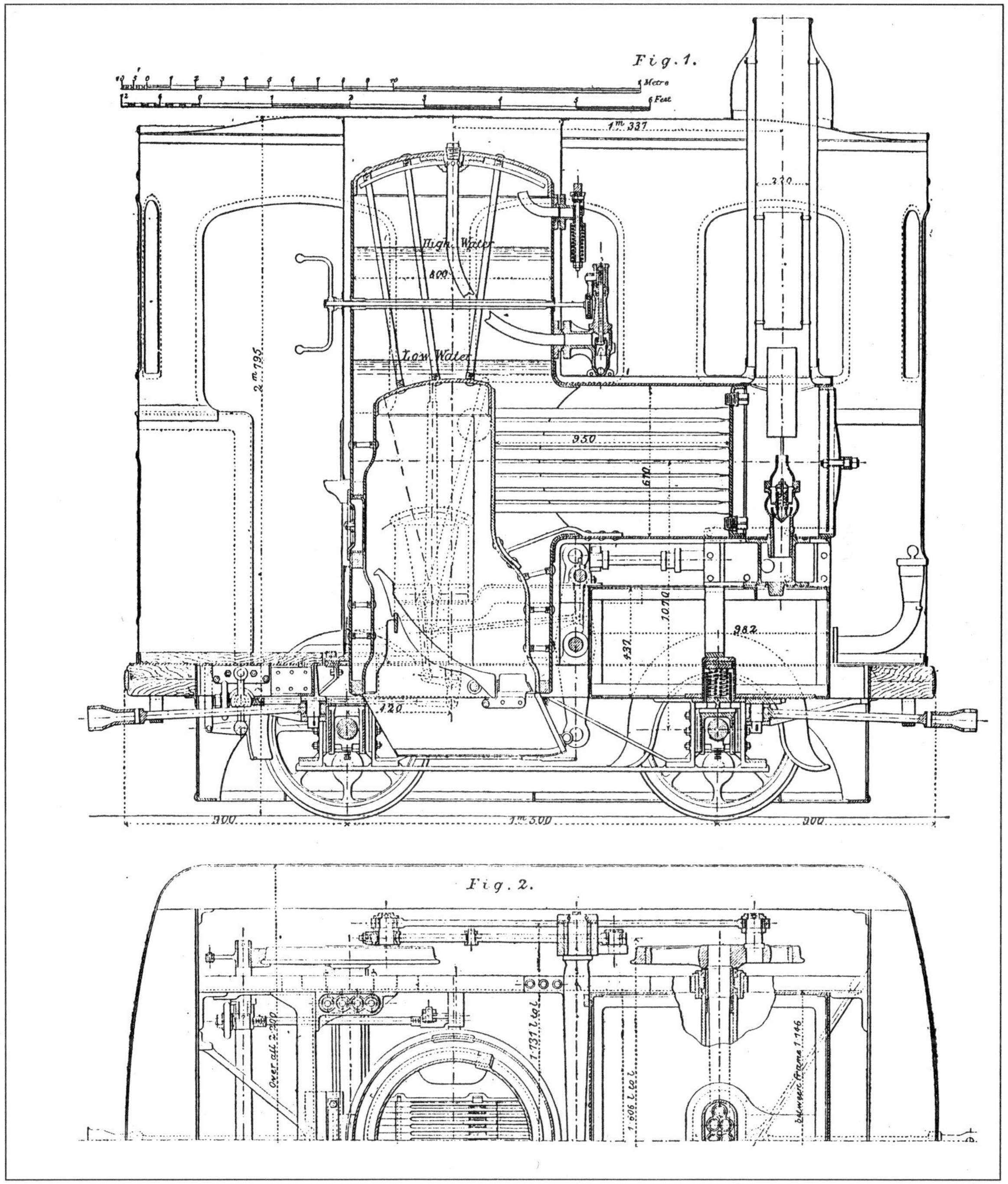

155. The engraved drawing from Engineering 16 January 1880 shows locomotive no.1 for the Sunderland Tramways Co. which was first run in service on 15 September 1880. Swiss-built, cylinders measured either (according to source) 6.3" or 5.5" x 11¾" stroke, and the engine weighed 7 tons. The drive used in Brown's Patent design is very clear, this allowed the cylinders and many other parts to be raised against the refuse and mud of the highways at the expense of more mechanical parts and joints to wear out, and increased 'slop' in the motion. This engine ran from Christ Church to Roker where the photograph of either no.2 or no.3 was taken around December 1880. These later engines were on the Brown designs – and if the order book is correct – contained many parts of the other engines supplied by Winterthur, but incorporated improvements put forward by the assemblers R. & W. Hawthorn of Gateshead. They may have remained in service for 9-12 months but were withdrawn due, it is said "to frequent breakdowns."

machines during 1880-1882 appearing as No.16 (New Castle on Tyne 6 Tramway – Locomotiven) in the SLM 'bestellten' (delivered) list of July 1882, at which time 178 were in service and 33 on order. In this context it is worth reproducing a table from the SLM list showing that Merryweather & Sons were, in 1882, their only real rivals in Europe.

It does seem probable that a number of this batch of locomotives was used on the line from Newcastle to Gosforth, but as details are, as yet, unclear, or at best contradictory, this will be covered when looking at the Newcastle tramways in volume 2.

Woods

Perhaps it is a proof of the innate superiority of British engineering and engineering training at the time that a very high percentage of all steam tramways throughout the world had British input, be it the surveyor, engineer, manager or in the provision of rolling stock.

This rather attractive combination car for Vienna was designed by Mr. E. Woods (a member of the Institute of Chartered Engineers). It was trialled on the Hoylake and Birkenhead Tramway, having been built by G. Starbuck of Birkenhead (who also provided many of the bogie cars used in Britain) but the boiler came from the Shand, Mason works. The Manager of the Vienna Tramway was Palmer Harding, another Englishman.

Presumably hoping that the machine could be sold here it was inspected by Colonel Hutchinson on 11 May 1876 but part of the bodywork broke, leading to failure of the bogie (another report states the bogie itself broke) and as a result there is some doubt whether No.1 ever went to Vienna. But it was 1876...

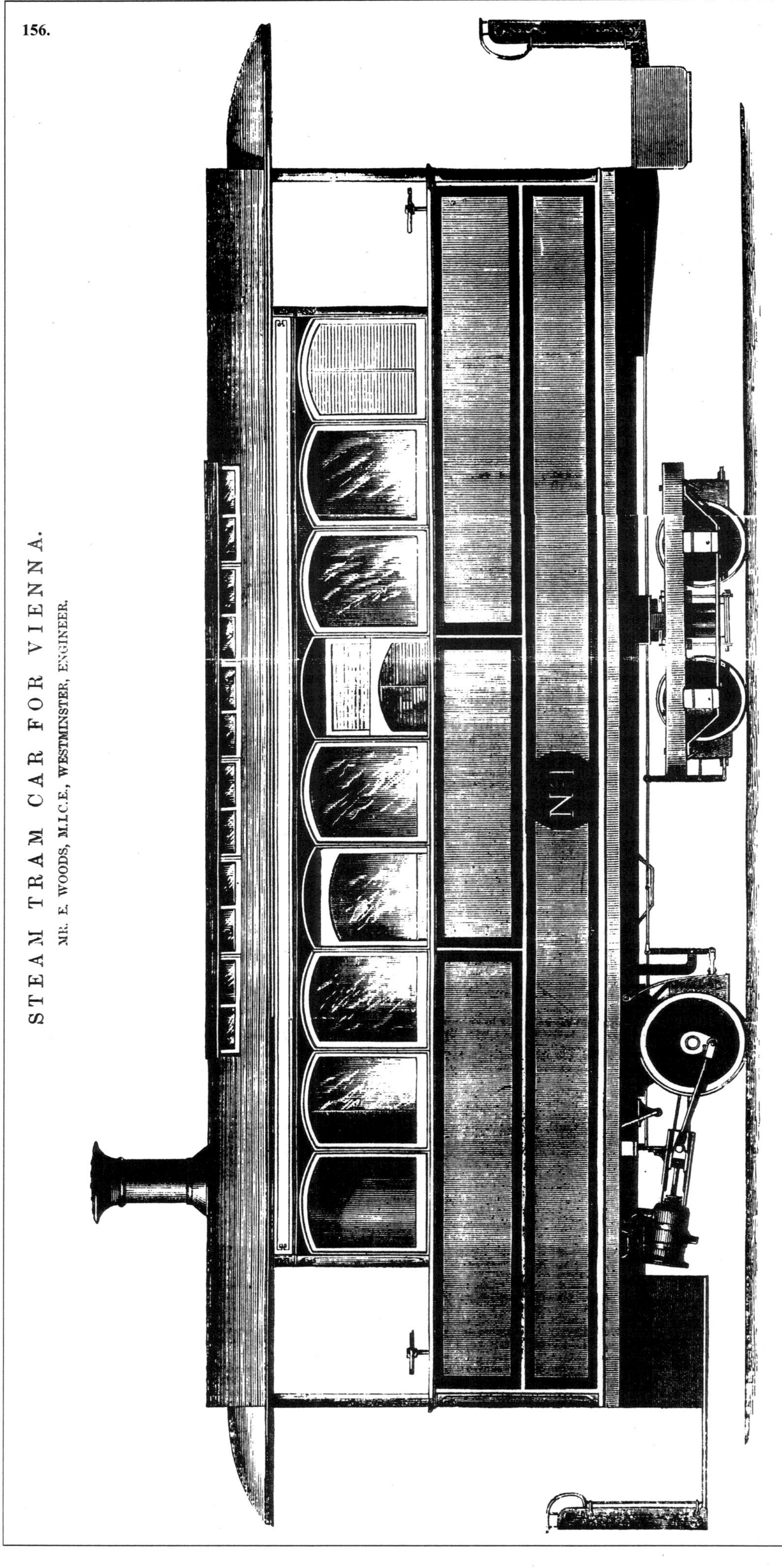

156.

Chapter 8

PEOPLE CARRIERS

Steam tram trailers were built by a surprising number of concerns, but the later versions were so alike that it is almost impossible now to know who built what for which company. Dr H.A. Whitcombe wrote down his findings in his History of the Steam Tram, and generally they are as accurate as could be attained, although later researchers have thrown up some errors. The primary difficulty lies in that the orders for these trailers were in such 'penny packets', that the builders did not often photograph the vehicles or indeed make any notes other than single lines in the order book; attrition of paperwork over the last century plus the mergers that took place in the industry have all affected records. Curiously, while reporters regularly enthused about the 'neatness' of a Kitson engine, 'new design' for Wilkinson products, 'exquisite workmanship' for Beyer Peacock engines, and so on, beyond stating that the trailers had lights "of a new pattern" and were well lit and/or painted brown/red/cream, they hardly noticed them at all until a few years after the opening of the lines when "lumbering behemoths" became the catch-phrase.

Most seated 58 (28 inside and 30 'outside' i.e. upstairs) with longitudinal undivided bench seats – as a personal note I may add that as a schoolboy on electric trams with this type of seating one either slid up and down if no one else was present, and the basilisk eye of the conductor was elsewhere, or if crowded one had great sympathy with a pea in a full pod, large or boney ladies making it difficult to even get to one's feet which dangled way above the floor, and how the girl to whom one offered the seat ever got into the space remains a miracle to me – although in later days steam tramways acquired stock with garden (cross) seating, albeit only upstairs.

Initially there was a rather quaint belief amongst operators that thriftily they could reuse their horse-trams, albeit with minor modifications, and as long as speeds were very low, the tishy springs or India-rubber blocks under the cars withstood the shocks, and photographs show two or three of these following their engines in for example Birmingham and Aston, Dewsbury, Dundee, Leeds and Sunderland. If there was any doubt about the future of steam on tramways it all made sense not to buy new vehicles that, in any event, would probably be too heavy at 3-4 tons empty for horses to drag. But the Board of Trade grew rather fretful at the thought of what were becoming railway trains running around the streets, and decreed that other than in special circumstances only one car would be towed, opening the way for the long bogie double deck trailer cars that became the norm. The first of these was claimed to have been built by Falcon for the South Staffs lines in July 1883. Due to their length (30'/9m) the plate frame bogies were placed at the extreme ends, the entrance and stair access being via the corner of the car rather than at the side as in electric cars. Many, many, accidents were caused by this difficult shape, particularly as the front

157. In early days the operators hoped that they would be allowed to tow trains of trailers along behind their steam trams. The Board of Trade almost outlawed this practice, and 4-wheelers like these Birmingham and Aston Starbuck-built cars soon became redundant, and were spliced together in pairs on new underframes to make 60-70 seaters. Kitson engine no.4 (T78 of 1883).

158. Blackburn and Over Darwen thriftily used existing horse trams during trials, eventually changing to 4-wheel Ashbury-built cars with upstairs screens at the leading end only. The engine is Kitson No.3 (works no T20).

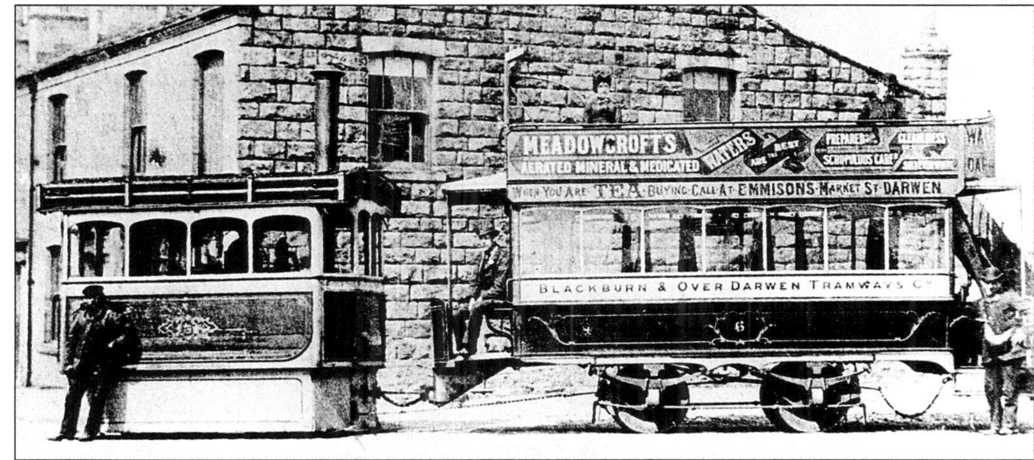

159. Burnley and District Tramways bought 7 trailers of the type shown here which were more or less identical to horsecars made by Starbuck. Engine no.4 in the fleet (Kitson works no T44/1881).

entrance/exit normally seems to have remained in use even as passengers loaded from the back. If you slipped under the car you died.

"Joseph Henry Morton, engine driver in the employ of the Midland Tramway Company, said he knew deceased. About 7.20 on Wednesday night he was in charge of an engine from Wolverhampton to Dudley, and when near Springfield House he passed ... deceased who was walking towards Sedgley. As soon as witness passed deceased he noticed that he commenced to run about five yards, and then made a jump as if to get hold of the handrail, missed his hold and fell between the car and the engine. Witness came to a standstill, and found deceased on the rails between the bogies of the car, unconscious. With the assistance of the inspector and the guard deceased was lifted on the car, and was left at Dr Hallenden's surgery. He then appeared to be dead. Men and boys were constantly trying to jump on the front of the cars, and he had often warned them of the danger they were incurring."

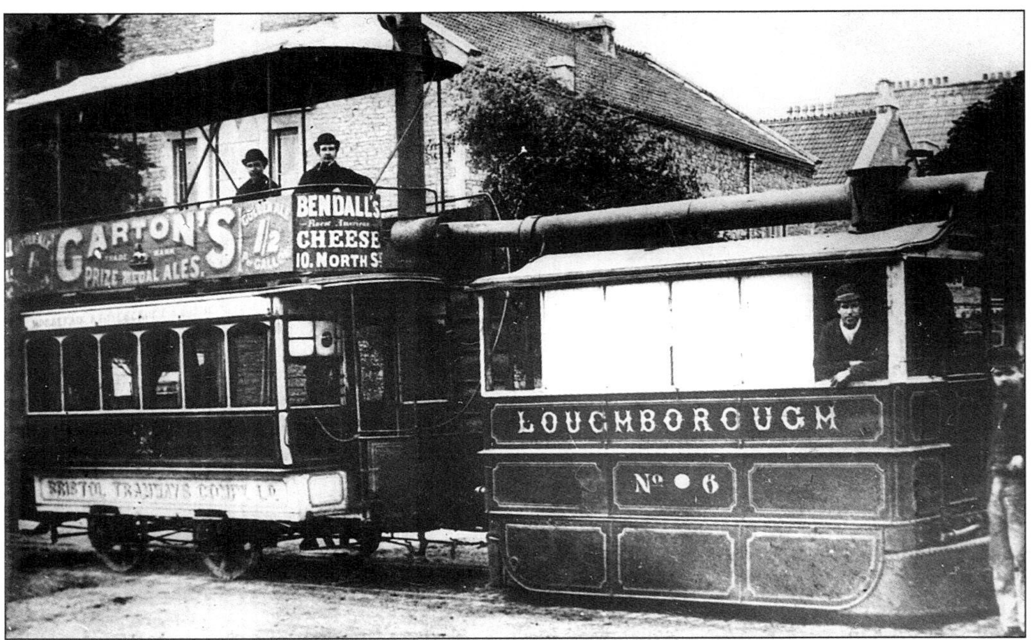

160. Normal horse cars were adapted to run behind the Hughes engines used by Bristol Tramways & Carriage Company's experiments on their line between the Tramways Centre and Horfield in 1881.

161. A Kitson/Starbuck combination running on the line from – as the company name explains – Dudley to Wolverhampton via Sedgley. The company went bankrupt and was replaced by the Midland Tramways Company who continued using the same rolling stock on rickety track until they, too, ceased operating.

162. Ormskirk Road, Pemberton with, in the foreground, the Wigan Tramway Company's line to their depot. Kitson engine and one of a tranche of cars attributed to a local firm, the West Lancashire Wagon Company. Just how dangerous the practice of riding on the drawbar was is clear here.

A daring trick was to go out the front of the car and ride on the drawbar between the tram engine and the trailer; one conductor described his dilemma when faced with this situation – if he shouted and the boy turned around he would go under, if the boy was surprised he could slip, and if he signalled the driver to stop the percussion through the bar could dislodge the boy's feet. Small wonder when the ensemble did stop he clouted the boy; the magistrates gave the conductor an absolute discharge.

A few early cars were open topped, but most were covered in due course against smoke, smuts, and fumes from the engine, although again abiding by the Board of Trade rules on narrow-gauge lines one or more windows were omitted upstairs; safer perhaps, but hardly conducive to comfort on a cold winter's night in Wigan. Eventually as reversing 'wyes' or triangles became commonplace, cars were either rebuilt as single ended vehicles or newly built thus, the finest being those put together by the City of Birmingham Tramways Company.

Lighting by all accounts was awful; colza or paraffin oils being used, the flickering flame being required to illuminate both the external running light and to very dimly relieve the gloom inside the car. Generally conductors carried their own oil lamps to see who was paying with what (forged) coins. (Curiously this technique albeit involving a small torch, was to

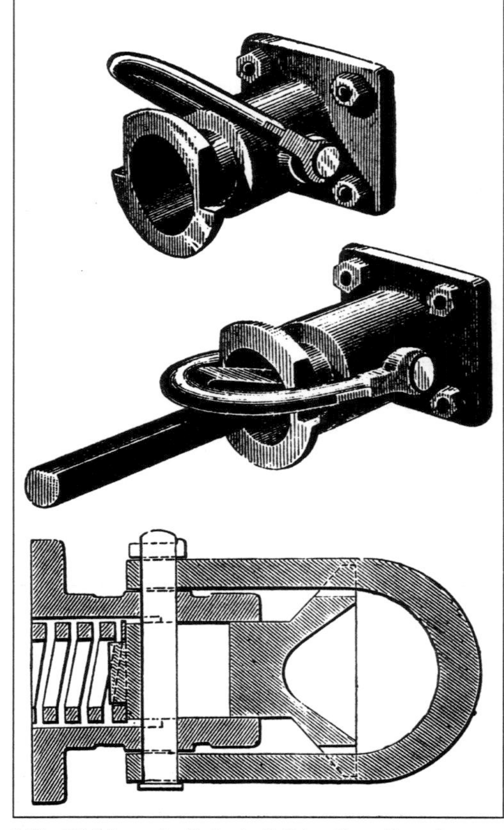

163. Dickinson's Patent Safety Coupling for use between engine and trailer.

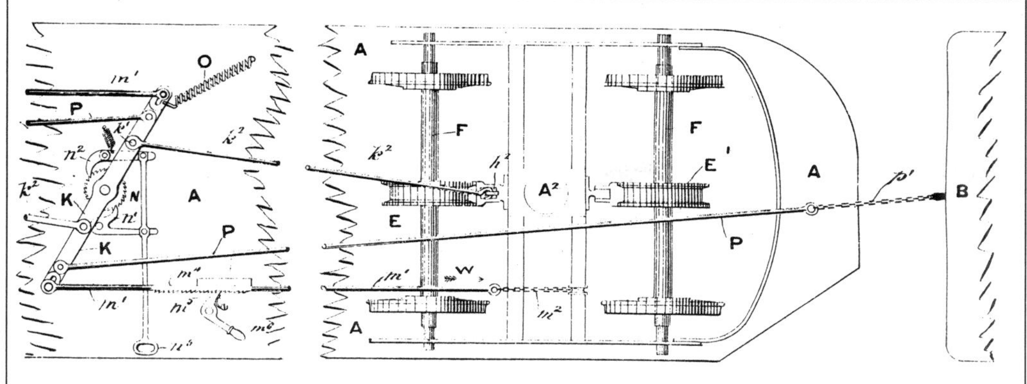

164. The brakes on most cars after 1890 utilised Dickinson's patent design; a simple and effective way of stopping trailers.

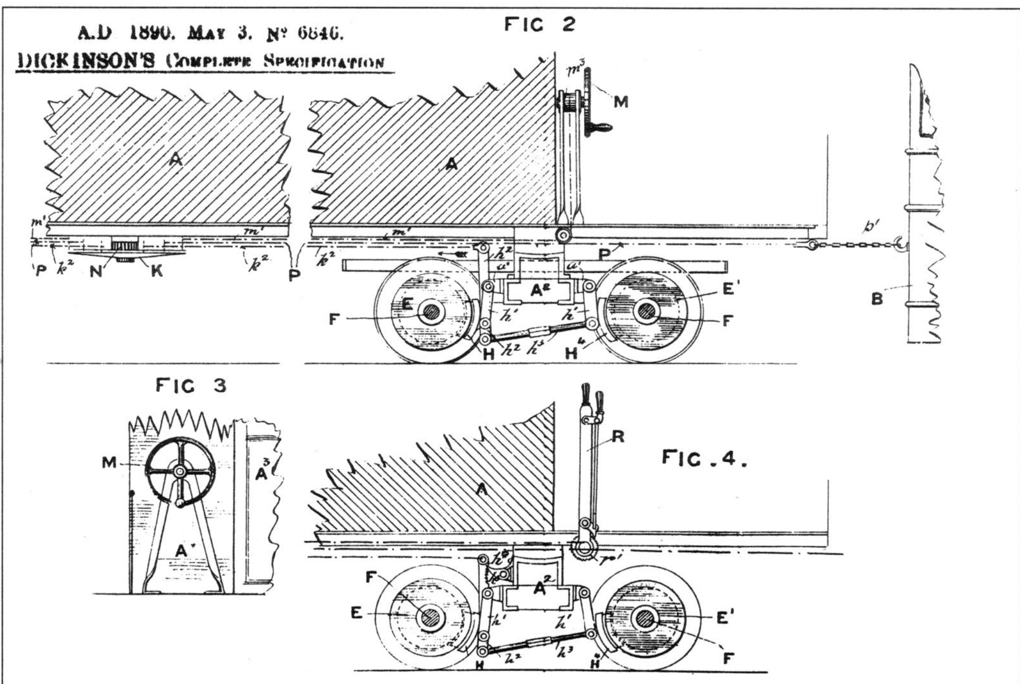

165. North London Tramways Merryweather tram no.11 and Milnes, Birkenhead trailer 18. An odd combination of open upstairs and curtained windows below.

re-appear during the second world war blackout – clippies being very careful to check cash!).

Although the springing within the bogie gave minimal deflection (around 1"/125mm between empty and loaded) the bogies could and did run light on their front axle.

One Saturday in October 1890, shortly before 11.00pm, the 10.10 tram from Stourbridge "had arrived at Brierley Hill, and when approaching the 'tournout' at the top of High Street, overturned on its right side. There were over thirty passengers on the car at the time, about two-thirds of these being inside, and all of them were shaken more or less severely. The oil lamps at either end of the car upset, and the curtains inside the car taking fire added to the general alarm and confusion." The interest in this accident, apart from its cause, lay in the oil lamps igniting the curtains. These curtains were by then six years old, but when similar curtains were introduced inside electric tramcars their lives were very short due to 'infestation'; did the coke fumes keep the fleas and similar life forms away from steam trailers?

There were many detail items which could have been easily rectified but which spoilt the trailers – either the pleasure of the passengers or bystanders. An editorial of 1887: "We are glad to see how much the ladies patronise the top of the cars, but would remind them of the danger when they are about to descend. The top rail to the left is very treacherous. It is not nearly high enough for the very narrow passage down stairs. We suggested some time ago that it would be well for the tramway companies to adopt some means of communication between the passengers on the top of the car and the driver. Several ladies, we know, have been carried considerably beyond the distance they wish to go in consequence of this deficiency." No bells could be fitted upstairs that worked with any degree of reliability until electric or battery operation became feasible, and even downstairs use could be difficult in 1885.

"THE PERRY BAR TRAMS – A COMPLAINT.

To the Editor of the Daily Gazette.
Sir, To-day, while travelling in one of these cars a lady desirous of alighting, found a considerable difficulty in communicating with the conductor, the car being full, and she being located at the end of the car near the engine, and he being busily engaged in conversation with several people on the platform outside the car. When, to assist the lady I ventured to pull the bell, it was immediately followed by an abrupt demand from the conductor for the name and address of the person who pulled that bell, as it was against the rules. No doubt I had ignorantly broken one of the company's rules, and when I ventured to ask Mr Inspector why they did not put the rules in the trams for the guidance and protection of the passengers (which I think they have a right to expect), he informed me that they had their rules in their pockets, and if he was to see anyone pull the bell (no matter who) he would have them locked up on his own responsibility. Now, Mr Editor, I have heard of and witnessed lately several instances of incivility on the part of one or two of the company's servants (though I may say that the majority, as a rule, are energetic, civil and obliging) and as I am not anxious to be incarcerated in durance vile, I shall not (unless sorely pressed) offend again; but be that as it may, civility is a commodity so cheap that these gentlemen in the company's cloth can afford to use it unsparingly. I feel sure these complaints have only to be brought before the notice of the directors to find their proper remedy. I am, yours respectfully, PRO BONO PUBLICO. Birchfield, Dec. 5."

Another editorial, this time from the north and 1889, although this complaint was still being made in the 1950s! – "In dry weather, especially when two trams are passing each other, the noise is something dreadful. Talk about a combination of the roaring of the 'deep' and an American tornado, it isn't in it. Now then 'Ye Patentees' what about a noiseless tyre for the wheels? Ah, that's to make the row more musical. Music indeed charms to soothe the savage beast."

In 1885 a writer in a midland newspaper highlighted a problem in poor design that, if true, must have led to some claims against the company concerned. It is uncertain whether this report refers to steam or cable cars, although looking at drawings, the former seems likely.

"Can nothing be done to save the headgear of the male passengers on the Handsworth tram-cars? Yesterday I saw no fewer than three hats bulged and ruined as their owners leapt upon the foot-board behind. Just above the point where, entering from one side, the incautious passenger places his foot, there projects a hard, angular, relentless lamp, which arrests his progress with the enterprise of a policeman on procession-days, and the precision and force of a steam hammer. If he be of moderate stature, it is his hat which suffers; if tall, his eye. In either case the matter is just as urgent as that of penny stages."

An oddity of 1889 was a formal protest to the "Managers of the Tramway Companies" which the Clerk to the Sedgley Local Board was directed to make, related to "the excessive noise of some of their engines when going along the roads", although one councillor at least pointed out that the trams were quieter than the iron tyres of heavy wagons, the phrase "They [trams] glided along" being used. The companies were also to cease the dangerous overcrowding of the steps of the cars. A rather poetic description elsewhere likened the passengers on the steps of a trailer as "bees around a honeypot, jostling for position."

At a distance of over 100 years it is difficult sometimes to wonder why companies seemingly varied so much in their treatment of passengers, as on the one hand we have the directors of the Birmingham & Aston Tramway claiming that in their new (1883) cars from Starbuck the seats would be covered by Utrecht Velvet* as they were "determined to fall in with the views of the public irrespective of monetary considerations", and yet the poor old Dudley, Sedgeley & Wolverhampton Company in 1887 were still under fire from a newspaper correspondent not only for their appalling timekeeping but "...the seats instead of being nicely cushioned like the railway carriages, they are hard wooden benches, which make one feel tired after sitting on it an hour, sometimes above. I am sure the company would do a lot more business if these things were attended to..." True indeed, but deaf ears hear no complaints!

Finally, the following epistle of 1885 is fascinating as until air conditioning arrived (and when it works!) whether windows should be opened or not was ever a bone of contention – as a conductor once I went upstairs following a complaint of excessive smoke and was met half way up by a 'roil' of blue cigarette-induced fog. I opened a window at the front amid various interesting comments, mainly about unheated cars and interfering officials, and before I was half-way back to the rear stairs at the next stop the top-light closed! I sympathise with Mr Brampton: "VENTILATION OF STEAM TRAM CARS. 1885. Sir, the provision made for ventilation in the steam tram cars consists of a row of small windows along each side, at the top

* Utrecht Velvet was first produced in Utrecht in the 17th century, and used extensively during the 18th century as upholstery fabric. It was made with mohair and cotton, similar to furniture plush.

166.

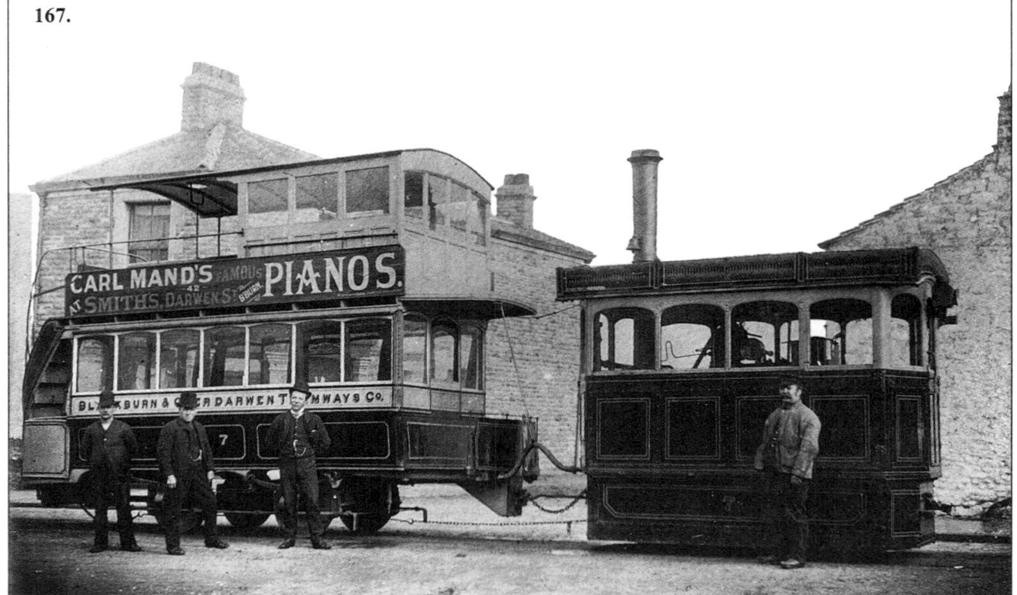

167.

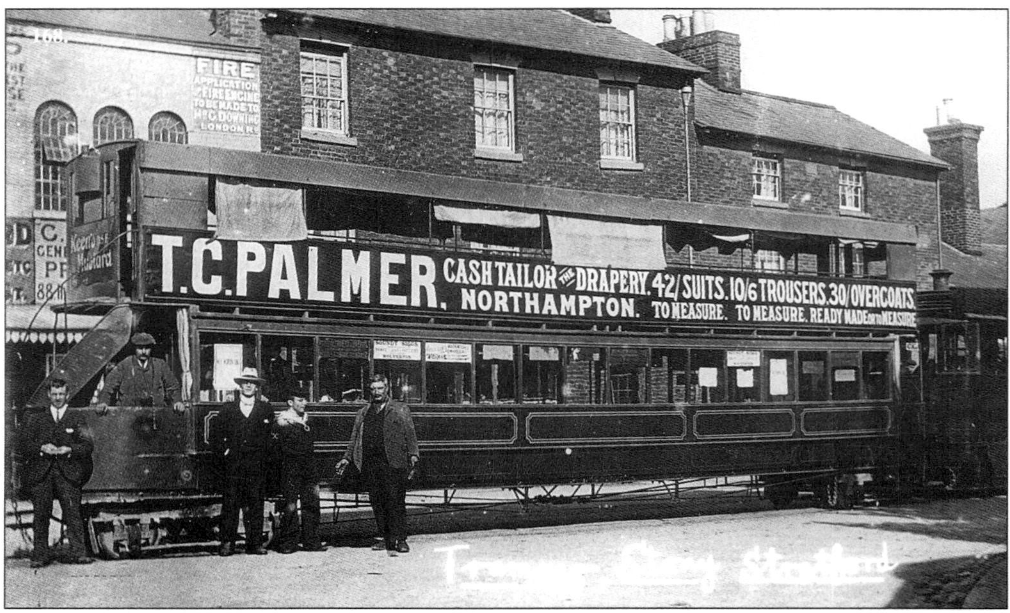

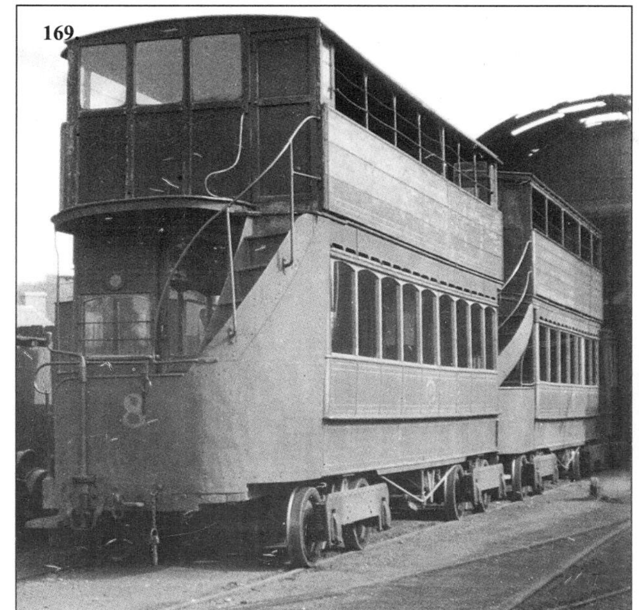

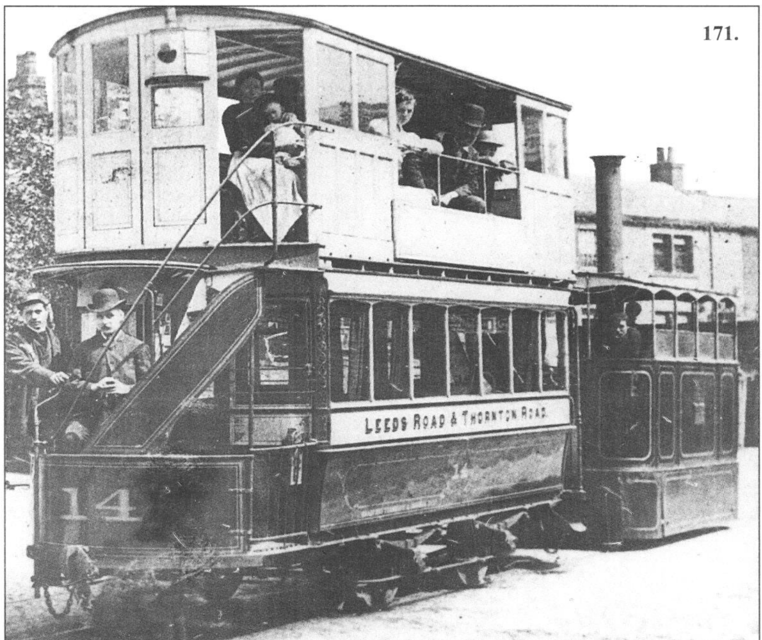

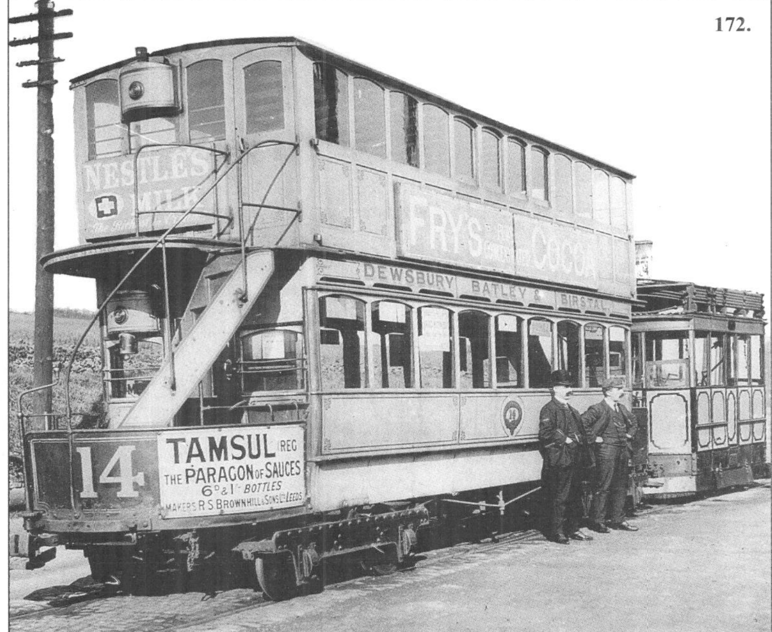

Variations in design; a selected montage to show the variety in both trams and their trailers found in early days, when each company was experimenting.

of the car, which can be opened and shut at pleasure. In summer time this answers very well, for nobody objects to have the windows open when the weather is warm; but in winter time the case is far otherwise, and the majority of people act upon the belief that ventilation on a frosty morning is a superfluity. Consequently there are to be seen, any cold morning, upwards of two dozen suburban intelligences packed inside a car, with the windows shut and the doors shut; and here they sit and stew for half-an-hour in an atmosphere redolent of coffee and bacon and highly suggestive of a 'stable under a cucumber frame'. If, however, someone should intimate that a little air would be an advantage, the individual would be regarded as an enthusiast and might perhaps be asked what he wanted with air on such a cold morning. The popular idea of ventilation is entirely governed by an idea of temperature. People think that if a room is cold the air in it is alright, but if it is hot it wants ventilating. Until this silly notion is dispelled – by a few minutes attention to the requirements of the human lungs – people will continue to regard ventilation as a fad, a theory, the adoption of which is optional ... Ventilation in a public conveyance ought not to be optional, for it remains a necessity, however much the majority vote otherwise. A Compulsory Ventilation Act would certainly be a novelty ... (but) ... the insidious working of consumption, asthma, bronchitis, etc., carry off a far greater percentage of our population than the attacks of smallpox yet the one is legislated for and the other ignored. Considering the many thousands of people who daily travel in the new tram cars it is by no means trivial that they should be made healthy.

The ventilating windows of the car should either be made so that they will not shut, or they should be replaced by perforated zinc panels, which would perhaps be less liable to the objection of down-draughts, the zinc serving to deflect the current. This would ensure a constant circulation of air in the cars ... (and) the tramcars will be at least fit for human beings to enter ... Yours etc. Walter Brampton."

The majority of trailers were built by private companies including:

George Starbuck & Co. (later Starbuck Carriage & Wagon Company).
The Midland Railway Carriage & Wagon Company.
Metropolitan Railway Carriage & Wagon Co.
Oldbury Railway Carriage & Wagon Co.
Ashbury Railway Carriage & Iron Co.
Lancaster Railway Carriage & Wagon Co.
Brown, Marshalls & Co..
Geo. F. Milnes & Co. (successors to Starbuck).
Falcon Engine & Car Works.

A few were home-built or re-built by the tramway companies (particularly in the City of Birmingham Tramways Company), or in the case of the Wisbech & Upwell, the Great Eastern Company.

Of these the Metropolitan R.C. & W., Brown Marshalls, Oldbury R.C. & W., Ashbury R.C. & I. all amalgamated in 1902 to form the Metropolitan Amalgamated Railway Carriage & Wagon Co., which many years later, after steam trams were long gone, metamorphosed into Metro-Cammell-Weymann Ltd., vacuuming up the relics of the Midland R.C. & W., and Milnes on the way, while Falcon became the Brush Electrical Engineering Co. Ltd.

Tramway builders' customers

Although incomplete partly due to missing documents and "lost" paperwork, the following list of who built what is as accurate as I can make it.

Metropolitan Railway Carriage & Wagon Co. Ltd.
J. Aird (contractor), Birmingham & Aston, Birmingham & District, Birmingham & Midland, Birmingham Tramways Co., Cavehill & Whitewell, Belfast, Dublin Tramways, Edinburgh & District, Edinburgh Northern, Mr. Felts (for pier tramway), Fintona (Ireland), Fisher & Parrish (contractor), Kreeft Howard (contractor), North Dublin, North London Suburban, North Staffordshire, P.W. Pearson (contractor), Phillips & Co. (contractor), Portstewart, South Shields, South Staffordshire, Stockton & Darlington, Taite & Carlton (contractor), Tynemouth, Universal Steam Tramway Co., Vale of Clyde, J. Whittall (contractor), F.C.Winby (contractor), R. Whyte (contractor)

Oldbury Railway Carriage & Wagon Co. Ltd.
The only two I am absolutely sure of are Birmingham & Midland, and the body for John Grantham's steam car, but I have no doubt there were others.

Ashbury Railway Carriage & Iron Co. Ltd.
Accrington, Bessbrook & Newry, Blackburn, Bradford, Darwen, Dewsbury, Dublin & Lucan, Glyn Valley, Lytham (gas trams), Southport Pier.

Southport Pier is also of interest as the winding 'engines' came from Wm. Wilkinson.

Lancaster Railway Carriage & Wagon Co. Ltd.
The following have been traced, but there were many more.
Blackpool, Bury, Neath (gas trams), Ryde Pier, South Staffs & Birmingham District, Trafford Park (there is a suggestion the Serpollet body came from Lancaster).

Brown Marshalls & Co. Ltd.
Again, only the following are definites, but other customers no doubt existed.
Birmingham Central, City of Birmingham, Dudley & Stourbridge, South Staffs & Birmingham District.

Geo. F. Milnes & Co. Ltd.
The late John Price was working on a definitive list of Geo. F. Milnes' customers which, if available, will be published in a later volume.

A couple of years prior to their amalgamation Brown Marshalls & Co. Ltd. appear to have thrown open their works to a number of railway journalists; and although this was past the steam trams' heyday, nonetheless a description of a manufacturer's methods of working over a hundred years ago is worth repeating, the quality alone making it small wonder the tramcars were almost indestructible.

Anyone travelling on the old Nor'Western line from Euston to Birmingham today would be hard pushed to recognise the Victorian landscape. "The train whirls through great stretches of white, shimmering faintly in the cold winter sunshine ... The hedgerows glistening like sprays of diamonds as the light falls on the particles of snow and ice which still adhere to their branches. No life of movement visible except here and there amongst a flock of sheep huddled around the food and shelter provided for them, their usual pasture being unattainable. Or an occasional wagon driving heavily along the snow-encumbered road, the creaking of the wheels, and the encouraging shouts of the driver lost in the rattle of our train."

And so they arrived at the Britannia Works of Brown Mashalls. "Outside the station we find ourselves paddling through a mixture of snow and slush of a pea soup consistency and colour, very different in appearance from the pearly white of the country, and breathing an atmosphere to which the adjacent brick works, and the tall chimneys of numerous manufactories contribute an element not particularly agreeable to lungs fresh from air of a purer, if less substantial nature."

The linkages between businesses a hundred years ago were strong and clear; the failure of a bank nearly finished the company, but in 1882, just over ten years after it was reformed (1870), Sir James Allport, Manager of the Midland Railway Company and Chairman of Brown Marshalls appointed as General Manager A.L. Shackleford who, to show the degree of professionalism entering the industry, was an associate member of both the Institutes of Civil Engineers and the Mechanical Engineers; a far cry from Mr Brown and Mr Marshall who hand built stage coaches. As a result of Schackleford's guidance and new methods imported from America (he had visited the Pullman Works in the USA and Canada with Mr Pullman himself) plus touring Buenos Aires and Brazil where orders, including tramcars, were obtained, shares in the company with a face value of £1 stood in 1900 at £1.90. Overall the works measured 12 acres, of which nine were covered – this area giving some clue why rail and tramway needed a high throughflow of vehicles; the heating, lighting and rates bills must have been horrendous, although the factory was one of the first to install electric lighting (by the Brush Electrical Company) in 1883.

The frame shop (poetically described by one writer as looking like a hospital ward full of iron bedsteads for a race of giants) measured 450 feet long (137m) by 110 feet wide (34m), and was where the underframes were riveted together, hydraulic presses handling any untoward shapes.

Without the aid of computers and slide-rules, a good number of draughtsmen were each drawing their specialities, the one detailing a tram bogie while another would be completing details of the marquetry panels for a new sleeping car.

Strangely in times of cutbacks, draughtsmen were often the first of the white collar workers to go, the manufacturers then only offering an already extant design; in later years this could stultify British industry.

The forge and fitting shop where, as it was said "steel is hammered and punched and drilled, and generally knocked about until it assumes the required form" was 250 feet long (76m) and 200 feet wide (61m), and held something over a hundred hearths for blacksmiths' welding and riveting work.

Like any heavy industrial forging shop of that era, on the one hand steam drop hammers formed the basic shapes out of the steel, shaking the entire building as they did so, and on the other myriads of screeching, yowling, relatively tiny, machines produced nuts, bolts and the humble but necessary washers. The incredible

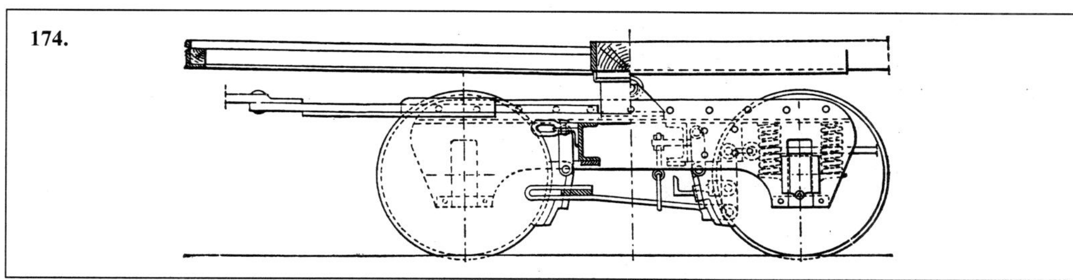
174.

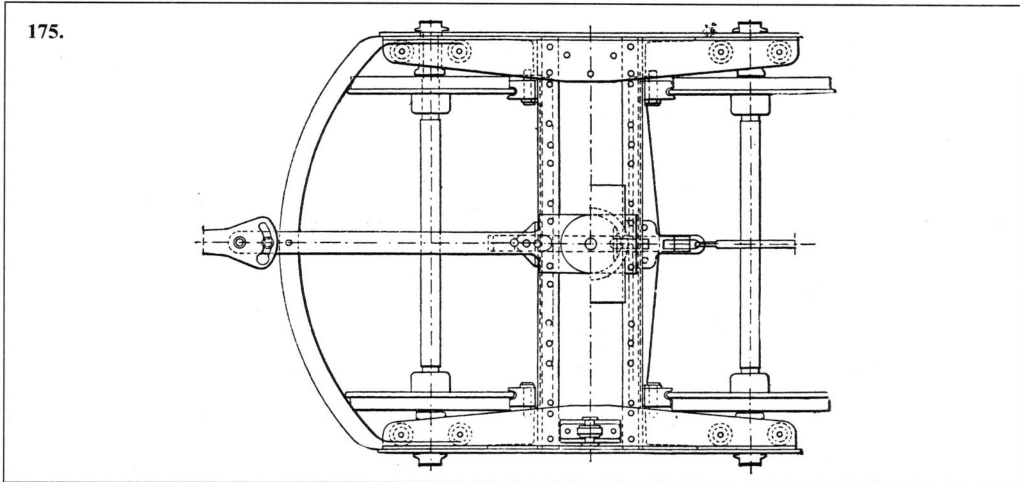
175.

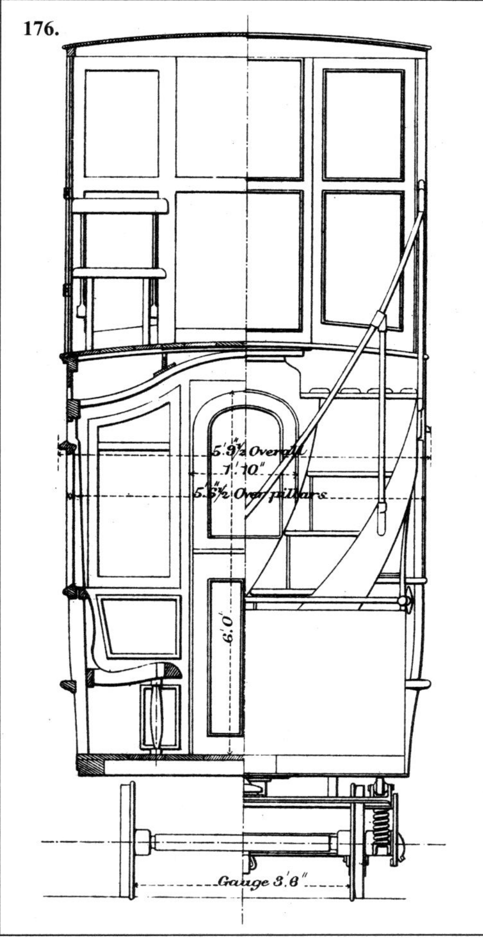

176.

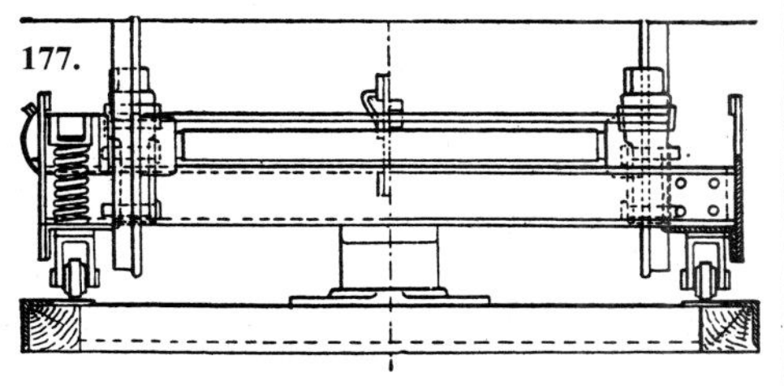
177.

cacophony emitting from such works has almost gone from Britain; I for one miss it!

Since vehicles, whether built for heavy or light rail, were predominantly made from wood, Brown, Marshalls had a massive timber yard (it was said a fire at Milnes finished them as all their seasoned timber was lost and they had to resort to green wood for framing. "In the drying houses immense stacks of wood of great value are being seasoned and dried, a process to which all wood is subjected on the premises for years before it is considered fit to be worked up. A variety of woods enter into composition of carriages and tram cars, oak, elm, teak, ash, pine, mahogany and walnut."

After the timber was rough sawn (although much came in plank form) heavy work was reduced, dimension saws, four- and five-cutters, planers and the rest, being equipped with rollers, in some cases chain driven to pull the wood into the cutting teeth. Only thirty or so years ago any man applying to work on high speed spindles (which shape or profile the thin face of timber) rather cynically was considered an amateur if he had not lost the top digit of his right hand fore-finger notwithstanding the existence of machine guards.

"At the same time those who assume that the individuality of the workman is lost in the machine he tends are mistaken. In connection with all these appliances, whether for working up wood or iron, much deftness and skill are required ... and men who bring such qualities to their work are as highly valued and paid as good wages now as at any former period."

One modernisation welcomed by all parties is that the sawdust was sucked up from the machines and deposited outside (from where, of course, it was bagged and sold), as not only was this extraction "an immense advantage to the health of the workpeople" but also an economy for the company in reducing the labour involved in collecting and barrowing the sawdust by hand from the purlieus of each machine as well as greatly reducing the fire risk.

The erecting shop was the largest in the works, being 400 feet long (122m) and 350 feet wide (107m) and, like all of its kind, the area where an apparent chaos of steel sections and different types of wood was finally bolted, screwed, glued, hammered and tacked until a tram car or railway carriage emerges.

Two paint shops were in use at the Britannia Works, one 200 feet square (61m x 61m) and the other 200 feet by 140 feet wide (61m x 43m); one where fourteen coats of paint and varnish were applied, and the other more of an upholstery area where cloth, leather and brass predominated as hordes of workmen tacked and sewed and glued together the visible parts of a vehicle.

Amid all this hustle and bustle (there were 1,200 employees at the turn of the century) more mundane, but paying freight vehicles went through the shops more or less continuously, whether coal wagons, hopper or gas tankers, all could be sold or leased to operators.

The Railway Magazine writer ended his report by referring to tramcars and although steam trailers had, by 1900, run their course, the similarities between the cars he saw and those trailers preserved, shows just how near the one was to its parent. "We have scarcely alluded to a very important part of the business, the making of tramcars. With the extension of tramways in this country and abroad has come a large increase in the demand for cars, and to Brown, Marshalls and Company has fallen a considerable share in supplying the want. They have built vehicles for all kinds of tram and traction, horse, steam, electric, and cable, for the 'home and export trade', including those for the cities of London and Glasgow, the Liverpool Elevated Railway, and many other important corporation and private companies. We saw, nearly completed, one of the cars forming part of a large order from the Edinburgh and District Cable Tramway. Its appearance is in marked contrast to that of the dingy, narrow vehicles placed on the earlier lines. The interior is spacious and comfortable; the ventilation is under the control of the conductor, who by working small levers outside can regulate it for the general benefit; a system more conducive to pace and harmony than leaving the adjustment to the discretion of individual passengers. The public generally have very conflicting ideas on the subject, the delicate looking female who looks as if a good puff of air would blow her away, usually finding the greatest pleasure in sitting in a draught, whilst the robust gentleman at her side shivers at the thought of the substantial cold of which it is laying the foundation. Of course he is too polite, or too timid, to suggest an abatement of the signals of distress made by her neighbours, in the shape of turn up coat collars, and the hasty buttoning of garments up to the chin ... The platforms of these cars at each end are sufficiently roomy to give plenty of space for passengers entering or leaving the inside without interfering with those to and from the top. The stairs, too, are of easy ascent, and wide enough to allow the more portly inhabitants of 'Auld Reekie' to pass up and down without the undignified squeeze gentlemen of liberal proportions are subjected to in many cars."

The Britannia Works of course no longer exist; Brown Marshalls closed in 1908, the works being sold to the Wolseley Car Company and finally Morris Commercial Cars built their lorries, vans and other vehicles on the site until

178.

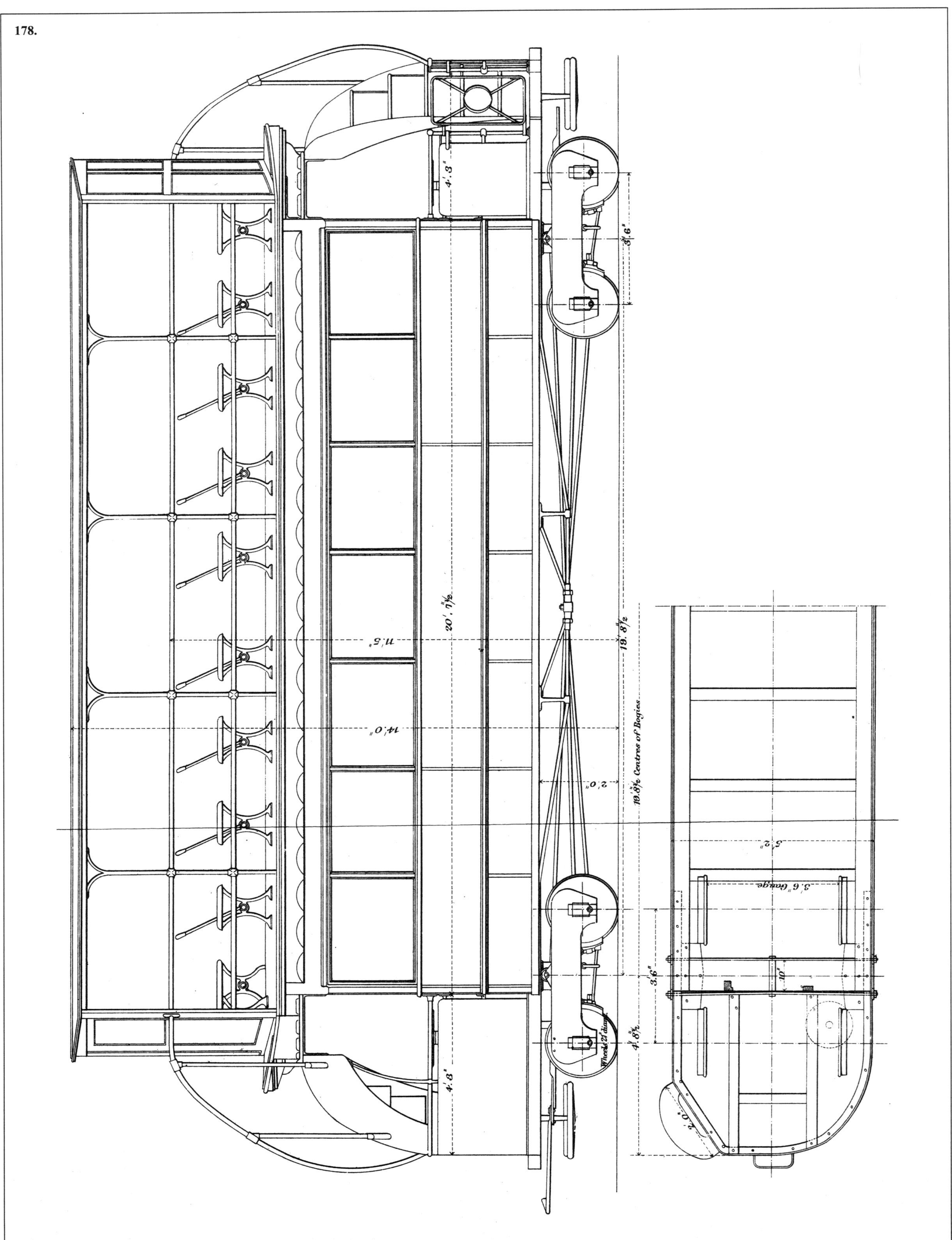

4' 3"
3' 6"
20' 7½"
19' 8½"
11' 5"
14' 0"
19' 8½ Centres of Bogies
2' 0"
5' 2"
5' 6" Gauge
10"
3' 6"
4' 8½"
4' 8"

relatively recently. Now Adderley Park Station is almost deserted.

D. Kinnear Clark has a useful look at a car constructed by the Falcon Engine and Car Works, Loughborough, at pp.371-375 of the second edition of his "Tramways, their construction and working" of 1894, and which I reproduce on pages 139 to 140 (Figs 174-178) to round off this chapter:

"This car was constructed for the Birmingham Central Tramways, on a gauge of 3½ feet, to carry thirty passengers inside and thirty outside. It runs on eight 21-inch wheels, set in two swivelling bogies. The body is of the usual street car type, having a platform and staircase at each end, and an awning over the top seats. The dimensions are –

Length inside body: 20 feet ¼ inch, or 16 inches per passenger.
Length over platforms: 29 feet 1½ inches.
Width outside pillars: 5 feet 6½ inches.
Width over all: 5 feet 9 inches.
Height: 14 feet.
Distance apart of bogies, between centres: 19 feet 8½ inches.

The bottom frame is of oak, put together with white lead, and where necessary, with oak pins. Each side is trussed. The side and corner pillars are of ash. The waist panels are of Honduras mahogany, and the rocker panels of whitewood. The inner sides of the panels are covered with canvas glued on. The panels are pinned to every pillar, except the end pillars, to which they are screwed; they are glue-blocked to the battens.

The floor is of 1-inch red deal, tongued and grooved, nailed sown to the bottom frame. Wearing grids are formed of longitudinal strips of white deal, nailed to the floor. The roof ribs are of American elm or English ash, bent to the curves and covered with pitchpine tongued and grooved. Canvas is put on with white lead, and painted outside with four coats of white lead paint. The doors have frames of cherry, panelled at the bottom with light wood and at the top with glass. They are hung on brackets and rollers at the top, and are fitted with friction-plates, handles, and catches.

The inside casings are framed together, and fitted with fancy wood patterns finished in their natural grain. A swing door with glass panel is fixed on the side where the car door slides in. The windows are of best polished plate-glass, and ¼-inch bare in thickness, fixed in grooved India-rubber. The blinds are of curtain form, of mohair mounted on polished brass rods. The seats and backs are of perforated veneer in one piece, suitably carved, finished in the natural grain, and French polished. The inside hand rails are of wrought-iron tube with screwed ends. They act as tension rods to keep the roof in proper form. A sufficient number of hand-straps are provided. There are two lamps, one at each end of the car. Their reflectors are fluted glass mirrors, showing a strong light to the car and a coloured signal light outside. Ventilators are fixed inside of the roof. Cords are provided to be connected with the gong on the engine.

The platforms are of 1-inch red deal, 4¼ feet long. The frames and supports are of angle-iron, with oak bearers. The off-sides are railed in. The entrances are fitted with gates and locks. The flooring is either tongued and grooved or open-jointed. The steps are of hard wood, on wrought-iron brackets. The dash or fence is formed of wrought-iron rails supported by suitable standards, with a hand-rail at the top, and shut in outside. A light staircase is fixed to each platform to give access to the seats on the roof. The stair has sheet-iron stringers and risers and wood treads. The risers are flanged to receive the treads and secure the stringers.

The frames of the bonnets are of ash or American elm, bent to the curves, and covered with pine and canvas, as specified for the roof; fixed to the ends of the cars with wrought-iron brackets.

The top seats are of slat-and-space construction, with reversible backs. The slats are of pitch-pine or other suitable wood, varnished the natural colour. A light wooden roof covered with canvas is supported by iron standards. The upper part of each end is glazed and fitted with a deal door. Wearing slats of deal are fitted alongside the roof and across the bonnets. A light and strong hand-rail, 2¾ feet high, of wrought-iron tube with wrought-iron feet, all screwed together, is securely fixed round the top of the car and on the outer side of each staircase.

The bogies... are of wrought-iron. The axles of each bogie are 3½ feet apart. The sides are cut out of ⅜-inch solid plates, forming guides for the axle-boxes. The centres are of cast iron, with convenient means for oiling. Friction rollers are fitted on each side to limit the tilting of the car. The wheels are of chilled cast iron, from America, 21 inches in diameter, bored to 2⅜ inches in diameter. The axles are of mild steel, turned, with 2⅛-inch journals, having 5¾ inches length of bearing. The wheels are forced into their proper places on the axles by hydraulic pressure. The axle-boxes are formed with oil wells, and to exclude dust and dirt. The bearings are of gun-metal. There are double-spring check plates to limit end play. The lids are of wrought iron, fixed with a book at the top and a bolt at the bottom. The springs are of coiled steel. The deflection of the springs, when fully loaded, amounts to ¾-inch.

A wrought-iron draw-bar is connected to each bogie as near as possible to its centre. Brake blocks of chilled cast iron, supplied one to each wheel; worked by means of a hand-wheel under the stair at each end of the car, and arranged to connect to the break-chain from the engine.

The iron work is of B B Staffordshire or other iron of equal quality. It is required to be of light but strong design and first-rate workmanship.

The outside of the car receives three coats of lead priming, eight coats of filling-up, stopped and rubbed down, painted, picked out, fine lined, and lettered according to colours, patterns, and wording, to be supplied by the purchaser. Finished with three coats of durable body varnish outside; and French polished inside, except the roof, which is varnished with finishing body varnish.

	Tons	cwt
Weight of car, unloaded	3	18
Do., fully loaded with 60 passengers, weighing 4 tons, at the rate of 15 passengers per ton	7	18

The gross weight may be taken as 8 tons, or 2 tons per axle, or 1 ton per wheel. The total horizontal bearing area of the journals may be taken at 50 square inches, and the gross load at

$$\frac{2240 \times 8}{50} = 358.4$$

or, as a round number, 360 lb per square inch.

The weight of the car unloaded is 1.30cwt per passenger."

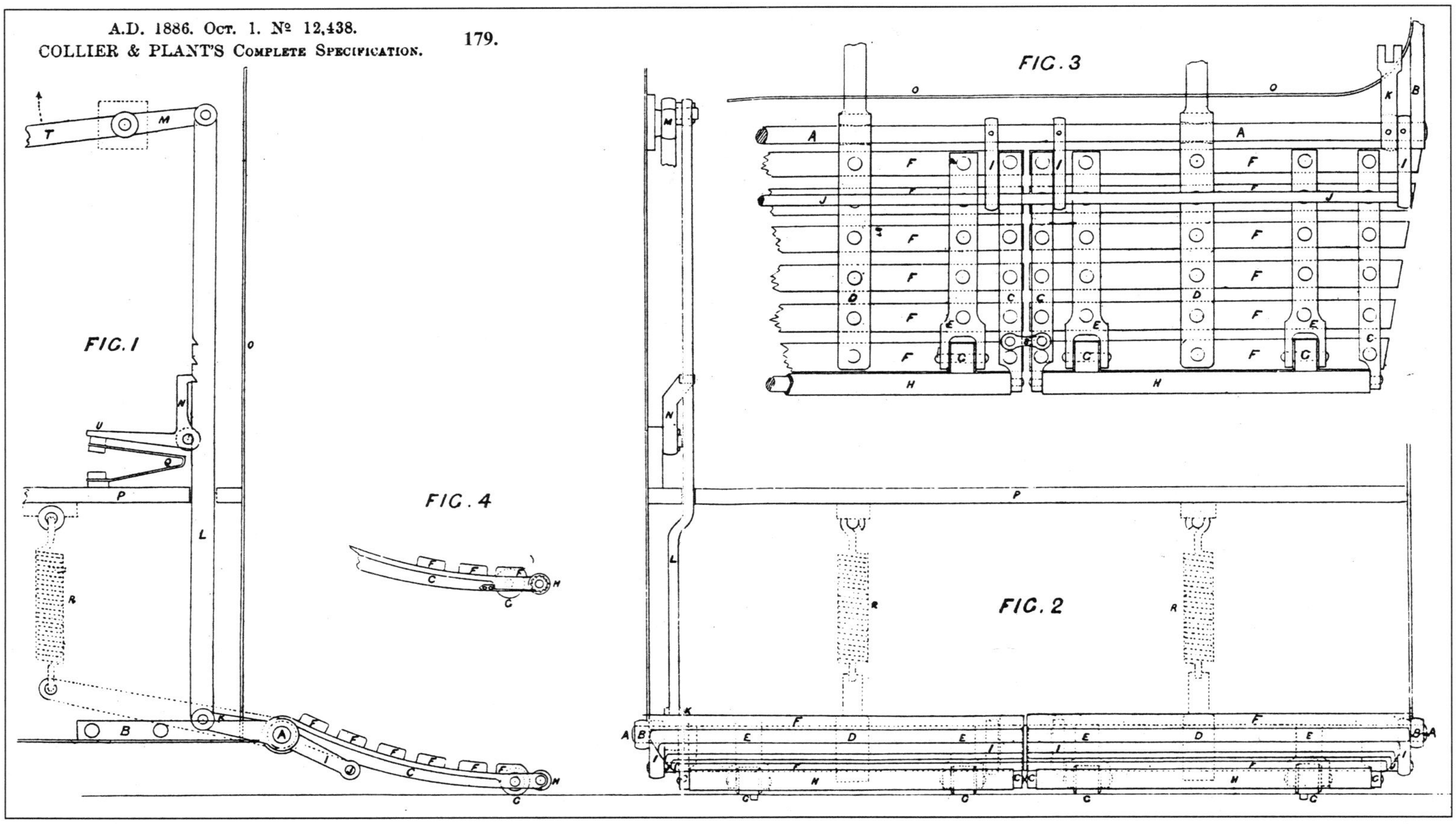

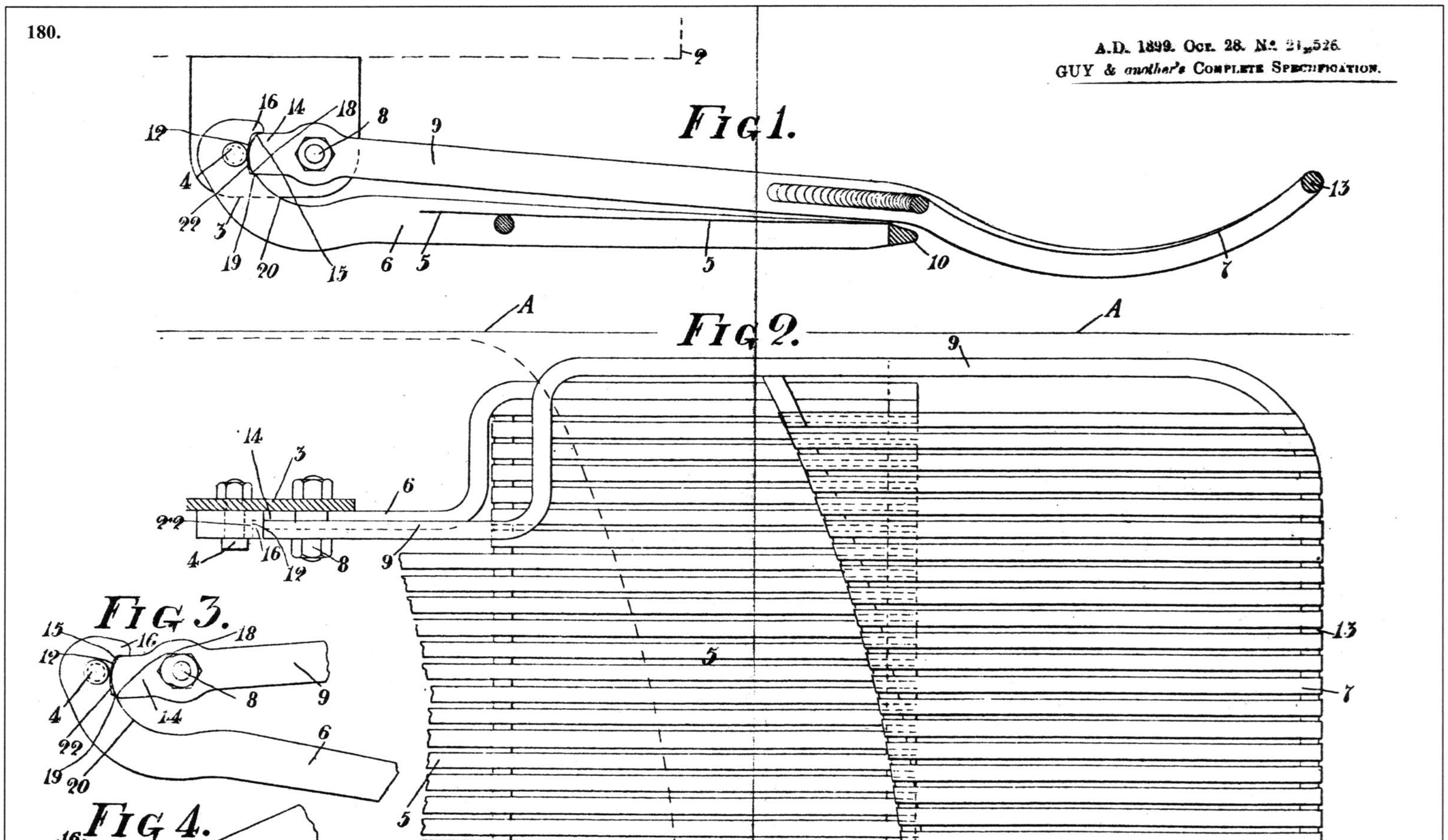

179.

A.D. 1886. Oct. 1. № 12,438.
COLLIER & PLANT'S Complete Specification.

FIG. 1

FIG. 2

FIG. 3

FIG. 4

180.

A.D. 1899. Oct. 28. № 21,526.
GUY & another's Complete Specification.

Fig 1.

Fig 2.

Fig 3.

Fig 4.

Two proposed lifeguards. Tests with (admittedly crude) models seem to indicate they work, but too many intricate parts complicated matters on service vehicles.

Chapter 9

LIFEGUARDS AND LIGHTS

The number of designs relating to lifeguards patented in the United Kingdom during our period runs well into three figures, although not all were even modelled let alone completed. For reasons of space I have only illustrated a handful, selected not necessarily because they were the most successful but to show their infinite variety. One however, the Tidswell, which was so successful under electric cars that the Board of Trade suggested its widespread adoption, is of particular interest inasmuch as James Tidswell, of 75 Bismarck Street, West Bowling, Bradford, was a steam tram driver who was obviously very attentive to matters about him and his mode of transport.

Samuel Collier, a wheelwright, and Richmond Plant, a Mechanician, saw trams in Birmingham and under their patent 12,428 of 1886 stated "This our Invention relates to the construction and arrangement of parts forming a Safety-guard intended to be attached to one or both ends of Tram Engines or Tram Cars in such a manner that if any person is seen by the driver in charge of the engine or car in danger of being run over, he can instantly lower the safety guard, and by so doing keep the said person from getting beneath the engine or car." Their guard might have worked, although it was dismissed during the trials due to those small wheels. Incidentally, one wonders if Richard Plant was in fact a tram driver – the word 'Mechanician' being commonly used in France for such a train (or tram) driver.

On 4 October 1886 patent no.12,584 was entered by Joseph Smith (of Wednesbury in the County of Stafford, Solicitor), who stated "My invention has for its main object the saving of life, but it has also the effect of removing obstructions from the front of Tramway Engines. At the present time a margin of four inches is allowed between the bottom of the screen plate of an engine and the ground level to allow for the wear and tear of wheels which in the case of a badly worn wheel brings the screen plate to say some two inches above the ground. Now experiments show that a screen say four inches clear of the ground will frequently mount over such objects as a good sized child while two inches or thereabouts will enable the screen to push away the child or other obstacle. It will thus be seen that as the wheel springs and other parts of the engine wear the space between the screen plate and the road level varies. My invention meets this variation and provides a safeguard to life and property."

The method of operation is clear although the set of false teeth "W" are the "pavement" or road surface. Lives were probably saved, although we know from one report that this spring loaded guard, in its Mk 2 mode, was under the control of a driver of a Central Tramways tram via a lever, i.e. no longer just bouncing along, when it initially stuck and then banged down on a luckless boy who was trying to scrabble or roll clear of the tram.

A year later Thomas Bolton Waterfield, a Dublin based Civil Engineer paid for no.13,176. He stated, correctly, "Guards as at present used in connection with tramcars locomotives and such like vehicles consist of a V shaped or hemispherically constructed apparatus which is rigidly attached to the frame work of the vehicle. By this method of attachment it is obvious that as the vehicle oscillates or pitches longitudinally the guard is necessarily carried with it and is consequently somewhat a source of trouble, owing of its tendency to strike or 'bump' the ground; and also for the same reason it cannot be carried sufficiently near the roadway to effect satisfactorily the object for which it is designed." His guard was to be attached to the axle boxes of the engine, "in other words" he stated "(it will) maintain a constant horizontal position irrespective of the rise and fall of the body of the vehicle..."

In 1899, 21,526 covered the invention of J.A. Guy, a wool merchant, and F.W.Bentham a 'Machine Comb Maker' which is mainly reproduced to show the drawings detail. If anyone wonders how it works (and in model form it does) the main outline can be gathered from "In case however the feeler is raised by meeting an obstacle in the track the under faces or corners 18 of the arms 14 engage the bottom 19 of the recesses 12 and force the guard down on to the track, and at the same time the arms pass out of the recess. The curved part 20 of each side bar of the guard is made of such a form that when the guard is thus forced down upon the track the centre from which such curve is struck is concentric with the stud 8 on each side, therefore any further upward movement of the feeler has no further action as regards depressing the guard, but the ends 22 of the arms 14 engage the curved parts of the side bars and prevent the guard being lifted."

Another very late patent 13,705 of 1904 came from a 'Baker and Confectioner' and a Publican (of the Craven Heifer) acting in concert, but which saw light of day under electric cars. Two pattern makers from Hyde, William Wilson and Thomas Bennett brought out No. 20,752 in 1899 which involved both little wheels and netting – all the time moving away from the basic simplicity demanded in service, but they showed unrewarded ingenuity.

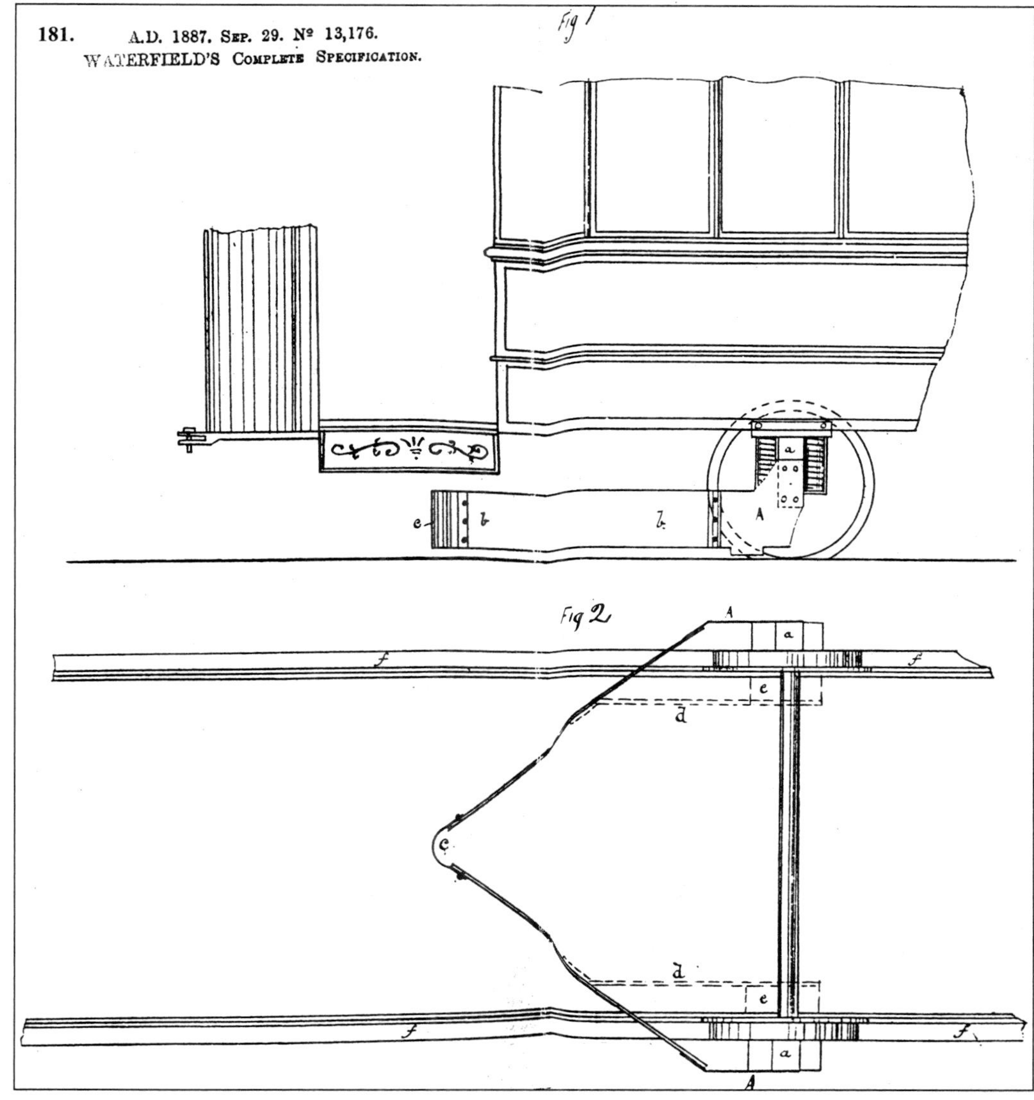

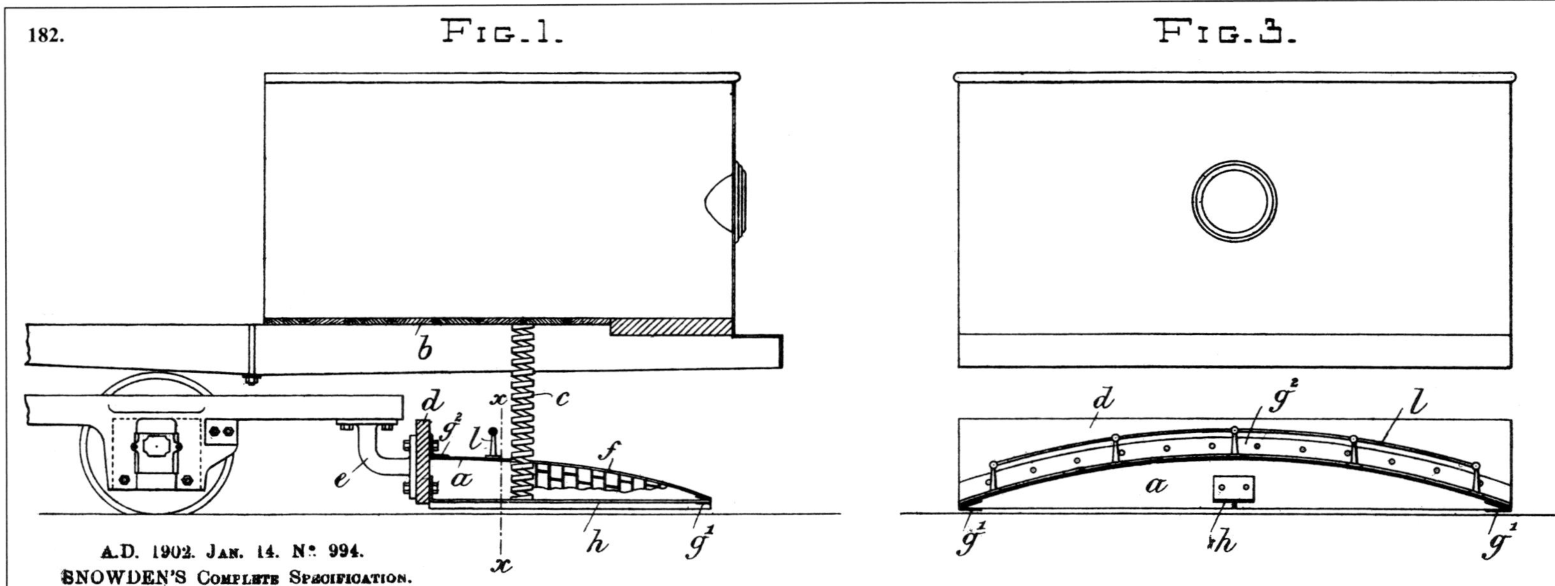

Johann Von Holt, a Hamburg labourer, had his set of angled rollers tried in Germany and patented them here (20,109/1899) just in case ... his fellow-countryman, one Wilhelm Metternich, a merchant of Cologne (Koln) stated correctly in his preamble to 14,958 of 1902 that the fixed shield commonly used did not always work as "These arrangements hitherto known for the removal of bodies from before street tram cars and the like and for the prevention of accidents therewith, consist essentially of a structure surrounding the entire car frame, and which is prolonged to a point before and behind at the ends of the car. These arrangements fulfil the object of pushing aside obstacles in front of the car in a very incomplete manner, and especially when designed to prevent accidents by running over persons, these structures fail entirely, because with them a crushing or squeezing of parts of the body, if not of the whole person, is unavoidable. This will be obvious when it is recognised that the structure for practical reasons cannot be set so low that it is almost in contact with the ground, in consequence whereof a portion of the body is always squeezed into a space between the ground and the lower edge of the structure and thereby broken or crushed." He used rollers with bristles or wires "which receiving a rotary motion in the opposite direction to that of the rotation of the car wheel ... [would] ... cause obstructions to roll and thus pass to one side without being crushed."

Manuel Carbonero y Sol, from Madrid, issued no.23,219 in 1901 and suggested not only was it suitable for tramcars *but also motor cars*. If he had known ... far too complex, but fascinating.

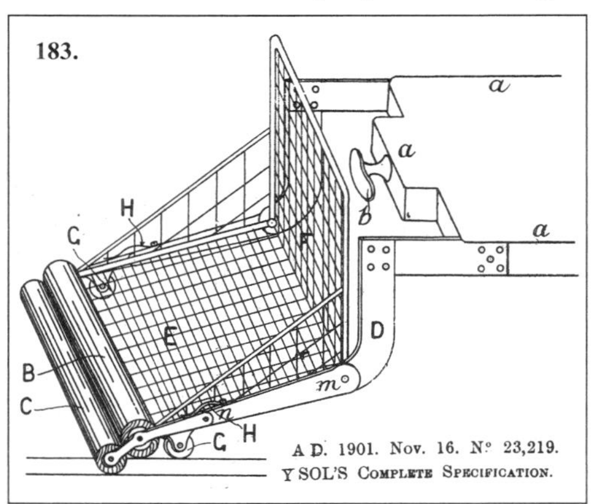

John Snowden, a boiler maker of Hull, (994 of 1902) was another who was worried about machines other than tramcars. "My invention relates to tramcars, motor cars and similar vehicles, and has for its object to provide an improved device for use in connection with such tramcars or the like for the purpose of preventing persons, animals, or the like being run over by such vehicles, thus acting as a safety guard or shield for protecting foot passengers, live stock or the like should they be in the way of such vehicles." This was another complex roller/netting arrangement shaped like half-a-mushroom.

A study of an unbelievably complex design (with, the patentee said, "peculiar features and arrangements and combinations") is rewarding. This was No. 3105 of 1895 from an American gentleman, A.E. Hughes.

Variants on the basic Bellamy life-guard (2246 of 1900) were extensively used under Liverpool Corporation electric cars – but Charles Revill Bellamy was their General Manager.

The Tidswell guard mentioned earlier (covered by No.18,457 of 1899) was for "electric tram cars and other tramway vehicles". No fool, James Tidswell could see the turning tide. His guard, too, was simple "its object is to provide a simple and efficient means to prevent the car from running over any caught in its track". Thousands of people of all ages and many motormen have had cause to thank Mr Tidswell.

"BIRMINGHAM GAZETTE 27 August 1887 THE STEAM TRAMS AND THE PUBLIC:
There is a reason to believe that the "dulled ears" of the body lately challenged by Mr Henry Hawkes in the Coroner's Court have not remained altogether insensible to the public feeling aroused by the tragedies that provoked the coroner's blast. The momentum created by the explosion has produced movement elsewhere, and while the subject is under considera-

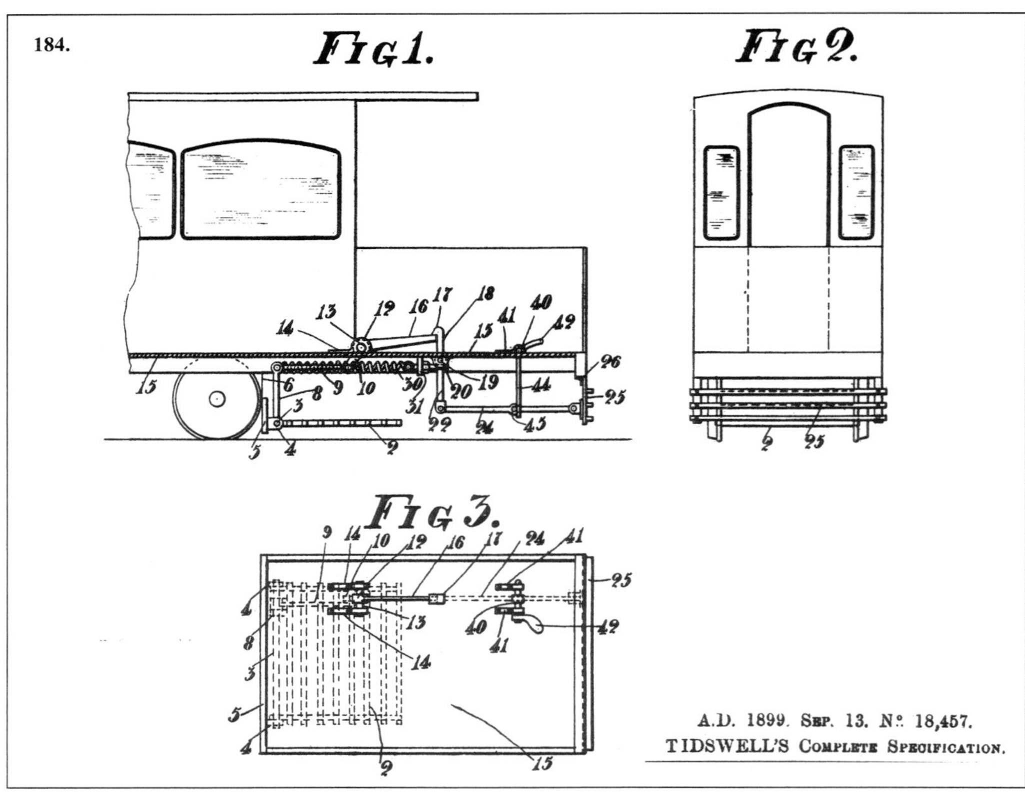

FIG_2_
FIG_4_
FIG_5_
FIG_6_
FIG_7_

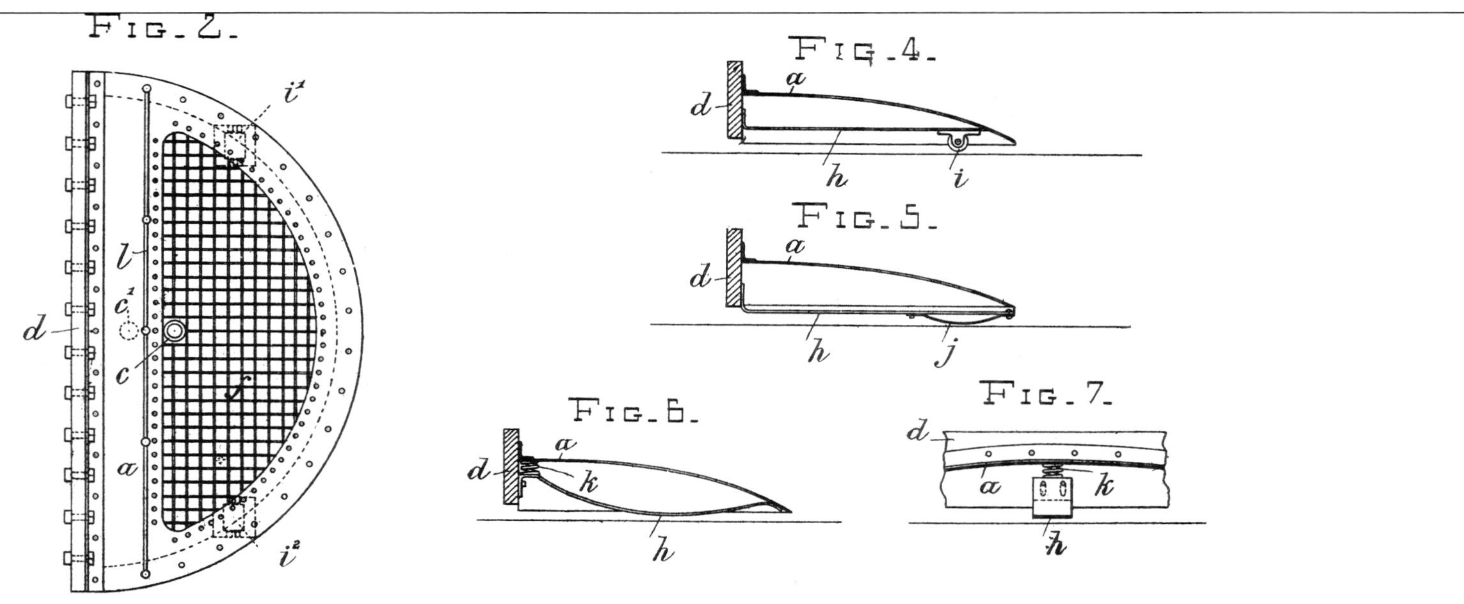

tion it may be as well to set down in black and white some of the chief evils of the steam tramway system as it exists in Birmingham. These evils require prompt and energetic action on the part of the local authorities, in the interests of the public and of the companies themselves. It is probable that steam as a motive power for tramways is comparatively in its infancy, but seeing that it will in all likelihood live, notwithstanding the development of the cable, electricity and other motors, it is high time that something was done to remove, or mitigate, the very glaring nuisances and dangers. Primarily the fatal accidents that have so repeatedly befallen children and others justify the demand for some life-saving apparatus to be affixed to the front of the engines. It is indeed imperative that some such contrivance should be at once adopted. None probably but those who have been eye witnesses can imagine the harrowing character of some of these disasters. The sickening sight of a child jammed under a tramway engine is an experience the most hardened among us would find it difficult to efface from his memory. What must the cruel trial be to a distracted mother? It is urged, and perhaps with some reason, that in nine cases out of ten the sufferers have themselves to thank for their carelessness. But old heads cannot be put on young shoulders. For the toddling babe who unwittingly takes a fatal walk on to the tram lines, and for the urchin who takes a ride on the cheap and pays the penalty with his life, the public voice calls loudly for some protective measures. The Public Works Committee, notwithstanding that their engineer, Mr Piercy, has inspected several different life-saving appliances seem totally unable to make any practical suggestion to the companies. It may be that the

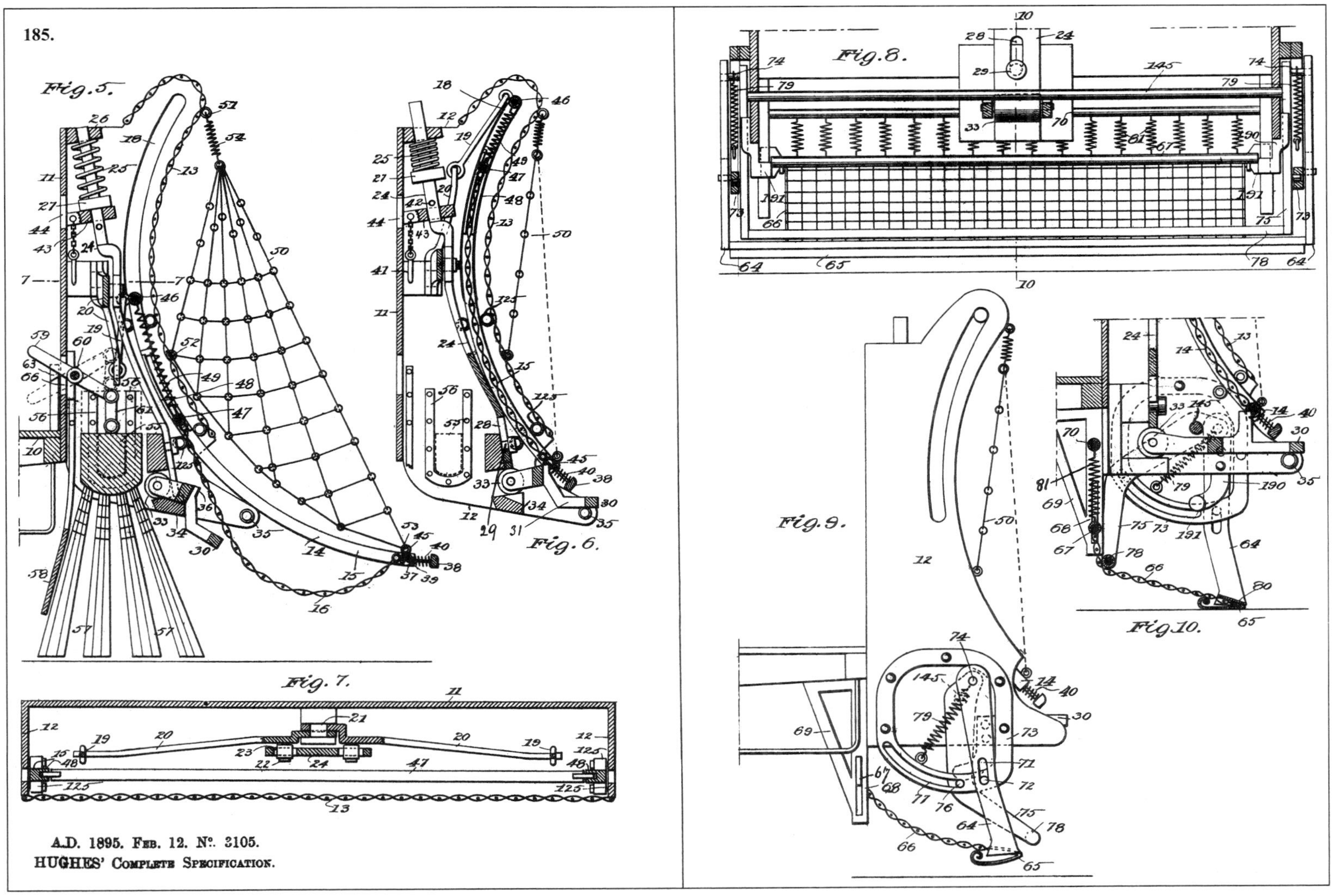

185.
Fig. 5.
Fig. 6.
Fig. 7.
Fig. 8.
Fig. 9.
Fig. 10.
A.D. 1895. Feb. 12. No. 3105.
HUGHES' Complete Specification.

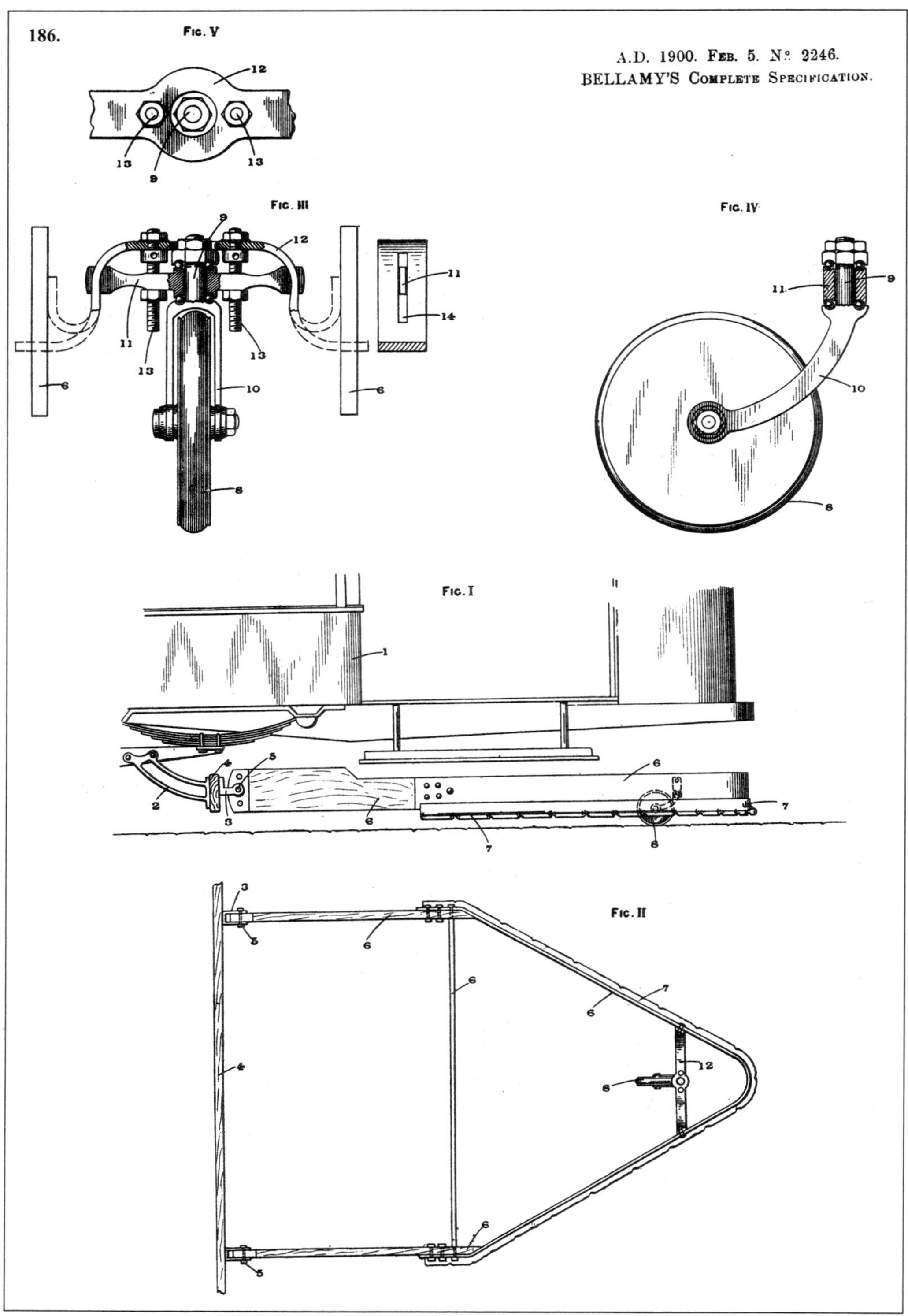

inventions brought forward are in a degree one and all wanting, and whilst they may tend to mitigate the horrors that as a rule surround these accidents, there is no reasonable hope that their adoption would have any greater advantage than that of maiming instead of killing. The question has again been revived consequent, no doubt, on the censorious utterance of the borough coroner. We understand that quite recently Mr Lawley Parker addressed a communication to Mr Joseph Smith, the chairman of the Birmingham Central Tramways Company, on the subject. We gather that the latter gentleman is quite prepared to recommend his co-directors on the Central Board to sanction the company incurring the expense of making and testing any appliance the Public Works Committee may consider would meet the requirements of the case. As to his own invention Mr Smith is naturally reticent, but we understand from the general manager of the South Stafford Steam Tramways Company that Mr Smith's "Life Protector" is in use on some of that company's engines. As before described in these columns, it consists of an iron guard, shaped to the engine, and carried in a projecting form some two inches from the permanent way. By means of compression springs the guard on coming in contact with any obstacle closes to the ground, thus preventing the engine mounting the obstacle. A great improvement has recently been made by connecting a lever on the foot-plate of the engine with the protector, thus enabling the driver on perceiving a child or other obstacle to apply the lever with his foot, whilst at the same time he can with his hands reverse the engine and apply the brakes. Forcibly compressed to the permanent way by means of this lever, it appears next to impossible for anything to get under the engine. On one occasion only has this invention encountered an emergency. In this particular instance a bullock was run into and knocked down by an engine travelling at a moderate speed, and, falling directly in front of the death-dealing machine was, thanks to the protector, pushed forward for a few yards until the engine could be stopped, when it was found that the animal had sustained no injury whatever. Viewing the question from a public standpoint, we think that nothing short of actual practical use of one or other of these appliances will demonstrate their value, and it is only by such means that the weak points will be disclosed. Why cannot Mr Smith cause one or two of the Central Company's engines to be fitted with life-protectors, constructed on the lines of his patent? Surely our tramway companies possess some mechanical talent which, being daily associated with the requirements of the case, is capable of introducing such improvements as will ultimately meet the views of the public and, we will hope, efficiently cope with the existing evil. The public demand is that some move in the directions of a preventative for these accidents should be made forthwith, and we do not know why the company should longer hesitate to make trial with one or other of the appliances at their disposal... There is one more point that we would draw attention to, and certainly it is a grave one. It is appalling to see at times a crowded steam tram rushing along some of the routes at a speed averaging from 13 to 20 miles per hour, and it would not be hard to picture what would be the consequences in the event of the brakes failing to act – a contingency not outside the range of possibilities. The practice is one that is becoming very common and it is highly important that it should at once be checked. The Board of Trade insist that the speed of engines working on the highways shall be mechanically regulated so as not to exceed 10 miles an hour. It is clear to any practical man that either the governors of the tramway engines do not act or that the speed indicators are interfered with by the drivers, thus making them to register a speed within the regulations whilst they may practically run at any rate they please. We do not say that this is so; at the same time the authorities may, if they have not already done so, think it advisable to solve the mystery."

There can be no doubt that the engineers and proprietors of steam tramways, together with the steam tram designers missed a chance to gain a psychological advantage over their enemies. One can well imagine that the shareholders would not appreciate the importance of life-guards but the poor design or non-existence of them led to many avoidable deaths among children and animals alike.

Typically, there was a belief among some of the middle classes that the children of the working classes (whose only playground was the streets) were almost expendable – cynical perhaps, but remember how the same 'carriage folk' as officers in the first world war believed the only way to win a battle was by attrition, pouring in more and more manpower until you had numerical superiority over your enemy and could then advance.

But there were those who queried this theory as much as there were influential people who deplored (for whatever political reason) the deaths the tramcars caused. Maybe steam road transport did represent progress but trams had (and still have) many enemies who varied between men and women who were genuinely afraid they might blow up or run amok (as they did from time to time) and those whose traps were upset by the rails. We cannot forget either that even if the death of a child from some stinking slum was 'regrettable', many respectable men and women were distressed when a dog was killed or maimed by a tram.

To some degree we should be even more grateful to these 'liberal' people as they were the selfsame group that so deplored the cruelty to horses inherent in the haulage of road vehicles (be they chars-à-banc, carts or trams) in hilly districts and directly or indirectly led to steam and later electric tram services. Other than a few flat routes (Isle of Man, Morecambe, etc.) power closed all horse operated lines very quickly – where it did not (the University towns, etc.) the motor bus did.

No doubt reflecting popular feeling among the ratepayers (voters then) of Birmingham on 5 February 1884 their Public Works Committee minuted that "...the use of steam as a motive power for tramways is safe. Your Committee are informed that it is much more economical than horse power, while an uniform speed can be obtained by it irrespective of the gradients of the lines. *It also commends itself in a town like Birmingham, in which there are many steep gradients, from humanitarian principles."*

To some degree the blame for the non-existence of lifeguards in early days can be placed at the door of the Board of Trade, as the tram companies, while metaphorically wringing their hands could point out, with justification, they were meeting all the stated requirements: "Every such engine shall be free of noise ... *and the machinery shall be concealed from view at all points above four inches from the level of the rails* and all fire used on such engine shall be concealed from view.

Every carriage used on the new tramways shall be so constructed as to provide for the safety of passengers and for their safe entrance to and exit from and accommodation in such carriage and *the protection of passengers from the machinery of any engine used for drawing or propelling such carriage."*

However, quite early on a number of very clever Victorian engineer/inventor patentees turned their minds to this problem, including H. Conradi, who patented various combined guards/track cleaners during 1884/5. His preamble sets the scene "During the several years I was engaged in superintending a steam tramway service, my attention was drawn to the fatal accidents often occurring [elsewhere]. Thanks to the ability and great care of my drivers and other workmen, I was fortunate enough in never having a single accident."

He then gives a rough outline of his latest patented device but expresses the opinion that the "cowcatcher" type of guard must be next to useless, and offers scientific calculations why this was so. "Assuming, for example, for horse cars, a mean speed of five miles per hour, the weight of a car only half filled with passengers, at 4 tons, the length of the car 20ft; then the accumulated work W in foot-pounds will be:

$W = h\,w$; h = height in feet through which the body falls,
w = weight in pound of body; v = velocity of body in feet per second,

187. Portstewart Tramway with their Kitson engine showing the standard Board of Trade lifeguard and, very clearly, the gap under both it and the skirting. Mixed train on a nice soft Irish day.

Assuming, further, the car stopping in 15ft; F = force imparted by the accumulated work in pounds; x = distance in feet to which any obstacle is moved by the car;
F = 498.3, say 500 foot-pounds force of the blow imparted, which by the application of an elastic guard, will be reduced to a minimum."

Victorian engineers seem to have had a great fondness for rather obtuse mathematics; I suspect algebra was taught to them from primary school days! He continued: "I arranged the apparatus therefore accordingly; I also combined with it a rail cleaner, to reduce the tractive power required of the already overworked horse. Each car thus cleans the permanent way, whenever necessary. The muddy state of rails requires, according to experiments, six times the amount of tractive power on clean rails. I am prevented to enter fully into the subject at the present moment not to trespass on the Patent Law, as my final specification was only filed on 31st October last. I shall be glad to show, to any party interested in this question of public benefit, the models I have made, so as perhaps to be enabled to bring the apparatus to practical application."

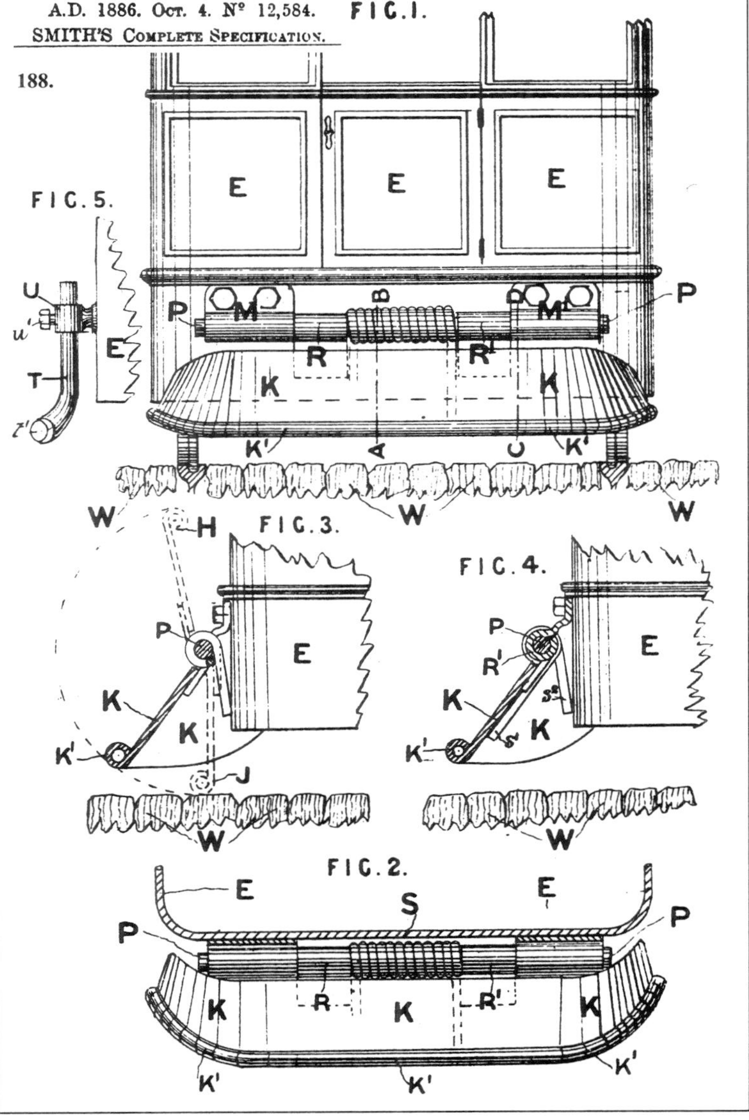

188.

By contrast at the same time Clement E. Stretton advocated a brush fixed to the tram in exactly the same manner as 'snow brushes' used on railways. For some three and a half years prior to 1884 all Leicester cars (horse drawn) had not had a single case where "persons and children" had gone under the wheels. He took in a letter a sly dig at Conradi by writing "the plan costs very little and, of course, is not patented".

But for all the high level discussion, patents and designs, the fact was that matters were getting worse with more accidents occurring; some curiously being blamed on the "stealthiness" and "quietness" of the tramcars, presumably being lost in the ever present clatter of mill machinery, thumping of forges and presses or the general racket of heavy industry. In some occupations, particularly cotton and woollen looms, a way was learned of communicating almost without speech so noisy was the workplace, while in our steelworks signs (often expressive!) had to be used; it made a tramcar motorman's life seemed a paragon of silence!

Surprisingly little factual material seems to have been printed regarding lifeguards but the Handsworth and Smethwick Free Press on 4 December 1886 gave an unusually full account of Joseph Smith's invention. Handsworth as a district were vehemently against tramways, which makes this matter-of-fact report rather surprising.

"SAFETY SHIELDS FOR TRAMWAY ENGINES;

The want of some mechanical contrivance that would in a measure tend to mitigate the serious accidents that now and again befall children and others consequent upon their coming in contact with tramway engines has long been recognised and several inventions with this object have been patented. Amongst some models and plans of such contrivances laid before the Birmingham Town Council a few days ago was one invented by Mr Joseph Smith, solicitor, of Wednesbury, a specimen of which is in actual use on the Birmingham and South Staffordshire District Steam Tramways. It consists of a piece of sheet-iron about six inches deep, which fits to the front of the engine and curves away at either side, being of similar shape to the old-fashioned kitchen fender. It curves slightly outwardly from the front of the engine, and is fixed by means of compression springs slightly above the permanent way. The invention has already been tried, and it has been found that on coming in contact with any object the weight acts on the springs and the projector is forced down to a perpendicular position, thus fitting close to the ground and rendering it next to impossible for any object to get underneath the engine. It will be well-known to those who have had experience of accidents on our tramways that fatalities have frequently arisen owing to the engine mounting the obstacle that it comes in contact with.

The invention named has been specially designed to fill up the gap between the engine and the ground, for it will be patent to anyone that if this is accomplished the danger has been considerably lessened. The invention further claims to push any obstacle along before it, and by means of its 'rounded sides' remove it from the track. Further improvements are in contemplation with a view to establish a connection between the protector and the steam-brake, so that on encountering any obstacle the brake would be automatically applied and the engine brought to a stop. Mr Smith's invention has during this week been in actual work on one of the Central Tramways Company's engines in Birmingham." The design was Alfred Dickinson's, the engineer to the South Staffs Tramway Company, being marketed by The

189.

A.D. 1884, 1st *February*. N° 2507.

An Improved Combined Safe Guard and Rail Cleaner for Tramways.

PROVISIONAL SPECIFICATION.

I, Henry Conradi of 18 Golden Square in the county of Middlesex, Engineer do hereby declare the nature of my said invention for An improved combined Safe guard and Rail cleaner for Tramways, to be as follows:—

It consists in general of a plough or similar shaped elastic buffer or cushion, provided with springs or similar elastic appliances and the necessary lever or rod arrangements. It is fixed to the vehicle and placed in front of the wheel in a certain inward position and prolonged at the outer side and ends as a protecting plate, going to the back of the wheel. The apparatus is fixed to the vehicle by a bolt or tapered rod, which is prolonged into the groove, its end forming a hook for the purpose of cleaning the groove. To it is attached above rail level a plate forming shovel to shift the mud aside. The elastic buffer or cushion is closed at the bottom or also at the top to protect the springs or similar elastic appliances, placed inside against the mud. The apparatus is also set on small jointed rollers.

Having had opportunity to study the Tramway traffic requirements during several years experience on some large lines at home and abroad; my attention was drawn to the many accidents occurring on the Tram lines both of horse and steam traffic, as well as to the great tractive power required of the horses owing to the unclean state of the permanent way.

To remedy those evils I have designed a simple and practical apparatus. It consists in general of a front part shaped like a plough or otherwise. It is placed in front of the wheel, being about half its height; forming an elastic buffer or cushion and is fixed to the vehicle, placed in a certain inward position. It is prolonged at the outer side and ends as a protecting plate, going to the back of the wheel. Therefore if any person by accident falls on the rails, instead of being run over as is unfortunately so often the case, he is prevented from being touched by the wheel, the projecting protector or guard, shifting him aside outwardly, without any injury. The apparatus is fixed to the vehicle by a bolt or tapered rod, which is prolonged into the groove, its end forming a single or double hook. This hook or similarly shaped bar, serves to clean the groove as far as is practically possible and is assisted in shifting the mud and dust from the rails, by a plate inclined both ways and fixed to it above rail level. This plate acts as a kind of shovel. Considering that in this manner each vehicle cleans its way during its run, the

[*Price 8d.*]

2 A.D. 1884.—N° 2507. Provisional Specification.

Conradi's Improved Combined Safe Guard and Rail Cleaner for Tramways.

permanent way will remain in practically clean conditions and therefore keep the tractive power of the horses in its normal conditions. It must hereby be remembered that the frictional resistance of the wheels, if the permanent way is in muddy conditions, increases on the level road to six times its normal value, to which in case of gradients the steepness has to be added.

To relieve the horses from the additional weight thrown on the vehicle by the apparatus, it is set on a small front and back roller, which can be arranged to run either in the groove or on the level of the tram rail.

The above named elastic buffer or cushion is made of a plate, bars, boards or any similar material. To it are fixed a number of springs or buffers or any other similar elastic appliances, as also an elastic sheet, say of india rubber, leather, or any other elastic material, which passes over their top end, from the inner side to the outer side and from the top to nearly the bottom of the plate, forming a wedge or rounded up, shaped front. A wedge or half round shaped elastic bulb is inserted between the plate and the elastic sheet, at its front end, going from top to bottom. The guard is fixed to a leaf spring or rod placed between the springs resting on the plate. To this leaf spring are attached levers connected together by a joint or are fixed firmly and which lever system is attached to the hook. To protect the inside of the elastic cushion from the mud a plate or any other kind of cover, is inserted at the bottom or if necessary also at the top, preserving hereby the free motions of the springs or buffers.

The bottom of the elastic sheet is formed by a strip bolted to the plate, to allow its easily being removed when worn out; without interfering with its remaining top part.

The above mentioned front and back rollers of the apparatus are jointed to allow of a free and easy run in the curves.

The elastic sheet projects above all edges to prevent any hurting.

The single or double hooked cleaner, can either be made out of one piece or be fixed firmly or socketed to the bolt, to be easily removed, when worn out.

For greater firmness of the particularly selected inward position of the guard or elastic cushion, it can be stayed by rods fixed to it and to the vehicle, or by other similar appliances, should the bolt alone not being found sufficient.

Dated this first day of February 1884.

HENRY CONRADI.

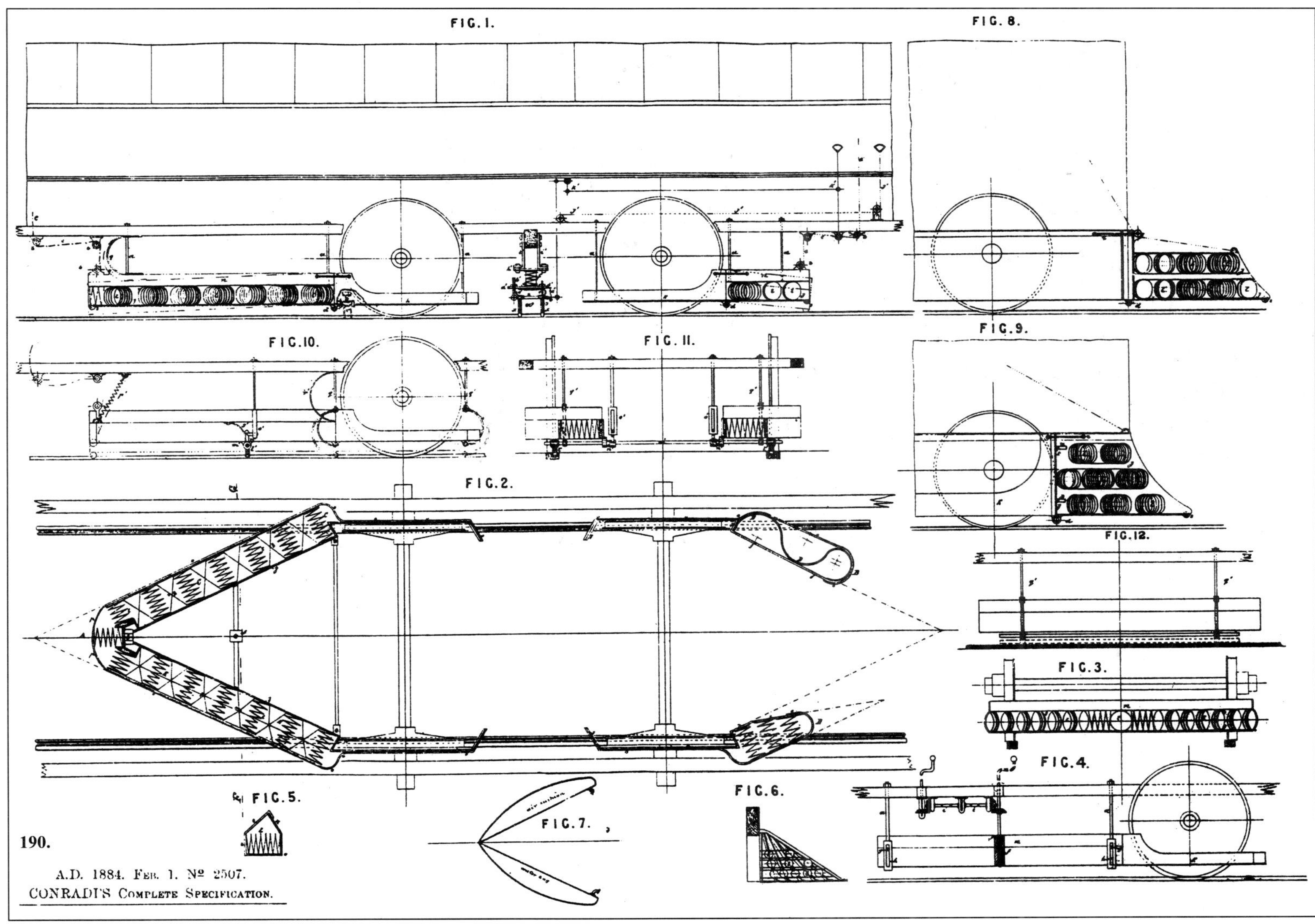

Dickinson Appliance Company – one of Joseph Smith's enterprises.

It is not clear exactly which accidents seem to have caused a great furore in 1887 but even the prose of a report by the Birmingham Public Works Committee cannot hide much disquiet. Part is given verbatim below, the last paragraph expressing a true but unpleasant truth.

"Your Committee, ever since the use of steam motive power upon the Tramways was sanctioned by the Council, have insisted upon the adoption by the several Tramway Companies of any invention calculated to lessen the danger to foot passengers, and especially to children. In 1886 they specially referred the matter to Mr H.J.T. Piercy, MIME., whom they have retained to advise them on Tramway matters, and laid before him models of inventions which had been submitted to them with this object in view. Mr Piercy has given the matter most careful attention, and he informs your Committee that in his opinion the models submitted would not effect the required purpose, and that so far as he knows no apparatus has yet been invented which would prevent the killing or maiming of any child that might place itself in the direct way of the engine. Your Committee have, however, directed the attention of the several Tramway Companies to the subject, and understand that experiments are being made by them with several inventions ... While your Committee are most anxious to use every effectual means that may be devised for preventing accidents to children by the trams, they are of opinion that the only safe preventative against accidents to children of tender years, whether by the ordinary vehicular traffic or by the Tramways, is for such children to be under proper guardianship, and not allowed to run alone in our crowded thoroughfares."

But by 1 October 1887 the patience of the Corporation of Birmingham was finally showing some strain with the direct threat, no longer just implied, that "public safety must be the first consideration of the Council, and that, however convenient steam may be as a motor to the travelling, unless the traffic can be conducted with safety there will be no alternative than the withdrawal of the permission to use steam on the Corporation lines". (In the town the lines were built by the Corporation and leased to the tramway company).

All the local newspapers and some national then reported on a couple of experiments carried out on 14 October 1887. It was amazing just how the Council's flat statement had concentrated the minds of the tramcar company's directors! The Dudley Herald whose 'patch' included three tramways and whose sales extended throughout the Midlands gave the most succinct report in its issue of 22 October. Given that there were no TV cameras, tape recorders or anything more complex than shorthand and that rarely were there 'press handouts' it is a wonder how thorough this reporting really was.

"LIFE SAVING APPLIANCES ON TRAM ENGINES.

Amongst the various appliances for protecting life on steam tramways, two inventions have recently been submitted to the Birmingham Central Company. Last week they were tested in the presence of the Mayor (Sir Thomas Martineau), Mr Lawley Parker (chairman of the Public Works Committee), Mr Till (borough surveyor), Mr Joseph Smith (chairman of the Board of Directors of the Central Tramway Company), Mr A. Dickinson (general manager of the South Staffordshire and Birmingham and District Steam Tramways' Company), Mr Read (manager of the Birmingham and Aston Tramways' Company, &c. A fortnight ago most of the above mentioned gentlemen witnessed a series of experiments with an apparatus which was formed on the principle of the 'cow catcher' in use on American railways, which was not only devised with the object of preventing an obstacle from being drawn under the engine and crushed, but to pick it up and carry it forward, thus preventing further injury than that caused by the collision. The tests, however, were not altogether satisfactory, the only occasion upon which the result was favourable being when the engine was driven at a slow walking pace. Then the dummy was deposited on the frame without sustaining any apparent injury. The apparatus tested last week were of an altogether different character. The first invention tried was that of Mr Smith (chairman of the Central Tramways Company). This consists of a substantially wrought-iron plate adjusted to the front of the engine and bent to the shape of the front. It is connected by a lever, which is under the control of the driver.

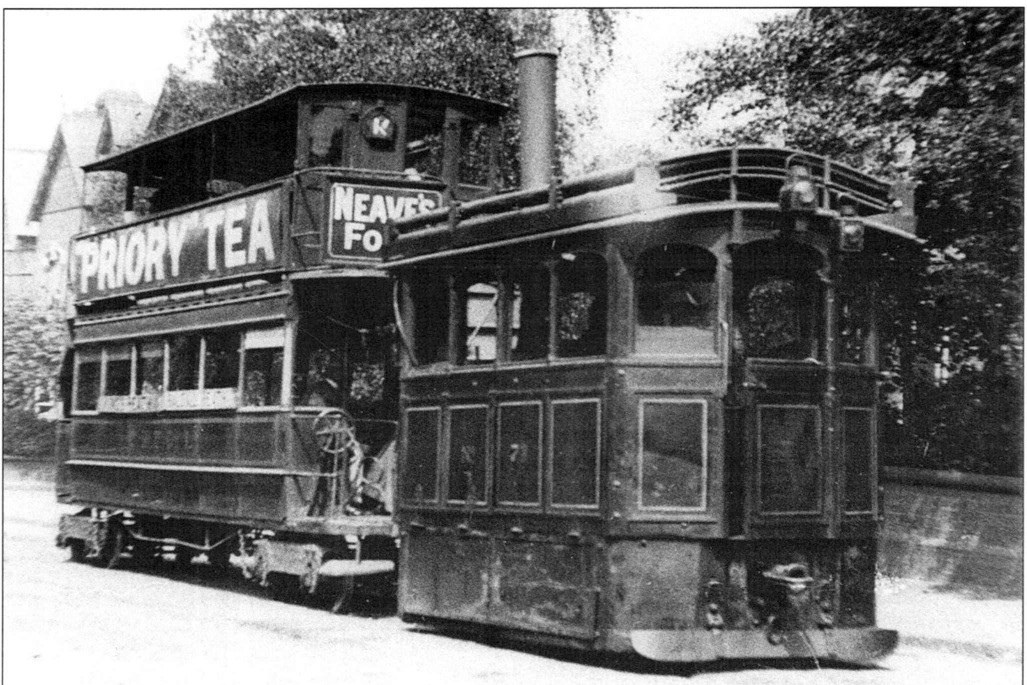

191. City of Birmingham Tramways engine, probably no.71 (Kitson T262/1893) showing its Smith's type lifesaver. This is a slightly later development than his patent pattern as a cut out allows for clearance on rough trackwork. "K" on the trailer indicates a Kings Heath bound car.

The apparatus projects slightly, but upon coming in contact with any obstacle it at once falls, thus closing up the space between the engine and the ground. It will, therefore, be seen that the invention works both automatically and by lever. The experiments were made with a dummy child, which was at first placed on the tramway in a standing position. The engine approached at the regulation speed, and when about a yard from the figure the driver touched the lever and let down the plate. The object was knocked down and pushed along the road for several yards. Upon the dummy being examined the limbs appeared to have escaped injury, the clothes only having suffered. The experiment was again tried with the dummy lying across the tramway, with the same result as before. In the other tests that were made the apparatus was allowed to work automatically. The result in some cases were hardly so satisfactory as when the lever was dropped by the driver. Once or twice the feet of the dummy appeared to have been crushed by the sudden fall of the plate, and eventually these limbs were altogether removed. The second apparatus is manufactured by Mr John Cheshire, machinist of 46 Wheeler Street. This is claimed to be so constructed as to save life, and is evidently intended solely for the protection of children. The arrangement is about two feet deep and extends across the feet of the engine in two sections, rising several inches from the ground. Only one of the sections was attached to the engine for the experiments. It opens in the shape of a pair of tongs and on either side network is constructed about a foot square. Two bars, which join in the centre, run along the bottom of the network and are fitted with springs so that the object on touching the bars is at once clutched and slightly raised. No provision appears to be made for anything lying on the tramway, and when the object happens to fall exactly on the bars the apparatus would be of little avail in saving life. The dummy used for the experiments last week was firmly clutched by the apparatus, but from its appearance afterwards the extremities appeared to have suffered severely. Mr Piercy, consulting engineer to the company, conducted the experiments which were made in Kyott's Lake Road and at the terminus at Sparkbrook."

Birmingham does seem to have been in the forefront of investigating these life-guards and in some areas neither newspapers or council Minutes seem to have even mentioned the subject; but perhaps life was more expendable. Between the Kyott's Lane experiments and August 1888 Mr Piercy had been busy, testing no less than 27 inventions out of the "large number" brought before him, and reckoned the Dickinson/Smith device the best including a report that "...a boy was knocked down by one of these engines running on the Perry Barr route (I believe on May 29th), and instead of the engine running over and crushing him, the Guard simply pushed him along the ground for some yards, and he got off with merely a shaking and a cut on the hand. Had this Guard not been on, another death would probably have been recorded." He concluded that the Joseph Smith design seemed, so far, to be the best submitted as:

"I It occupies less projecting space in front of the engine than any of the others we have tried, and is therefore no source of danger to vehicles or pedestrians.
II It is simplest in construction, i.e. it has fewer parts.
III It does not require to be kept in motion as the engine travels, and requires no support in the shape of wheels to run upon the ground, which would soon become useless from the accumulation of dust and dirt, and quickly wear away.
IV As the guard shuts tightly down upon the ground, the possibility of a child passing the guard and getting under the engine is reduced to a minimum.
V It is not costly to put upon the engines, and is not likely to get out of order.
VI If it should get out of order it is very easily repaired."

Having paid Mr Piercy, no doubt the Committee thought it best to agree and told the Companies they had to adopt this device "unless the Companies submit some other invention which they are prepared to adopt at once, and which is thought by the Committee to be equally effective."

The primary problem facing lifeguard designers and patentees lay in the very design of the steam tram and trailer combination. Earlier experiments had already established that ultimately the tram engines' wheel flanges against rails acted like a crude guillotine or bacon-slicer on whatever part of a body (human or animal) got dragged under the skirts, but prior to this it was apparent that the skirt (despite the ten tons or so weight of the engine) tended to lift over the arm or leg or indeed to roll over them, while the underframe and the ashpan could catch on clothing. It was therefore apparent and imperative that the body must be pushed to one side or at least deflected, and to this end all items liable to

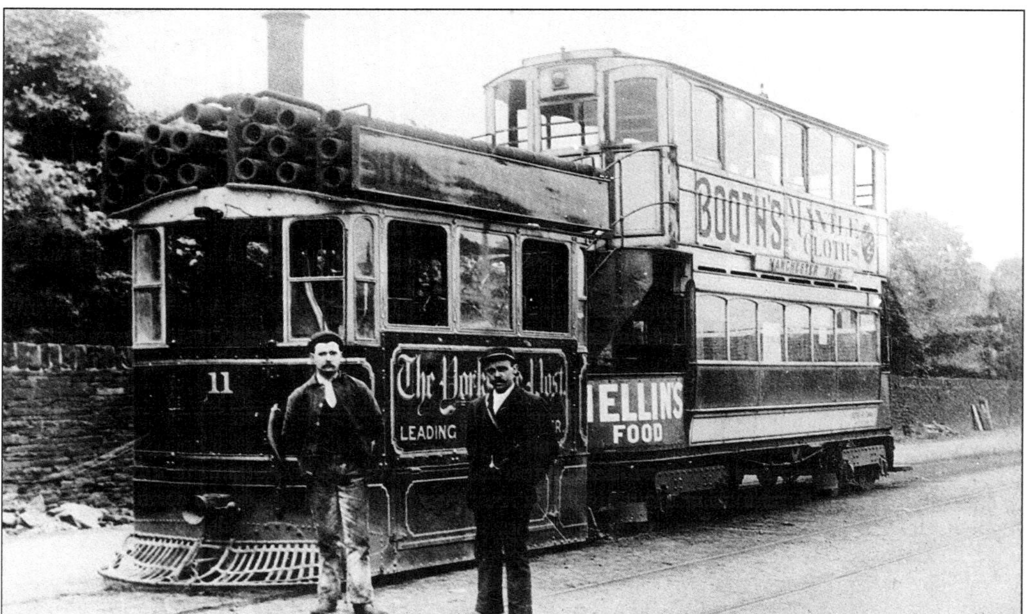

192. From time to time I sympathise with the horses that saw this locomotive, Bradford and Shelf Tramways Co No.11 (Greens works no 94/1892) bearing down on them, but the wire type lifeguard or 'tray' gave some protection to children ... and dogs! The pipe by the driver's arm is for the vacuum brake, rare on British tramways.

snag a person (be it a child stumbling or a drunk bumbling) must be streamlined, as far as possible, but a surprisingly high number of would-be 'experts' appear not to have realised this basic truth; whereas an unattentive pedestrian could have had his coats pockets and sleeves or their scarves caught by car mirrors, door handles or loose trim in the 1950s, now smoother vehicles, at least in theory, tend to deflect bodies and their clothing away.

Inescapable with steam trams was the movement of the machine in all possible directions. They pitched up and down especially on rough track and at points and rail joints, they swayed longitudinally according to the action of the pistons coupled to worn wheel flanges and oversize grooves, they also oscillated and waggled. All this motion was magnified by the trailer wandering along behind. It had all the same tricks as the motor, plus its relatively soft springing allowed a nice healthy sway to build up, movements all translated to the engine via the drawbar. And somehow a life-guard was supposed to be flexible enough to cope with all this.

But about 1895 the choice of lifeguard seemed to depend on whatever the manufacturers fitted; on photographic evidence Accrington, Leeds, Rossendale and Rochdale used fixed wire mesh 'scrapers' on most (but not all) of their engines, while the Bury, Rochdale and Oldham, and Burnley companies seemed to fancy the brush, normally raised but unhitchable by the driver. The Wisbech & Upwell (Great Eastern Railway) used real American-style cow-catchers, the Wantage & Wolverton companies nothing much. Wigan used riveted V-shaped plates painted white, while half-a-dozen other concerns used the same design but omitted the paint.

193. Heywood Corporation Tramways' last car, a Beyer Peacock-built Wilkinson-type tram engine shows its brush lifeguard. Normally it should be raised, but presumably the chain has slackened over the years. And contrary to common belief, the driver is not the author, but a relative!

Steam tramway accidents did not always have fatal results. Indeed, by and large a high number of both adults and children survived such encounters, even if they were bruised or otherwise damaged. While in a history like this there is a tendency to emphasise their nature, and even more so for today's writers to exaggerate modern accidents, it was not so in contemporary days. This particular happening was reported in the Northern Daily Mail (actually an evening paper) on Saturday 30 August 1890, page 3, and was sandwiched between a report on a railway accident at Milngavie Junction, the Guatemalan Revolt ("a tragic deed"), Grimsby fish prices, Cleveland Miners' wages, Robbing a daughter ("a father sent to gaol") and the Frightful Accident at Birtley ("buried under slag"). The letter appeared on the Monday, 1 September, was less conspicuous and received no editorial comment.

194. Now that is how a tram-train should look. The lovely old Wisbech and Upwell line, before the end of passenger traffic on 31 December 1927. Great Eastern Railway-built no. 0125, completed at Stratford under order D85 in 1921. 12" x 15" (305 x 381mm) cylinders, 180 lb/sq.in. boiler pressure, spark arresters on the top of the chimney, governers limiting speed to 8mph (12.87kph) later relaxed, and the steam from the safety valves was discharged into a receiver and hence into the tanks where it was condensed. And as can be seen, cow-catchers. Nothing fancy, just a logical design by James Holden, the engineer. 0125 was scrapped as BR 68224 in March 1952.

"THE TRAM-CAR FATALITY INQUEST AND VERDICT

An inquest was held last evening at the Hartlepool Police-Court, before Mr Coroner Settle, touching the death of a little girl named Jane Warren, who was killed on Wednesday last by being run over by a tram-car on the Clarence road, near West Hartlepool Police-station. Mr Wilson appeared on behalf of the friends of the deceased, and Mr H.G. Winship was present in the interests of the Hartlepools Tramway Co.

Alfred Warren, sworn, said he was a seaman and lived at 35 Arthur-street, off Stockton-street, West Hartlepool. He had identified the body of deceased as that of his daughter. He saw her last alive about 8 o'clock am on the day of the accident. The first information he received of the circumstance was from deceased's companion, who ran to his house, saying his daughter had been run over by a tram-car. Deceased had been carrying her uncle's dinner to the Central Marine Engine Works.

Hannah Blume, head nurse at the Hartlepools Hospital, proved the admittance of deceased into that institution about a quarter to two on Wednesday afternoon last. She was suffering from two broken legs and a fractured skull. There appeared no hope of her recovery from the time of her admission, though she was immediately attended by Dr Morgan, the house surgeon, and Dr Ainsley, one of the surgical staff. Deceased died about fifteen minutes afterwards.

Minnie Parr, nine years of age, daughter of Edward Parr, West Hartlepool, said on the day in question she took her father's dinner to the Central Marine Works. She was accompanied by deceased, and on returning they both met at the Gas Works in Middleton-road. They purposed walking back home. Neither of them had any money for tramway fares. They knew the cars stopped at the Gas Works, and as they reached the place one of the cars from Hartlepool was standing. After it had remained about three minutes deceased approached the end of the tram nearest the engine and got upon one of the steps, witness following. Both stood upon the step, and the engine started. Nothing happened until the football field was passed, when deceased became dizzy and fell off the step between the car and the engine. Witness also fell off, but the wheels did not touch her.

By Mr Wilson: There was a small gate at the end of the tram, which was open. A Mr Shields, of Fawcett-street, shouted after deceased and witness fell off the step. It would be two or three minutes before the car was stopped. Mr Shields afterwards picked up deceased.

John Burns, sworn, said he was a "spare" engine-driver, employed by the Hartlepools Tramway Company, and resided at Throxton. He was riding at the back end of the car, going to West Hartlepool as a passenger, when the accident occurred. The inside of the car was nearly full, though there was plenty of room above. He first saw deceased beneath the car near the end bogey. She appeared to be dragging by her foot when discovered. She was extricated by backing the car a few inches. She was then placed inside the car and conveyed to Hartlepool. The rate at which the tram was travelling when the accident happened was about four miles an hour. He believed the conductor would be unable to see the children when standing on the step, though he was collecting the fares inside.

By the Foreman: As soon as witness saw deceased he rung the bell and applied the brakes, while the conductor was attending to his duties inside the car.

Neither the driver or conductor of the tram, both of whom appear to have been exempt from any blame, were called, and the jury returned a verdict of "Accidental death", recommending at the same time that some means should be devised whereby the steps of the car not in use should be folded back, so as to prevent people from standing upon them.

Mr Winship informed the jury that their suggestion would be conveyed to the proper authorities, though at the same time he was of opinion that the idea was impracticable."

In the correspondence section of the same paper for September 1 1890:

Sir, – Having read the evidence given ... in your Saturday night's issue, I beg to refute the following statement, which is incorrect, and given by the witness Minnie Parr: "There was a small gate at the end of the tram, which was open. A Mr Shields, of Fawcett-street, shouted after deceased, and witness fell off the step." Now, sir, I think this statement is misleading, and I wish it to be understood that I never saw deceased (Jane Warren) until the tram was stopped, and I then extricated her with all possible haste from the wheels. I did shout at the witness to stay on until the engine was stopped, when she alone was riding. I was not aware anyone else was there until the tram was stopped. By inserting the above you will oblige. – Yours truly, JOHN SHIELD.

VEHICLE LIGHTS

In the 21st century our motor vehicles, be they electric, steam petrol or diesel, have their lighting requirements very clearly defined, at a consistent and regulated distance apart, height above road surface, etc., even to the lumens output permitted. Horse-drawn vehicles and many pieces of farm equipment appear to be exempt from such rules for varying reasons. In the world of steam tramways over a hundred years ago the definition of lighting was far from consistent – rural horse wagons for example might have one guttering, smokey, oil lamp on the offside, showing white to the front and possibly red to the rear, while a 'toff' in his landau would probably have two brilliant candle lamps which mounted on each side of his vehicle and fitted with bevelled and polished glass mirrors gave a brilliant light in town or country.

Our tram engine would have one (or more) white lights at the front ... although they might show a green aspect ... the trailers had one light facing forward, probably white and mounted high up on the vehicle, with one or more lamps at the rear which might be white ... or red ... or green!

In the County Express (covering Stourbridge etc) for 20 November 1897 under the heading "Bye-laws as to lights upon vehicles" a report on a Home Office paper shows, in part, just what chaos existed just seven years before the first London-Brighton run took place.

"The Home office has issued a return giving information concerning the bye-laws made by the councils of counties and boroughs as to lights upon vehicles. This shows that 29 boroughs have made bye-laws which, speaking generally, impose upon vehicles in streets, highways, and other public places an obligation to carry lights at night similar to that laid upon cyclists with, in some cases, the additional requirement that vehicles carrying loads which project towards the rear should carry a rear light. As it is obviously undesirable that persons passing from one county or borough to another should have to comply with different and sometimes inconsistent requirements, the Secretary of State has aimed at securing as far as possible uniformity in the regulations. Among the main points of difference, it may be mentioned that while the hours usually prescribed for carrying lights are from one hour after sunset till one hour before sunrise, in Warwickshire and Bishop's Castle the period fixed is between one after sunset and 2am, except such part, if any, of that period as is between the rising and the setting of the moon. In Birmingham and Kidderminster lights are required also during fogs. Usually the bye-law applies to the whole year, but in Herefordshire, Staffordshire, and Walsall the four months from May to August, and in Northamptonshire the six months from April to September are excepted. Many of the bye-laws have been confined to vehicles drawn by animal power, on the ground that locomotives of various kinds are dealt with, to some extent, by statute. But in Bedfordshire, Cumberland, Northamptonshire, Staffordshire, Warwickshire, Bishop's Castle, Richmond, Thornaby-on-Tees, Walsall, West Bromwich and Worcester, vehicles driven by steam, electricity or other mechanical power are included. Vehicles carrying loads which project towards the rear are commonly required to carry rear lamps showing towards persons overtaking them. In some cases this is confined to timber wagons – the type of vehicle which gave rise to the bye-laws. It is usually provided, as regards the direction in which the vehicle proceeds, that 'a lamp or lamps' be carried, and that if only one is carried, it shall be fixed on the right or off side of the vehicle; but in Anglesey, Durham, Glamorganshire, and Northumberland lamps on each side are required. The front lamps are generally required either by express provision or by implication to show a white or uncoloured light, and the rear lamp to show a red light. This provision as to the rear lamps the Home Secretary thinks it right to insist upon wherever possible, and the only exceptions to the rule occur in Gloucestershire, Somersetshire, Warwickshire and Warrington."

[Some further information has emerged re lifeguards, and will be included in the appendices].

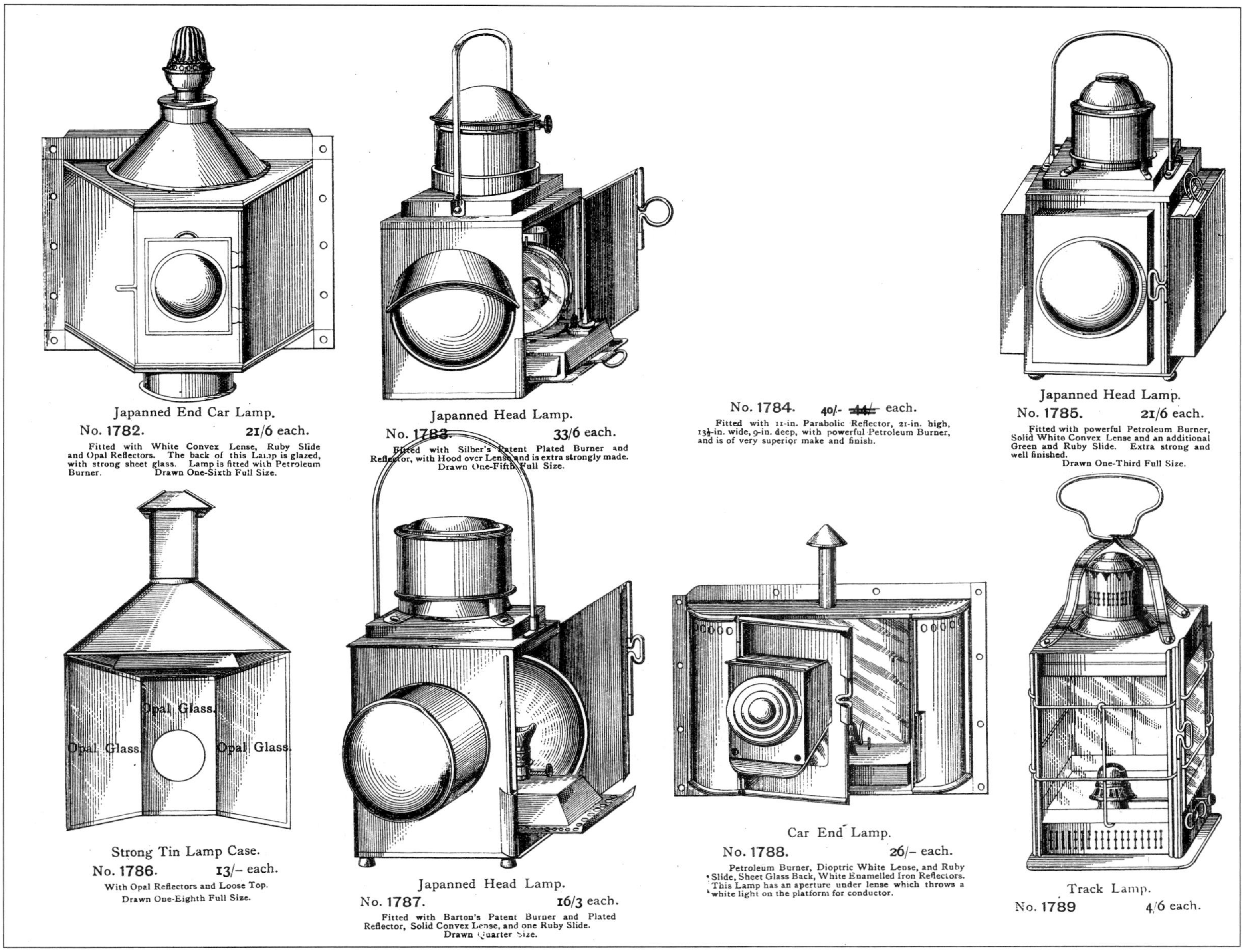

Japanned End Car Lamp.
No. 1782. 21/6 each.
Fitted with White Convex Lense, Ruby Slide and Opal Reflectors. The back of this Lamp is glazed, with strong sheet glass. Lamp is fitted with Petroleum Burner. Drawn One-Sixth Full Size.

Japanned Head Lamp.
No. 1783. 33/6 each.
Fitted with Silber's Patent Plated Burner and Reflector, with Hood over Lense and is extra strongly made. Drawn One-Fifth Full Size.

No. 1784. 40/- ~~44/-~~ each.
Fitted with 11-in. Parabolic Reflector, 21-in. high, 13½-in. wide, 9-in. deep, with powerful Petroleum Burner, and is of very superior make and finish.

Japanned Head Lamp.
No. 1785. 21/6 each.
Fitted with powerful Petroleum Burner, Solid White Convex Lense and an additional Green and Ruby Slide. Extra strong and well finished.
Drawn One-Third Full Size.

Opal Glass.
Opal Glass.
Opal Glass.

Strong Tin Lamp Case.
No. 1786. 13/– each.
With Opal Reflectors and Loose Top.
Drawn One-Eighth Full Size.

Japanned Head Lamp.
No. 1787. 16/3 each.
Fitted with Barton's Patent Burner and Plated Reflector, Solid Convex Lense, and one Ruby Slide.
Drawn Quarter Size.

Car End Lamp.
No. 1788. 26/– each.
Petroleum Burner, Dioptric White Lense, and Ruby Slide, Sheet Glass Back, White Enamelled Iron Reflectors. This Lamp has an aperture under lense which throws a white light on the platform for conductor.

Track Lamp.
No. 1789 4/6 each.

195. Extract from Gabriel & Co.'s catalogue of tram car fittings.

196. A typical summer Swansea and Mumbles tram-train drawn by No. 4 engine, a powerful 0-6-0 tank built in 1899 by the Hunslet Engine Co., Ltd. (Works No. 697) with 13" x 18" cylinders. Side skirts have gone, but fore and aft lifeguards remain. A contemporary report tells us that "the invasion of the Mumbles by holidaymakers from Swansea ... commenced at an unusually early hour ... the Mumbles trains were heavily laden from about 9.30am, and are said to have during the day carried approximately 48,000 persons ..." Small wonder most photographs show the passenger-carrying vehicles (I hesitate to call them trams!) as being grossly overloaded.

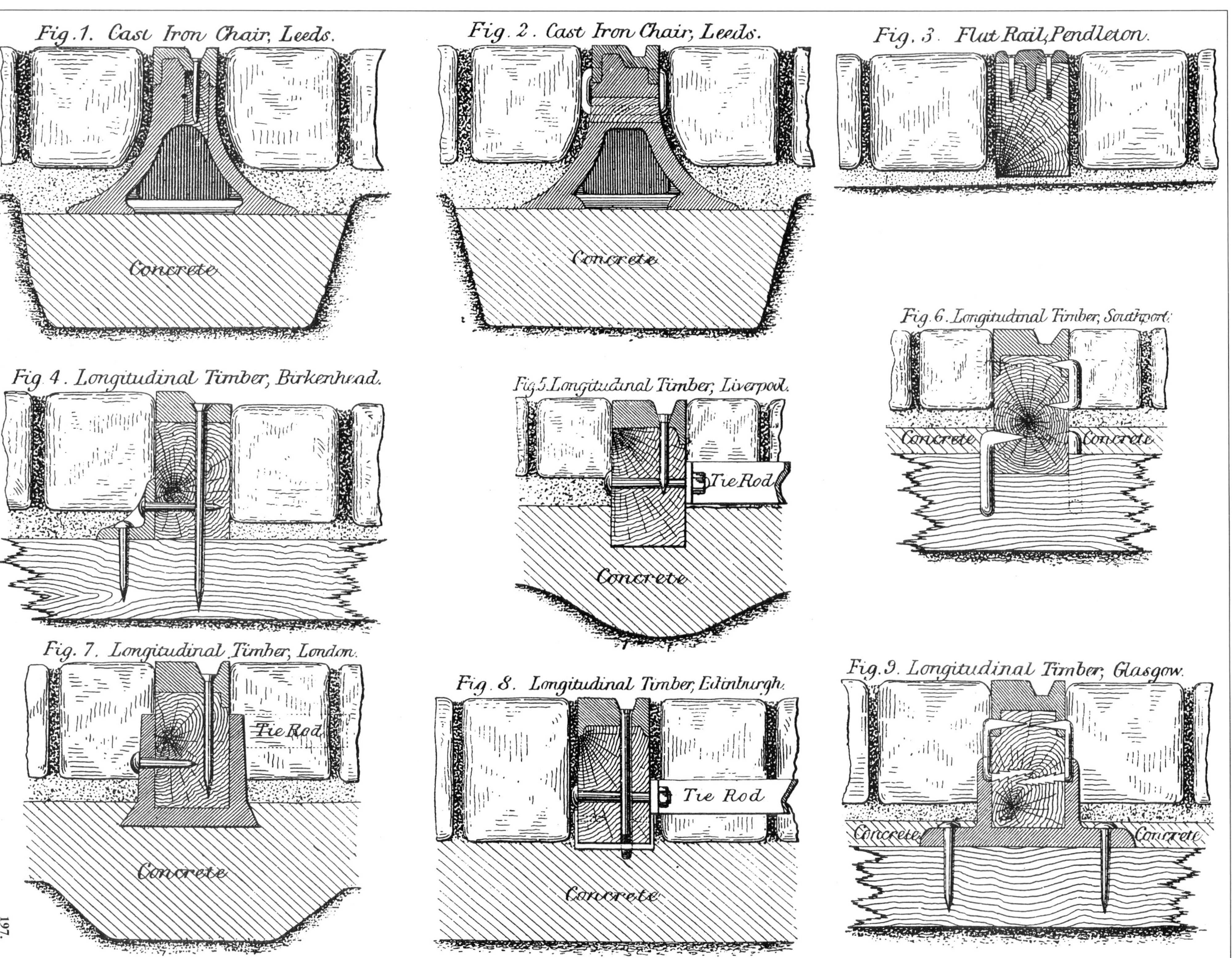
Fig. 1. Cast Iron Chair, Leeds.
Concrete
Fig. 2. Cast Iron Chair, Leeds.
Concrete
Fig. 3. Flat Rail, Pendleton.
Fig 4. Longitudinal Timber, Birkenhead.
Fig. 5 Longitudinal Timber, Liverpool.
Tie Rod
Concrete
Fig. 6. Longitudinal Timber, Southport.
Concrete
Concrete
Fig. 7. Longitudinal Timber, London.
Tie Rod
Concrete
Fig. 8. Longitudinal Timber, Edinburgh.
Tie Rod
Concrete
Fig. 9. Longitudinal Timber, Glasgow.
Concrete
Concrete
197.

Chapter 10

PERMANENT WAY

Obviously it is a sine qua non that permanent way should be just that, or at least give a good simulation of being permanent. Unfortunately, as is apparent from the individual histories of some steam tram companies, this ideal was rarely met. The 1870s and early 1880s were a great time for patentees of 'better, 'more stable' and 'wear proof' tram rails. Too many of these inventors, even some of those who had at least some knowledge of trams' habits, overlooked the fact that their fancy rail section might be technically almost impossible to produce by the iron or steel works, and even when it could be manufactured, not only would it cost figures in £s that tram company accountants saw in their nightmares, but that quality might prove to be incredibly variable. One rather curious X-shaped rail with two slots top and bottom proved impossible to roll, and in the end the 1" slots were machined from wasp-waisted bar 8" square. A few yards were made before commonsense entered the calculation.

However, these esoteric fancies apart, what we basically needed was a track bed which according to engineers' taste was either to be rigid or flexible. And great were the outpourings from the protagonists of both. Although obviously having some bearing on the lines to be used for steam, much of what had been painfully learned building a tramway suitable for horse trams had to be rapidly unlearned. Steam tram engines came in a number of variants, but generally they weighed between 8 and 12 tons, were twin cylindered with drive via one or another pattern of linkage, and with all four wheels coupled, normally with a 4' 6" wheelbase to enable tight radius curves to be passed over without too much wear on either the wheels or the rails. In passing it should be mentioned that some slight extra gauge width was not unknown on the tightest corners even in electric days; for a while as new track and wheels wore together, the skirling, screeching, yowling din was guaranteed to wake the deepest sleeper especially as we howled our way back to the shed with the last empty tram!

The bulk of the steam trams had some gesture towards springing – as much as 1½" travel – but generally every bad rail joint was going to be punished, and of course lumbering along behind was a behemoth of a trailer weighing 4 tons empty (but double that loaded), mounted on quite primitive bogies, themselves with minimal springing.

If your tramway wished to use Wilkinson-pattern vertical boilered engines then, since these utilised gear drive, they were by design springless and going to give the trackbed an even greater pounding, although there was a gain insofar as the cylinders were normally vertical and the 'shouldering' motion found in orthodox short wheelbase engines absent, but all those unbalanced lumps of metal hurtling about were not conducive to permanent way men's sleep.

But it all brings us back to where we started. A flexible bed, as defined in railway practice, allows for some degree of movement and has the power to absorb some shocks. In some cases, on 'tender' embankments for example, a hard base was undesirable as ground movement was easily set up, particularly when railways were young (even in the 1880s many were only 30 years old).

So this means our tramway engineer could use longitudinal or transverse sleepers in some kind of hardwood with the rails spiked – totally unsatisfactory – or bolted through to the underside of the sleepers. Barbed or 'jagged' tram-nails for track work remained one of the last hand-made products by Halesowen nailmakers, although in later years the demand was probably more for use on industrial sites.

Gauge could be maintained either by cross (transverse) sleepers or tiebars (a length of strip steel threaded at both ends). Jointing of rails could

The Engineer May 1879

MECHANICAL POWER ON TRAMWAYS

Sir, The construction and maintenance of the permanent way should ... be left in the hands of the owners of the engines and rolling stock, rather than in the hands of the tram company, or, according to arrangements in the hands of the traction contractor, but not in the hands of the local authorities. The engines must be fit for the road, and the road fit for the engine; they must both work and be well fitted together to work well. Nobody better than the driver can tell where places of the iron road are bad or begin to be so, and nothing more than engines and cars are severely suffering from it, but not so much the public road itself. The owner of the rolling stock is therefore certainly the party most anxious to keep the iron road in good condition, not only to prevent the wear and tear of engines and car, but also to prevent accidents, as going off the line &c. That the local authorities are not the most anxious party to keep the permanent way in good order I experienced in Paris, where the maintenance of the road is in the hand of the town authorities ... [but paid for by] the tramway company. Wherever there were bad places, as holes under the rails, bad joints and crossings, of shifting, bad curves or wrong gauge, difficult to pass and dangerous as to the straining of axles and whole mechanism. I telegraphed sometimes twice a day that I would stop the engine if the repair was not done immediately, and consequently disturb the whole traffic regulations of the company. The consequence was I got it done a day or two, sometimes few days afterwards, while in a well-organised steam tram company the rolling stock and permanent way are under the superintendence of the manager who has the repairs of the road made at a moment's notice by own gang of men, that is to say, at any rate, in the course of a few hours and then according to requirements. On the Paris lines the repairs were made as to the understanding of the platelayers, without special superintendence, and there was always something left undone ... [and then] came the pavior of the town of Paris. They again repaired the pavement as to their convenience, and paved the places such as either too narrow, say for about 1½ in., and sometimes too wide, so that the whole work had to be done over again, and always at the expense of the tram company. All such terrible nuisance and reckless waste of money to the tram company would not occur if the construction and maintenance of the line – at any rate the latter – and the rolling stock were left under one and the same management, that is to say, in the hands of those whose interest are the most involved in the well-working of the line to the satisfaction of the public, and to make it a successful, beneficial undertaking.
H. CONRADI.

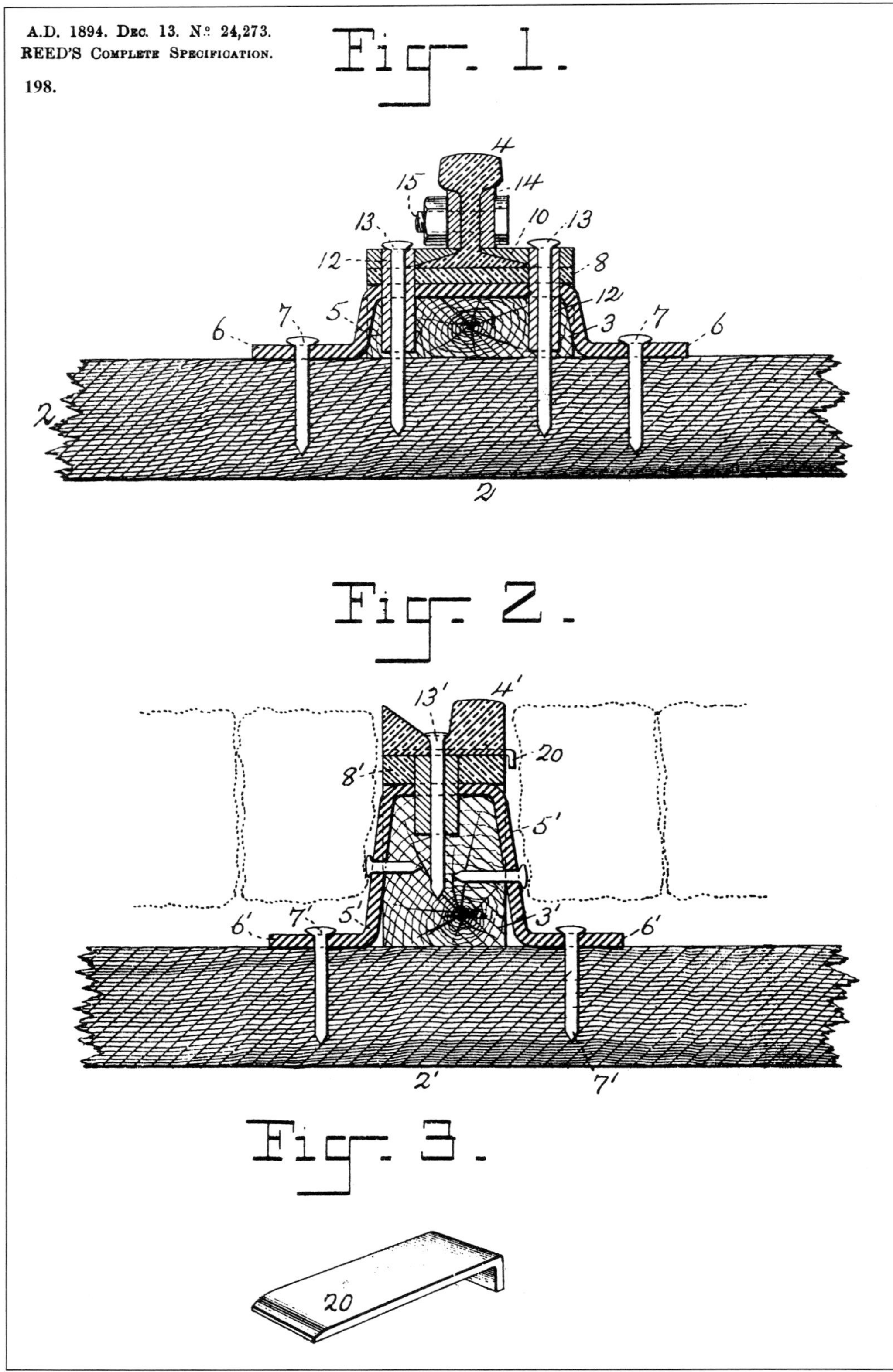

be carried out by railway style fishplates nipped up tight. The whole tramway would be quite economic and reasonably satisfactory except ... what railway line is buried in a road, surrounded by pressure from setts (granite or other stone), or worse still wood blocks? Drainage, without which any railway would quickly fail, was almost unknown in our steam tramway days and even where primitive soakaways existed, there was not the inspection system of cast iron mudholes utilised in electric days.

But instead of drainage our tram engineer faced seepage from above which must have started its insidious attack on the lines' foundations almost from day one. And the seepage was not just water, but basically urine from incontinent horses mixed with, in places, quite disgusting industrial waste, including sulphur based compounds. And what railway line was especially favoured by carters and carriers to run on? For them the area of the tramway was paradise compared with the quagmire that in winter was the rest of the road.

The alternative is a total re-think, getting away from a flexible base to one that is, within limits, self draining and having an absolutely solid bed, keeping the rails straight and true by the very squareness of the concrete base and to bolt the rails down so rigidly no movement is possible. Fishplates would be longer, bolted up tight and often extending under the rails. If sleepers were to be used, let them be in iron, almost impervious to anything that might surround them.

But, and buts abound in this life, what were the tools available to carry out this engineering? And it really was often engineering at its highest because for example at no time must the rails protrude above the surface of the road, but the road itself may be little better than a combination of mud and loose stone, all well churned by carts, wagons and their four-hoofed tractors. Where was the natural level of the road? Not only was there no kerbing, but carters, in winter, often deserted the mudbath for fresh ground on each side (much as motorists regard pavements as extensions of the highway today), and this road rose and fell according to the contours of the countryside. And, unlike railways, tram road builders could not normally put the road in a cutting or use waste to fill a declivity; this did happen, but it was the exception rather than the rule – however much easier it might have made the work of the tram engine. It might also seem logical to put the rails on one side of the road (as at Wantage) but the engineers were constrained by the infamous nine foot six inches (2.93m) clearance required between kerbs and the rails required under Board of Trade regulations.

From time to time the line had to be built in a lazy curve veering from the left hand side of the road right over to the right in order to pass around a corner. When the tram followed this S-bend it really excited carters who did not know the district. Most reversing 'wyes' tended to be asymmetric to avoid or reduce problems raised by local councils. Obviously buffer-blocks as used on railways could not be put down in the middle of the road, and many photographs show where trams (steam or electric 1881 or 2001!) had trespassed past the end of the line, to the detriment of the road surface. One wonders if any steamers ever 'nosed-in' and had to be rescued. Difficult to explain that! And of course at the termini water points had to be installed in the form of a sunken hydrant, and a suitable location for sacks of coke made available.

The width of the road taken up by the companies varied according to the gauge of rails selected, but normally the paving had to include eighteen inches (457mm) on each side of each rail plus the area in between, thus the responsibility of the tramway company using 'standard' gauge at 4' 8½" (1435mm) included, roughly, an eight foot (2438mm) width of roadway, or if using 'narrow' gauge at 3' 6" (1067mm) about 6' 9" (2057mm). The location of each crossing place, turnout, or loop (nomenclature varied around the country) was specified in the enabling Act of Parliament, but could be altered by agreement with the Council and the Board of Trade, the latter a formality, the former not always so. The points used initially were fairly primitive with only one movable blade, trams always entering the side of the loop which gave a straight run in, departing via the curve giving, we are told, fairly horrendous jerks as they did so, a matter which could greatly restrict the driver's ability to accelerate.

In general, as steam tramways were quite short, one contractor would be appointed for the whole work, although he might well then sub-contract, either for a complete length, or in the supply of labour or materials. On the other hand when tracks were laid by the Corporation, direct labour was employed under the supervision of a resident engineer or at least the Borough

Surveyor, and to some extent his reputation must have rested on the choice of rail used; many seem to have experimented gradually introducing improvements or at least cost cutting methods. This is very apparent in the great horse networks of Liverpool, London or Sheffield where trackwork evolved over a few years.

However, for our purposes we will assume there is a reasonable contractor, overseen by a fit engineer (and they needed to be, to handle 19th century contractors, and to walk or ride the works' length several times a day), and that the narrow Midland gauge of 3' 6" (1067mm) is in use, requiring a 7' (2134mm) trench to be cut out of the road along a surveyed length, always subject to carters' and carriers' ribaldry and occasional elements of violence. Strikers from outside industries could be another difficulty, as occasionally they were egged on to try to damage the works on some obscure argument that the ability to bring men in from outside would help the bosses. Mercifully this was rare, but the denunciation of any Sunday work by some vicar or priest, foaming in his pulpit about 'The Devil's Work', and threatening all forms of mayhem was not unusual. The fact that Sunday work was only carried out when the alternative was to delay the work and lay off men, seems to have by-passed these people.

Manual labour was an absolute necessity when tramways were first laid, and by way of contrast with the machinery used today for digging even the smallest hole, I reproduce below a checklist issued to an apprentice/student together with the relevant notes: "...the following may be taken as a list of what should be provided for a complete construction 'gang', i.e. the squad of men working on a section which is opened out at one time. This would be about a quarter of a mile in length, and would include work in all stages of progress, from the breaking up of the macadam roadway in front to the finished paved tramway behind. The carting is a separate item, and is often arranged with a local haulier.

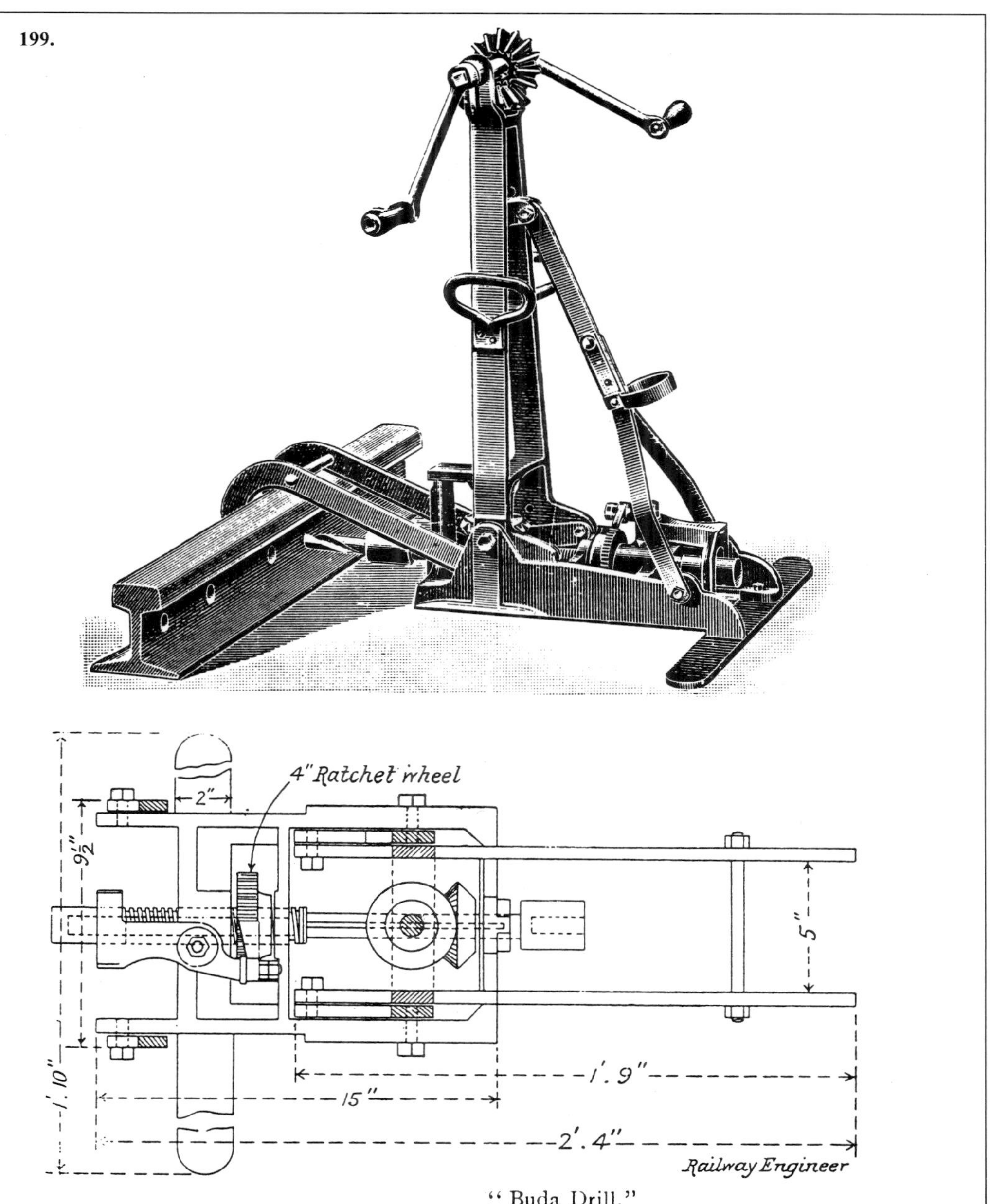

"Buda Drill."

EXCAVATORS
[not to be confused with JCBs and the like!]
4 doz. 2ft.6in. x 1¾ in. octagon steel wedges
4 doz. sledge hammers
4 doz. round shovels
4 doz. square shovels
20 ash levers for breaking up macadam
8 doz. picks
12 doz. pick shafts
30 wheelbarrows
21 yard gauge boxes
2½ yard gauge boxes
4 large concreting boards
3 water stand pipes
4 tarpaulin cement covers
20 water-cans
30 buckets
3 straight edges, 8ft. to 12ft. long

PAVIORS
1 doz. cane brushes
2 pitch boilers
4 pitch scoops
12 pitch buckets
6 rammers
6 chisel pointed crow-bars (small)
1 doz. 18 in. x 5/8 in. round pins
1½ doz. reel hammers
1 doz. cutting hammers
3 tool boxes

PLATELAYERS
1 doz. fish-bolt spanners
1 doz. tie-bar spanners
2 track gauges
2 doz. beaters, for packing rails
2 jim crows, 1 large, 1 small
2 doz. cold sates
2 drilling machines and drills
2 ratchet braces, cramps and drills
4 tool boxes.

GENERAL
1 pay office
4 watch boxes
4 doz. red lamps
4 doz. fencing standards
500 yds. fencing rope or chain
3 notice boards
12 fire buckets
2 sets of boning rods
½ doz. ranging rods
120 yards strong setting-out line
2 doz. iron pins, 18 ins x ¾in. round
3 doz. 2 in. x 2 in. x 18 in. wood pegs
1 measuring chain
2 measuring tapes
Supply of pens, ink, paper, chalk, time-books, carters' check tickets and sundries."

There was some degree of semi-mechanical equipment available, the quantity and condition depending on the contractor's situation; rarely in this life is everything new and working simultaneously!

Each rail would require a minimum of four holes drilled in it to take fishplates plus others for tiebars. For no reason that is apparent, this work was not always carried out before the rails were delivered – one can only assume cartage and labour costs came into the equation.

Our apprentice would come across a number of patterns of drills varying from the ratchet and brace, which was fine for use in wood but in rails "the form of cutting tool is bad, so are the intermittent action and still more intermittent feed, and so also is the sitting posture of the workman ... it is long outclassed". This was written right at the end of our period when two American machines, the 'Buda' and the 'Paulus' were commonly available. Both were designed for use on the final form of tram track.

Of the two it was claimed the Buda was the better as it could be wound in to maintain the cutting action, although at 90lb (41kg) it was nearly twice as heavy as the Paulus; thus for ¾" or 1" (25mm) holes the former was to be preferred, with a good workman and freshly sharpened drill-bit (if only...!) the half-inch (13mm) web of girder rail could have a one inch hole drilled through in as little as two minutes.

Rail saws were obviously vital tools, although "the ordinary way of cutting a rail is to nick it all round with a cold sate [cold chisel with 4" handle], and then break it with a Jim Crow [see later]. This is noisy and objectionable especially in town, and it is impossible thus to so cut a rail as to make a close butted joint. This can only be done when the rail is sawn through..."

However mechanical, or at least 'manumatic' saws were available which were for the period really quite efficient. The method of operation is quite clear:

"The saw and its gearing are mounted on a cast iron pedestal, separate from the base frame. This straddles the rail to be cut, the jaws in front grasping it firmly, and the whole machine then being steadied by legs at the outer corners, adjustable to suit the irregularities of the ground. The saw is driven by a double train of cog wheels, the saw itself being the last wheel of the train; the back of each saw tooth coming into gear with the driving pinion in the same way as the tooth of an ordinary spur wheel. The saw is fed downwards by a slow automatic motion of the usual character."

Even the design of this machine was improved from time-to-time; ultimately not only a square cut but any angle up to 45° became possible without loss of efficiency. Mind you, given the foul conditions these machines worked in, and the variable quality of the workmen, one wonders how long it was before those exposed gears wore away. "It is essential to the smooth working of (any) saw that the sharpening be properly attended to, and the cutting edges of the teeth kept accurately spaced from the centre: this is not a suitable job for a three-cornered file, as the blade is ¾" thick. The sharpening is done by an emery wheel on a special frame carrying the saw, which is so mounted that each tooth can be brought up to and across the face of the wheel, an adjustable stop limiting the motion of the frame towards the wheel so as to ensure the saw teeth being all left of the same length and angle of rake; the back of the tooth, which acts as a cog, is not touched".

200.

Whardown Rail Saw.

201.

"Paulus" Drill.

There were a number of alternatives including the German 'Sundale' saws:

The smaller relied primarily upon its own weight (80lb/36kg) for its cutting ability. The handle on the right is used in a reciprocating manner, but the strain on the operator and sheer mind-bending boredom probably helps to explain why these men drank. Fifteen to twenty minutes cutting time through a rail in 'modern' (1895) steel was average, although by reversing the thing it could be wheeled away to another site ... assuming a rail was already laid. The alternative combined saw and vertical drill was designed for railway work from sleepers to fencing and would have relatively little use on a tramway site.

202.

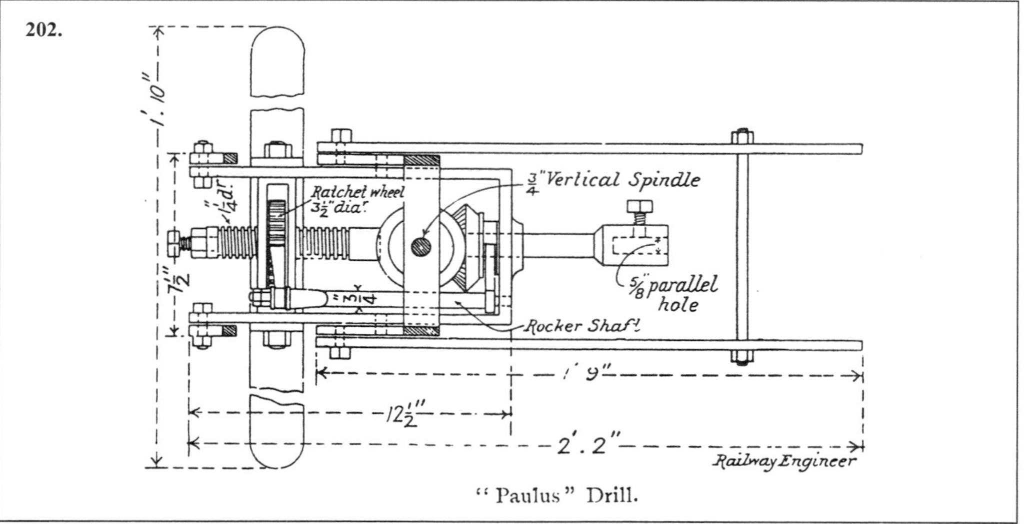

"Paulus" Drill.

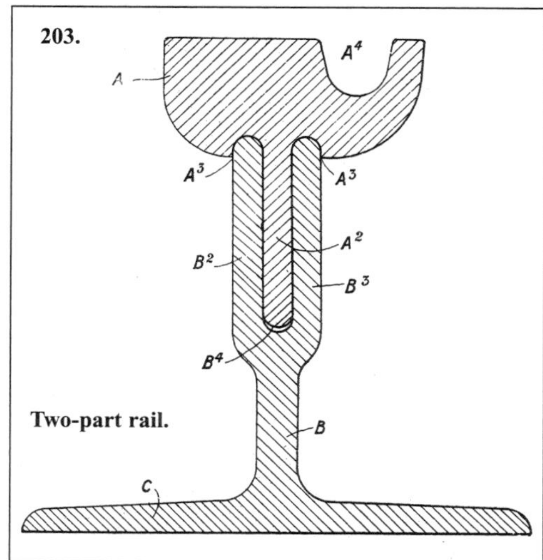

203. Two-part rail.

205. "Sundale" Portable Rail Saw.

The third and most vital tool used on tramways and railways of all ages and most types was (and still is even today) the "Jim Crow" or rail bender. It was the ability to use simple tools like this that, in part, led to the girder rail becoming the only choice, as some of the more fancy designs relied upon curved rails being cast in the iron works to fixed radii which must have handicapped engineer, contractor and workmen alike. Other patent shapes could be bent but where they were in two parts one can imagine how coaxing could turn to profanity when the two segments declined to mate.

The Jim Crow was, I have to admit, my favourite tool when I managed to be on a permanent way site; there was something magical about the way half-a-dozen of us without vast sweat could take an recalcitrant tram rail, cold and inert, and induce in it a gentle sweeping curve without kink or twist. Early Jim Crows were used to bend the foot of the rail which was only entirely satisfactory on light rail, as on heavy section, "the web has to transmit this bending strain from the foot to the head; this can only be done imperfectly and in consequence the web is tilted over, so that the bent rail is distorted and the web and foot are no longer perpendicular: there is thus a difficulty in getting the top flat, and at the same time true to gauge, and this difficulty increases with the length of rail operated upon."

This led to the development of a sophisticated variant, the Kenway, which matched the profile of the actual rail, thus creating an even stress

206. "Sundale" Circular Saw.

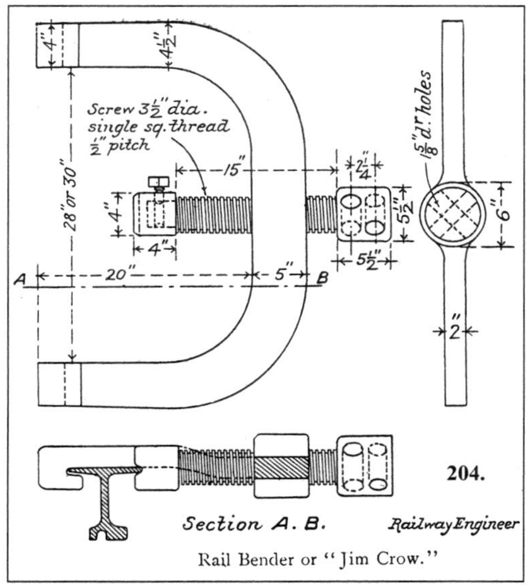

204. Rail Bender or "Jim Crow."

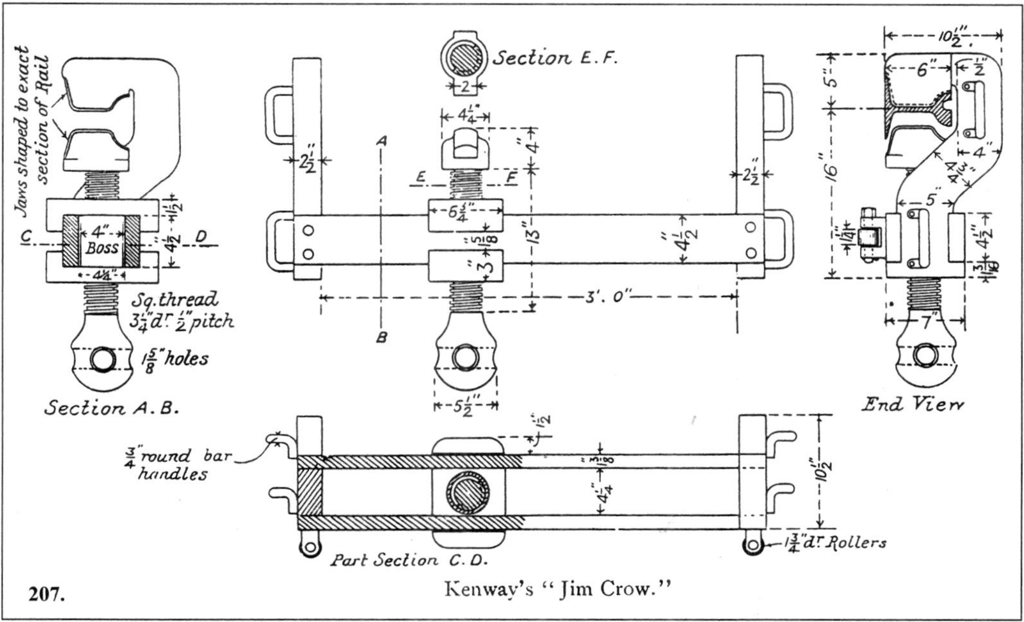

207. Kenway's "Jim Crow."

208.

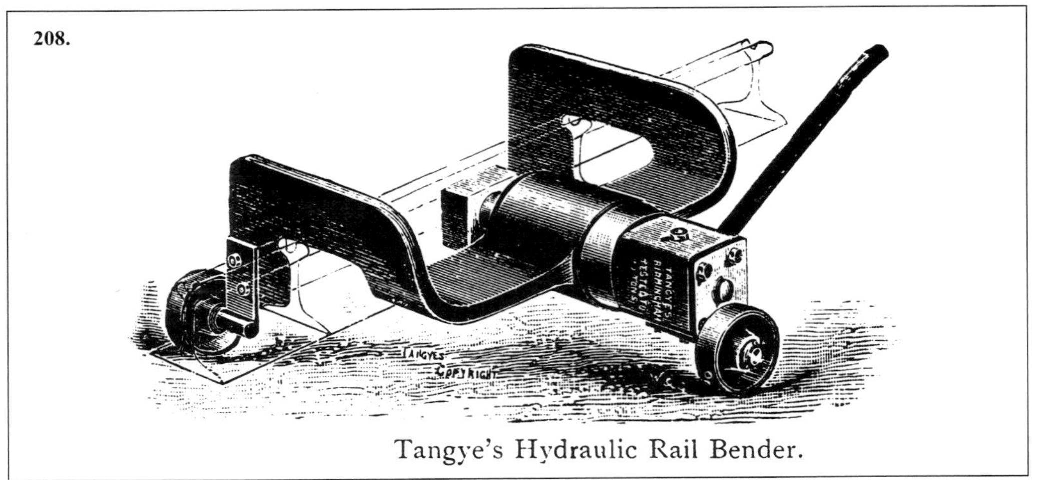

Tangye's Hydraulic Rail Bender.

from top to bottom and obviating any twist.

One problem that was never really resolved until the introduction of modern machinery was that of inducing a gentle curve throughout the rail *including rail joints*, as the curve must then include the fishplate, Even a cursory look at lightly laid lines will show the problem as the rails fight to straighten out. 'Threepenny bit' (or today 50p) segmental bends were anathema to all.

The nearest our tram engineer had to mechanical assistance for this work was an early hydraulic Jim Crow; in this case made by that British engineering firm par excellence, Tangyes, Cornwall Works, Smethwick. It was heavy at around 600lb (272kg) and obviously more suited for use in the contractors' works or the tram shed (if built!), but with jaws 28" (710mm) wide and with a breaking strain of 60 tons there were few rails that could withstand its pressure.

Having established what equipment was available to do the job, our apprentice had next to understand exactly what happened on the ground. We must assume for simplicity that this is a new extension being built in the middle of the steam tram period, using girder rails on a good concrete base and incorporating some but not all of the lessons that have been learned.

First of all the trench has to be excavated and all re-usable materials recovered; broken sharp stone commonly used in waterbound macadam is one of the recommended elements in concrete, whereas gravel is quite useless for our purposes. There was a common fallacy that rubble from demolished buildings, or any other waste, was adequate for concrete. This our apprentice would quickly learn was not so, due to contamination by 'foreign' materials.

How much road do we open up? Bye-laws must inhibit any tendency to overdo the excavating, and anyway all we need is sufficient to keep our gang rolling along, once they get a rhythm our job should be limited to ensuring that all materials are in hand at the right time. No telephones of course, but an excellent telegram system, with even in a town like Dudley or Wigan having up to ten letter collections daily and four or five deliveries. A letter posted by midday will be at most destinations the following day, and in London it will reach other London addresses the same day.

And if for any reason supplies of rails or their fixings are not forthcoming, the railway will find them quickly, so that last minute panics should not occur.

Let us say then that initially the equivalent of two rail lengths is roughly dug out (say 50-60 feet/16-20m). The following period the men will bottom out two further rail lengths and roughly excavate two further sections in advance. This done, our bottomed sections can have the concrete laid while sections 5 and 6 are bottomed out. Assuming all goes well, in a few days our excavation should look something like this table:

Sections 1 & 2 rails laid	Sections 3 & 4 concrete laid (rails loose on top)	Sections 5 & 6 bottomed out (shuttering ready)	Sections 7 & 8 rough dug
Another couple of days and the engineer would like to see:			
setts in place	rails laid	concrete laid	bottomed out
and Sections 9 & 10 rough dug			

What we must not do is to lay too much concrete at a time as it would be difficult to protect it against the weather, and neither must we lay too much unprotected rail, as expansion and contraction can both damage the alignment and the packing. Neither can our excavation team work too far ahead, (we already have a 200' long trench!), as the council's surveyor will be on the prowl, and neither they nor our engineer or contractors want any accidents – a nightsoil horse and cart floundering around in our wet concrete would wreak havoc, as well as introducing pollutants in the mix – as is said to have happened at least once!

The main emphasis throughout the works is on supervision, for while workmen can generally be trusted to carry out routine work, they will ease up if they can. If they have been laid off due to bad weather it is as well to arrange daily 'subs' for a while, and to ensure a hot pie man is in attendance at the works. Sometimes overlooked in planning we must ensure we have a portable forge to allow our blacksmith and his striker to repair, sharpen and rework edge tools. And if the blacksmith is hungry work will stop, it gives one a terrible queasy feeling to work on an empty stomach!

It will be explained to our apprentice there is another reason to take some interest in men's welfare – it keeps them out of pubs! Obviously as there were no portaloos they are going to use a pub for this purpose (or the side of the excavation!) but if their absences can be reduced that is a gain. The hours the men work may need to be limited if we want quality rather than quantity, as there are physical limits to the amount of heavy mauling work a man can do. A report in Sheffield refers to working hours: "seven while [until] dusk in winter, and seven while [until] seven or eight in summer with an hour's nap at dinner time".

A couple of other don'ts for a sensible apprentice – don't cut down the number of men on the rail lifting gang. Some may be capable of lifting two hundredweights (9100kg), others cannot: one man to a yard is reasonable, and don't allow the rails and sets to be dropped by the carter any old how; tipping sets on or by newly laid rail will twist it on its bed, and on new concrete must cause damage.

So the excavation is dug and bottomed out if possible, if still soft, broken stone will generally harden it up; but in very wet places (and with an eye to costings) it may be desirable to dig out a soakaway and lay herring-bone drains.

One advantage of being near a great manufacturing centre is the presence of clinker hills from which local councils draw their supplies for road repairing, and from which after grinding and sieving we shall have the basic material of our concrete. Roadstone may be perfection but clinker is cheap! Using Portland cement, a mixture of four parts of clinker (which will pass through sieves of 2½" mesh maximum and of ½" minimum), two of sand and one of cement will be quite satisfactory.

A curiosity our apprentice will notice when reading his textbooks is that a number of 'fancy' tests are suggested for concreting, including making up a small pat of cement and placing it in water as soon as it is properly set, the cement being considered suitable for use if no cracks develop in four or five days. Similarly it was suggested that a block of concrete made from the materials supplied should be made up, allowed to dry (between seven and twenty-eight days according to climactic conditions) and then tested to destruction which should not occur before the hammer is loaded to 175lb (80kg). Any thought of such tests will be brusquely dismissed!

If, as one should, we aim for perfection, then after seeing that the shuttering boards are properly located, the actual mixing of the concrete can begin. In all cases the physical activity of mixing must take place on a clean boarded stage, swept clear of detritus. According to circumstances either a cube yard bottomless box is first filled with the broken stone or clinker, a small box (say half the first) is placed on top of the stone and filled with sand, and then the whole is surmounted with another, smaller, box holding the cement. If the proportions 4:2:1 are adhered to the carpenter can knock up these boxes as required without fancy calculations. After

209.

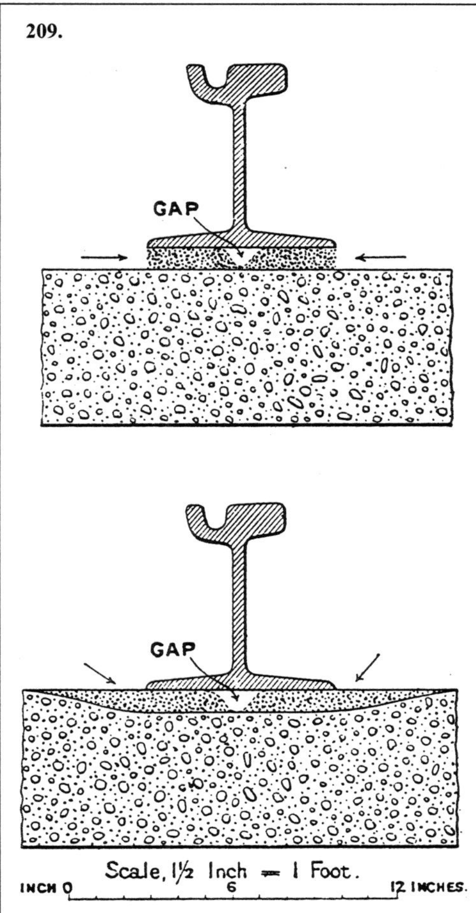

removing the boxes the whole compound, working from sides in, is dry mixed twice. During a third turning, involving perhaps six men, water is added **through a rose.** Commonsense says that if the water is just slung on to speed up the work, the cement will run through and away. The mix is then turned again and worked as it is shovelled into the excavation. If for any reason boxes cannot be made available, then the dry mixing must take place on the staging leaving a rim, rather like a saucer, some 4" high, water is then added and the mixing completed, although the loss of cement can be higher.

One alteration in working after 1885 was that rails were laid in place on bricks or other material before the concrete was poured in. But still a gap of 2"-3" was left between the rails and the concrete; if they are bedded in it is impossible not to have voids between the foot of the rail and the bulk of the concrete, especially as this may shrink.

Having laid the concrete and ensured it has a good surface, and that is far from easy when working on a gradient, as having to leave wet concrete unattended it may drift to the lower end of the section: "providing the concrete foundation is sound, and apart from the question of rail joints, there is not the slightest doubt that the majority of track maintenance problems are due to faulty packing". Three reasons existed, firstly that the rails may not have been properly and systematically packed when the track was laid (reason: bad or lacking supervision); secondly that although the packing was well done initially, it was disturbed by traffic (reason: lack of, or poor, watchmen at night); or finally, the materials used may not have been of suitable quality (reason: unsupervised contractors always cut corners).

As a rule before 1895 it was accepted the gap between the rails' base or flange and the base concrete should be no more than 1½" (38mm). Packing was then made from ¾" chippings (free of dust), which mixed with a cement at a proportion of 2½:1 and just moistened gives a good strong mixture. Application was by hard labour, skill and specialised tools. It will be remembered our rails were laid on old bricks, setts or anything stone that would hold them at the correct height and the concrete laid beneath them, integrating the 'stands' in the concrete. As these were at roughly three feet apart the rails should be fairly level. The composition, mixed as above, is then packed beneath the rails from both sides using square mouthed shovels so that it is evenly spread beneath the rails. It should then be carefully beaten solid by means of specialised 'beater picks' whose packing edge, blacksmith made or modified, should be bull-nosed, and about 2½" wide by ¾" thick (63mm x 19mm). The technique now long forgotten, but fresh to our apprentice, was executed thus: "six men are usually 'set on' to pack a length of rail [probably 20 feet/6m], two with shovels and four with beaters, and they work from opposite sides ... each man places one foot against the edge of the rail flange [base] while packing from the other side, so as to prevent the packing from being forced out by the beaters. The method of beating should consist of a number of short half-arm strokes until the packing is quite hard and unyielding. The two front men should beat in all the material required and the two rear men should follow inch by inch in their traces and finally consolidate the material." The men should, if they so wish, be rotated, but one job for your apprentice or the foreman platelayer is to continuously get down on his knees, and sighting along the rail, ensure that it has not been 'hogged' or gone out of alignment. Although a length of rail weighs a quarter of a ton or so, enthusiastic beaters can hog or bow this as much as 2" out of level. The rails when packed should be absolutely level (or at the correct angle for the line) and there should not be any difference in level from one rail to another; a good test for soundness of the packing is to strike the head of the rail with a hammer, when there should be no vibration.

With a good engineer who is his own master (and contractors rarely were), no more than one track length should be packed, as the continuous expansion and contraction of the rail from day to night will abrade and weaken the packing, and no matter how well the setts are laid, the road will always be weak. And our apprentice in his seven years 'learning' (but is it not true a good engineer is always learning?) will find that rails have a life of their own as they always seek to rise or fall or twist.

There was a problem sometimes found in badly packed rails that gaps are left due to imperfect work with the beater-picks and "should these occur they will eventually become filled with water, through condensation, seepage or sweating, and every tramcar passing over the rail forces the water into the packing" [like a squeegee]; "the car having passed on, the rail assumes its original level and the water is sucked into the gap, bringing with it particles of the packing". Given that on a tramway like the Wigan main line or the Dudley & Stourbridge, trams passed over single line sections every ten minutes for twelve to fourteen hours a day, the abrasive effect can easily be imagined. Eventually of course the weakened rail sags and the setts begin to lift – realistically it can be said they are blown out of their places. Relaying becomes necessary sooner rather than later.

It was to some degree due to the problem of indifferent workmanship or supervision that the pitch compound was developed as a substitute for the cement mix; but until the turn of the century engineers were still feeling their way as

210.

tar, rather than water-based roads were still rare, and the tramway engineers were, in some ways, in the forefront of progress. The technique still called for a packing of stone under the rails, albeit absolutely dry, and then on each side of the rail a sand bund or barrier a few inches high is made, and into this is poured a mixture or pitch or tar (6 parts pitch to 3 part Tarvia or similar ready prepared tar) raised to a temperature of 220°F (118°C) (although authorities quoted a range of ±50°F!) at which level it will run like tapwater into and through the chippings.

There were (and are) problems with this type of work, insofar as the site had to be dry (the results of a 'blowback' at that temperature are spectacular, destructive and downright dangerous) and the air and ground temperature had to be checked, uneven chilling of the mix meant a waste of time and the dratted stuff had to be hacked out again ... one engineer had a recommended method of dealing with these poor places, but his workmen had equipment most, including our apprentice, probably never saw in a year! "A very good plan is to raise the rail the merest trifle with very thin steel wedges, dry the underside of the rail base with a blow lamp and finally grout beneath the rail with hot well-tempered prepared pitch, after which the wedges should be immediately withdrawn, thus letting the rail down on its bed".

As can be imagined, if this work is not done well then the packing will be disturbed on each side of the repair work (a problem which arises not only on 'real' railways and tramways but models too), and care always had to be taken not to put a 'bow' in the rail: such practices are "very difficult to detect and keep under supervision". Not surprisingly given the conditions of labour in 1880-1910, "this has also been known to have been taken advantage of by unscrupulous workmen for securing the permanency of their employment".

As long as the tramway was laid along the crown of the road, levels were maintained and a good base laid, there should have been little difficulty in giving the cars a sweet run, but "Bad workmen always complain of their tools, hence the tramway permanent way is blamed for proving unsuitable for locos made on railway principles. The road is, in truth, bad enough, but it is begging the question to expect that a rail laid in a street can be treated as independently as one laid on a railway. We must expect on curves the wrong rail to be elevated, and often, for miles, one rail to be considerably lower than the other. As Mr Scott Russell suggested, the only remedy is to make an engine whose nether limbs are insulated from the trunk, so that the irregularities of the road and its varying resistance are effectually cut off from the motive machinery thus rendered indifferent to the state of the road ... J.W.HADDON, Late Manager, Paris Steam Tramways. 6 June 1879".

If one thinks about almost any normal road, it does not take much imagination to consider how much extra weight is borne by motor-cars' tyres which are nearest to the kerb and manufacturers now adjust suspension to allow for this; a tram engine with its wheels 4' 6" (1.37m) apart, weighing ten tons and pulling a top heavy 8 ton trailer, will always be trying to run down to the gutter while being forced to permanently climb up the camber of the road by its wheels being imprisoned in grooves. And every 20' along its journey there will be one or more rail joints. Before modern welding techniques became available (1905 on) the stresses on the rails and their joints must have been almost intolerable and it is not surprising much time and ingenuity was expected to design the perfect fishplate. And the success of a fishplate depends on how well the rails are laid, how well the tie bars holding the gauge and squareness of the rails have been tightened up, and that in turn relies upon the anchors for the rails. A good modern anchor properly placed in the concrete (as practised from 1895 on) and properly locked to the rail by wedges, is almost immovable, and if one of the anchors is placed a foot (30cm) from the end of each, the fishplates should lock the whole assembly rock solid. Before this time though where the rail depended upon being spiked to a sleeper or upon the packing to keep it in line, then the fishplates could only defer eventual movement.

"In making a fish-plate joint, both skill and patience are required: it is not a handy man's job ... given that the fish plates and rails are well designed, it is of the utmost importance that the minutiae of the design should be adhered to..." If the rails are drilled at the works, if the rails are a true fit to the fishplates, and if both items are obtained from the same steelworks, and the one had been tested against the other from time to time, and if the rolls producing the rails had not become worn, and if (almost an impossibility) the metal being rolled had not cooled or 'chattered' in its passage through the rolls, then the job was almost a 'doddle'. But if the rails came from Germany, the fishplates from Belgium and the nuts and bolts from Smethwick, what then? Given that engineering tolerances were wide, where there was supervision the chances were that ideally someone – our apprentice no less – was going to have to match fishplates to rail ends and number them. Do I hear a hollow laugh? Then the rails had to be squared up at the ends which might yet again throw the holes out of alignment, if arrises (bevels) were formed on the rail-heads these had also to be filed square. "In preparing a fish-plate joint, all traces of black and red oxide scale must be removed from both the rail ends and the fishplates by means of files, wire brushes and scrapers. New fish plates, having been 'dipped' [in hot oil as a rust preventative] have occasionally some coagulated oil about the bearing surfaces, which either prevents a good fit from being made or conveys a false impression of tightness: these should be removed of course" ... so there we have it, a November night in the middle of a noisy, sulphurous, factory area, sheeting down with rain, with most workmen having had a drink or two and getting a bit surly. Lighting by paraffin lamps is poor, as two of the men are driving home the bolts with 'Thursday', the 7lb sledgehammers, to the detriment of the threads although they know if they are quick enough to codge the job there will not be any nuts to worry about, (the bag had long been trodden in the mud and lost anyway), when up trots our keen apprentice who immediately notes after all his work matching fish plates to rails the fishplate is number 110 and the rail ends numbered 106 and 112. Does he say anything? Now our sagacious foreman platelayer "who must possess an accurate 'eye', must be able to line his rails as accurately as a surveyor can range a line, must be able to bend a rail so as to produce a faultless curve, must be skilled in the use of tape, rule and spirit level and [who] must also have some considerable knowledge of smiths' work, drilling and filling", where is he? Probably elsewhere on the site, so when our workmen look at the apprentice like hungry Kodiak bears just wakened from hibernation, if he has any sense he will mumble something and disappear into the gloom, to the sound of 'Thursday' once again bashing bolts. Oh, it happened, even in the 20th century.

There were always objections to the use of rail anchors at joints, not the least being the cost of drilling the rails and the difficulty of laying concrete around and underneath them; furthermore using a length of steel as an anchor makes a very hard base. As the rest of the rail is in effect suspended between the joints, it will give until an undulating road is formed, and...

211.

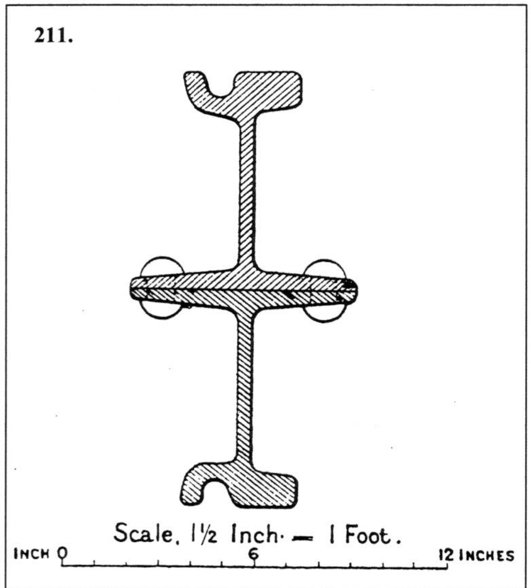

...the inevitable hammering is merely transferred from the joint to points immediately adjacent on either side. One alternative was to use fishplates of an enveloping form, where the section [EE] which took the foot of the rail was slightly narrow and had to be 'sprung' around the rail and then bolted up tight. But the 'springing' was only attained by using 'Tuesday', the 28lb sledgehammer, which must again have damaged any adjacent concrete bedding.

212.

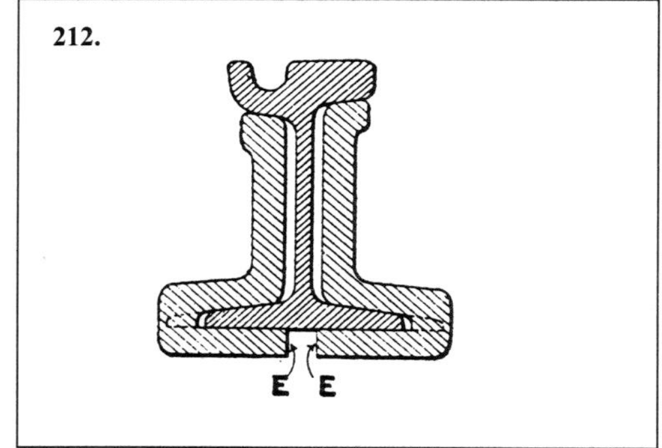

Henry Whytehead, the Manager of the North Staffs Tramways, where they were plagued with rail problems, designed an ingenious chair that deserved success, although first cost mitigated against this.

The quoted description is worth repeating: "The inventor has aimed at making the maintenance of tramway track more easy by reducing the number of bolts and nuts to a minimum, and by so arranging the parts that these nuts can be got at with but little more trouble than on an

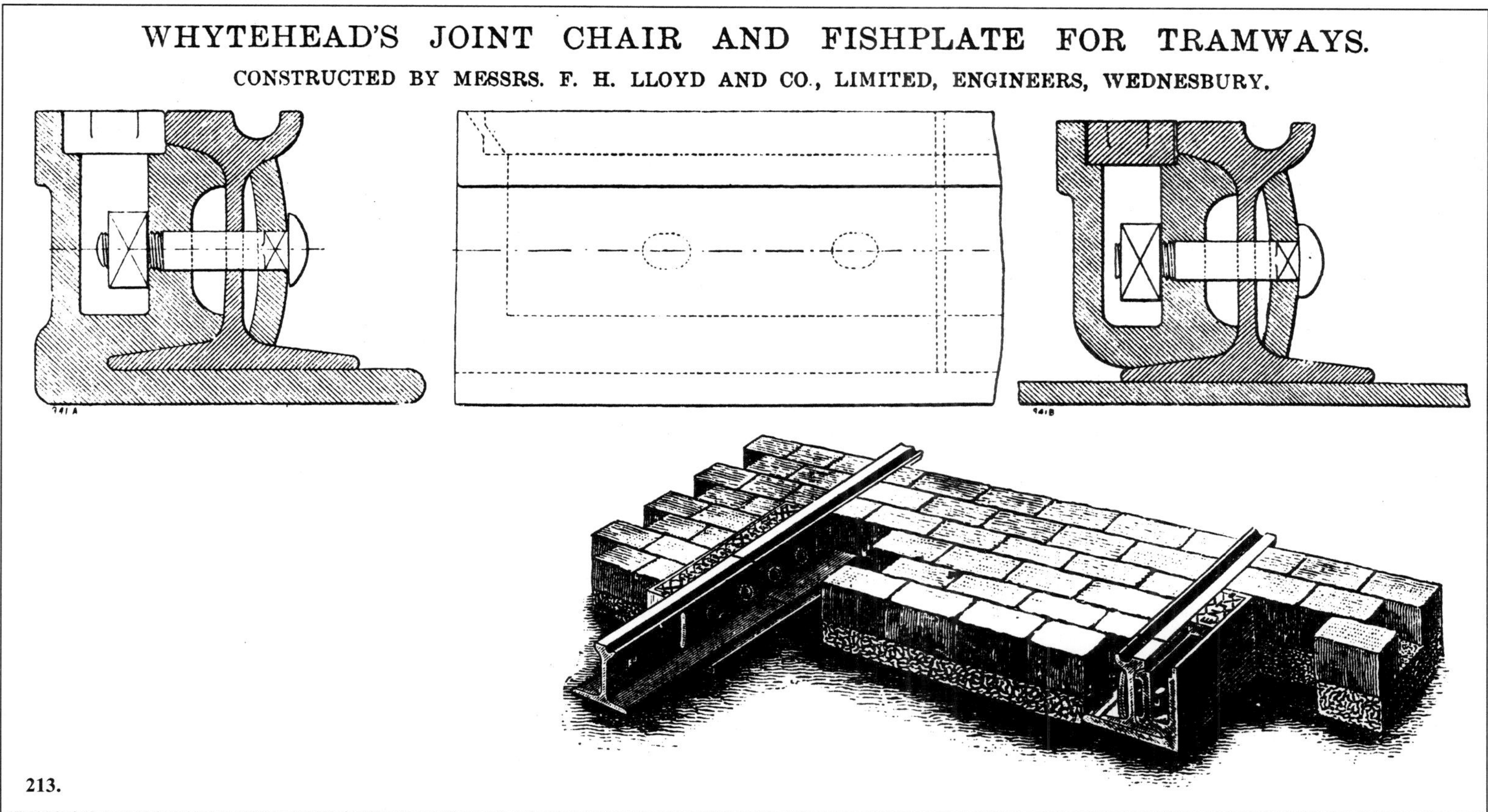

213.

ordinary railway line. Mr Whytehead believes that no form of lock-nut can be relied upon to maintain the tightness of a rail joint under traffic, and that the only reliable plan of doing so is to tighten the nuts periodically. With most tramway joints, this, however, necessitates taking up a part of the roadway to get at the nuts and to avoid this, his improved chair has a recess cast in, in which the nuts lie, as shown in the engravings, Figs. 1, 2, 3 and 4. This recess is covered by a lid, which can easily be removed by a suitable tool, the other end of which is shaped as a scoop to clear out any mud which may have entered the recess. The nuts can then be tightened with an ordinary spanner, and the whole operation is but little more troublesome than on a railway line".

214.

FIGURE 1

FIGURE 2

FIGURE 3

FIGURE 4

Any patented invention cost the hapless inventor (and his family) some considerable cash outlay, especially as in many cases (Downes loco for example) they built or had built full size prototypes. Arthur James Hamilton-Smythe, a Civil Engineer of Westminster, dreamed up a 'different' tram rail in 1893, and had his patent accepted in 1895. Whether he ever sold the batch of castings he is supposed to have made is doubtful. The parts, and there were an impracticably high number of them, were as follows:

A = tie rods
B = bolts
C = bent and perforated metal plates
D = concrete
E = perforated railway or tramway rails
F = perforated fishplates or waster-plates
G = nuts
J = (optional) spring washers

The mode of working, incredibly simplified (!), is to lay concrete D inside the plates C, and when it is hardened place E in their positions "by passing holes drilled through the said rails E at the required intervals on to the end of bolts B". Fit F outside the rails (E), screw up nuts G with or without spring washers J. It is not clear what holds the baseplate H in position, or how you keep the muck out of the U shaped ends of H as the Sections C are put in position, or what (apart from the concrete) prevents the two sections C from creeping in towards one another. Clever though, if akin to using a sledgehammer to crack a hazel-nut.

At this point it is as well to give a breakdown of a tramway's costs, the most accurate (as far as can be checked) and certainly the most detailed, was dated 21st May 1886 and relates to the new works in Liverpool. It is true that Liverpool prior to electric cars only ever had horse trams, but their trackwork, laid by direct labour, was far better than most installed for steam traction.

"The prices paid for materials and labour are as follows:—

Bessemer steel rails, straight	£8 15 6 to £7 12 0 per ton.
" " curved	Bent by Corporation workmen on the works.
Cast steel fixed points..	1 6 9 per cwt.
" movable points	1 6 9 "
Cast iron sleepers, straight	5 14 0 per ton to 4 15 0 per ton.
" " curved	6 0 0 " 5 5 0 "
" " special	7 15 0 "
Wrought iron holding-down jaws, double	0 14 3 per cwt.
Wrought iron holding-down jaws, single	0 13 3 "
Phosphor bronze bolts..	9 10 0 per cwt. to 8 8 4 per cwt.
Wrought iron nuts	1 11 9 "
Syenite sets, 3½ × 6½in. on quays ..	1 8 0 per ton to 1 6 9 per ton.
" 3½ × 7½in. " ..	1 7 0
" 6½ × 3½ × 3½in. (block sets).	1 8 0 "
" specials	1 12 6 " 1 10 0 "
Shingle (on quays)..	0 6 3 " 0 5 6 "
Gravel "	0 5 0 " 0 3 10 ".
Coal tar pitch	1 13 0 " 1 4 0 "
Creosote oil	2½d. to 1½d. per gallon.
Coke	0 11 8 per ton to 0 5 0 per ton.
Portland cement	2 0 0 " 1 19 0 "
Breakers	0 7 0 " 0 4 6 "
Burr pitching..	0 2 6 " 0 2 0 "
Broken stone	0 5 6 "

NOTE.—The above prices were for delivery on the works free of all charges, except where otherwise stated.

Rates of Wages Paid.

	Piecework.	Day work.
Platelayers		5s. 4d. to 5s. per day.
Blacksmiths		5s. "
Paviors	Outside tramway limits, inclusive of all labourers' work, from the completion of the finished surface of the concrete (with the exception of pitch carrying, for which one penny extra per yard is allowed), 5½d. per superficial yard. Inside ditto ditto, 9d. per superficial yard..	5s. 4d. "
Masons	Flagging laid complete, inclusive of all labourers' work, 6d. to 1s. per superficial yard. Curbs, channels, &c., ditto ditto, 4d. to 6d. per lineal yd.	6s. to 5s. 6d. "
Set dressers..	Ordinary sets, 7s. 6d. per ton .. Small " 11s. " .. Special " 16s. " ..	6s. "
Platelayers' labourers..		4s., 3s. 6d. "
Paviors' and masons' labourers		4s., 3s. 6d. "
Ordinary labourers		4s. 4d. to 3s. "
Watchmen		3s. 4d. "

Costs involved in the laying of trackwork. Liverpool, May 1886, can be seen above.

One experiment which showed either absolute optimism or desperation, was to lay *glass* sleepers on the line of the North Metropolitan Tramways in High Street, Stratford. It appears Frederick Siemens of Dresden developed a new way of hardening glass in 1878 so that it had some of the characteristics of cast iron. Laid as rectangular sleepers 3 feet long (90cm), 4 inches wide (10cm), and 5 inches deep they replaced the existing wooden sleepers like for like, although iron bearing plates were fitted at the joints so that the rails could be bolted down. Clearly the glass could not be drilled for retaining bolts. The suggested economy lay in the fact that had they proved serviceable, being indestructible by moisture, these sleepers could be used and re-used indefinitely. But both this tramway experiment and one on the London & North Western Railway at Crewe proved unsuccessful, the sleepers shattering transversely into 1" (25mm) pieces.

Our apprentice will be duly grateful that our tramway is only using normal equipment. The concreting is progressing, the track is laid in situ for two or three lengths and properly packed, while the gang of men are working ahead hacking out another length of road.

Tramway paving was not too much of a problem for a good engineer, but the local Councils always had a say in what could be used, sometimes arguing over a slight difference on the dimension of setts.

In April 1882 the Upper Sedgley Local Board had a long interview "with Mr Frankland, engineer for the construction of the tramway from Dudley to Wolverhampton ... in reference to the outside setts or 'randoms' – Mr Bevan moved they consist of five-inch Mount Sorrel granite – seconded by Mr Church – Mr J. Law moved they be four-inch. He did not think they would cripple the Tramway Company, they wanted the trams, and they ought to do all they could to get them – this was seconded by Mr Pugh, and carried by 9 to 7.

After a long, all day, discussion around the same time Dudley Council (Sedgley's neighbour) expressed much unhappiness over the ¾" (19mm) groove chosen "as it has been found that a groove of the width proposed is very inconvenient to vehicular traffic and does great injury to gigs and traps of all descriptions..." They wanted a narrower groove, different, less slippery setts, and even thought the engineer (Kincaid) should abandon his type of rails and substitute "Mr Deacon's system" (a two part rail theoretically obviating any necessity to lift setts when wear occurred). They wrote to the Board of Trade and told them so. The BOT wrote in May stating:

1. Width of rails at top 2⅞"
2. Width of rails at bottom 6¾" i.e. girder rails
3. Groove to be 1"
4. Grouting of pitch and tar
5. Concrete packing next to rails to be packed and rammed.
6. Paving setts to be 5" x 3" throughout and of granite unless otherwise agreed
7. Bedding for setts to be of fine gravel
8. Additional thickness of concrete when required to be settled by Promoters.

And that was that.

Standard textbooks showed the wearing characteristics of various stones which could be sourced from Penmaenmawr, Llandbredrog, Pwllweli, Clee Hill, Rowley Hills (the famous Rowley Rag), Mountsorrel, Guernsey (C.I.), Stoney Stanton with even Cornish or Newry (N.I.) stone being suggested. The problem was that for the steam tram operator a stone which could be dressed with exactitude, and never wore down was ideal; whereas a horse tram operator and for that matter a horse cart driver were well aware a horse's iron horseshoe on a wet hard stone could have him over in seconds, and that rougher stone gave some traction . A legal wrangle which ended up in the House of Lords (judgement 27th November 1902) stated that where a smooth hard granite had been used in Dublin, since it gave insufficient grip the road surface must be sanded. The sand will of course further polish the setts, so this was a judgement of Solomon – standing on his head!

At the AGM of the North Staffordshire Tramway Company held just after Christmas 1881 the Chairman, Mr T. Beattie had a confession to make: "In fulfilment of the promise made to you at our last annual meeting, the directors intend to take the shareholders into their fullest confidence; I will, therefore, now explain what has been done since we last met. On that occasion, it was stated that the line from Stoke to Longton had been completed and only awaited the Government inspection. This took place in January last, but the line was not passed, owing to the immensely heavy traffic along the road having worn the Macclesfield setts with which the tramway was paved in accordance with the contract to such an extent as to render it necessary to replace them with granite setts, thereby causing so much delay that it was not until April we were enabled to obtain the certificate of the Board of Trade authorising us to commence working." He was then severely gnawed by a very irate shareholder who pointed out the engineer had received £2,400 (a vast amount of money when a tram driver got £1.50 a week) and seemed to have passed the setts as suitable, and yet now they were condemned because they could not stand the wear on them.

His reply was surprisingly unapologetic – but it was an O'Hagan tramway. "As regards the Macclesfield setts, I agree with a good deal the gentleman has said about our troubles, but in justice to the engineer, I must say that the Macclesfield setts were put down at the suggestion of the local authorities. It is the best known stone in the district, and they thought it would be suitable for our purpose; but experience pretty soon showed us that it was not. It was too friable a stone and wore away too quickly. The original intention was to lay the tramway on a Macadam road, with granite setts on each side of the rails, but that was altered to the Macclesfield setts. A SHAREHOLDER: Did the engineer object to it in the first instance? No sir, as regards the engineer, I need hardly remind you that a civil engineer is not supposed to know much about mechanical engineering. A SHAREHOLDER: I cannot agree with you there. The CHAIRMAN: It is very rarely you can get a combination of both qualities."

The recommended size for setts was in depth 1" less than the overall depth of the chosen rail, the width between three and four inches, and the length should never be more than 8". Modern paving is often longer than this and shows why the Victorian engineers chose 8" (203mm) as, inevitably, there will be hard high spots in the bedding material and the longer stone will always rock.

Another matter which affected the stone supplied was the cost of transport, whether by canal boat, train or cart, as this was governed by weight. One ton of a medium stone cut in 8" x 5" x 3" setts will cover 4 square yards, but the variation between different quarries was quite important – Penmaenmawr weighed 172lb per cubic foot, Mountsorrel 164, Stoney Stanton

168, Clee Hill 179, Penryn 185. Even when the setts are to hand (and weather, strikes and faulty seams wreaked havoc with many a contractor's schedule) one job our apprentice might get was to sort them out. Those which did not have true bottoms (i.e. were lumpy or wedged) were rejected, and all the others had to be sorted so that each batch as the paviors came to them were within ¼" (6mm) of the same dimensions. Up to 20% were regularly rejected and used for infill or as half setts to butt against the rails. Part of the skill of paviors and their rammermen lay in the ability to 'make do' with materials to hand, but not only was this wasteful of their time, but when that stretch is lifted for repairs or disturbed for other work, inevitably the setts will not return to their original location and the result will be a mess. "...In Glasgow, as well as in London, Liverpool, Leeds, Edinburgh, and many American cities, the points and crossings of tramways have failed, equally with the joints, just on account of the adoption of the wood sleeper system. There are many glaring instances of this fact in Glasgow, as any ordinary observer may see for himself, especially if he makes his inspection on a wet day. Some of these instances seem to become more and more glaring on the return of wet weather after the lapse of a week or two, or even a few days. Constant repairs are consequently required, not only upon the continuous track, but more especially where there are any points or crossings. The circumstance is very patent to persons whose professional labours necessitate their being on the streets very late at night and during the 'wee short hours ayont the twal' to use a quotation from Burns. The repairs to the track are of necessity made under very great difficulties, and at very considerable expense, whether made by day or during the traffic, or by night when the traffic is suspended. Even after the repairs have been effected it almost invariably happens that a very uneven surface is left; indeed, in the circumstances of the case it could scarcely be otherwise, inasmuch as the bond of the paving is destroyed..."

The alternative to stone in early days was to use wood blocks. These were normally fitted in the road adjacent to hospitals, Courts and similar buildings, sometimes including the Mayor's Chamber or the Council Meeting House. Even a church might be able to bring enough pressure to bear to require use of wood blocks outside.

Whatever the location, wood paving was anathema to the accountant due to the cost, and to the engineer because apart from the noise reduction "in any other desirable quality every variety of it is inferior to granite. It is not so heavy and it is therefore less stable and more easily affected by vibration arising in the rails. It wears faster and therefore has to be relaid and replaced more frequently". When they were wet, despite tar dressing, wood blocks expanded and placed an intolerable pressure on the rails, and as they dried and shrank, so road detritis filled the gaps. On the next expansion the blocks would 'cockle' until the roadway looked rippled with the occasional toe-bender located to catch the unwary cyclist. However, during the bombing in London and doubtless many other cities, dislodged blocks made useful material to burn on open fires, albeit they gave off oddly coloured flames and spat like a venomous woman! Our apprentice would learn that there was a vast choice in timber from Danzig ('Baltic') pine to Australian Jarrah. Like the stone setts, wood blocks had their own specification, for the timber was to be "properly seasoned, close and uniform in grain, free from sapwood, shakes, and large or loose knots ... the most serious defect is the prevalence of immature sapwood; it is soft and most liable to decay, and is the first part of the surface to wear into holes..." Pressure creosoting, while vital for underground timberwork, was not regarded as essential for the wood blocks as they would be worn out before they rotted. Conversely pickling the wood in creosote was held to assist the pitch grout (where used) to form a better bond. But there was a problem in this process. "[It] ... has one very objectionable feature when the timber has not been previously selected; it hides most of the imperfections and makes green and sappy blocks look very much like good material".

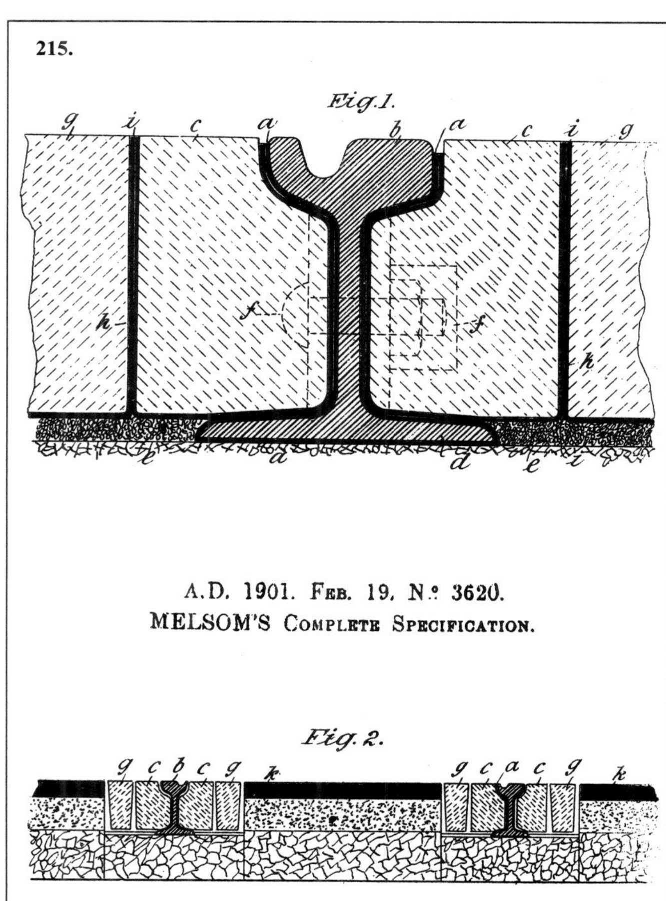

Pressure creosoting was an interesting process and it is known that one or two tramways had mobile units; the vessels were, however, prone to exploding with unpleasant results. Creosote is a dark brown oil produced from oil distillation at between 400°F and 700°F (205°C and 370°) containing various phenols which can be used in a refined form as a disinfectant.

The pressure chamber was filled with timber, warmed creosote added and the temperature raised to 220°F (105°C). Additional oil was then pumped in until a pressure of 100-120psi was attained. Generally wood will 'take up' about 10 lb of creosote per cubic foot. Another expense involved in using wood blocks was that of using either pure pitch or a pitch/tar compound as grouting. Tables of consumption were available but our apprentice was more likely to have seen the old mixture of a 'nut' of pitch (it looks like black glass when cold) to a gallon (4.5 litres) of tar. The 'nut' should weigh 1 lb (454g) but it was rather hit and miss. This mixture was then heated to bubbling hot and poured in the interstices, which were normally about ¼" wide. If Jarrah or Karri woods from Australia were used, then no preservatives were required, both being of the eucalyptus family, they contained natural resins. Timbers of this type, which are almost inert, were laid 'hard to hard' with as tight a joint as possible.

One fascinating patent (3620, 19th February 1901) by Henry Melsom, proposed "inserting bituminous cloth, or cloth covered in bitumin, between the [tram] rail and the paving blocks adjacent to the rail; also inserting a row of taper or wedged shaped paving blocks, with bituminous cloth joints next [to] the rail paving blocks so that these taper paving blocks, and afterwards the other blocks, can be removed without injury when required to get at or remove the rail, and can be used over again...", as an additional scheme (shown in the drawing) Mr Melsom proposed bedding the rails in his bituminous cloth. I do not know whether or not his scheme was tried, certainly it seems a logical way of sealing the joints although compression of the cloth might be a problem.

The setts should have been neatly stacked by the tram lines, and it is at this point the paviors and their rammermen make their appearance, and since they are almost inevitably on piecework, pressure is placed on the digging, concreting and platelaying gangs ahead of them. Two types of bedding material are commonly found, the first our pitch/tar compound so mixed that when it goes off it makes a rubber-like substance. The great advantage of this mixture is that it has the ability to absorb some of the inevitable vibration inherent in the rails. "If good clean pitch is boiled with creosoted oil in the proper proportions, the product is a ductile, adhesive, watertight substance..." said one of our textbooks, but it was again emphasised that *all the materials must be dry.*

It was held that the elasticity of pitch grout was due "to the volatile gases of the oil being held imprisoned in the interstices of the molecules of the melted pitch". It was understood these volatile oils would evaporate out in time, but no quicker than the sets would wear. If using the compound the recommended method was to pour onto the underlying concrete bed a 1½" (38mm) layer, the setts then being worked into position and further hot mixture poured in the gaps around the setts, albeit leaving ½" clear at the top.

It was known that pitch grout expanded in summer and by oozing out between the setts caused problems for predestrians and horses' hoofs alike. Normal practice was to brush a mixture of sand and cement down the missing top half inch between the setts. Where ladies passed to and fro across the road, boy crossing-keepers normally strewed sand or sawdust to

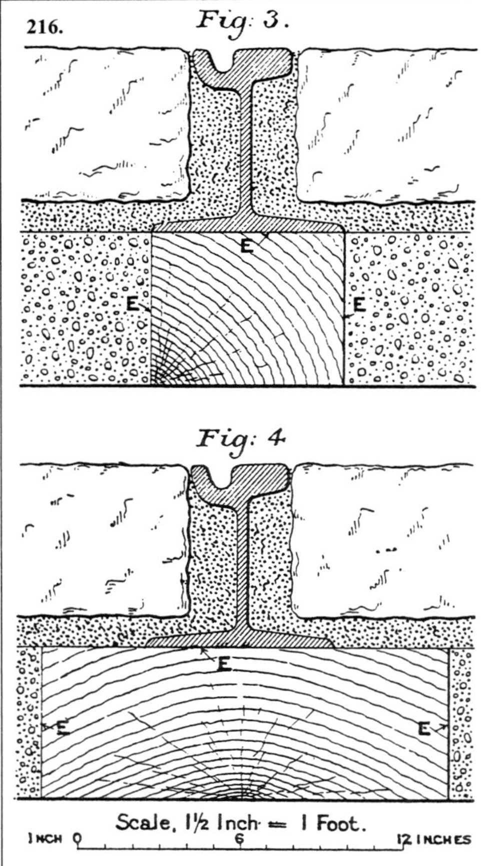

keep the tar from their skirts; thereby earning the boy a farthing or so (a farthing = 0.1p, but many a Victorian mickle made a muckle!).

Although this technique was, for the time, the acme of perfection, it was expensive and our contractor was more likely to follow an older method of working. First a 4:1 mixture of fine sand and cement was just moistened and spread evenly over the concrete bed. "The pavior [then] takes a sett in his left hand, and with a broad-ended paving hammer he shapes the bedding to receive the stone, which is gently placed in position. If the sett is not low enough it should on no account be struck with the hammer ... but should be removed, the bedding lowered and then placed back. The pavior, by pressing on the sett with his hammer, is able to detect at once whether it will rock or not. If it rocks or is too low, it must be taken up and additional bedding must be carefully spread before the sett is replaced; on no account [as practised by inferior paviors] must the paving hammer be used for beating extra bedding beneath the sett". The ramming of setts required good and dedicated workmen "... it is the paviors' duty to bed the setts and the rammerman's duty to ram them uniformly into the bedding".

It was always emphasised to apprentices that setts should be laid and rammed so as to end up level with the rails, whereas a pavior always tended to leave the courses next to the rails slightly high as he would feel the wagon wheels would wear them away quicker than the rails, but the difficulty lay that when the iron tyres of the wheels laid down from the setts to the lower-level rails, they would grind off the edges and eventually shatter the stones, causing 'rutting' which not only broke the water-proof seal betwixt rail and sett but accelerated the very evil these high setts were supposed to ameliorate, that of wear. And excessive wear meant premature maintenance...

In 1874 James Henry Lynde was granted a patent wherein he foretold not only the practices of the following decade but, modified, 'Light Rail' systems a century and a quarter later. "The object of my Invention is to construct a tramway that shall present the least possible obstruction to the ordinary traffic; that shall supersede the present objectionable straight joint in the paving of the street on each side of the rail or tram, which is always the source of ruts; that shall be absolutely immovable without the use of any fastenings whatever; and that shall be more durable in its foundation than any system at present is use on account of the imperishable nature of the materials used. My Invention consists in the combination of a metallic grooved rail cement, concrete, or asphalte. This invention is more suitable for paved streets, but can also be applied to macadamised roads. Where streets are already paved I removed those sets or blocks that interfere with the grooved metallic rail, which is about three inches broad, leaving a broken or irregular or indented edge to the paving on each side of the rail or tram, I then fill in the space to within about two-and-a-quarter inches of the surface with cement or lime, concrete, or other similar material or asphalte, and upon this when properly set I support the metallic rail temporarily and pour in liquid or viscous asphalte, or fill in with compressed asphalte or cement, or cement or lime concrete, with either a flat or an indented surface. The rail is provided with a small projection on each side at its base to form a key or dovetail, and it is joggled horizontally at the ends to render it still more secure. I prefer to procure the rails as clean and fresh from the mill as possible, and at once to coat them with some bituminous material as a paint in order to preserve them from rust and to ensure that when asphalte is used it shall adhere firmly to them, but this it not indispensable. When I apply this Invention to a macadamised or unpaved road I first excavate and remove the surface of the road to a depth of eight inches for a width of eight feet or more. I then pave with sets or blocks in the ordinary way so much of such excavated space as will leave two spaces in the lines of the rails or trams, having broken or irregular, or indented edges, as before described. I then proceed in the same manner as if the road had been paved with sets or blocks in the first instance."

One has to feel proud that a man with such an ingenious brain was British!

217. The alternative rather pragmatic approach to track laying is to, in effect, just run a light railway alongside the road. This is the Cavan & Leitram 3' 0" gauge line between Drumshambo and Arigna, opened in 1888 as a mongrel tram/railway line, 15 miles long, mainly for freight. The cost of modernising the line caused closure in 1959 – they even wanted fences!

Table of weights and leading dimensions of steel girder rails

The tables which follow are those which were published in 1895 showing the tram rail sections available from Dick, Kerr & Company, in their guise as contractors. By and large, each engineer had his own idea of what type of rail would suit his traffic conditions, thus where heavy road verhicles crossed or ran over the rails a larger foot was desirable; elsewhere a council would demand a narrow groove, although the 7/16th of an inch (11mm) quoted for Birmingham, Leeds etc. was unbelievable – the wheel flanges would be like razors, and the stresses on curves enourmous – probably sufficient to twist and break an axle.

The list is obviously incomplete, as some tramways ordered their rails direct or used other contractors; this seems to have applied particularly in the Midlands where among others the Dudley-based tramways are omitted, as are Liverpool and Sheffield. A number of horse tramways have been included, generally but not necessarily using a lighter section. Certainly some attempts at using steam trams were undermined (literally) by track collapse, and even the rail splitting; but towards the end of electric trams the loss of one side of the head was not uncommon.

A note on nomenclature: a tram rail was regarded as comprising three parts, the HEAD which carried the groove, the WEB or SHANK and, thirdly the FLANGE BASE, FOOT or (rarely) the TAIL. Ideally the vertical centre groove, and the joint between the base and the web, should be thickened to a half circle, thus reducing distortion.

Table of Weights and Leading Dimensions of Steel Tram Girder Rails.

(Reduced from the Section Sheets of Messrs. Dick, Kerr & Co.)

Order number.	Names of tramways.	Weight of rail per yard.	Height by width of base.	Width of head over all.	Width of groove.	Minimum thickness of web.	Thickness of base. At edges	Thickness of base. Near web.
No.	Tramways.	Lbs.	Ins. by ins.	Ins.	Ins.	Inch	Inch.	Inch.
2	Spanish	50 to 53	$4\frac{1}{2} \times 4$	3	1	$\frac{7}{16}$	$\frac{1}{4}$	$\frac{1}{2}$
3	Gateshead-on-Tyne. Woolwich and South-east London Wigan Ipswich	56 ,, 58	$5\frac{1}{2} \times 4$	3	1	$\frac{3}{8}$	$\frac{1}{4}$	$\frac{1}{2}$
6	Madrid Bucharest Brighton Malaya Panama	60 ,, 63	5×5	3	1	$\frac{1}{4}$ $\frac{3}{32}$	$\frac{1}{4}$	$\frac{1}{2}$
9	Norwood & Croydon Hartlepool	74 ,, 77	6×6	3	1	$\frac{3}{8}$	$\frac{5}{16}$	$\frac{5}{8}$
10	South Staffordshire. Cardiff Southampton La Plata	75 ,, 78	6×6	3	1	$\frac{3}{8}$	$\frac{5}{16}$	$\frac{5}{8}$
11	Accrington Port Glasgow Birmingham Midland	75 ,, 78	6×6	$3\frac{3}{16}$	1	$\frac{3}{8}$	$\frac{5}{16}$	$\frac{5}{8}$
13	Manchester, Bury, and Rochdale	88 ,, 92	6×7	$3\frac{1}{16}$	1	$\frac{7}{16}$	$\frac{5}{16}$	$\frac{5}{8}$
14	Newcastle-on-Tyne.	90 ,, 94	7×7	3	1	$\frac{3}{8}$	$\frac{5}{16}$	$\frac{5}{16}$
15	Manchester, Bury, and Rochdale	90 ,, 94	7×7	$3\frac{1}{8}$	1	$\frac{1}{2}$	$\frac{1}{4}$ full.	$\frac{5}{8}$
16	Dublin United	90 ,, 94	7×7	3	$\frac{7}{8}$	$\frac{3}{8}$	$\frac{5}{16}$ bare.	$\frac{5}{8}$
17	Brazilian	35	$3\frac{1}{2} \times 3$	$2\frac{5}{8}$	1	$\frac{1}{4}$	$\frac{3}{16}$	$\frac{3}{8}$
18	Bridgetown	40 ,, 42	$3\frac{1}{2} \times 3$	$2\frac{3}{4}$	1	$\frac{5}{16}$	$\frac{3}{16}$	$\frac{3}{8}$
19	London, Camberwell, and East Dulwich. Portsmouth	65 ,, 68	$5\frac{1}{2} \times 5$	$3\frac{1}{16}$	1	$\frac{3}{8}$	$\frac{1}{4}$	$\frac{1}{2}$ bare.
20	Brisbane Seville	55 ,, 57	$4\frac{1}{2} \times 4$	3	1	$\frac{3}{8}$	$\frac{1}{4}$	$\frac{7}{16}$
21	Brisbane	77 ,, 80	$6 \times 6\frac{1}{2}$	3	1	$\frac{3}{8}$	$\frac{1}{4}$	$\frac{7}{16}$

332 CONSTRUCTION OF TRAMWAYS.

Table of Weights and Leading Dimensions of Steel Tram Girder Rails.

(Reduced from the Section Sheets of Messrs. Dick, Kerr & Co.)

Order number.	Names of tramways.	Weight of rail per yard.	Height by width of base.	Width of head over all.	Width of groove.	Minimum thickness of web.	Thickness of base. At edges	Thickness of base. Near web.
No.	Tramways.	Lbs.	Ins. by ins.	Ins.	Ins.	Inch	Inch.	Inch.
2	Spanish	50 to 53	$4\frac{1}{2} \times 4$	3	1	$\frac{7}{16}$	$\frac{1}{4}$	$\frac{1}{2}$
3	Gateshead-on-Tyne. Woolwich and South-east London Wigan Ipswich	56 ,, 58	$5\frac{1}{2} \times 4$	3	1	$\frac{3}{8}$	$\frac{1}{4}$	$\frac{1}{2}$
6	Madrid Bucharest Brighton Malaya Panama	60 ,, 63	5×5	3	1	$\frac{1}{4}$ $\frac{3}{32}$	$\frac{1}{4}$	$\frac{1}{2}$
9	Norwood & Croydon Hartlepool	74 ,, 77	6×6	3	1	$\frac{3}{8}$	$\frac{5}{16}$	$\frac{5}{8}$
10	South Staffordshire. Cardiff Southampton La Plata	75 ,, 78	6×6	3	1	$\frac{3}{8}$	$\frac{5}{16}$	$\frac{5}{8}$
11	Accrington Port Glasgow Birmingham Midland	75 ,, 78	6×6	$3\frac{3}{16}$	1	$\frac{3}{8}$	$\frac{5}{16}$	$\frac{5}{8}$
13	Manchester, Bury, and Rochdale	88 ,, 92	6×7	$3\frac{1}{16}$	1	$\frac{7}{16}$	$\frac{5}{16}$	$\frac{5}{8}$
14	Newcastle-on-Tyne.	90 ,, 94	7×7	3	1	$\frac{3}{8}$	$\frac{5}{16}$	$\frac{5}{16}$
15	Manchester, Bury, and Rochdale	90 ,, 94	7×7	$3\frac{1}{8}$	1	$\frac{1}{2}$	$\frac{1}{4}$ full.	$\frac{5}{8}$
16	Dublin United	90 ,, 94	7×7	3	$\frac{7}{8}$	$\frac{3}{8}$	$\frac{5}{16}$ bare.	$\frac{5}{8}$
17	Brazilian	35	$3\frac{1}{2} \times 3$	$2\frac{5}{8}$	1	$\frac{1}{4}$	$\frac{3}{16}$	$\frac{3}{8}$
18	Bridgetown	40 ,, 42	$3\frac{1}{2} \times 3$	$2\frac{3}{4}$	1	$\frac{5}{16}$	$\frac{3}{16}$	$\frac{3}{8}$
19	London, Camberwell, and East Dulwich. Portsmouth	65 ,, 68	$5\frac{1}{2} \times 5$	$3\frac{1}{16}$	1	$\frac{3}{8}$	$\frac{1}{4}$	$\frac{1}{2}$ bare.
20	Brisbane Seville	55 ,, 57	$4\frac{1}{2} \times 4$	3	1	$\frac{3}{8}$	$\frac{1}{4}$	$\frac{7}{16}$
21	Brisbane	77 ,, 80	$6 \times 6\frac{1}{2}$	3	1	$\frac{3}{8}$	$\frac{1}{4}$	$\frac{7}{16}$

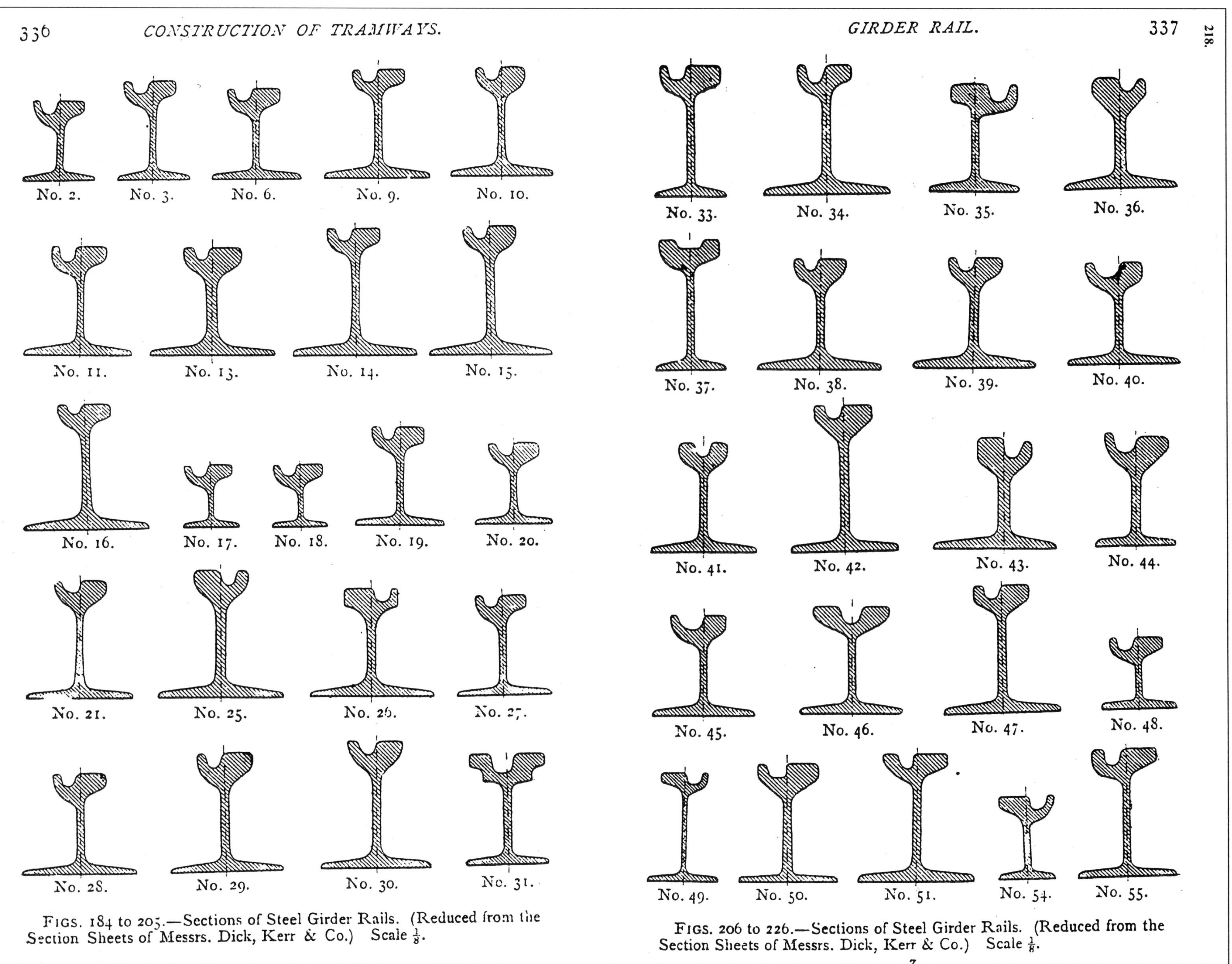

Figs. 184 to 205.—Sections of Steel Girder Rails. (Reduced from the Section Sheets of Messrs. Dick, Kerr & Co.) Scale $\frac{1}{8}$.

Figs. 206 to 226.—Sections of Steel Girder Rails. (Reduced from the Section Sheets of Messrs. Dick, Kerr & Co.) Scale $\frac{1}{8}$.

GREEN'S ANCHOR CHAIR
(PATENT).

Over 35,000 in use on the LEEDS, AYR, MORLEY, and other Corporation Tramways.

Reduce cost of Maintenance. Increase Life of Track. Small First Cost and in Fixing.

Will fit any section of Rail—no drilling, no bolts, no loose parts. Rails easily and quickly changed without twisting, or disturbing concrete.

Our improved "Rail Grinding Machine" removes and prevents corrugation in Track and hammering of Rail Joints.

Write or Wire for Particulars and Prices to—

THOMAS GREEN & SON, Ltd., LEEDS and LONDON.

219.

FIBRASTIC.
The Ideal Medium for
RAIL PACKING.

The object of this Packing is to give either
RIGID OR RESILIENT TRACK TO SUIT ALL LOCAL CONDITIONS.

GREAT SAVING IN MAINTENANCE.

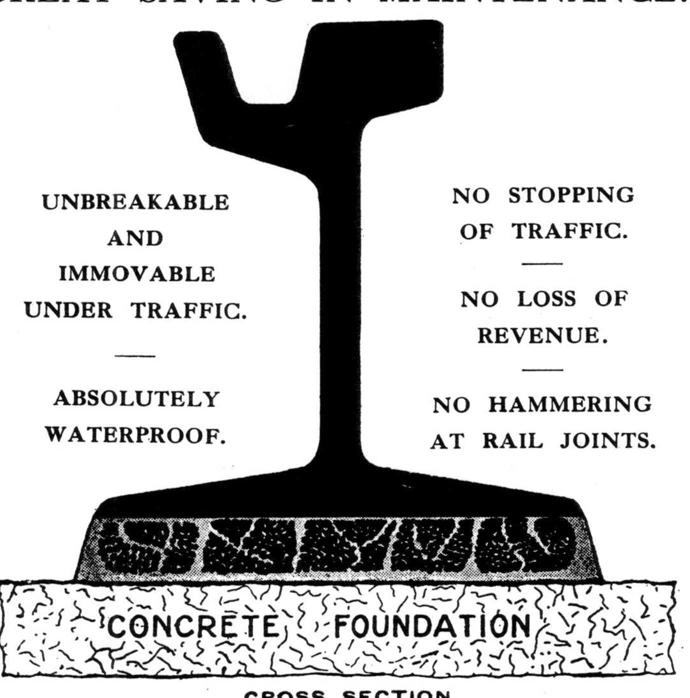

UNBREAKABLE AND IMMOVABLE UNDER TRAFFIC.

ABSOLUTELY WATERPROOF.

NO STOPPING OF TRAFFIC.

NO LOSS OF REVENUE.

NO HAMMERING AT RAIL JOINTS.

CROSS SECTION.
IN USE AT LEEDS.

Full particulars from the Manufacturers—

ROBBINS & CO.,
11, TOTHILL STREET, WESTMINSTER, S.W.
Telephone—VICTORIA 4531.

220.

ILLINGWORTH INGHAM & CO. LTD.
TIMBER IMPORTERS AND CREOSOTERS
50, BLACK BULL STREET, LEEDS

CREOSOTED PAVING BLOCKS

Tel. No. 70 (Four Lines) Telegrams: "TIMBER," LEEDS

221.

PARGING BLOCKS for TRAMWAY RAILS

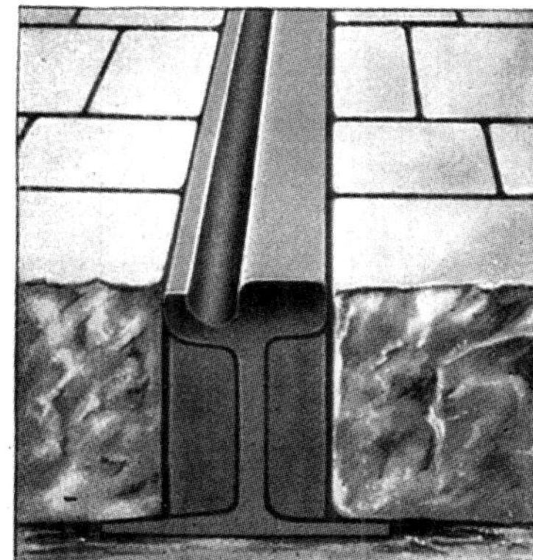

Sales Agent:
J. G. Ames, 48, Granville Rd., Fallowfield, Manchester.

Supplied to 26 Corporations and Tramway Companies

May we send you Particulars and Prices?

SHEPHERD'S PARGING BLOCK CO.,
Milkstone, Rochdale.

222.

WILLIAM GRIFFITHS & CO., LIMITED,
ENGINEERS AND CONTRACTORS
FOR
TRAMWAY CONSTRUCTION.

QUARRY OWNERS, WOOD & GRANITE PAVIORS, Etc.

Quarries: ST. SAMPSONS, GUERNSEY.
GRIFF, Nr. NUNEATON.
KIT HILL, CORNWALL.

Hamilton House, Bishopsgate, London, E.C.

Telephone: London Wall 2496. (3 Lines.) Telegrams: "GRIFFITHS STONE, AVE, LONDON."

223.

A selection of cures for perceived problems. Even Thomas Green offered their wares.

WALTER SCOTT Ld.,
Leeds Steel Works,
LEEDS.

Manufacturers of

ORDINARY TRAM RAILS

All British Standard Sections.

Special Sections Rolled by Arrangement.

Lengths up to 60 ft.

Stocks kept at the Works.

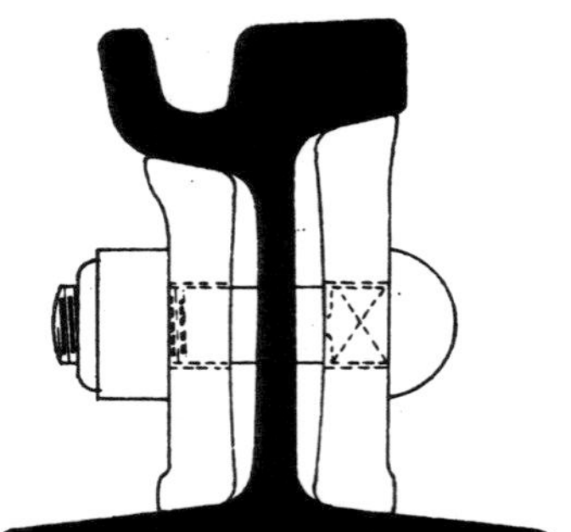

TRAM RAILS:—
Suitable for
DOCKS,
WORKS, SIDINGS.

Width of Groove ... $2\frac{3}{32}$ in.
Depth of Groove ... $1\frac{15}{16}$ in.

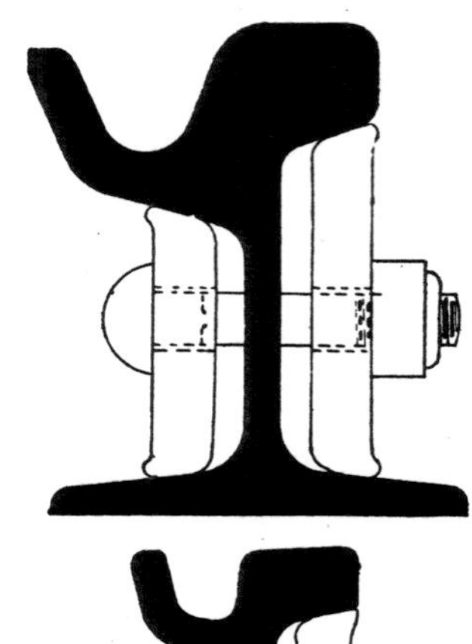

TRAM RAILS:—
Suitable for
Temporary Track Work.

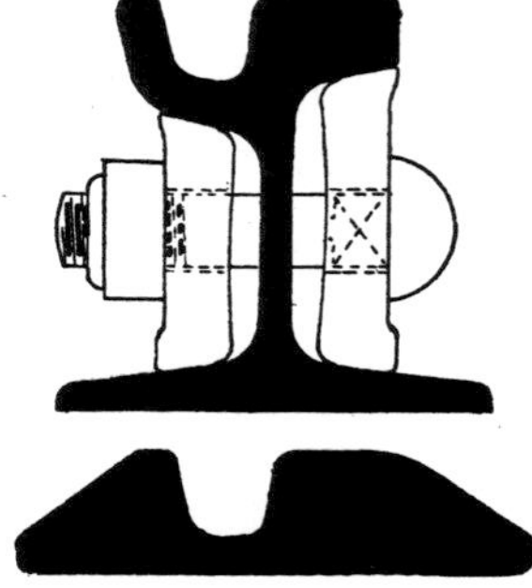

As used by many of The Large Corporations in the United Kingdom.

224.

225.

LIFTING TACKLE,
RAIL AND TRAM TOOLS.

ASK FOR LIST No. 29c.

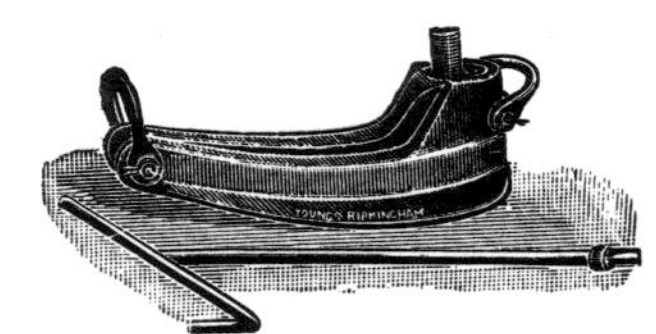

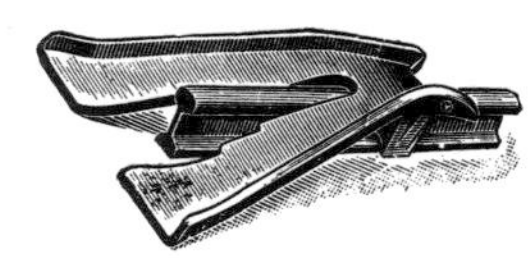

YOUNGS, Ryland St. Works, BIRMINGHAM. ::

Tailpiece

In a future volume of this series more of the 'smaller' companies – smaller in the sense that their production of tram engines was miniscule – will follow. In many cases it has been necessary to omit these as accurate details have been hard to find, good illustrations are scarce, or simply because all research is on-going and we (the publisher, my colleagues and I) have deadlines to meet.

But as a taster I promise all the following concerns and many others will have their space in this series:
Aveling & Porter (photo A),
Andrew Barclay,
Charles Burrell,
Dübs,
John Fowler,
Kerr Stuart (photo C),
Lifu,
Peckett,
Sentinel (photo B),
Sharp Stewart,
Yorkshire Engine.

And as a further taster I also offer photographs of two engines towing real live tramcars.

226. A. Aveling & Porter works no. 807 of 1872 photographed on 27 March 1951 at works of Henry Martin Ltd. at Nether Heyford. It is a tram engine: the drawing (which will appear later with all dimensions to aid modellers) says so!

227. B. Steam at its finest is seen on the fish quay, Great Yarmouth 26 June 1947, Sentinel type D.E.D.G., LNER class Y10. Two were supplied in 1930 at cost of £4,720, numbered 8403/4 they were used on the Wisbech & Upwell tramway, until May 1931 when they were sent to the quayside. Sentinel works nos. 8147/8 'our' engine outlived her sister and survived until February 1952.

228. *C. Sir Harry Bullard*, **Kerr Stuart works no. 71 was supplied in 1892 to operate on the extremely narrow (30" gauge) tracks belonging to the Great Yarmouth Pier & Harbour Commissioners. With 8" x 12" cylinders, other than in gauge,** ***Sir Harry*** **was very similar to two other tram engines supplied by Kerr Stuart the same year to Avilles, Spain.**

229. D (left). Officially no. 5, nicknamed ***"Jane"*** **but once** ***"Shannon"*****, this Wantage Tramway was in no normal sense whatsoever a tram engine, being built by George England of Hatcham Ironworks, New Cross, London in 1857 as a perfectly ordinary 0-4-0 well tank locomotive for service on the Sandy & Potton Railway. After many vicissitudes this little beauty served the Wantage well from 1878 to 1946 and was subsequently preserved. But** ***Jane*** **has in tow a pair of real tram cars, nos. 4 (Hurst Nelson), 1900, converted double deck open top car, and No. 5 (Hurst Nelson, 1904 ex-Nidd Valley Light Railway). No wonder enthusiasts flocked to the line!**

230. E (below). This photograph from the Roger Kidner collection shows a 'train' leaving Torrington on the Torrington and Marland Light Railway, serving the Devonshire Mineral Works. Taken in January or September 1931, other than the goods vehicles we have two connections with steam trams. The locomotive is ***Mary*****, Black Hawthorn works no. 576 built in 1880, 3' 0" gauge, cylinders 7½" x 10" and supplied new. The two horse cars are ex-North Metropolitan (London) which in due course absorbed the steam tram operator, North London Tramways.**

INDEX

Note from the publisher: it is intended to keep pagination continuous throughout the four proposed volumes, and that the final volume will have a master index. I have curtailed the index in this volume to exclude subjects such as the mechanics of steam trams, condensing etc. as the references are so numerous, but the extent of the final index will be reviewed for the final volume. Entries in italics are either the titles of publications or the names of trams and ships.